FAR AWAY COWS

FAR AWAY COWS

Veterinary Vignettes from the Third World

Patrick Guilbride

'Far away cows have long horns' – Anon

The Book Guild Ltd
Sussex, England

The Book Guild Ltd.
25 High Street
Lewes, Sussex

First published 1998
© Patrick Guilbride 1998

Set in Times
Typesetting by
Acorn Bookwork, Salisbury, Wiltshire

Printed in Great Britain by
Bookcraft (Bath) Ltd, Avon

A catalogue record for this book is
available from the British Library

ISBN 1 85776 234 7

CONTENTS

PART 1   NORTHERN RHODESIA (1943–1946)   1

I meet Dame Africa   3

Rum Mum and other Abercorn characters   16

Beating the border   26

Bwana Piet   32

Castle in the bush   38

Ngombe from Nyasaland   42

Bureaucracy in the *Bundu*   55

Bush music   59

Panda's epic run   60

A deep and angry lake   64

How rabid can you get?   68

North Luangwa and the Mafingas   73

White Fathers and white ants   82

Christmas at Broken Hill   87

Kalambo Falls   90

Lions and lycanthropy   94

Lake Mweru   96

Lake Bangweulu   111

My future in a cleft stick   124

Blue eyed bureaucrats   132

Of foot and mouth and other ant-ticks   140

Au revoir Africa   146

v

PART 2 JAMAICA (1946–1957) 151

Magic Isle 153
'Cow sick, come quick' 161
Bush surgery 166
Dipping problems 169
The widow of Woodfield 172
A house by the sea 175
TB and Bang's 180
Prolapses and parasites 183
Dr. Billy 186
Fighting cocks 188
Calypsos and cricket 191
Ian Fleming's Golden Eye 192
Promotion and politics 195
Coral kingdoms 201
A hot and dirty job 206
Film stars and roast pork 210
Pocomania 220
Professional up-date 223
A cure for 'cauliflowers' 226
Ill-treated mules 230
A very high wind 233
A near miss 237
Jamaica-Hopes 239
Ironshore disease 241
'Tissic' and typhus 245
Caribbean conferences 247
'Seek and ye shall find' 252

Zoo quest   257
Big Syd   258
Jamaica farewell   263

PART 3 UGANDA (1957–1963)   267

The Land of *Bado Kidogo*   269
Research opportunities   275
Recollections of a rocking horse   279
TB or not TB   283
Expatriates at play   285
Lake flies and furniture   288
The cows that cried   292
Operation buffalo   295
Trial by holidays   300
Copper plated sheep   308
Naked warriors   309
Operation hippo   314
An elusive parasite   320
An FAO bull   322

PART 4 PERU (1963–1973)   329

'City of the Kings'   331
Cows in the clouds   337
A house in the sandhills   347
Alpacalandia   352
Amazon jungle   360
High up – but hatching   366
Pets   369

First of the few 375

The school run and other fun 380

Shock waves 385

Poultry for the *campesino* 389

The Karate Queen 392

The Four Stooges 395

Si, si, senor, manaña 401

Vicuña 403

Prof. Jack and *mal de altura* 407

Enemies within 408

In the red 411

Vitar extended – Mary too 414

Paiche, pastures and *Pintadas* 418

Syphilis and Salmonella 424

A parasite's parasite 426

Shivy just makes it 430

An Alpaca dream 433

Rabies galore 436

Holocaust at Huaraz 440

A jungle heroine 443

Time to move on 448

PART 5   BRAZIL (1973–1975) 455

Recife – Venice of the new world 457

Research remains remote 465

Peruvian postscript 472

EMBRAPA emerges 477

Surubim for starters 481

The watchman   484

New faces and a new house   486

EMBRAPA muddles it up   491

There are horses at the bottom of our garden   492

Cats on the keys   494

Too many cooks   500

Ben into battle   503

Guy's special epithet   505

Death squads   507

Killer bees and creeping eruption   510

Supernatural goings on   513

Nova Jerusalem and Carnaval   515

Floods   517

A time for tears   519

Coping with calamities   520

The beginning of the end   522

Back to Africa   524

PART 6 MOZAMBIQUE (1975–1982)   529

Comrades all   531

A nearby oasis   536

The left-overs   538

Exposure to education   542

We win a mansion   544

The Nordics step in   551

A dog answers our advert   555

A secretary and other experts   557

Bush into beef   564

Buckets of milk 566

Who's next? 570

Botheration at the border 577

Fagin's followers 579

Survival of the fittest 583

The Milkateers 585

An outcast shepherdess 588

A smattering of arts. Lindley rescued 591

'They little know of England...' 593

Comrades love committees 594

A hero bites the dust 597

Time for a change 599

Tackling tuberculosis 601

Rhodesian raiders 604

Rabies again 606

Renamo ransacks Muabsa 609

One to help, one to hinder 610

Luanda 613

Monkey business 617

Viva international aid 621

Guests of Big Brother 626

Politics sour the milk 635

Centurions from Rome 640

A finch too frequent 644

A medal for the Minister 647

Bulls from Comrade Castro 649

Put out to grass 653

x

INTRODUCTION

Till I was five I scrambled barefoot beneath Uganda's equatorial sun, stalking imaginary lions with a flimsy bow and arrow. Alas for those halcyon days! The eleventh commandment for colonial families decreed that the gentler climate of 'Home' was essential for the nurturing of their young. So 'Home' we went, Terry and I, aged six and five respectively. Bare toes, freckles and pith helmets were swiftly replaced by chilblains, grey skies and cod liver oil.

Then, at the age of eight, sitting up an apple tree, I read Ryder Haggard's *King Solomon's Mines*. Immediately, the spark of tropical sunshine and adventure, dormant since Kampala, sprang to life and later after devouring John Masefield's *Sard Harker* and *ODTAA*, I knew that I could never accept a life under sunless skies. Finally, while watching the treatment of my Aunt's ailing Sealyham, I knew exactly what I wanted to be. Train drivers were out. I would be a vet.

I was lucky in both my aspirations and *Far Away Cows* is a condensation of how it all worked out.

To the many, many people, my wife Mary, our family, colleagues and friends whether they appear in these pages or not, who helped me enjoy my life, and to those who encouraged these notes, I can only offer my deepest gratitude.

Mount Chaos,
Rosetta,   June 1995
Natal, 3301
Rep. South Africa

Note: Although written many years later I have tried to describe each event as I thought and felt at the time. Allowances should be made for this, especially in Part 1. The few rough sketches are from note books or pieces of paper that have survived a lifetime of moving.

PART 1

NORTHERN RHODESIA

(1943–1946)

I would like to acknowledge the assistance of the late Mrs Pat Montgomery in typing the draft of Part 1.

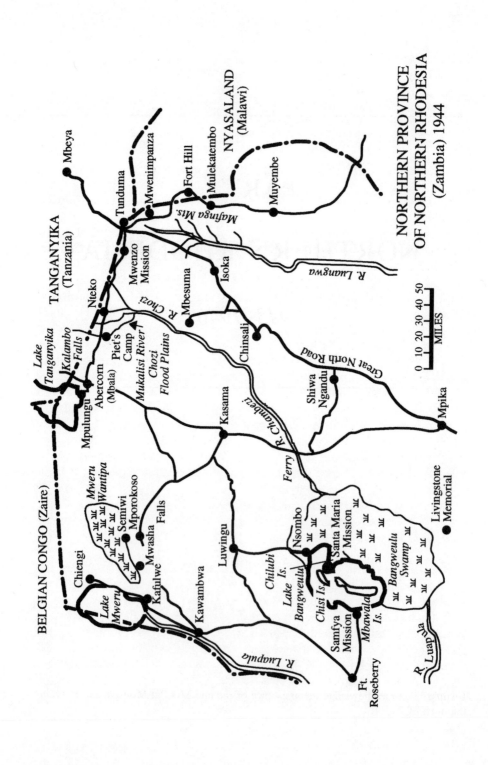

NORTHERN PROVINCE
OF NORTHERN RHODESIA
(Zambia) 1944

I MEET DAME AFRICA

I was determined to hate Africa.

Nothing, but nothing, could compensate for the shattering loss of those palm-fringed coral isles and the sparkling blue Caribbean – not to mention the ravishing girls I had pictured strolling golden strands – all of which had so nearly been mine.

Once more I looked at the letter from the Colonial Office. 'Owing to the exigencies of the service, etc. etc.', they regretted that it had been necessary to change my posting from the West Indies to Northern Rhodesia.

Northern Rhodesia? For God's sake! My atlas of Africa showed the damn place bang in the middle of that dreary continent, hundreds of miles from the sea. 'Exigencies of the service,' my foot! I knew exactly what had brought about this switch of continents – Charlie, and that catastrophic 21st house party.

After I had graduated as a Veterinary Surgeon in 1942, the Colonial Office had grabbed me from the jaws of the Royal Army Veterinary Corps and sent me to Cambridge University, together with three other colleagues, including the redoubtable Charlie, on what was termed, euphemistically, a Colonial Veterinary Research Fellowship. The sole object of this generosity, I suspected, although no-one actually said so, was to allow the social cloth of that august institution to polish us up to a point where we 'cow doctors' could distinguish a soup spoon from a dessert spoon, and uphold similar fine traditions of His Majesty's Colonial Service. Between brief periods in the laboratory, Charlie and I broadened our rustic minds by studying anthropology, practicing Judo and punting the fairer sex up and down the Cam.

Several nights a week we volunteered for fire-watching at the University library on the offchance that Hitler might still be capable of dropping a few more incendiary bombs. Prowling the endless shelves in the dark hours, I came across a section stuffed with tomes on treasure hunting. Admittedly, not a subject likely to make much impact on animal health in the colonies, nevertheless, it soon had me hooked. Within a month or two I knew every treasure trove from Oak Island to the Cocos, every shipwreck site and every route that the Spanish galleons had followed from Vera Cruz to Havana and Spain. So, when we were asked in what part of our Empire we would prefer to serve King and Country, I had no hesitation in opting firmly for the treasure-strewn isles of the West Indies with their tantalizing chimera of doubloons for the digging.

3

Then came the fateful house party to which both Charlie and I had been invited. On the last morning of that monumental four-day binge we had tried to steady our hands and clear our vision by potting at a row of windfall apples. Our weapon was an antiquated small-bore rifle. My turn came.

'Try these high-velocity bullets,' suggested our young host. I put one in the breach, closed the bolt and aimed.

'Hold on.' Charlie grabbed the gun. 'You're waving it all over the place. You'll kill someone. Better let me try.'

Charlie, no steadier than I, raised the gun and aimed. At the report, he swung round dropping the weapon and clutching his face with both hands. In hospital they found that powder and metal filings had been blown back under the worn bolt mechanism by the extra power of the high-velocity bullet. He would retain his sight but he would need special treatment for some time. Fair enough, but what really hurt – me, that is – was that the specialist care would only be available in – you've guessed it – *my* West Indies! Our postings had been swapped around; Charlie would now sail away to the coral-emblazoned isles of my dreams, while I would have to make the best of the lustreless, landlocked wastes of Northern Rhodesia. So it was not surprising that as the little *SS Sarpedon* tossed southwards across stormy December seas, I felt fully entitled to despise anything to do with Africa.

It was in this mood that one evening, two days before Christmas and after five weeks of dodging German submarines, we slipped into Cape Town harbour. I watched, fascinated, as Table Mountain spread her festive cloth of downy cumulus before changing into a sequined gown of a thousand twinkling lights, brightest where her hem touched the water, thinning gradually towards her waist to dissolve into the darkening star-bejewelled sky. If only Africa could all be like this!

I gaped at the trays of Swiss watches, uncouponed clothes and unlimited food, half-forgotten during four years of wartime Britain, and at the sun-ripened girls etched beneath thin cotton frocks who scurried by, chatting in a strange accent, intent on last-minute purchases. The air was filled with the gay rhythms of bands parading through streets scorched by the midday sun, save where an occasional curbside tree threw down a small puddle of shade. I was willing to concede that it might represent paradise to some, but I would still have swopped it all for one coral reef.

I bought a plain silver ring for the girl I had left behind and had it engraved 'P2' (since we were both 'Pats'), and sent it off, wistfully, to

4

the Fleet Air Arm station in Lancashire, where she was serving as a WREN. We had become very close during my last year at university, but war was apt to confuse and upset priorities. It was not really an engagement ring, but Patricia would understand.

At dusk, our train jolted out of Cape Town's main station on wheels that would carry me 2,500 miles towards the centre of Africa. What lay at the end I preferred not to contemplate, but it would, I feared, be different from the Cape – very, very, different. Dame Africa, I suspected, had let me glimpse her painted lips only to emphasize the drabness of her body.

I lay on the hard, shiny leather of an upper bunk, one of four in the compartment, my head level with the half-open window, gazing at the ghostly expanse of the moonlit Karoo. From time to time the lights of a small station would blink through the palm fronds and orders would be shouted along the platform in a strange language.

For three long days we puffed through the Karoo and the Kalahari, hoping for the desert to give way to misty mountains, deep rivers and tropical forests more in keeping with travellers' tales than these desolate plains. But as the miles rattled past, my hopes began to fade, reviving briefly as the train idled across the giant bridge spanning the Zambesi gorge and into Northern Rhodesia in full sight of the magnificent Victoria Falls. Tall dark trees and thick undergrowth bordered the river course and a fine spray sent aloft by the thunderous cataract turned everything green. Oh, to take a shower in it! This was more like the genuine article, more like the romantic hunting grounds of Livingstone and Stanley, the unexplored forests of Trader Horn and Prester John.

Alas, after Livingstone the flat monotonous scrub unfolded once more, unrelieved except by the irksome stops at each railway official's shack. Until recently, it had been normal for the engine driver and any passenger suitably equipped to spend an hour or two hunting *en route*. But those carefree days had now gone and trains, I imagined, were more on schedule. There were no 'expresses' or 'non-stops' but the thrice-weekly 'Mail' was said to be slightly faster and less aggravating than the daily 'Kaffir Mail', which catered principally to the indigenous population.

I had been instructed to get off at Mazabuka, 'Three thousand feet above sea level' – so it said on the station sign. I expected the seat of the country's Veterinary and Agricultural Services to be a little more sophisticated, but Mazabuka appeared to be just another half-street *dorp*, indistinguishable in the growing dusk from all the others we had passed through. On one side of the railway ran a dusty road along which skulked a handful of tin-roofed Indian stores, a one-pump petrol station and a bungaloid hotel. My God! Was this the place where I was to begin my professional career and make far-reaching discoveries?

Mercifully, there was no-one to meet me. The customary enthusiasm which new arrivals are expected to display would have been impossible to fake, so I tagged along behind Jack, an agricultural officer who had come out on the same boat and was being shepherded by his boss towards the bar of the crummy, tin-roofed hotel.

Beer flowed as we chatted about the journey, wartime England and, of course, conditions of service in Northern Rhodesia, the 'old-timers' being only too happy to put the 'new boys' wise as to just what a miserable country it was. Their bellyaches matched my own dejected state of mind and I sat listening to their tales of woe, marshalling my hatred of everything African.

The iced beer soon sent me scurrying to 'have a look at Africa' somewhere behind the hotel. Here, with the crickets ticking all around and an electric light plant chugging nearby, I realized how naked I was in this strange new world. Old values would have to be revised, a colour bar introduced, my vocabulary enlarged to include such words as 'ticky' for a threepenny bit, 'bwana' for a European, 'munt' for an African, to say 'PK' (picanniny kaia – little house) instead of toilet, 'bioscope' instead of cinema, and shed such heinous crimes as offering someone 'another' drink. Another drink! That was plain rude. Every drink, no matter how long the party had been going on, was just a drink; never, never, 'another drink'.

Later, someone dropped me at the house of the Director of Veterinary Services. A tall, almost gaunt, man with black hair and moustache, dressed in cream bush shirt and slacks, came down the verandah steps, fending off a couple of small, hyperactive boys intent on sampling the mug of beer he was holding just out of their reach. An equally dark-haired lady followed him.

'Didn't expect you till next week,' they said.

Seated with my tankard on the mosquito-gauzed verandah, I reflected ruefully on the marvellous week I could have spent swimming at the Cape. No-one would have missed me!

John explained the importance of copper (the country's largest industry) to the war effort and the duty of the Department to supply mine labour with meat. It sounded more like a marketing organization than Veterinary Service. They needed salesmen, not vets!

From time to time I would take a swig from my mug which I had placed on the floor beside me. About the fourth time I raised it, it was empty. What the hell? I thought. Then a snigger behind my armchair gave the game away.

'Bed, Simon,' roared his father, 'you've already had half of mine.'

The Director proved to be one of those rarities in the Civil Services: a 'go-getter'. Brilliant academically, a bold thinker, decisive, and as practical as a spark plug, he was equally at home on the golf course, cricket field, tennis court, or airing his endless repertoire of jokes at the club bar as he was piloting his De Havilland Hornet. Still in his thirties, he had already collected an OBE.

'Our policy is simple,' he explained as we sat in his office the next morning. 'Apart from ensuring meat supplies to the copper mines and larger towns, we have to control or eradicate the major epizootics like bovine pleuro-pneumonia and foot and mouth disease, and keep out others like rinderpest. Then we must improve the animal husbandry and feeding so that we can import better stock to upgrade our present herds. It'll take time, but there shouldn't be any real difficulties. If we *do* come across any, we'll simply knock 'em out.' I was to find that this was John's attitude to most problems.

I looked up at the great map on the wall behind him. 'You'll probably go to Abercorn,' he said, tilting his chair backwards and pointing over his head with his left arm. 'Or possibly to Mongu,' his right arm flung over to the west of the map. 'Wherever you go, you'll be the boss of that district; I'll take your advice unless it's plain stupid, and you'll carry out my decisions even if you don't agree with them. If you make a bloody fool of yourself, I'll kick your backside. If you are a success – well, that's what you're paid for. Anyway, stick around for a while and learn how to be a civil servant, it takes longer than you think.'

So I stuck around, reading old reports; learning new abbreviations, such as PWD for the Public Works Department, known popularly as 'Procrastination, Waste and Delay' or the 'People who Won't Do it' and buying more appropriate clothes than those which the tropical outfitters in London had thought fit to supply. I compromised between the 'slacks' and 'shorts' schools of thought, by buying both, deciding that the tunic type 'bush shirt' was a great advance on the 'tuck-in' shirt.

We celebrated the New Year, the Russian victories, the Eighth Army advances and anything else that happened along, and I began to acquire, somewhat painfully, a working relationship with the most readily available form of alcohol, South African Brandy, better known as 'dop'. I 'sundowned' with the Provincial Commissioner (PC), the District Commissioner (DC), the Medical Officer (MO), the Director of Agriculture (DA), and many other worthies, having first left my card on the silver tray that every civil servant of standing placed on his hall table.

'What Africa needs,' said the Director, as we strolled round the station one morning, 'is an efficient way to preserve grass.' Tilting his green pork-pie hat over his eyes, he pointed to a paddock. 'If we could cut that grass two or three times during the rains and preserve it, we would have enough fodder to tide ourselves over most of the dry season.' It was obvious, but no-one had done it.

Further on, John pointed at a heap of metal to which some remnants of wood still clung. 'Lesson for today. Six months ago that was a brand new cultivator. Then some idiot left it outside and the white ants got it. Look at it now; only the metal parts left. Termites rule Africa – don't ever forget it.'

We followed a road over the rise past the laboratories. To the north, the grey-green carpet of the Kafue Flats stretched to the horizon. Not a tree, not a mound disturbed that expanse of hot waving reeds. Africa was beginning to impress me!

* * *

Well-intentioned advice battered me from all sides. Advice on clothes, the most suitable calibre of rifle, what to eat, what to drink, how to take care of my feet, protection against snake-bite, which end of an elephant to aim at, whether to take five grains of quinine daily or fifteen grains once a week, who to like and who to avoid. 'I'll remember that,' or 'It's very good of you to tell me', I would murmur, hoping to live long enough to find out for myself.

The nearest cinema or bioscope, was in Lusaka, 150 miles to the north. Tennis and golf were well patronized and there was a cricket field and, of course, the '19th hole' at the club, the most popular venue of all.

It was with John, one afternoon, that I made my first and only attempt to play golf. He'd lent me a wooden shafted driver. I tee'd up, full of confidence and energy. Swoosh! Crack! Only half the club remained in my hands.

'Oh, well. Perhaps we'd better have a drink, instead,' he suggested sourly. 'Clubs are almost irreplaceable.'

He must have had more success teaching his son. Forty years later, Simon was playing in the Masters!

War news dominated all discussion. No-one moved very far from their radio, and, if it wasn't the news bulletins it was the nostalgic serial 'The Archers', which was liable to interrupt all other activities.

My first personal servant was a Barotse, a tribe in the north-west of

8

the territory. Simangolwa looked so old that I dared not speak harshly to him or ask him to lift anything heavy. His eyes were bloodshot and squint. His teeth (both that could be seen) were as black as his skin, and his legs were short and bowed.

The accepted form of communication between master and minion seemed to be shouting, but since I didn't know where I would be posted, I didn't know in which of the four regional languages I should learn to shout! Chinyanja would be spoken in the east, Chibemba in the north, Chitonga in the centre and Lozi in the west. And then, there was that mixture of English, Swahili, Hottentot, Dutch and many other languages, the *lingua franca* of Central and Southern Africa which almost everyone understood – 'Kitchen Kaffir'. But I knew none of these, and Simangolwa knew little English. The Chinyanja phrase book I had been recommended started with a small vocabulary of essential nouns and verbs like 'house' 'chair' 'come' 'put', the last being '*choka*', meaning 'get out!'. Instead of 'I say, old man, would you mind bringing the lamp?' I soon found myself bawling 'Come put lamp table, scram.' However, when we parted, some months later, it was as the best of friends. He promised to pray for me every day. Would I do the same for him? I said I would try. I doubt if my prayers would have been strong enough and I don't think his did much for me. Perhaps, like me, he forgot.

Until then, I had judged the African by the *elite* few that had found their way to public schools and universities in Britain, like Harry Wharton's chums in the *Magnet*, for the most part the cream of the West African Colonies, differing from the European only in skin colour and background, who could talk the same language and think the same thoughts. Things were a little different in Northern Rhodesia, where there was a strong South African influence.

'Tell the *munt* what to do in words of one syllable and see that he does it. If he doesn't, kick his backside. It's the only language he understands. Never let him think for himself or you're in trouble – and never trust him. The day you trust him, sack him.'

Hardly the relations I had expected between whites and blacks, nevertheless I was soon to find that my philanthropic attitude towards my dusky cousins, whom I had been determined to help up (or was it down?) the road to civilization, was fast eroding. In my ignorance I judged them by my own customs and background and they failed, just as I would have failed had they judged me by theirs.

One thing was certain; technically immature he may have been, but 'Billy Bantu', as he was sometimes referred to, was no fool. He sized up his *bwana* very shrewdly, giving him a nickname to match his habits. 'He who shouts in the office.' 'He with the behind like a

9

sack.' 'The one who takes three paces forward and one backwards.'
'He who speaks to your feet.' 'The *bwana* with three wives.'
Outwardly, they called me the *piccanin bwana* – the young master –
but I'm sure that they had a private and less flattering nickname for
me.

* * *

'Like a short *ulendo* into the *bundu*?' John asked a few days after my
arrival.

'A what into the where?'

'A trip into the bush, sticks, countryside, whatever. Bill, the
provincial veterinary officer, is going to buy slaughter cattle for the
Copperbelt. It'll give you an idea of what you're in for.'

Oh no! Was it for this that I had spent six years at university –
buying cattle? Bloody hell!

The sale was to be held at Mwanachingwala, some 30 miles south
of Mazabuka. We took the main Livingstone–Lusaka road – in those
days no more than a couple of muddy ruts zigzagging through the
bush. The camp site was an equally muddy clearing enclosed by a
high grass fence, with a thatched barn in the centre shaded by two
enormous fig trees. We pitched our tents near the barn but away
from the fig trees, in case of lightning. Some of the storms were truly
terrifying.

Mac, the good-natured, corpulent, Scots veterinary officer from
Lusaka, came down to lend Bill a hand. I shared a tent with him and
his heroic snores. Also present were Ian, the local Stock Inspector,
the District Commissioner, who thought that a couple of days out of
the office would do him good, and so had offered to lend his weight
and influence to the proceedings, and five or six European cattle
buyers for the mines.

Chief Mwanachingwala sent word that he would visit us the following morning. I was excited at meeting an African chief. No doubt he
would be a resplendent fellow, decked out in gold and silver; a
shrewd man, worshipped by his subjects. How Dame Africa must
have chortled! This moth-eaten, hung-over potentate, draped in dusty
black rags and garnished with Woolworth beads, tottered into camp
the next morning brandishing a bedraggled fly switch and followed
closely by a minion, who carried a three-legged stool onto which his
master frequently collapsed. He sidled up to us, knelt and clapped a
greeting. One of the chief's retainers opened the dialogue.

'Chief Mwanachingwala greets you, *bwanas*.'

'Tell the Chief that we greet him also and hope his people have a
lot of cattle to sell,' answered Bill.

A shrug was His Worship's only comment. He and his people would first see what prices they could expect before committing themselves. Another of the Chief's party came forward with a couple of scrawny chickens and a bag of mealie meal, the usual *bonsellas* or presents, for which the old reprobate obviously expected us to pay.

The District Commissioner opened proceedings with a pep talk embracing the war, the importance of copper and the need to supply meat to the miners. As far as I could see, no one understood or cared.

Bill and Mac sat themselves beneath a tarpaulin shelter at the exit to the stockade, estimating the weight of each animal offered for sale. Behind them the cattle dealers from Lusaka and the Copperbelt, their pockets bulging with banknotes, waited to make their offers. Payment in coin was more popular since paper had a tendency to disappear in smoke, while a lump of molten silver still had a certain value.

Buying continued all day. Competition between the plump, sweating dealers grew keener as the sun grew hotter and the humidity rose, but it was not until they came to drive their purchases away, that they found that Billy Bantu's flair for business was equal to their own. Numbers didn't tally. It was clear that some of the animals sold had been stealthily smuggled back into the bush and, in all probability, would be offered for sale again the following day.

Mac took me back with him to the capital, Lusaka. The Grand Hotel, where I lodged, was 'Grand' only in name. Mosquitoes were everywhere, and I found a spring from the mattress sticking up through my sheets! If this was the standard of the capital, I thought, God help the other towns!

A two-mile tarmac strip connected the business district to the hill on which Government House, the Secretariat, and all the official residences were built. It was as if business and officialdom had nothing to share, and didn't propose to explore the possibility. Most farmers were 'Dutch' speaking Afrikaners who struck me as hard-working, intelligent and friendly, a view I confirmed when I took over the district two years later.

One evening I visited the bioscope. After the newsreel and a couple of shorts, there was an interval. It seemed that the gentleman who owned the cinema also owned the adjoining bar and saw to it that the intermission was always long enough for the patrons to satisfy their fairly considerable thirsts. There was an unkempt area opposite. I strolled across to it and found a small path in the tall grass. Soon I was alone save for the fireflies, the crickets and the bullfrogs. A full moon shone down with tropical brilliance and I realized, with a certain shock, that I actually *was* in Central Africa, surrounded by six-foot-tall grass, wearing a white washable suit, 5,000 miles from home and all my friends. I wondered what Patricia was doing at that very moment. As I stood there listening to the alien noises of the bush, I felt a little frightened and very, very lonely.

* * *

Later, John flew me down to Livingstone in his De Havilland Hornet. I had never flown before, and was decidedly nervous as we bumped over the grassy paddock which acted as his airstrip and just made it above the fence. It was the first of many flights over that endless scrub where only an occasional river or village broke the dirty-green carpet. The plane's cabin boasted an altimeter, clock and compass. That was it – not even a radio, so John decided to play it safe and follow the railway line, which was clearly visible from 2,000 feet. The only time we left it was when we had to deviate for a storm. We could, however, hardly have missed our destination; the spray from the Victoria Falls could be seen an hour away.

In Livingstone, John pointed out the residence of the late Harry Sussman, a wealthy and popular old pioneer of Middle Eastern origin, said to have been almost illiterate and whose malapropisms were legendary. His classic description of a visit to the Farnborough airshow was perhaps his best: 'All dose iroplans manuring in de sky; vot a vonderful shite.' And, at a party in his honour, he had thanked the participants from the bottom of his heart. 'And from my vife's bottom also.'

I woke the next morning with a throbbing just behind my knee. I located a boil and squeezed it. My eyes bulged as a large maggot emerged. 'I'm being eaten alive,' I called across to John, who was smoking a cigarette in the other bed.

'That's just a "putsi" fly larva,' he chuckled. 'You'll get plenty more. One of our kids had fifteen.'

The 'putsi' fly, (*Dermatobia hominis*), laid its eggs on chairs, mats, unironed clothing or anything that was likely to come in contact with a human or animal body. When it did, the egg would hatch and the larva burrow into the skin, ultimately turning into a large white, wriggling maggot. I felt like a piece of Gorgonzola.

We flew another 90 miles up the Zambesi to the tiny railhead of Mulombezi in Bartoseland, where Dr Piet, the Veterinary Research Officer, was carrying out experiments on bovine pleuro-pneumonia (BPP), an insidious, fatal lung condition of cattle caused by a virus-like organism, very difficult to diagnose in the early stages. Vaccines were unreliable and treatment was impossible, so the only means of control was to quarantine infected areas, one of which was Barotseland, only permitting animals out for immediate slaughter. Mulombezi was the exit point from which cattle were railed to the slaughterhouse in Livingstone.

Piet's quarters were basic. The rough, oblong, wooden petrol boxes, used throughout Africa to transport two four-gallon tins, or *debbes*, of petrol, formed the bookcases, cupboards and storage space for specimens, as well as providing most of the tables and chairs.

In the paraffin-operated Electrolux were squashed butter, bread, vaccines, specimens of diseased lungs and his meat supply, a considerable portion of which fell out each time the door was opened. The proximity of food and infection didn't seem to worry Piet. Screwing up his deep-set, grey-blue eyes behind steel-framed glasses, he would pick up the fallen objects, rub his high grimy forehead or his three-day stubble and discourse on the probable outcome of his experiments.

Piet roused me early to autopsy an experimental animal he had infected with pleuro-pneumonia. He was soon inside the carcass, flinging out chunks of lung and other organs for my scrutiny. Then he attacked the stomachs and intestines, scooping out their wormy treasures into jars of preservative. After extracting everything of interest we left the carcase and returned for breakfast.

'Bread?' Piet enquired, wiping his blood-stained hands on his already filthy slacks and grabbing a loaf. I shuddered. Not the type of Empire Builder who bathed and changed into a dinner jacket each evening, or shaved every day, but he was a brilliant scientist and one of the profession's most outstanding parasitologists.

John had promised me a close-up view of the Victoria Falls, which we could see as a white cloud in the distance almost as soon as we took off. We circled around above them while I clicked away with my Retina 1. The Zambesi was over half a mile wide before it plunged into a rocky gorge, several hundred feet deep and only 50 yards across. It was as if a giant had taken his knife and slashed a fissure across the river's path. John was worried that we might attract the attention of the ack-ack guns which guarded this vital target, but nothing happened. He told me that a daredevil pilot, Ted Spencer, had once flown under the Falls bridge. It seemed impossible. Even at 1,500 feet the turbulence made our little plane dance about.

John had to stay on in Livingstone for a meeting, but as I had to catch the weekly mail lorry from Broken Hill to Abercorn (now Mbala), where it had been decided to station me, I had to leave at once. By ill luck, the only transport going north was a goods train with open trucks and a 'compo' on the end. A 'compo' was a luggage van with one passenger compartment at the rear. No one pretended that it would be comfy.

Dust covered the interior. The door to the luggage van opened and slammed all night. The window crashed open at every jerk, the seats were wooden slats and the electric light was not connected. The small sister of a college friend had given me a penlight torch – 'In case you meet a lion in the dark.' I had still to meet the lion, but it helped me to make a rough bed from my dirty clothes and a raincoat. Even so, sleep was impossible, it took all my efforts just to stay on the slatted seat. The guard, whose compartment was in front of mine, looked in once with a cup of lukewarm coffee. '*Got jong*,' he said in a strong South African accent, 'you're in for a helluva ride.' He was right.

At two o'clock the following afternoon we pulled into Mazabuka. It had taken less than two hours to fly down and eighteen to train back.

I caught the mail train to Broken Hill, a friendly, happy town with distant mine workings thrusting darkly against the blue sky. The air of officialdom and bureaucratic gloom that had pervaded Lusaka had been flushed out by private enterprise. There as a bustle in the streets and citizens shouted greetings to each other. Here there was no civil servant pecking order.

After Broken Hill, one could continue by rail northwards through the rest of the Copperbelt towns of Ndola, Luanshya, Nkana and Mufilira to enter the Belgian Congo (Zaire), but travellers for the Northern Province or for Tanganyika (Tanzania), left the railway line at nearby Kapiri Mposhi and had to proceed by the Great North Road, a highway thick in dust or deep in mud, depending on the season. By car it could be tolerable, but on the square wheels of the transport services trucks it was not, and in the rains the road could be impassable for weeks. It would be another 25 years before the Chinese-built railway would link Kapiri Mposhi and the Copperbelt with Dar-es-Salaam.

I left Broken Hill with regret. It would be the last time for many months that I should be able to look on a bit of femininity, or see a movie. Perhaps the bush would have other compensations, but I doubted it. Whisky-besotted old fogies or ancient missionaries would probably be my only companions, neither would there be any sports or cultural inspiration, and almost certainly no proper veterinary work. It was a terrifying prospect to gregarious young bachelor eager for life, and filled with visions of research and great discoveries. I'll probably go mad, I thought, or commit suicide or, preferably, die of drink. If I could have foreseen the future then, I would have been even more worried. Not for the last time I cursed both the Colonial Office for overriding the Veterinary Corps, and that wretched 21st birthday party.

The journey up the Great North Road was uneventful. What little excitement I had conjured up died within the first 50 miles as the flat bush continued to unroll before me. There were two welcome respites; an overnight stop at Mkushi, a delightful rest-house, where a small stream giggled and gurgled below a garden of roses, and a breakfast stop at Kanona, home of Captain Mills, a 70-year old Australian elephant hunter.

Edward, the truck driver, was the half-caste son of a celebrated pioneer, Chirupula Stevenson, whom I saw fleetingly when we stopped to offload some goods at his home. Chirupula could have been Smuts' double with his pith helmet, white goatee and bush shirt. In fact, he had been a close friend of both the General and Cecil Rhodes. He had two African wives and had spent the last 30 years trying to protect the local tribes from exploitation. (His book, *Chirapula's Tale*, unfortunately, was more a history of the Copperbelt than an autobiography, but Kathaleen Rukavina's *Jungle Pathfinder* (Hutchinson, London 1951) has now filled this gap.)

At Mpika we branched off the Great North Road and took the left fork to Kasama. About halfway, on the banks of the hundred-yard wide Chambeshi river, the trucks were unloaded and goods, mail and passengers ferried across to continue their journey in the vehicles of another company. I shared my last bottle of beer with a wizened old-timer on his way to the Copperbelt to try and recuperate a little of what he had lost prospecting in the bush.

The last stop before Abercorn was the provincial headquarters of Kasama. We arrived after dark, due to trouble with the 'carbuletor'. To most African drivers there seemed to be only two things that could go wrong with a vehicle, apart from broken springs and punctures ... the carburettor and the plugs. No matter the symptoms, the carburettor would be confidently dismantled, wiped out, blown into and then, with far less dexterity, reassembled. Next, the plugs would be removed and knocked about. If the vehicle still refused to go, some drivers were willing to take the whole engine to pieces – but not when I was there.

Kasama, with a population of about 30 Europeans, was a sizeable town for the *bundu*. I soon twigged that Africans didn't count in general population statistics, only Europeans.

Jimmy, the veterinary officer whom I was to relieve at Abercorn, met me here; a large, jovial, round-faced, 30-year old Scotsman. I

15

also met Lanky, the Game Warden, Dick, the PWD engineer and several others, all of whom would become close friends in the following years.

Jimmy drove me the last hundred miles in the comparative luxury of the Veterinary Department's vanette, a Ford half-ton pickup with a canvas cover, which was to cause me much anxiety over the next two years. For most of the time it had no brakes whatsoever, as spares were unattainable, so if I wished to stop I had to change down rapidly and turn the engine off or run into the bank. The left side was soon stripped of paint by bushes and rough verges, but with less than one other vehicle encountered per 500 miles, there was little danger to life or limb, and I became extremely adept at dealing with steep hills and sudden emergencies.

It seemed to me that there was a continuous cloudburst for the rest of the journey, and we were either ploughing upstream against a torrent or shooting rapids as we plunged downhill. What little I could see through the deluge looked identical to the rest of the country since leaving Broken Hill: scrub, ant hills, occasional *kopjes*, little roadside villages and PWD camps of thatched mud huts.

God! What *had* I let myself in for?

I had expected to see mountains as we approached the vicinity of Lake Tanganyika, but nothing changed. As we skidded down the hill on the outskirts of Abercorn, past the thatched club house and grassy landing strip, the only new scenery was a belt of palms strung along the Mbulu stream at the foot of the hill, and as we laboured up the other side and into the little township, the red, red soil.

RUM MUM AND OTHER ABERCORN CHARACTERS

It was market day.

Well – there was no actual market, but Friday afternoons were great moments in the life of this little station. It was the day that the weekly mail lorry arrived.

The handful of settlers and missionaries around the township would pump up the tyres of their ancient vehicles, push start them down the slope on which they had been parked (batteries were a luxury in wartime), and bump off into Abercorn to collect their mail, cash their cheques, purchase their weekly supplies and listen to the latest gossip.

The centre of activity was a lofty, tin-roofed, bat-infested hall, the Tanganyika Victoria Memorial Institute, or TVMI, presumably built in honour of Her Revered Majesty and now used as a library. Here, while the good citizens tried to find a book they hadn't already read twice, fruits, vegetables and other donated goods were sold and a cake raffled in aid of the Red Cross. Presiding over the sales and raffle was a voluptuous, silver-haired, rose-cheeked lady.

'Let me introduce you to Rum Mum.' Jimmy strode over and planted a loud kiss on her plump, sunny face.

To describe Rum Mum as enormous was simply a statement of fact, but I could never think of her as 'fat'. There was a determination in her old face, a sympathy in her smiling eyes and spontaneous chuckles that made one overlook the rolls of quivering flesh, considering it natural that one with so big a heart must need a body large enough to house it. Between issuing raffle tickets, collecting money from the sales and slipping sweets to the high-spirited children who raced round the table, Rum Mum welcomed me to Abercorn and told me a little of her life. I was to learn more, sipping 'dop' in her room. She had spent a large portion of her 70 years trekking over the great plateau of Northern Rhodesia with her surveyor husband. Now, almost a cripple, she spent her time knitting for the Red Cross and doing those odd jobs for friends that only she had the time and patience to perform. I was to find her a permanent source of fun, and many a hilarious party would start or finish in her room at the

'Pop' the Postmaster

17

hotel, where her cheery laugh and apt Scots repartee would make the gloomiest of homesick youngsters smile.

Jimmy introduced me to many other people that afternoon: Mike, his Afrikaner Stock Inspector, all six foot two of him; Ian, the recently arrived District Officer Cadet; Jack, the Medical Officer; Hans, the ebullient Belgian Co-Director of the Locust Control Centre; Piet, the young Afrikaner game ranger; Pop, the Postmaster; Sylvia, the Nursing Sister, and others, all of whom had their particular niche in the microcosm of that bush community that was Abercorn, and all of whom would play an important part in my future.

Later that evening, a party was held in the thatched, barn-like tennis club as a send-off for Jimmy, who was to return to Mazabuka, and as a welcome to me. I was hardly in the mood for gaiety; the anti-climax of having arrived and the prospect of three years in this African Siberia was too appalling. There was some dancing, but most of the women seemed to me (more accustomed to wild student 'hops'), to be in their dotage, shuffling to music of a byegone age from records long overdue the dustbin, and played on a barely audible wind-up trumpet gramophone. The one thing that stands out clearly, even to this day, apart from an acute shortage of beer, was Jimmy, standing on the bar, reciting a marathon poem on the antics of a rather liberal-minded Eskimo lady.

We arrived home around midnight. As we stood on the lawn in front of the house, 'looking at Africa', I heard my first hyena. There was no doubt that it was laughing at me, its eerie howl rising to a shriek.

'You're here, my lad,' it cackled, 'and here you're going to stay. Ha, ha, ha, ha.'

* * *

Across the road in front of my house stood a four foot high brick pillar commemorating the 1467 Africans who served the British Army as carriers and were killed or died of wounds or sickness.

'Here on the 25th of November 1918 the German forces in East Africa surrendered.'

Later, a monument was erected to the German General, Paul von Lettow Vorbeck, who, with a handful of *shutztruppe*, led the British, Belgian and Portuguese armies a frustrating dance for over two years, remaining undefeated at the end. Like Rommel in World War Two, von Lettow Vorbeck was regarded as much a hero by the British as he was by the Germans.

The road in front of our house continued up the hill past the Nursing

Sister's house to disappear in a grove of blue gums and jacarandas which shaded the centre of the township. Two branch roads led down the hillside, one to the native hospital, a modern whitewashed building with a green corrugated iron roof, the other, Jimmy told me, to the African Compound.

'Compound?' I asked. 'What's that?'

'Village; location; the African half of Abercorn.'

We were now passing a red, tin-roofed bungalow, separated from the road by a semi-circular gravel drive and a crescent of unkempt garden.

'That's the Abercorn Arms Hotel. You'll probably spend a lot of time there.' Jimmy prophesied. 'The bar is at the end of the verandah. It's the hub of Abercorn's social wheel.'

Opposite the hotel a road disappeared into the long grass. 'That goes up to the Polish Refugee Camp.'

'The what?'

'Polish refugees. We have six hundred of the buggers here.'

'Six hundred Poles in Abercorn?' I was dumbfounded. 'Any of them women?' I asked, hopefully.

'About eighty per cent, but cool it. They're mainly old bags or children.'

Never mind, I thought, there must be one or two worth looking at, and the younger ones would be maturing all the time! Things were looking up.

We passed the Veterinary Office and the Game Ranger's office, and drew up in front of the African Lakes Co store, better known as Mandala. The slight, bespectacled Scots manager greeted us and announced joyfully that he had received a consignment of potatoes on the previous day's truck.

'First in months. Better take a sack before they're all gone.' He sent a boy to put one in Jimmy's vanette, and invited us for a cup of tea in his office.

He told me that the African Lakes Co had started in Glasgow as a semi-philanthropic organization, aimed at supplying the growing band of Central African missionaries with basic necessities. Soon, the Scots eye for business developed the concern into a chain of trading stores. The name Mandala, by which the company was always known, was the native name of a long-dead store keeper and meant 'he with the spectacles'. During his long service, the name became synonymous with the store and was eventually adopted by the company.

There were several more buildings beyond Mandala's, the most important of which was the red-brick *Boma*, from which the District Commissioner administered his domain.

19

At the crest of the hill, we caught a glimpse of Abercorn's only scenic attraction, little Lake Chila. A cool breeze blew down from Tanganyika's distant hills, ruffling the surface of the water, swaying the stately blue gums and carpeting the ground with purple blossoms from the jacarandas. Here the road pondered before dropping to curve round the lake shore and jump the Lucheche stream beneath a grotto of bamboos. This accomplished, it skirted a forested hill, the original site of Abercorn before the Germans destroyed it in World War One, and now the site of the European cemetery. Thereafter, it wandered disconsolately northwards across the Tanganyikan border to its next resting place, the small town of Sumbawanga.

Lake Chila was where the township should have been re-built, I thought. Neat houses on the high ground, green lawns and terraces stretching down to the water's edge, a club house, golf course, a few boats, fishing. It was a bit late now, but the possibilities were enormous. So, of course, were the snags. We did not yet have DDT to deal with mosquitos, and the priorities of war precluded any development. Anyway, who would have footed the bill? Most inhabitants were birds of passage, officials changing their station every few years. Settlers and missionaries had their farms and mission stations scattered in the bush. There weren't more than 30 Europeans within a radius of 50 miles, except the Poles, who kept to themselves in the camp and didn't count. Ironically, the only building whose inmates would have had an unrestricted view of the lake, if it hadn't been for the high brick walls, was the gaol.

Perhaps, when the war was over, Abercorn would become the showplace of the Northern Province. But many things were to change after the war – not all as predicted, or for the better.

I was anxious to inspect my office, which we had passed earlier. In my mind, I was already equipping a laboratory for research, but what exactly I was going to investigate, I hadn't yet worked out. Whatever it was, I knew it would make me famous, a most important objective for the young.

As we drove up to the tin-roofed, whitewashed building, two Africans in blue vests and shorts rose from their petrol box seats on the verandah and saluted smartly.

'Meet the brothers Simbaya, Kenaan and Cephas. They're a couple of rogues, but they do a lot of useful work.' The brothers grinned and saluted again.

The building, although newly constructed, proved a disappointment. Its three rooms, labelled 'Office', 'Store' and 'Lab', were almost

20

entirely furnished with petrol boxes. The only pieces of orthodox office equipment were the desk and the metal filing cabinet, the latter filled with old magazines, ammunition of various calibres and motor vehicle spares. The top drawer, alone, contained a few grubby files and order books. Only two books of the dusty six-volume library were of this century, probably the student pride of veterinarians long since deceased, and now collectors' items.

The room labelled 'Store' contained a mess of uniforms, bicycles, hoes, tyres, tins of oil, unlabelled packages and bottles, official forms and branding irons, all thrown into empty petrol boxes stacked sideways, one on top of the other, from floor to ceiling. My spirits rose a little as we entered the 'Lab'; a modern binocular Zeiss microscope was on a bench by the window. My rhapsody over this enviable piece of equipment ended before the month was out; a telegram from Mazabuka instructed me to send it down to headquarters immediately!

'There are monthly reports and returns to be sent in,' Jimmy warned, 'but apart from that there's damn all to worry you. There's no mad rush about anything; it takes three weeks for a reply to reach you from head office.'

We turned to the wall maps.

'The district is about the size of Spain, and not a single policeman in the whole bloody place.'

'So what about law and order?'

'*Boma* Messengers. Those fellows in red *fezes*. They carry out the law under the District Commissioners. The Veterinary Department has its own messengers in blue *fezes*, like Kenaan and Cephas, to enforce its regulations. We also have Zone Guards along the border.'

Although the district was enormous, the cattle population was more or less confined to the area along the borders of Tanganyika (Tanzania) and Nyasaland (Malawi), which was free of tsetse fly. Jimmy told me how, a few years before, rinderpest had swept southwards through Tanganyika and how they had had to build 160 miles of fence, like a Hadrian's Wall, to stop it. The fence, completed in three months, had prevented game moving south until all cattle on the Rhodesian side had been vaccinated. Guards had now been stationed every 15 miles, with orders to shoot anything that tried to cross. In addition, rangers were ordered to shoot all game within 20 miles on either side. Tens of thousands of large and small buck, buffalo, wild pigs and other animals had been wiped out in the last few years. 'Conservation' was a concept still to be implemented.

21

I had heard tell of rinderpest in my student days, a virulent virus disease which could rapidly wipe out large populations of cattle and game. Introduced into Eastern Europe from Asia by the Goths, it had reached the Danube by the third century. Then the Huns under Attila had scattered it westwards to Italy and France. By the ninth century it was all over Europe including Britain, where outbreaks occurred regularly up to the eighteenth century.

Some authorities considered that the devastation caused by rinderpest had been responsible for the founding of the first Veterinary School in France, in 1761, and the consequent rapid progress of animal health measures in Europe.

'You can forget rinderpest,' Jimmy went on, 'but the fence still helps to keep out East Coast fever.'

This insidious, tick-borne disease of cattle was also new to me. The great danger of East Coast fever (ECF), Jimmy told me, was that whereas local breeds in an ECF area acquired a certain immunity from being infected from birth, any other cattle, especially European breeds brought in to improve the local African breeds, had no immunity at all, and would quickly turn up their trotters when bitten by an infective tick.

While we were chatting, a slightly-built man in khaki shirt and shorts came bustling up the path.

'Here's the DC,' Jimmy moaned. 'I'll introduce you.'

The District Commissioner, however, got in first.

'Look here, old man, did you get my note on the sale of cuckoos? What about ninepence as a fair price?'

'Well ... er ... I'd like you to meet...'

'Or should we make it a shilling?'

'May I first introduce...'

'Eh ... what?'

'For God's sake, Victor, I'm trying to introduce my successor. This is the bloke you'll have to argue with, not me. I'm off tomorrow.'

'Oh, sorry, sorry. How are you, old man?' We shook hands.

'What do you think? Should we control the price of cuckoos, or leave it alone?'

This seemed to be addressed to me as much as to Jimmy, so I admitted that I hadn't the faintest idea, and wasn't aware that cuckoos were a commercial proposition.

'Chickens, old man. K-U-K-U, the native fowl, ha, ha, ha.' Victor went off into what I came to recognize as one of his characteristic paroxysms.

'Anyway,' Jimmy continued, 'the point is that you could never enforce a control price. The Poles are already paying five shillings a bird.'

'Now look here,' Victor retaliated, 'the Poles don't buy much, and after all, they've had a hell of a journey through Russia and India. You can't blame them, it's a sort of anti-starvation reaction.'

I studied Victor, a convert to Rome who regarded the Catholic Poles as his special wards. The long sensitive face and high, rather square forehead, gave the impression that his head was a little too big for his body. He spoke rapidly, rather nervously, coiling a forelock with his left hand. I found that when he became really agitated his right hand would come into play as well, and he would use both to twist and untwist that long-suffering tuft of hair.

We agreed that price control was a bad bureaucratic idea, and hoped that the extra demand for *kukus* would stimulate their increased production.

* * *

Ian, the young District Officer cadet from Scotland, who had arrived shortly before me to help Victor in his ministrations of law and order, was occupying a gloomy, bat-infested barn of a house. As soon as Jimmy left, I suggested that he move into my modern three-bedroomed house and share the housekeeping at five pounds a month.

Ian was a wiry, mousy-haired lad from 'Auld Reekie', where his father was head of the Scottish Region BBC. Dry-humoured, hard as nails and as plucky as hell, he had been in line for a Scottish rugger cap until the war and the unfortunate recoil of a field gun onto his kneecap had put an end to his sporting hopes. So, here he was, in an office chair, about as far from civilization and the war as it was possible to get, a demobbed captain of gunners, starting a new career in the Colonial Service.

His knee was constant agony. A trip to Johannesburg for a lengthy operation left him no better. The pain and consequent lack of sleep made him look older than his 23 years and put a rasp in his voice, but he refused to let it impinge on his activities and only the occasional limp in his long determined stride would indicate that the elastic bandage was anything more than a temporary support. The Africans respected him utterly. Kenaan once confided that Ian was 'too like lion' but, nevertheless, a 'too good *bwana*'. For sheer guts and determination, Ian had few equals. We were a contrast. Ian was exacting, precise, methodical, mechanically minded. I, day-dreaming, artistic (so I liked to think) and slap-dash; but for eighteen months we never regretted sharing quarters – at least, I didn't. Maybe he bore it all along with his knee!

Mike, my Stock Inspector, also mucked in with us. He would show me the ropes before he, too, left on transfer the following month. He

23

was a huge young man, well over six feet and broad, with a delightfully open, freckled, boyish face and grey-blue, smiling eyes beneath perpetually tousled, light brown hair. His physical strength was a byword, as Kenaan constantly informed me. Amongst his feats, Mike had lifted the veterinary vanette off Kenaan's arm after the jack had slipped. Previously he had been living at Nteko, a dismal isolated, mud-and-wattle house along the border, where I was soon to spend one of the worst nights of my life.

It was on Kenaan Simbaya, my Head Messenger, that I depended for all practical applications of the Department's work. He was like a Regimental Sergeant-Major and a tower of strength, both moral and physical, to his atrociously naive boss. About 45 years old (arrived at by counting the years since he was first married at – he thought – the age of 14), he had been in the department for 16 years and was known and respected by everyone in the district.

I nick-named him '*Nsofu*, the Elephant, because of his enormous chest and bellowing commands, and the Director, on one of his visits, dubbed him 'Bovril', which he didn't understand but thought a huge joke. His English was lively but inaccurate; the verbs 'to hope', 'to think', 'to wish', 'to be sure' and 'to expect', were interchangeable.

Kenaan, like many of his colleagues, was a member of the Ainamwanga, a small tribe, many of whom lived across the border in Tanganyika. They were the only tribe that had a woman as their head, Queen Waitweka. Together with several other small border tribes, they had been dominated for centuries by the warlike Awemba. The Awemba, it seemed, were too ignorant or too lazy to keep their own cattle, or perhaps the tsetse fly, with which they shared much of their territory, had something to do with it. Whatever the cause, they found it easier to raid the Ainamwanga, the Wiwa or the Mambwe for their Sunday steaks. Kenaan's opinion was that they were all 'too much bloody thieves and liars', and it was probably due to this distrust that not one of my Messengers and Zone Guards was an Awemba. The Awemba did have one saving grace. They made excellent soldiers and fought with distinction in Burma.

Kenaan's half-brother, Cephas Simbaya, was the Second Messenger. Slimmer and with much less built-in authority than his sibling, he had started life as a schoolmaster at a mission and reckoned he knew all there was to know about rhetoric. His English was good, but one had to get used to the biblical flavour of his idioms, such as 'and so it came to pass', or 'the District Commissioner said unto me', with lots of 'thus's' thrown in for good measure. It was difficult not to murmur 'Amen' at the end of his discourses.

Cephas's real claim to fame, however, lay in his *fez*. Between his

24

short, black curly wool and his blue Turkish headpiece, he stored practically all his worldly belongings. Letters, his pay, three or four notebooks, a pencil, a packet of gunpowder, a box of matches, tobacco and many other items nestled snugly on top of his scalp. I had only to ask him for a piece of string, a rubber band or some solution to mend a tyre, for him to bow, topple his *fez* into his hands and, with far less fuss than it takes a lady to ransack her handbag, produce the desired article.

Several of the Zone Guards, employed to check and count cattle in the district, were probably related to Kenaan – perhaps they all were, because whenever I needed a new man, he always had just the one I wanted... 'He too good man. *Bwana* must give he job.'

That was fine with me; I made him responsible for anyone he recommended and, usually, they came up to scratch. With one notable exception. I had asked him to procure me a houseboy. Simangolwa had just departed, and I hadn't yet been able to replace him. Kenaan soon herded before me a thin, nervous young man.

'This Solomon, *bwana*. He too good boy.' He added that he had worked for a former Stock Inspector, a most exacting man. So I took him on forthwith. That same evening, Ian and I had some friends for dinner. Everything was fine until we sat down. As we spread our napkins, a shaking Solomon entered carrying the soup, which was slopping out on both sides of the tureen. Thinking he might be having a bout of malaria, I slipped into the kitchen to ask if he was all right. He assured me he was, but when he began to clear away the soup plates and bring in the vegetables, the clatter stopped all conversation. Furthermore, his hands shook so violently that it was quite a feat to collar a spud or a spoonful of greens, especially as he stood several feet away. Next day I asked him why he had been so nervous.

'Not do this work,' he explained.

'But you worked for *bwana* Rob for three years.'

'Yes, *bwana*. *Bwana* Rob say I best boy.'

'He wouldn't have if he'd seen you last night. You were no better than a herdsman.'

'That's right, *bwana*. I *bwana* Rob's best cattle boy.'

Luckily, the next of Kenaan's proteges proved a gem. Kosam was a rather bashful lad but an excellent laundryman and cook, although his knowledge of some of the finer points of the cuisine was sadly lacking. I had ordered a Gorgonzola cheese from a supplier at Broken Hill, at great expense. I asked Kosam to bring it after supper.

'Cheese no good, *bwana*. I burn it.'

'You what! Why?'

'It all green inside, *bwana*. It rotten.'

25

BEATING THE BORDER

Jimmy had left for Mazabuka, Mike would soon be gone and, as yet, I had hardly seen anything of my district.

'I have to pay the Zone Guards,' Mike told me, 'so I can show you most of the cattle area at the same time. We could also pop across to Tanganyika and visit the Veterinary Officer in Mbeya, if you like. He might be of help to you, sometime.'

'Great,' I agreed. I was eager to see what there was in the way of tropical jungle and wildlife. To date, the country had proved a complete flop; barren, flat, uninteresting, and lacking all those excitements one expected of Central Africa. I had already made a fool of myself asking stupid questions.

'Where are all the pygmies?'

'In the Belgian Congo, of course.'

'And the tropical forests?'

'In the same place.'

'What about those mysterious ruins whose builders are still unknown?'

'Zimbabwe? In Southern Rhodesia.'

'And where's all the witchcraft and ju-ju?'

'That's on the West Coast. You seem to have got on the wrong boat, old man.'

Heading south on the Kasama road early the next morning, we passed between two half-moon-shaped marshes, the Ningi pans, formed by the road embankment which sliced across the centre of a large swamp. Soon afterwards the road slid into a wide forested gorge, at the foot of which the deep, dark, crocodile-infested Saisi river flowed northwards into Tanganyika.

Mike kept up a running commentary, pointing out where he had shot a bushbuck or leopard, or where his car had skidded into the ditch. The road varied from fair to very bad, and the bush changed from open *veld* with many wild flowers to forest and *dambos*, those marshy culverts with a small stream running down the centre obscured by the long grass or trees. It was wise, Mike said, to stop and test the rickety bridges before crossing them.

Occasionally, small rocky *kopjes* gleamed down through the trees. I resolved to climb them on my next trip. I made the same resolution every time I passed, but always seemed to be in too much of a hurry, and in the end I never climbed any.

I noticed that near each village, patches of trees had had their branches cut off. Some of these clearings appeared recent, others

26

older, with new branches already sprouting again. It gave the impression that the forest was suffering from mange.

'*Chitemene*,' said Mike. 'They lop off the branches at the end of the dry season, collect them together in a smaller area and burn them. The wood ash makes a good fertilizer for *malezi*, a type of millet which is their staple food and, more importantly, the source of their beer.'

'How long does the garden last?' I asked. 'It looks as if a lot have been abandoned.'

'They cut new gardens every year. They used to cut the whole tree down, but that's now illegal, so there's not so much deforestation as before. The problem is that when the gardens are burnt the rest of the forest goes up with them. They've no idea of preserving their resources.'

Indeed, I found that the whole province went up in smoke each dry season – but not only because of *chitemene*, arson seemed to be a national sport, even a duty. As Kenaan explained, 'Must burn, *bwana*. If not burn *bundu*, grass too thick and lion be hidey and catchey black man.'

I'm sure he had a point, but a more probable reason was that immediately after burning, fresh green blades would spring up through the ashes. These attracted the hungry buck, which had been existing on fibrous grass and leaves during the dry months, into the open, making them easy prey for Billy Bantu with his bow and arrow, hiding atop an ant-hill.

Whatever the real reasons for the annual conflagration, a local pilot told me that flying over Northern Rhodesia in the dry season was like flying over a London smog. The smoke made visual navigation impossible.

Halfway along the border Mike swung the vanette to the left onto a rough track.

'Welcome to Nteko, where I spent the last two miserable years,' he growled. 'Bloody awful place.'

A wobbly bridge spanned the Nombwe stream, swollen by the rains, the torrent making the poles vibrate menacingly. Although I was to have it strengthened several times, it continued to creak and sway as soon as my front wheels ran onto it. Reaching the other side was always a great relief.

The thatched house could, at first glance, have been taken for an old English barn, except for the mango trees and mulberry bushes that jostled the mosquito-gauzed verandahs. Two halves of a *debbe* tin which hung on each side of the front door held the dried remnants of once-coddled flowers. Clumsily framed pictures of film stars and pin-up girls decorated the whitewashed walls and a bamboo screen, divided the large central room into dining and sitting areas. A petrol box bookshelf was filled with worm-eaten semi-religious books, cheap paperbacks and tattered magazines. A few old notebooks and torn scraps of paper with messages and jottings hinted, only too vividly, of a young active lad, lonely to distraction, trying to make the best of a hermit's life.

The middle-aged Stock Inspector who had originally selected the site and built the house had been a bit of a recluse, only too happy to get as far away from civilization as possible. Ironically, no sooner was the house complete than he found himself married. History does not record his wife's comments when he introduced her to their love-nest.

We found eight Zone Guards in blue vests, shorts and *fezes*, lined up outside ready for inspection. The senior guard, Philemon, taller than the others with an angular, Arab-like face, stepped forward and yelled 'Shun' with all the vigour he possessed. At this, a few moved their feet together, while the others either hopped into the air or stood at ease and saluted. At that moment another guard arrived and, rushing up to the others, jumped to attention and saluted. Unfortunately, his feet slid from under him on the slippery soil, and he came down hard on the seat of his blue shorts. Nevertheless, with commendable discipline, he remained where he was on his back, rigidly saluting the sky.

Each Guard, Mike told me, had charge of a Veterinary Zone. Their duty was to count and classify all the cattle, sheep and goats in each village, record the numbers of births and deaths and give reasons for unusual increases or decreases. Under the guise of disease control, bureaucracy had invaded darkest Africa!

The only excitement that day was a report of 15 goats having been killed by a honey badger which had then gone to sleep in the kraal, where it was found and killed. This was most unusual; honey badgers fed chiefly on insects and the honey and grubs of wild bees; although, occasionally, they would attack snakes.

Sometimes I would catch one of the Zone Guards 'cooking' the results. Wrath of the *Bwana* Doctor *Ngombe* would then descend on the miscreant. My tirade, in English, little of which he could follow, but whose tone he could well recognize, would end in a suitable passage in German or Latin, spat out with a curl of the lip. Gaelic, I felt, might have been an excellent tongue for the purpose but, alas, I knew none. If it happened too often, the culprit would be moved to a less agreeable Zone, or sent behind the house with a couple of Guards and a leather thong. Six of the best was an accepted practice.

It was not unknown for a housewife to send her cook or garden boy up to the *boma* with a note, 'A little stimulation would greatly improve this lad', and see him walk back, a little stiffly, having been stimulated on his nether end! One smart boy circumvented his mistresses intentions by asking an unsuspecting fellow he met on the way, to take his note to the DC!

Once, a Guard proudly reported that while visiting a village, he had killed a lion with a spear. This was indeed a brave act and earned him five shillings from the 'bull bag'.

The 'bull bag' was an old bush institution, operated by every field official, but heartily disproved of by accountants and auditors. It consisted of all the odd shillings and pence which could not, or should not, be accounted for: illegal fines imposed as a minor disciplinary measure, unofficial sales of unlisted articles and any other cash, the origin of which might be awkward to explain.

Its original purpose was to buy animals for the *boma* herd which supplied the station with milk and an occasional steak, for which no official funds were allocated. In practice it paid for anything unofficial – rewards, small purchases for the upkeep of the station, celebrations and such like.

There were always numerous complaints and numerous requests. Bicycles needed repair, uniforms were worn out, pencils required replacing, a wife had died and the Guard wished to be transferred because he was being bewitched. Or, perhaps, loans were sought for a wedding. These and innumerable other nigglances had to be settled.

After meat, salt was the most prized commodity, and Africans, like wild animals, would go to great lengths to acquire it. Sacks of salt always took up a large part of the vanette on my trips to pay the Zone Guards.

I estimated that five or six per cent of all domestic livestock were killed annually by lions, leopards, cheetahs and hunting dogs, usually because of badly made or dilapidated kraals. In an effort to encourage more substantial enclosures, I would fine village headmen five shillings for every animal killed in their kraal. I was green then, so green that when the next month's returns came in and no animals were killed by vermin, I thought I had achieved a major administrative victory. But I noticed an increasing number of animals had died from sickness, or 'by thin', as the Guards so quaintly put it. Later on, when I stopped the fines, the lions returned and my statistics were more accurate.

Skulls of buffalo, lion, leopard and a variety of buck lay bleaching in the sun behind the Nteko house, proof of Mike's skill as a marksman. His most spectacular exploit had been the previous year. Lions

29

were killing the Nteko cattle regularly, so he built a platform beside the kraal and baited the ground with meat. On the second night the lions returned, seven of them. Mike got every one.

I noticed a collection of small bones hanging from a nail above the door of his old store.

'What's that for?' I asked.

'Man, that's magic. Worth its weight in gold.'

'Doesn't look very valuable to me.'

'*Jong*, that little thing has saved me pounds. It's very strong *muti*, no-one will steal anything while it's hanging there. Here, you'll need it.' He unhooked it and gave it me.

It consisted of the collarbone of a leopard, the wishbone of a chicken and a digit from a lion's foot. I hung it outside my pantry in Abercorn. Simangolwa, for the short time he was with me, was unimpressed; perhaps he figured that Ainamwanga magic was impotent against a man from Barotseland, because he continued to help himself to my sugar, soap and tobacco until I put a lock on the door. Kosam, my subsequent boy, was, I like to think, honest, or perhaps he recognized the magic, for nothing ever disappeared – even after I gave him the key for safe keeping.

* * *

We called at Mwenzo Medical Mission, further along the border, near Tunduma. It was an unwritten rule that no-one passed a mission, a DC's *boma* or PWD foreman's camp, without calling in. Help might be needed, or there might be letters to post, or telegrams to be sent, or important information to be had about the road ahead. Anyway, visitors were so few and far between, it was really a social obligation.

I came to know the Scottish missionaries at Mwenzo well, especially the good wife's cooking. Her sole desire in life seemed to be to cheer passers-by with her culinary delights. Drop scones, tarts, puddings and meat courses were always ready and waiting whenever I happened to call, all of which she managed with a small kerosene refrigerator and a wood-burning 'Dover' stove.

'I must tell you this,' she said one day, 'but, of course, you won't believe me. Last week we went to Mbeya to replenish our larder and buy shoes for the children. On the way back Ian shot a duiker. We put it in the back of the vanette with the other things. When we got home I told the girl to cook a couple of steaks from the *nyama* (meat) which we had brought. You can imagine our reaction when she dished up two roasted shoes!'

I gaped at her.

30

'I knew you wouldn't believe me, but it's true. We've even included "footwear" in our pre-prandial Grace! I think the Lord gets a good laugh out of it!'

Tunduma, on the border with Tanganyika, was an ugly little settlement by any standard. A few Indian stores straggled over an eroded, windswept ridge, their roofs – made of a mica-like material – sparkling in the sunlight. But what Tunduma lacked in man-made beauty was amply compensated for by the view it commanded.

To the north, a great valley stretched away in green and gold to a range of purple mountains, a magnificent panorama forever changing in tone and colour as if Dame Africa could not leave her canvas alone, improving it all through the day before washing it clean at night, to start afresh the next morning.

We headed north to Mbeya, the capital of Tanganyika's Southern Highlands Province. Mountains began to corrugate the horizon, replacing the dull, flat bush with sudden escarpments, gorges and curiously shaped hills, as befitted the tail-end of the Rift Valley.

We caught glimpses of neat coffee and citrus plantations and tidy, well-laid-out farms. The German colonists had certainly put their hearts into making beautiful and prosperous *shambas* – until the war had ended their ventures. It was sad that so many of these properties were being broken up and sold, for the most part to Indians who opted for quick profit rather than aesthetic beauty and land conservation. Tanganyika, it seemed to me, would be a lot poorer without a sprinkling of the 'Master Race' to farm it.

Sitting quietly in the wide lap of the Mbeya and Poroto ranges, a thousand feet higher than Abercorn, with jacaranda and flame trees everywhere, the air cool and clear, Mbeya seemed the perfect residential site. Perhaps it was too perfect – too relaxing. It was Saturday morning, but before midday, the usual start of the weekend, nearly every European official we met had beaten the gun by several hours and was decidedly merry. The official at the Post Office, whom we asked to send a telegram, was perhaps the furthest overboard, but the PWD engineer and even the Medical Officer were running pretty close. We joined them later at the club and rapidly caught up!

The Veterinary Officer, big, bluff and Irish, proudly showed us the new offices and lab he had built, and assured me of help any time I needed it. However, the social success of our visit was due mainly to Elsie, the short, rotund, capable matron of the European boarding school, and to the six or seven young female staff, recently arrived from England, who gave the two girl-starved bachelors a warm

31

welcome. At midnight, we drove back to the hotel in the back of someone's vanette, shouting bawdy songs to the moon, the cold mountain air tingling our ears. Life was looking up: half a dozen luscious females, and only a day's drive away!

On the way back to Abercorn we deviated onto the Stevenson Road, a scarcely usable border track which crossed the sombre Saisi river on a long, tortuous and very rickety bridge. The closely laid logs perched on wobbly poles zigzagged precariously across the deep, fast flowing water for a hundred yards or more. I closed my eyes in terror, convinced that we were about to provide a banquet for the thousands of crocodiles which Mike casually told me were lurking in the reeds along the banks. (In fact, we were the last people ever to run the gauntlet of that terrifying bridge. The following week, the whole middle section was washed away.)

A few miles from Abercorn, we called at Kawimbe mission, a collection of neat brick houses hidden amongst pine and jacaranda trees. It was deserted save for numerous brightly coloured butterflies which danced around the flowers. Strange, we thought, and then realized it was Sunday. Everyone was in church.

We drifted on slowly through the cool morning air. Thousands of multi-coloured *veld* flowers, washed clean by overnight rain, carpeted the roadside like confetti. We skirted Lake Chila, her glassy surface undisturbed except for a few water-birds that swam near the outlet, and a couple of naked children from the Polish camp paddling on the far side. What a lovely spot, I thought.

I was forgetting to hate Africa!

BWANA PIET

I owed a lot to Piet, the young Game Ranger.

Like Mike, Piet was an Afrikaner. Slight and sinewy, his large dark eyes, fringed by long, almost feminine eyelashes, would avoid contact with yours until he knew you better. A crop of coarse black hair, clipped neatly round small, close-set ears, thatched a high, prominent forehead, making the lower part of his face appear too small in proportion. A thin, tight mouth just managed to squeeze between a slender nose and a small, but aggressive, cleft chin. To strangers, his handshake appeared hesitant, almost apologetic.

Piet was, in all respects, a tidy person. Even after a month in the bush, he looked neat and kempt in his well-fitting khaki shirt and slacks, a packet of Cape to Cairo cigarettes bulging his breast pocket. Devoid of social graces, shy and retiring in strange company, he had only to feel a gun in his hand to become a different being, decisive and confident. Perhaps self-confidence was his most notable characteristic. Whatever he tackled, he would be quite sure of his own personal success in the venture because, should something go wrong, he would easily convince himself that it had not been his fault. His was very much the aggressive spirit of the old *voortrekkers* who had had to battle climate, infertile soil, disease, African tribes and, not least, the interfering, arrogant British, who had been driven to Imperial frenzy in their scramble for land, gold and diamonds.

Piet came into Abercorn once or twice a month from his camp on the Mukalisi River, not far from Nteko, bunking down on a camp bed in the Game Dept's office, opposite mine.

The first time I called at his Mukalisi camp, I found him on his camp cot, reading a paperback Western. A radio, blaring full pitch on his bedside table, was attached to the battery in his vanette by two cables through the window of the thatched rondavel. Seven or eight dogs milled around, barking and growling, as much at each other as at me. Piet shooed them off and yelled through the window for coffee.

Later, we strolled round his camp. Game skulls were strewn behind the store, and a stack of smelly, maggoty leopard and buck skins was heaped against the wall under the overhanging roof. His kitchen garden, a half-acre of orderly beds dug into the dark cotton soil where the Mukalisi formed a loop below his camp, displayed a variety of vegetables. As we returned for a sundowner, his herd of 30 cattle were driven into a stake kraal by a diminutive herder.

Zero, a big black mongrel, was leader of the dog pack, then came Dogsi, Tiger and five or six others whose names were apt to change according to their own escapades, or the hero of the book their master was currently reading. They slept on or beside Piet's bed, the doors and windows always open. Two or three times that first night I was awakened by the pack in full cry as they chased some animal intruder, real or imagined.

Piet had a simple method for ridding his bed of the fleas which his pets inevitably left behind. After bathing them in Jeyes, he would hold them by the legs and drag them up and down the bedclothes, his theory being that the fleas would jump back on to their now clean hosts. He swore it worked, but even after a bath, his cleanest dog was still hopping with them and probably left as many again as it collected.

What bugged me most at Mukalisi – and bug is unquestionably the right verb – were the midges. They didn't even wait for the sun to go down, but attacked at any time of day. Long-sleeved shirts and thick woollen socks they ignored; citronella repellent was useless, and insecticide sprays were still a decade away. There was only one remedy, as Piet kept telling me.

'Dop, man. After a few slugs of Limousin brandy you can't feel them, or they become so drunk they can no longer bite.'

A gun to Piet was like a briefcase to a businessman. It was always within reach, to be handled lovingly and with the same delicacy one might expect from a duchess raising her teacup. Constant siting on imaginary victims made aiming second nature. His favourite weapon was his 7mm, which he used for all game, including elephant and buffalo, although he claimed that he had shot both these species with his .22.

He was completely at home in the bush. As a youth, he would pocket a handful of rounds and some biltong, sling his rifle over his shoulder and disappear into the bush for a week. These sorties had developed in him an uncanny sense of direction as well as other survival instincts. Many times when out hunting, he would ask me in which direction the camp lay.

'Over there,' I would reply confidently.

'OK, *jong*, you go that way, but I am going this way. *Tot siens*.' And away he would stride. I soon learned to follow.

It was only too easy to become lost in the flat, featureless bush. Piet told me of two friends on the mines who went hunting. They were completely inexperienced and had no licence. Hiding their car in the undergrowth, they set off to stalk their prey. After a fruitless day they wearily tried to retrace their steps, only to find they were lost. They had been going round in circles for an hour or more when night began to fall. Suddenly, one put his hand on his companion's shoulder and pointed to a grey shape in the bush.

'Rhino,' he whispered.

Without further thought they let fly. The shape didn't move. They gave it another burst and approached, stealthily, guns at the ready ... to discover their car – its radiator full of holes!

Piet had plenty of odd tales to tell about his own hunting trips. The one I liked most was the time he shot a lion just before dark. He was far from camp and tired, so he decided to sleep where he was. He had no blankets, and a recent storm had made everything wet and cold – everything, that is, except his victim. Arranging the carcass with the wound underneath, he propped his rifle beside him and lay down on the lifeless, but still warm and dry, King of the Jungle. He didn't sleep – King Leo was covered in lice which rapidly transferred

34

themselves from the cooling carcass to the welcoming warmth of Piet's body.

Piet was an excellent mechanic. He once replaced the engine of the Game Department's truck on a lonely road in the middle of the night, with an angry, vociferous lion circling the proceedings. A couple of rounds fired into the bush now and then finally convinced Leo that he wasn't welcome.

He had little respect for germs and would drink from the filthiest pools and streams.

'I'll fix it when we get back to camp,' he'd say, which he did by gulping a mouthful of petrol, lamenting at the same time that he wouldn't be able to smoke for a couple of hours in case he exploded!

His attitude to medicine was equally bizarre. When he diagnosed constipation in his dogs from eating too much gristle and bones, he administered large doses of vinegar to dissolve the offending substances – with almost instant success. Once, when his chicks were sick, I had difficulty in persuading him not to cut off the tips of their tongues which, he insisted, would be a certain cure!

He was adamant that only slacks should be worn in the bush, never shorts.

'Might as well go naked,' he'd say. 'The chemists make their fortunes from idiots who wear shorts.'

I proved him right, time and again. I hated the hot stickiness that slacks produced, but every time I weakened and wore shorts, I suffered. Scratches rapidly turned into 'veldt sores', a type of ulcer, extremely painful and slow to heal.

Piet's greatest preoccupation was his lack of education, especially since it had been rumoured that future Game Rangers would require university degrees.

'Man,' he'd growl, 'I'd like to see a ranger trying to stop a charging buffalo with a diploma.'

Nevertheless, he wrote off for school books and for a time tried, doggedly, to master mathematics and other subjects for his matric so he could enter a university – unsuccessfully, I fear, but perhaps just as well. Had he made it, it would have only helped to propel him towards a desk job, which he would have hated.

There were three other members of the Game Dept in the Northern Province. The first was Lanky, the Provincial Game Warden, more of whom later. Another, and by far the oldest and most flamboyant government employee I have ever come across, was Chitty, a five-foot, clean-shaven gnome with sparse grey hair, thick, strong legs, a Cockney accent and over 60 years' experience. Chitty had been around Central Africa since the previous century.

'We hijacked a railway engine once, in the Congo, me an' me pals, an' drove it back into Northern Rhodesia. Eee, that was a lark. Got us three months each.'

He was the only person I've ever seen actually fall off a bar stool, unconscious. His legs being too short to reach the ground, he simply toppled sideways in a heap. Nevertheless, he was back on the job bright and early next day. He once showed me a small figure, half man and half lion, carved out of a green stone which he said he had picked up in a river bed. He wouldn't tell me where. Even at his advanced age – he said he was over 90 – he would walk 15 miles a day along the game fence.

The third character was the Elephant Control Officer, one of the most knowledgeable persons on game in the country. Unfortunately, he relied on Johnnie Walker for most of his sustenance, periodically disappearing into the bush with a dozen crates. It was inevitable that before long he came to be known as the 'Pink Elephant Control Officer'!

* * *

My first hunting trip with Piet was to the Chozi 'flats'. These 'flats' were the flood plains of the Chozi river that ran south from Tanganyika to join the Chambezi, which would eventually form the mighty Congo River. Piet made two or three trips to this area each year to ensure that no buffalo herds were moving into the game-free buffer zone along the fence.

Turning south off the Tunduma road near Nteko at an enormous *mulombwa* tree (the African mahogany), we followed the track which Piet had made some years previously through the long grass and trees. An hour later, we reached some higher ground overlooking a large flood plain. Here we pitched camp – a simple matter of unloading a table and two chairs and rigging up a tarpaulin between the trees under which we had driven the vanette, spreading blankets in the back of it for our bed, and making a large fire around which the Messengers would later sleep.

It was the end of the rains and the grass still much too long for serious hunting, but we needed something for supper so, with my 6.5 Mannlicher-Mauser (which Piet had sold me the day before for five pounds) slung over my shoulder, I set off with Kenaan in one direction while Piet with his chief hunter, Spider, set off in another. We agreed to meet where the old Kasama-Fife waggon road crossed the Sanchi stream, a fording which Kenaan was sure he could find. There were several old abandoned roads in this area chief amongst which was this one down which the Germans had advanced in 1915, and the Stevenson Road which had run from Abercorn through Tunduma (Fife in those days) to Nyasaland. (Not in our wildest dreams did we imagine that a railway would plough through this virgin bush in another 25 years.)

Half an hour later, having disturbed a couple of small buck without seeing them in the long grass, I spied a movement at the base of an anthill 50 yards in front. I unslung my weapon; it would be my first chance to use it.

I waited. Sure enough, a portion of brown hide appeared through the grass and disappeared immediately. I climbed the nearest anthill and pushed a round up the spout, my heart beating like never before. More movement – hell, a small herd of buffalo! Without further thought, I aimed at the next open space through which they would have to pass and held my breath.

'*Bwana*, wait,' wailed Kenaan frantically from below. I ignored him.

Then, just as I had calmed my nerves and had my finger on the trigger, there was a shrill human cry and four native cattle ran into the clearing, followed by their herdboy.

Relief overrode disappointment. I would never have lived it down. My God! I might even have shot the damn herdboy! The nearest village, Ntatumbila, was at least six miles away; why the cattle had been taken so far afield, with all that abundance of luscious grass near at hand, was a mystery I never solved – but it was a lesson I never forgot.

I found Piet at the Sanchi as planned. He'd not seen anything, either.

'Let's go back through the higher timber belt,' he suggested. 'The grass will be shorter.'

To get to it, we had to wade, waist deep, through a *dambo*, our rifles held high, trying not to stumble and trying to forget the leeches and snakes around us. It was incredibly hot – even with half of our bodies under water. We emerged and sat on an old log to smoke and dry out.

'Christ!' Piet yelled, suddenly jumping up and running away.

'What's wrong?' I called after him.

'Run, man, run! *Serui* ants.' I ran, but I was already covered in the little brutes. We stripped and helped each other to de-ant, gouging out their heads, which they left behind in our skin. *Serui* (*Siafu* in Swahili) ants are the most vicious little devils. Moving in long, mud-covered tunnels or in wide sheets of billions, they would clean out a larder in a couple of hours or devour your chickens

37

or any other caged or helpless animal in their path. This gruesome potential of theirs had once been used as a method of execution.

I was told of a mature lady missionary out for a stroll with a young District Officer cadet. Suddenly, she pulled up her skirt and began prancing about. The cadet was further shocked when the lady threw away her skirt and tore off her panties. Being a gentleman (perhaps he'd been to Cambridge, too), he turned away, only to have the lady shriek, 'For God's sake come here and help get these damned ants off me.

Serui ants could certainly be great levellers!

Before abandoning our hunt for supper, Piet decided to call up a duiker. Rolling a leaf into a cylinder, he blew down it like a whistle, experimenting until he produced a plaintive bleat. This, he said, was supposed to mimic the wail of a youngster in distress, or maybe a mating call. Almost immediately a little russet duiker came prancing through the bush to investigate. Its huge enquiring eyes and its answering bleat were so comical that I exploded with laughter, sending the delicate Bambi-like creature scurrying back into the safety of the bush.

Neither Piet nor his hunter, saw anything to laugh at, and Kenaan – well, what *was* he to think? He was still writhing in disgrace. Hadn't his *bwana*, less than an hour ago, almost shot an *ngombe*? Now this! What sin had he committed to be subjected to such mortification?

CASTLE IN THE BUSH

'Telegram from Shiwa, *bwana*,' Kenaan placed the pink form on my desk.

'URGENT TWO BULLS SICK GRATEFUL VISIT STOP
FRITZ SHIWA.

I had heard a lot about Shiwa Ngandu, a fabulous citrus and cattle estate in the middle of nowhere, and of its eccentric owner, Sir Stewart. A visit to Shiwa would also give me the chance of calling at Mbesuma Ranch, the largest cattle operation in the province, which was tucked away in the same semi-charted bush, a hundred miles further north.

I lost no time packing the vanette, and two hours later we were off. South of Kasama I turned east onto a dirt track which wound through dull, monotonous bush. I couldn't believe that anyone could grow citrus in such poor, stony soil until, coming over a low hill, I was astounded by the sudden transition to tall forest with a lake, guarded at the distant end by rocky crags. An oasis if ever there was one! An avenue of cypresses and blue gums ran up from the water to the biggest surprise of all: a real, live, medieval manor, half-hidden by tall trees.

Patches of bougainvillea and a multitude of bright flowers gave the scene a somewhat tropical air, but the overall impression was European – Swiss perhaps, or Austrian. The castle-like manor, the white, rocky tips of the crags that could have been snow, the steeply pitched roofs of the Swiss-like chalets on the hillside, the scent of oranges and limes which so easily could have been mistaken for a European orchard, even the plump rosy-faced man in a green pork-pie hat and tightly stretched shorts resembling *lederhosen*, who greeted me in a strong German accent, and whom I presumed to be Fritz; all contributed to the feeling of a country estate in Europe.

The creator of this spectacular haven, Sir Stewart, had stumbled on the little Lake Young while serving on a boundary commission before World War One. It must have made an unforgettable impression, for on his return from the trenches he had set about building his Shangri-La, calling it Shiwa Ngandu, 'The Lake of the Royal Crocodiles'.

Fritz, a refugee from Hitler's Germany and now manager, took me immediately to see the two sick bulls. Both looked miserable with high temperatures and almost white gums, and one was passing mahogany-coloured urine. These symptoms were typical of the tick-borne disease redwater, a close relative of biliary fever in dogs, both caused by a microscopic blood protozoan called Babesia. Treatment was by injecting an anti-protozoal drug, in those days Acaprin, a very effective remedy if it didn't kill the animal, which it could well do in advanced cases.

I inspected the dip tank through which the cattle plunged to kill the ticks. It was half full of mud, and the arsenic concentration of the dip fluid was hardly detectable. I told Fritz to clean it out, refill it at the correct strength and dip the herd weekly, instead of monthly, as he was doing.

We walked through the groves of citrus which covered the lower slopes of the hills and past sheds from which emanated the overpowering scent of oranges and limes.

'Where do you sell the fruit?' I asked, puzzled. I could think of no markets within several hundred miles.

'We don't. We extract essential oils for export.'

The manor house, or 'castle' as everyone called it, was impressively baronial, if a little impractical. The sun found it hard to penetrate the small windows, some of which were mere slits in the thick stone walls, so that the interior was always chilly and uninviting. The medieval dining hall with its echoing flagstones, 15-feet-long *mulombwa* table, heavy, carved chairs and austere portraits, was dark, depressing and icy cold.

The curving stone staircase, as in all genuine castles, had niches filled with coats of armour, and led to the much more friendly bedrooms and a tower where the lady of the house, Lady Lorna, had made her study, and from which, when she was in residence, she directed the estate. Her little garret looked down on the avenue of cypresses and blue gums that ran down to the sparkling silver medallion of Lake Young.

I wondered if the 'castle' was yet haunted and whether black ghosts roamed its corridors at night. It was certainly eerie enough. Although I couldn't help but admire this nostalgic replica of an ancestral retreat, it was not a place in which I could be comfortable.

I only met Sir Stewart once, as his duties on the Legislative Council kept him in Lusaka. He was a shortish, red-faced, monocled 'Colonel Blimp' type and, for all his liberal leanings, liable to fly off the handle and take it out on any African who crossed him, with a *chikoti* (sjambok)! Whether it was because of his quick temper or because he had shot a rhino on his first visit to Shiwa, his native name was *chipelembe* – the rhinoceros. I was too young and shy to ask this senior member of Legislative Council why he had built such an incongruous abode in the middle of the African bush, but I suspected that it was simply a Rhodes-like statement of British Imperialism.

After two delightful days, I said goodbye to Fritz and set off for Mbesuma following a little-used track (judging by the frequent anthills I had to circumnavigate) which soon began to drop and reveal the distant flood plain of the Chambezi river and a homestead halfway down the escarpment.

Fred, the owner of Mbesuma, was a small, shy man in his late forties who spoke with a Cockney accent. Words gushed from him as he led me into his long, low, thatched farmhouse, every wall of which was adorned with the heads of game.

I arrived shortly before lunch – his first visitor in three months, he told me. At eleven that night we were still chatting at the table, a Tilley lamp hissing in a corner where it attracted the larger flying insects away from us. The only interludes were visits to the toilet. Food and tea were brought and removed almost unnoticed as he recounted his adventures, contorting his weather-beaten features into almost music hall expressions to emphasize his points.

Fred had come to Africa at the age of 17 and fought in the 1914–18 war, where he had distinguished himself by carrying news of the Armistice to an isolated bunch of German troops a week after peace had been signed.

The bastards kept shootin' at me although I was wavin' me white 'an'kerchief on a stick – an' it wasn't *that* dirty! But they gave me an MBE for me trouble.'

He also explained why he had never married – a white woman, that is.

'Y' know, when yer young, yer takes what's offered, 'an in those days the only ones were black. I didn't think it were right to go with white women after that. But I've a good old lady out at the back 'an a couple of kids around.' I never saw them.

Fred's greatest problem was lions. At the time of my visit he had killed over 460, as well as numerous leopards, cheetahs and hunting dogs. Five years later he wrote that he had killed his 500th lion, one of the biggest he'd ever seen, 12 feet 2 inches from nose to tail, with a skull measuring 14½ by 10 inches. 'He took nine of me cows before I got him,' he added, 'so he had his run.'

His 3,000 head of cattle were a mixture of long-horned Afrikander, Shorthorn and Sussex. They were nearly all fat and sleek, as they should have been with miles and miles of the Chambezi flood plain to graze on, but here and there I would observe an animal that was thin or deformed.

'Better cut that one's throat to save its life,' I would joke.

'Maybe; but you see that dark cow over there?' ... indicating a beautiful beast. 'It's 'er best friend. She'd be lonely if I killed 'er best friend.' Or, 'I nursed that one night an' day after she was mauled by a lion. I couldn't kill 'er now, even if she is lame.'

His kraals were fenced with a particularly thorny Lentana bush, impossible for lions to penetrate, which some well-intentioned stockowner had imported from Australia. Now birds had carried the seed all over the province, making it the number one pest.

Once a year, Fred would drive 500 or 600 steers down to the railhead at Kapiri Mposhi, 700 miles to the south. He would lose a number, but it was his only market.

By far the best view from Fred's house was from his 'PK'. This little room, situated at one end of his bungalow, was a variation on the usual 'dull thump' toilet. It would have been more correct to call it the 'delayed splash', since he had built it over an underground stream, which I could hear gurgling away 20 feet below my posterior!

The panorama from this remarkable convenience took in the whole sweep of the Chambesi and its flood plain, with the grey-green bush dissolving imperceptibly into the grey-blue sky of the distant horizon. It was truly a royal 'throne'.

I would like to have known more about Fred, how he had hit on Mbesuma and how he got started, but somehow we never broached the subject. Perhaps I was too shy to ask, or there was too much else to talk about. He wasn't an educated man and I doubt if he came from a moneyed family. I heard later that he had written his memoirs, but I have been unable to trace them.

'Freds' were not uncommon in East and Central Africa, driftwood from the Boer War or World War One perhaps, hating what they had seen of civilization: adventurers at the end of their wanderings, or genuine 'loners'. Whatever the reason, they contributed much to the development of the bush.

NGOMBE FROM NYASALAND

'It'll be a bloody headache,' Jimmy had warned before he left. 'Glad it's you, not me.'

His words came back to me as I read the letter from Mazabuka telling me that I should now go ahead with the importation of cattle from Nyasaland (Malawi).

I unearthed the relevant file and read up the background to the scheme. It seemed that a recent border revision had cut off a number of villagers from their cattle, which were still grazing on the other side of the new Nyasaland border. Since regulations prohibited any bovine from crossing the border from Nyasaland into Northern Rhodesia, in case they brought in East Coast fever, the owners had virtually lost control of their herds.

The obvious solution was for these dispossessed villagers to sell their cattle in Nyasaland and use the proceeds to buy replacements in Northern Rhodesia – except that, unfortunately for them, cattle were plentiful and cheap in Nyasaland while on the Rhodesian side they were scarce and expensive. They would lose heavily on such a deal.

After months of argument, it had been agreed to let them bring over their cattle, but only to sell for slaughter under veterinary supervision. The Government would buy them, quarantine them for a month, sell them to butchers and then supervise their distribution to the various centres in the Northern Province. The risk of introducing disease would thus be minimized and the Government-controlled prices would be sufficient for the ex-owners to buy replacements.

There was another reason for starting these importations. Regular, controlled imports of slaughter stock would help solve the acute meat shortage of the Northern Province. This operation was to be looked upon as a trial run.

I wrote to Head Office for more information and last-minute instructions regarding funds for the scheme. Knowing that it would take several weeks for a reply, I took a trip down to the border to see just what I was in for.

Fifteen miles south of Tunduma, I turned off the Great North Road and followed a little-used, sandy road along the border to Fort Hill and Nyasaland. Immediately, the soil and vegetation changed. Rocky outcrops appeared. Huge stalagmite-like needles thrust skywards while massive rock faces solemnly guarded the road on either side.

At Nyala, the site of a long abandoned administration post, I came across a sad reminder of those who had once come to help establish *Pax Britannica* in Central Africa. A few yards from the road in a small clearing, rough headstones marked the graves of two officials who had died there in 1898; John Patrick Marshall Drysdale and E.J. Millar. There was no longer any evidence of a *boma* or settlement. Bush covered the lonely spot where these two pioneers had upheld the White Man's Burden, laughed their laughs, sighed their sighs, dreamed their dreams and in the end given their all for their Queen and Empire.

The Zone Guards gave me a list of some 60 cattle owners wishing to bring their cattle across for sale, so I told them to construct a large quarantine kraal near the border village of Mwenimpanza, where an emergency landing ground would provide good open grazing. The track to Mwenimpanza, they warned me, was very bad and several bridges needed repair before I could drive there. They suggested I start buying near the Fort Hill road. I headed back to Abercorn, well pleased at my arrangements. Jimmy had obviously exaggerated; there was nothing to it. It would be a piece of cake.

The day before I was due to return to Mwenimpanza, I called in at the Abercorn *boma* to draw the purchase money.

'Where's your authority?' Victor, the District Commissioner, asked.

'I've received an official OK from headquarters to go ahead, and you have had copies of all the correspondence.'

'Not the same, old man. You don't know these accountants like I do.'

'But damn it all, Victor, everything's fixed. The sale starts in a couple of days. I'm leaving tomorrow for the border.'

'All right. Draw out what you want, but for God's sake be careful. I'm the one who's responsible. I'll notify your Director.'

I took £700, all in half-crowns, shillings and sixpences. I told Kenaan to fetch another two messengers to help him carry the money box to the vanette.

'Is all right, *bwana*,' he boasted 'I too strong. Not need help.'

His pride sagged a bit when he found he could barely pull the box along the floor. £700 in silver is pretty weighty, and the heavy metal strongbox added at least another 30 pounds.

It was mid-afternoon when I reached the Game Department's hut near Kaombe's village, where I would be staying and where the track to Mwenimpanza turned off the Fort Hill road. After unloading I left Kosam to cook the evening meal while Kenaan, his brother Cephas and I, went off with the Zone Guards, to inspect the quarantine kraal. The five miles of semi-cleared bush that acted as a road were, without doubt, the worst I had ever travelled. The Guards hadn't lied when they said it was very bad. I was either bumping up hill in bottom gear or lunging downhill in bottom gear, the vanette dipping and rocking like a dinghy in a choppy sea. The bridges across the steep gullies had been repaired with thick branches laid closely on top of rickety poles. They looked anything but safe. The five miles took us over half an hour.

'At least it's driveable, we won't have to walk it,' I joked to Kenaan as we arrived at the kraal.

The Zone Guards had done an excellent job. The stockade of ten-foot stakes lashed together with bark rope was large enough for 200 cattle. I hoped it would be as vermin-proof as it looked; this was Five Star, Grade A lion and leopard country!

On top of a nearby hill, I found the Emergency Landing Strip. While the foot-high, waving grass would be an ideal place for cattle to graze, the strip was anything but ideal for landing an aircraft. Perhaps the white-haired caretaker had heard that a *bwana* was coming, for there he was, digging away feverishly in the middle of the runway. Proudly, he showed me his handiwork.

I shouldn't have been so surprised. All Emergency Landing Grounds were marked with a large letter 'A' in whitewashed stones sunk into the centre of the runway. Our friend at Mwenimpanza, who had never seen that mythical beast, the aeroplane, had embellished his efforts by erecting a three-foot-high, beautifully white-washed beacon of rocks on top of the 'A' surrounded by an 18-inch-deep trench. Patiently, with the help of diagrams in the dust, I explained that the ground must be level and what would happen if an aeroplane were to land at that moment.

I left him energetically destroying his handiwork and filling the trench with rocks from the beacon.

There was always someone collecting something, and I had promised to collect butterflies for one of the station wives whenever I was on *ulendo*. Thousands (butterflies, not wives,) were bobbing and dancing all over the field, so I spent a joyous half-hour stalking them with my hat. White ones there were with red-tipped wings, and brown ones and a little sky-blue variety, and occasionally a darting, pointed-winged, green and purple monster which defied capture. Game droppings, I had noticed, were invariably covered with a white and yellow species. Later, to save myself the trouble of hunting down individuals, I tied a butterfly net to the front bumper of the vanette and thus collected thousands of insects, including butterflies, as I drove along.

I was congratulating myself on how well everything was going as we bumped back down the track to Kaombe. But I had forgotten my rash boast to Kenaan that we wouldn't have to walk up from Kaombe each day. Scarcely were my rear wheels on the logs of the last rickety bridge when there was a loud crack and I was thrown across onto the passenger seat. Kenaan let out a screech of terror as he discovered there was nothing between him and the stream at the bottom of the gulley!

Christ! I thought: we're going to tip over. Luckily, the vehicle held firm, even if it was at a frightening angle. We climbed out warily. Both the front and rear wheels on the left side had gone through the bridge, and we had been saved from total disaster only by a thicker log in the centre of the structure. It took two hours to jack the vanette up, insert stronger logs and reach the other side.

I had suspected for some time that an invisible adversary, perhaps a band of little Black Imps working in cahoots with Dame Africa (who must have known by now what I felt about her), was bent on making things as difficult for me as possible. Several minor annoyances had occurred since I reached Abercorn, starting with the recall of the beautiful Zeiss microscope to Mazabuka, the destruction by *dudus* of my vegetable garden and, a few days previously, the loss of my only two bottles of beer, which I had been keeping for this *ulendo*, when they mysteriously fell off a shelf in my store. Now here was further proof. Dame Africa must have heard me bragging to Kenaan, and set her Black Imps to work! But I'd show her. No Black Imp was going to get away with this. The bridge could certainly be repaired in a couple of days.

I had brought the *boma* radio which had been issued to Ian, as District Officer, and which we connected to the battery of my vanette when I was in Abercorn. Since Ian had no vehicle and couldn't use it when I was on *ulendo* (there were no spare batteries in Abercorn), I took it along with me. This sturdy Philips had been sunned upon, rained upon, smothered in dust, jostled, jolted, bumped and dropped, but it still brought in Tommy Handley and the BBC news. I had just finished listening to the latest BBC bulletin when I heard Kenaan cough behind me.

'Headman Kaombe greets you,' he intoned, shuffling forward. 'Headman' was a step lower than a chief.

Kenaan always reminded me of a guilty schoolboy on these occasions, his head bowed, hands behind his back and a 'sorry to disturb you' smirk, as he tried hard to excuse his office as chief '*bwana* botherer'.

Headman Kaombe, however, was worth meeting. He spoke fair English and had travelled. His most prized possession was a .303 rifle, a one-shot affair, dated 1887, given to his father by a former Resident Magistrate. It was a real collector's item. Unlike most other headmen, Kaombe was interested in current affairs – and he didn't beg. Politely, he refused payment for the mealie meal and eggs he had brought but said that if I could find any .303 ammunition for his rifle, he would accept it as a present between friends. I found a few rounds in the ammunition box and gave them to him. Later, when we both fired a couple to test the accuracy of his rifle, neither of us could hit a piece of paper a foot square, pinned to a tree at 20 yards!

Kaombe was especially pleased to see me, he said, because lions had killed some cattle two nights before and now I could shoot them. The African's faith in the White Man as a slayer of lions was unshakeable. If the occasion arose, I hoped I wouldn't be found wanting either in valour or accuracy!

I had arranged to meet the Veterinary Officer from Northern Nyasaland at Fort Hill, 40 miles to the south. I strolled over to where Kenaan's legs were protruding from beneath the vanette.

'Everything ready?' I asked brightly.

'Sorry, *bwana*, but two springs break.'

'Impossible!'

'True, *bwana*. *Bwana* must look.'

Sure enough. The left front spring had come adrift and the left rear had two blades broken. How we had driven back last night was a mystery. Now, even if the bridge was repaired, I no longer had a vehicle. The Black Imps had thought of everything! But I wasn't beaten yet. A missionary had told me how he had reached home on a spring made from grass. I decided to try it. Kenaan made a sheaf of tough dried grass, two feet long and six inches in diameter, tightly bound with bark rope, with which he replaced the front spring. Then he bound up the rear spring with a leather *riem*, a thong of dried cattle hide. All went well until I tried to turn a corner. The grass was too weak to stand the strain of steering and tore away. (I had better luck the following year, when I repaired the ball-and-socket joint on the steering rod with a beer bottle cap, which took me 80 miles back to the station!). I helped push the vehicle back to camp, thinking that my missionary friend must have had a stronger faith than I, and was, no doubt, also protected against Black Imps!

I sent a Zone Guard on his bicycle with a note to Fort Hill telling the Veterinary Officer I was immobilized, and then despatched Cephas on a bicycle with the broken springs to await the weekly mail lorry at Tunduma, which would take them to Abercorn for welding. He was full of objections. There were too many lions and leopards. *Bwana* was sending him to certain death. So I gave him a gun and told him on no account to travel at night. I was well equipped to spend a few days by the roadside. My camera and sketching materials I always carried with me, and I had several books from the TVMI, including the autobiography of a burglar, *Low Company*, from which I extracted 96 words I had never heard before! I was illiterate compared to this crook. No wonder they had sent me to Cambridge! The only commodity in really short supply was drinking water. The water from Kaombe's stream was a dirty grey, even after straining through a sock and boiling, and the taste matched its colour!

The radio told of the Allied advances in France and I tried to pass on a simplified version to Kenaan and Headman Kaombe, the only two who would be able to understand. Kenaan had had some experience in the 1914–18 show, helping with supplies behind the lines.

'You weren't a fighting soldier, then?' I asked.

'*Awe, bwana*. Fighting soldiers soon deaded. I not fight. I not bloody fool.'

A car pulled into the camp late that afternoon and a large, fair-haired man introduced himself as the Veterinary Officer, Northern Nyasaland. He suggested we went to Fort Hill and spend the next day together before the buying started.

Gray was the first person I had met who admitted to liking Africa. I had taken it for granted that no-one could actually like the place, so to find someone who was actually happy and content was a shock. Stroking his bushy blonde moustache, he told me that he had served in the Army, New Zealand, the Sudan and Tanganyika, but he liked his present post the best.

Customs Post, Fort Hill, Nyasaland.

On my map, Fort Hill was inscribed in letters of the same size as those used for towns on the railway, but all I could see in the growing dusk were three thatched, wattle-and-daub huts and an avenue of 'pregnant palms' (so-called because of the bulge halfway up their trunks) that lined the road. The largest hut was the Rest House, one of many which the Government put up for the use of officials on tour. The other two were the customs and immigration post from which a telephone line ran south; and a small African branch of Mandala's stores. The Rest House caretaker, the Customs Clerk and the storekeeper were the black aristocracy of Fort Hill.

There was no room for me at the Government farm where Gray was staying, so he dropped me at the Rest House. While I was changing, there was a knock on the door. I opened it.

''Ello,' said a small figure.

At first, all I could see was long straggly grey hair and a massive grey beard. Then as the figure moved nearer to my flickering hurricane lamp, I saw in the midst of the unkempt fuzz a rosy weather-beaten face sliced by a toothless grin. We shook hands and introduced ourselves.

Charlie Woods had been in Africa since Adam was a boy, first as a professional hunter and collector, then farming, prospecting and odd-jobbing, and now, in his declining years (Charlie wasn't a day under 70), he was 'strolling about', taking it easy. He had two daughters in London, he said, but had forgotten their married names. He invited me to dinner.

48

'I ain't got no money, But I've got some grub,' he chuckled.

When he said 'no money', he meant just that and was camping in the Rest House car shelter, unable to find the five shillings (about 25p) for a room. The meal was entertaining. Charlie had to hold his 18-inch beard to one side with his left hand while he fed himself with his right. On account of no teeth, natural or false, he was restricted to soups and mushy stews, and there was a good deal of slurping. Thinking to give him a treat, I offered him some chocolate. He grabbed the half-pound bar and polished it off without stopping. It was my last.

'That's the first chocolate I 'ave had for five years, and you're the first white man I've spoken to for six months,' he told me.

With his tousled, unkempt locks, dirty khaki shirt and trousers, and much-mended boots, he certainly didn't look as if he had been gracing society lately. What I could see of his neck was wrinkled and black with grime, and from the colour of his hands he could have been an African. We parted late, Charlie (like Fred at Mbesuma) had hardly once stopped talking, but I was glad to listen; a man cannot survive half a century in the African bush without something to tell.

Unlike the burning heat of the day, the night sent a chilly breeze. I snuggled under two blankets with a pullover on top of my pyjamas, listening to the 'pregnant palms' rustling their fronds.

The early morning view from the Rest House was memorable. The valley which rolled away westwards to the blue Mafinga Mountains was covered with a ground mist, turning it into a silver lake out of which jutted tree-covered islands. Gray and I spent the day visiting local herds.

That evening, Charlie Woods (still talking) and I (still listening) strolled down the avenue of 'pregnant palms'. I wondered whether the two men whose pathetic graves I had seen at Nyala had anything to do with their planting. The dark outline of the Mafingas swelled up to the south-west behind the setting sun, their peaks beckoning and sending little thrills down my spine. It looked as if sheep might do well on those high treeless terraces; it would be excuse enough to explore them.

The next morning, Gray drove me to Mukubwe, a village near Kaombe, where buying was due to start.

'I think two or three days should be long enough to buy a hundred head,' I told him.

'Should be if they decide to come,' he replied. 'They're a queer lot when it comes to selling cattle.'

'Well, they've had a month's notice and a lot of reminding and, dammit, it's at their request.'

49

'Doesn't mean a thing, old man.'

The chap's crazy, I thought.

A table and chairs had been set up for us beneath a shady tree on the edge of a clearing.

'Where are the cattle?' I asked the Zone Guard in charge.

'Not yet come, *bwana*.' He didn't look very happy.

'But it's nine o'clock. Some should have come by now.'

My friend smiled. 'We'd better wait a bit, just in case some do turn up.'

'What d'you mean just in case? They'd better turn up, and quick.' What was the matter with the fellow?

But by eleven, it was obvious that none would. Only three men and a picannin had slunk out of the bush to stare.

'Don't let it get you down,' said Gray. 'This is normal. You'll get used to it.'

Like hell I will, I thought. I do things differently. I asked Kenaan why no-one had come.

'You see, *bwana*, all people want too much bring cattle but not sell. So they wait and see.'

I had to do something, the whole scheme and future importations could be at stake. I asked Gray what the East Coast fever situation was across the border and, on his assurance that it was almost unknown this far north, I gave out that I would buy cattle from anyone in the area, on either side of the border and that they should bring them to the kraal at Mwenimpanza each morning, which would be the only place I could reach easily without a vehicle. I stomped back to Gray's vanette in a deliberate show of anger.

'Leave me at Kaombe,' I told him. 'It'll probably take longer than I thought.'

'Probably,' was his only comment.

On the way, a huge leopard crossed the road just in front of us. I grabbed my gun and opened the door, but Gray put out a restraining hand. 'Shouldn't if I were you. If you wound it, remember that apart from yourself, there are two boys in the back, unprotected.'

It was a nice way of saying 'Don't be a bloody fool.'

The next evening I was told that five cattle were at the kraal for sale. It was a start.

I set out at dawn, arriving at Mwenimpanza an hour and a half later, exhausted. The walk seemed endless. I never knew that five miles could be so long. Admittedly, the kraal was 800 feet higher than Kaombe's village and there were four or five steep-sided gorges *en route*.

The strongbox with the cash presented a problem. It was too heavy to carry up and back each day, so after lugging it up the first morning, slung in a bark net from a pole between two porters, I left it at the kraal, taking the key with me. I wondered what Victor would have said if he had known that his precious money was lying in a grass hut on the border, with a solitary Zone Guard sleeping by it. But theft in the bush, in those days, was unheard of.

To add a little amusement to the routine, I told Kenaan one morning that I had forgotten the key and would he run back for it 'Quick, quick, you lazy old man.' Then, when he had gone a hundred yards at an unwilling shuffle, I shouted that I had found it, after all. He returned, all smiles and chuckles, like a schoolboy who had escaped punishment, knowing full well that I had tricked him.

Another morning, however, I did forget the key and sent Kenaan back with precise instructions as to where to find it. He arrived back at the kraal with a long face.

'I not find it *bwana*.'

'What? Did you look in the pocket of my jacket, like I said?'

'*Ndio, bwana*.

'And Kosam not find it?'

'*Awé, bwana*.'

'Well that's that for to-day.'

I went through my pockets in one last hope. Nothing.

I was about to start back when I noticed Kenaan's face pucker into a grin. Then squeaky noises escaped from his contorted body and at last he held out the key. The Guards were equally delirious. Kenaan had really fooled the *bwana*. I had to laugh too. After all, who had started it?

Some days only two or three cattle appeared, other days up to 15. I decided the price of each animal in consultation with Kenaan and a Zone Guard, depending on its estimated weight. Immediately after purchase, the cattle were branded with a big 'S' on their shoulder so the Zone Guards could recognize them later if they hadn't been slaughtered within the specified period.

The only really unpleasant part of the proceedings was the fine black dust mixed with dried dung, that was kicked up in clouds by the animals milling round the kraal, and which caked my eyes and nostrils.

To make the morning walk more interesting, I tried to reduce my time each day. My best was sixty five minutes. After that I contracted a nasty bout of athlete's foot and had to give up racing myself. In those days there was no specific treatment for this fungal disease, Johnson's baby powder shaken into my socks being the only alleviative.

51

Zone Guards branding cattle.

One day I asked Kenaan about the big black 'soldier' ants which scurried across the road in mobile ribbons.

'Where are they going, *Nsofu*?'

'To war, *bwana*.'

'Who with?'

'With white ants, *bwana*. They all time fight white ants.'

'And who wins?'

'I not know, *bwana*. Sometime black ant he win, sometime white ant.'

We laughed, both recognizing the analogy.

I collected scores of insects, trying to identify each in my copy of Imms' *Entomology*, which I always took on *ulendo*. One of the most fascinating was the *nakatwitwi*, the patient little ant-lion whose small conical excavations pitted the sandy ground all over the camp. Burying himself at the bottom of his pit, the cunning creature would wait until an insect slipped in, then, by throwing up particles of sand onto the sloping sides, he would start small avalanches and force the victim to slide down into his drooling jaws.

I had been at Kaombe a week when, on returning from the kraal, I found a batch of letters and a note from Lanky, the Senior Game Warden, saying that he had intended to join me that night, but had broken down five miles to the south and could I pick him up. His messenger had continued on to Tunduma to send a message to Abercorn for a mechanic. Thoughtfully, Lanky had brought my mail.

There was an aerogramme (a wartime weight-saving, photocopy device on a four-by-five-inch sheet) from Patricia. Dances, officers she had met (I felt jealous and more than a little anxious), reminiscences and pleas not to go into the bush alone. I laughed, it was probably more dangerous to walk down Piccadilly – I often wished it *was* a little more exciting.

I sent Cephas with a message to Lanky saying that I was also *kaput*, but would walk down and meet him halfway at three that afternoon. I set off alone, but within a mile I met Cephas returning on his bicycle, with a note from Lanky saying that he couldn't make it that day but would walk over in the morning and stay with me till his truck was repaired. After Cephas had cycled off back to Kaombe, I sat on a log, smoking and whittling a stick. Only the calls of ground doves could be heard, a sound which to this day takes me right back to that lonely road. Tiring of inactivity, I followed a duiker spoor which led me along a dried-up river bed. I loved wandering in the forest and along river beds sparkling with mica dust, my stomach churning with excitement and suspense. One had to be alert, of course, there were real dangers – lions, snakes, a frightened buck or bushpig, and game pits; all of which could easily spell disaster.

I lost the duiker spoor and returned to the road to see Kenaan running towards me from the direction of Lanky's camp, carrying my rifle and very worried and out of breath.

'*Bwana, bwana!*'

'What's wrong?'

'I sleep when *bwana* go and when I wake I ask "Where *bwana*?" and Kosam tell me say *bwana* gone see *bwana* Lankesti. Then Cephas come back and say *bwana* still on road. Then I see *bwana* gun, and run take it to *bwana*. But I not see *bwana* and *bwana* Lankesti boy say *bwana* not come. Then I too fright so I run fasti, fasti in case lion eat *bwana*.' Here he looked at me sorrowfully. '*Bwana* too brave, or *bwana* too much bloody fool!'

He was right. I'd made a fool of myself again. It was asking for trouble to go off alone without a gun. I wondered what Patricia would have said. I tried to laugh it off.

'But look, *Nsofu*. I have my knife.'

He thought this was a huge joke and squatted on the ground beside me, chuckling and puffing on the cigarette I'd given him.

'No-one kill lion with knife, *bwana*.'

'Yes, one man. *Mukulamba sana* hunter in South Africa.' And I told him how Harry Wolhuther, a ranger in the Kruger Park, had stabbed a lion through the heart as it was dragging him away.

Lanky was waiting for me when I returned from the kraal the following day. In his early fifties, he was still a bachelor, a state he continually threatened to remedy. Fortunately for some unknown lass, he never did. Lanky was a man's man and inseparable from the bush. There was nowhere he could have put a woman.

The black-and-white photo which I took of him in the bar of the Abercorn Arms, now before me as I write, shows a man of medium height with an inquisitive, rather ferrety face, wearing a bush shirt, a pith helmet tilted back to show a deeply wrinkled forehead, and a spotted handkerchief round his throat. I do not ever remember him without his helmet, even at table, or for that matter, without his spotted neckerchief. His left hand is supporting the bowl of a very old (and very smelly) pipe, the other end of which is held between almost prehensile lips. If the photo had been in colour it might have been possible to make out the light amethyst eyes, but even a black-and-white print could not hide the deep tan of his face and forearms.

Lanky was self-educated. Leaving school before his sixteenth birthday, he had relied on books and experience to make him one of the Game Department's most knowledgeable authorities. His library at Kasama filled four walls of a large room, and there was nothing he liked better, between puffs of his reeking pipe, than to air his theory of man's origin around the great lakes of Central Africa. His grasp of anthropology always surprised me, as did his appreciation of art. He once gave me a small guide for art collectors published by his father who had been an art dealer. I could have asked for no more interesting a companion to while away the days at Kaombe.

It was several days before a mechanic, a coloured lad, arrived from Abercorn, bringing my springs with him. We towed Lanky's truck into the camp at Kaombe so the mechanic could work at night, in safety. While he hammered and banged at the truck's innards, Lanky and I sat in front of a log fire, sipping brandy beneath a full moon and listening to the shrill persistent wail of the *walitumpa*, a type of bushbaby whose name meant 'bloody fool'.

It didn't strike me that there was anything unusual in being stranded hundreds of miles from civilization, surrounded by lion-infested bush with a dubious supply of water and uncertain source of food. Six months had made me a bit blasé about the bush!

Back in Abercorn, I separated my private mail from the official 'cag', and took it down to Lake Chila to read. Charlie wrote glowing accounts of the Jamaican beaches, sailing, girls and night clubs, which rekindled all my old desires and made me so envious and frustrated that I tore up the letter without finishing it.

Bloody liar, I thought, I bet he's sweating it out the same as I am. But, somehow, I knew he wasn't.

BUREAUCRACY IN THE BUNDU

'Shun.' Kenaan's voice boomed out as I approached the office and Cephas, usually the only other person present, jumped to attention and saluted.

So began another day. Later, when I had added a Veterinary Assistant and a clerk to my retinue, these worthies would bow themselves into my office after I was seated, to tender their personal aspirations for my continued good health.

After a busy morning doing absolutely nothing of importance, except perhaps filling in my travel claim (five shillings for each night spent away from the station), Ian might stroll down from the *boma* and together, if it was warm enough (even central Africa can be chilly at 5,500 feet), we would drive down to the Red Locust Control headquarters where Hans, the Belgian co-director, had diverted a stream through an old clay pit to make a swimming pool. Others might join us. Sylvia, the Nursing Sister, daughter of a local missionary; Jack, the doctor, or Westy, the tall, skinny ex-Singapore policeman, now Quartermaster of the Polish camp. A drink with Hans and Lislotte in their creeper-covered bungalow and a bite at home, then it was back for another two hours in the office.

Wednesdays and Saturdays were tennis days at the club, where seven or eight of us would bang very worn balls about a hard mud court. Occasionally, Westy would arrange a game of football. These games were rather confused as there were remains of anthills on the field and the players, both white and black, were inclined to rewrite the rules as the game progressed. But it was fun – and gave us much-needed exercise.

Evenings were spent at home or in the bar of the Abercorn Arms, or dining with friends, and once a month there was a gramophone concert at the club. A wooden box with a handle to wind it up and a large trumpet through which the music emerged was all we had to fill the high raftered hall of the thatched, wattle-and-daub clubhouse with the strains of Beethoven or Mozart. Astonishingly, there was a large selection of classical records (all '78's', of course) to be had amongst the few Europeans. Gramophone needles, those short thick pins which had to be fixed into the sound box, were unobtainable. Instead, fibre needles cut from a variety of woody plants were used, the operator disappearing outside now and then to cut a new batch, as one needle would only last for one side of the old 78 record.

As far as official duties were concerned, the Director had been right, it wasn't easy to become a 'simple serpent'. Even in the bush bureaucracy flourished just as well as at Headquarters. I began to distinguish two distinct subspecies of bureaucrats, the 'conformists' and the 'non-conformists'. The first adhered to each word of the regulations, the latter took the commonsense, progressive approach and interpreted the rules only as far as they got things done. There were continual battles between the two groups, often accompanied by sly poems. One, said to have originated in the United Services Club in Calcutta, I kept.

Form of Daily Service for use in Government Departments

> Let us pray:
> 'O Lord, grant that this day we come to no decisions,
> Neither run into any kind of responsibility,
> But that all our doings may be ordered to establish
> New and quite unwarranted departments;
> For ever and ever. Amen'

> Hymn:
> O Thou who seest all things below,
> Grant that thy servants may go slow,
> That they may study to comply
> With regulations till they die.

> Teach us, Lord, to reverence
> Committees more than common sense;
> Impress our minds to make no plan,
> But pass the baby when we can.

> And when our tempter seems to give
> Us feelings of initiative,
> Or when alone we go too far,
> Chastise us with a circular.

> Mid war and tumult, fire and storms,
> Strengthen us, we pray, with forms.
> Thus will thy servants ever be,
> A flock of perfect sheep to thee.

I even made up one myself:

The mills of God grind slowly,
But they grind exceeding small,
Colonial mills grind slower still –
That's if they grind at all!

I was rather proud of it.

Cephas Simbaya

Sometimes a po-faced administrator would carry his convictions to absurd lengths. One District Commissioner and his young District Officer were accustomed to go hunting at weekends. Monday morning a grim-faced DC summoned his DO into his office.

'I'm very sorry, old man, but I'll have to put you in court this morning. One of the birds you shot yesterday was a protected species. I just looked it up.'

'But you also shot one.' The DO was rather put out at these accusations.

'I know, so you will have to prosecute me afterwards,' the DC replied. 'It's just routine, of course, to show that no-one is above the law.'

The old man must be going crackers, thought the DO as he stood in the dock listening to the DC pronouncing sentence – 'A fine of ten shillings.'

The DO and his superior then swopped places. It was now the DO's chance to score off his bone-headed chief.

'This is the second case of this nature we have had this morning,' he intoned pompously. 'I feel it is my duty to make an example – thirty days or twenty pounds.'

History does not record whether they ever went hunting together again!

* * *

I had spent the voyage out swotting up my tropical medicine so as not to appear too green on arrival. But dreams of well-equipped laboratories, bustling technicians, and important investigations culminating in a PhD, had fallen rather flat – my responsibility, I was told, was simply to prevent and control animal disease in the Northern Province, an area larger than Spain, and I soon realized that the 'high heed yins' were far more concerned as to whether I could judge the weight of an ox accurately, organize cattle markets and vaccination campaigns, erect a good building, repair a broken-down vehicle, fill in forms and handle the natives, than whether I could carry out scientific studies. Common sense and public relations had a much higher rating than academic learning.

Clinical work was non-existent. Distances and lack of communications made attention to individual animals almost impossible. It was better to kill and eat a sick ox before it lost too much flesh. Apart from the treatment of tick-borne diseases in valuable imported grade stock, and there were only four farms with such animals in the whole of the province, it was left to the occasional pet dog or cat to test my professional expertise.

Well, even if the veterinary field was a non-starter, anthropology and archaeology might satisfy my enquiring nature. I decided to explore every nook and cranny of my domain and read every book on the area that I could find. Why shouldn't I be a tourist while I had the chance? I wouldn't get another opportunity to swan around an area of Central Africa, the size of the Iberian peninsula, at Government expense!

Doubloons might be rare on this dark continent, but there were probably other treasures just as exciting.

BUSH MUSIC

A thing that gave me increasing delight was my piano accordion.

'Right, I'll send it up a lorry next week. Must get rid of the damn thing before Susan comes back from school. Drove us bats last holidays.'

The burly PWD superintendent took my cheque for ten pounds, got into his vanette and waved me goodbye.

And that was how, quite by chance and on the spur of the moment, I acquired my first piano accordion, a 48-bass Hohner, quite adequate for a beginner and the ideal instrument for rowdy parties where noise was an important ingredient.

I took it with me everywhere, across the Luangwa valley and up the Mafinga Mountains, and even into the Bangweulu swamp. Many a wild beast must have wondered at the strange vibrations that filtered through the forest at sundown. The messengers and Zone Guards thought it was great, and I made up special tunes for them.

I had always considered myself musically inclined. At the age of 14 I had taken up the violin, which I played in the school orchestra, and with my brother Terry, a competent flautist, began to compose a symphony, of which I still have the opening bars. In an effort to gain musical recognition, I also wrote a violin solo and a hymn tune, hoping that they would be performed at the annual Corpus Christi Founders' Day celebrations. They weren't! I gave up the violin at University and bought a mouth organ which I could play anywhere at any time – and did.

This piano accordion, however, was a great jump ahead. It only took a couple of weeks to relate the chord buttons on the left hand to the piano keys on the right, and regulate the squeezing, and even if it didn't please everyone, it gave me a certain sense of musical achievement. Only Flea was rude enough to object. He would begin

Self caricature

to howl the minute he saw me reach for the devilish device, slinking off, ashamed that any master of his could be responsible for such a ghastly noise.

It seemed that you either loved it or you hated it, and Flea was determined to leave no doubt in anyone's mind as to which side he was on!

PANDA'S EPIC RUN

'He'll soon fatten out,' said my friend. 'He's only six weeks old. Mixture of ridgeback and pointer, not a bad cross.'

I looked at the large head, long tail and skinny ribs. He wasn't quite the type I had dreamed about, but pups were scarce. Once home, I gave him a meal while I picked fleas off my legs. Then I mixed up some Jeyes and bathed him.

'You're just a ruddy flea factory,' I told him. 'In fact that's exactly what I'm going to call you – Flea.'

A few days later, an African brought a baby jackal to the door. It would be company for Flea, I thought. I gave him a 'ticky' (three-penny bit) for it.

Ticky and Flea were immediate friends, except at meal times when Ticky became vicious if interrupted. But the friendship wasn't allowed to blossom. One day the mosquito control gang, who kept the grass short round the houses, came across Ticky frolicking in the long grass and killed him. Probably it was as well, he could have taught Flea all sorts of bad habits, and jackals were not easy to domesticate.

Flea grew rapidly into a sleek yellow hound with large floppy ears, olive eyes and an incredible burst of speed. Kipling's 'yellow dog Dingo' described him exactly. He would terrorize the piccanins we encountered on *ulendo*, driving them up the nearest tree, where he kept them until told to desist. But I never remember him biting anyone. He liked to sit beside me in the vanette, his eyes fixed on the road, drooling with anticipation. No matter at what speed I was travelling, he only needed to glimpse a hare or a buck to be through the window, rolling over and over as he hit the ground, before he was off in pursuit. Panda, who came a little later, did the same.

Panda was quite a different type. She was procreated in my spare room, by the union of Ian's bull-terrier bitch Topsy, probably the most stupid and undoubtedly the most stubborn animal alive, with Sammy, a pertinaceous fox-terrier belonging to the manager of Mandala's store.

Ian was in South Africa undergoing an operation on his knee when Topsy came on heat. He had given me strict instructions to prevent any mixing with *shense* (mongrel) animals, so I barricaded her in the spare room. It was the only place I thought she would be safe. The garden was unfenced, there was no garage and keeping her on a rope would have made her a sitting target – so to speak.

All went well for some days, if you discounted the partial destruction of the spare room door and Topsy's sleep-disturbing wails. Sammy and his randy cronies circled the house night and day, but were kept at bay by a variety of missiles and the occasional bullet fired into the ground under their tails.

Then, one night, I was awakened by a tremendous crash and the sound of breaking glass.

'Clumsy sort of thief,' I thought, jumping out of bed and grabbing my gun. The thief theory was soon dispelled by unmistakeably pleasurable whimpers coming from the spare room. Sammy was in full cry. I fetched a broom and belaboured him with it. He didn't even look up. Such were the joys of copulation.

Topsy, Panda's mother

What the hell, I thought, breathing heavily. I need my sleep. I've done all I can. 'Enjoy yourselves,' I told them and shutting the door, went back to bed. And after all, Sammy was no *shense*, he was a pure bred fox-terrier. It proved to be one of my happier decisions.

Ian was not overjoyed when he returned, but was delighted when the pups arrived. Four were pure white bull-terrier types but the fifth had two black splodges, one on the rump and one covering the right eye. She looked like a baby Panda, so that was what I called her.

Panda inherited the intelligence of Sammy and the determination of both parents. She was brave, faithful and loving, but her greatest feat occurred on the Nyasaland border. I had to investigate some cattle deaths in the Mulekatembo area of my district that could only be reached through Fort Hill in Nyasaland. Unfortunately, dogs were not permitted to cross the border and, although there was absolutely no-one to stop my taking them backwards and forwards, I figured that a Veterinary Officer should at least be seen to uphold the animal quarantine laws.

I left them both, late one afternoon, with Piet at the Old Fife Game Ranger's camp, a few miles from Tunduma, where the Fort Hill road turned off. The sun was already low. A little later, Piet's cookboy went to fetch water at a nearby stream. Piet's dogs, together with Flea and Panda, went down the road with him. Suddenly Panda, who had been sniffing about, took off and sped away down the dusty surface and out of sight. The cookboy hurried back and told Piet, who immediately sent one of his Game Guards after her on his bicycle since the carburettor of his vanette was in pieces. The thickly forested, sparsely populated terrain made this one of the wildest areas of the district. Rocky outcrops, stately trees, *dambos* sprinkled with game and, at night, lion and leopard on the road. In fact, it was one of the most leopard-ridden parts of the country. And leopards loved dogs above almost any other dish!

The Game Guard followed Panda's spoor, overprinted on the tracks of my vehicle, for eight miles until it became too dark and himself too scared. One thing he noticed; before each of the two villages he passed Panda's spoor would disappear into the bush, to reappear again on the other side. No villager had seen her pass.

Meanwhile, in ignorance of all this, I had spent the night at the Fort Hill Rest House, had risen at dawn to inspect the problem cattle and had returned to Fort Hill for breakfast. My meal was disturbed by a continual whining and barking coming from an outside store. I finished my coffee and went to investigate.

'Why don't you let your bloody dog out?' I asked the Rest House caretaker.

'Not my dog, *bwana*,' he replied.

'Whose is it?'

'Don't know, *bwana*. He come this morning.'

'Well, let it out, anyway.'

He hesitated. 'It very *kali*, *bwana*.'

'I don't mind how fierce it is. Let it out.' The thought did strike me that it might have rabies, but I was becoming rather irritated with the fellow.

He pulled back the wooden door and a skinny, dull-brown, cringing little creature limped out into the sunlight, its tail wagging nervously between its legs.

'Doesn't look very fierce to me,' I said.

Kenaan gasped. 'That *bwana* dog.'

'Which *bwana*?' I asked.

'You *bwana*. You dog.'

It was now grovelling at my feet. I knelt down and it licked my hand. Good God! could this dirty, emaciated runt belong to me? But now, through the layer of mud and dust, I could make out the dark patch over its eye.

Panda! I cradled her in my arms. Her paws were raw and she was half her normal weight. I carried her away so that no-one could see the tears that were running down my face. I couldn't believe it. She had spoored my vehicle for 60 miles, at night, through the most leopard-infested country imaginable, only to be locked up by a son of a bitch caretaker. No wonder she felt a bit *kali* – so did I!

When I could speak, I told Kenaan to fetch water and some *nyama* from the Rest house kitchen, the best he could find. I didn't think Panda would ever stop drinking.

Anger was boiling up inside me as I faced the caretaker.

'You locked it up without even giving it water?' I shouted.

He shrugged. It was only a dog. Suddenly, I lost control. Gripping the unfortunate fellow by the neck of his *kansu*, I shook him as hard as I could.

'If – I – ever – hear – of – you – treating – a – dog – like – that – again – ' I hissed at him through half-closed teeth, 'I – will – KILL – you.'

It was quite unreasonable of me, but I was mad with rage. The really frightening thing was that I meant every word.

Panda's exploit was published (not by me) in the *Bulawayo Chronicle*. It was claimed that it was a record. Since no-one refuted this, I presumed that it was. Brave little Panda, Champion Canine Tracker. Nothing was ever too good for her after that.

Forty-five years later, I cannot think of that day without a lump in my throat.

A DEEP AND ANGRY LAKE

At the southern tip of Lake Tanganyika, 11 miles north of Abercorn as the spurwing flew and 2,000 feet nearer sea level, sweltered Mpulungu, Northern Rhodesia's only port.

A deep channel separated the jetty and warehouse from the thickly forested, uninhabited Kambulu island, a quarter mile offshore. The island helped protect the anchorage from the quick-tempered winds and squalls that swept down between the purple cradling mountains to tease the surface of the lake until it punched back with a million leaping fists, heedless of the small canoes caught upon it.

Twenty-eight miles of ingeniously graded road connected Abercorn to Mpulungu, sliding gently at first past two or three almost derelict European farms, their owners gone to war, before dropping abruptly to tunnel through thick tsetse-infested bush below the dark green Chibulula hills. At 2,500 feet above sea level, the road levelled out opposite a couple of neatly thatched rondavels whose white-washed walls contrasted with the dark green mango trees, the poster-red poinsettias and the deep blue of the lake.

Mpulungu was not a busy port. There was only one regular caller. Every three weeks the *SS Liemba*, once the *Gotzen* and flagship of the German navy on the lake in the previous war, would throb her way south from her Tanganyikan base at Kigoma, bringing a handful of passengers and a load of petrol, salt and other goods.

Each visit was an eagerly awaited social occasion, a break from the monotony of station life and a chance to hear news from East Africa instead of only from the south, to sink a few scotch and sodas in place of dop and to experience the rather bitter, fizzy, but quite delightful Tusker beer from Dar-es Salaam. English cigarettes, fresh butter, bacon, beer and sausages could be procured at, for us, ridiculously low prices. Custom formalities were overlooked, but 'Pop', the postmaster and part-time customs officer knew, and we knew he knew, and he knew we knew he knew, so all was above board and legal – or so we told ourselves. And even if it wasn't, a fellow had to live and there were all too few perks in the bush.

Early in the morning when patches of mist still floated on the water, the sleek shining bows of the *Liemba* would nudge round Kambulu island and head for the jetty. As soon as she had been hawsered and the medical officer had pronounced her 'clear', the odd settler and those whose official duties could be overlooked for the day would jump aboard and head for the bar on the main deck for an early morning, ice-cold Tusker.

Below, on the well-deck, multi-coloured mats, wide-brimmed raffia hats and baskets, bunches of bananas, heaps of groundnuts and other foods would be displayed for sale. A melee of black citizens, some clothed in long white *kansus*, others with half-naked, sweating bodies, bartered fiercely amongst a babble of Swahili, Chinyanja and Chibemba. Alongside the vessel piccanins, unashamed of the bodies God had given them, and scorning the numerous crocodiles which could be seen from time to time surfacing at a distance, dived for coins thrown in response to their untiring cries of 'Penny *bwana*', 'Penny *mukwaï*', 'Ticky *bwana*'.

Surveying his ship from the bridge, a long thin-stemmed pipe gripped between his teeth, would be Eric, the skipper, a tall, spare, good-looking Britisher on the right side of middle age, with sleepy, smiling eyes and a mouth that would laugh more readily than talk. He and Margaret, his charming wife, daughter of that grand old warrior Rum Mum, made the *Liemba* a brief holiday home for travellers.

Somewhere, bustling about below decks, popping his head out now and then for a cheery greeting, would be Barney, the rotund, randy Chief Engineer from Runcorn, whose fund of stories was as great as his girth. Forever slimming but forever gaining weight and good humour, Barney ensured the social (especially for the ladies) as well as the mechanical success of each trip.

Not the least of the crew was Davy Jones, the saucy little sausage dog, trained to a pan in Eric's cabin, who had never been known to be sea-sick.

As the sun rose higher and the liquor took effect, the conversation in the bar would dwindle, and after an early lunch the remaining diehards would creep ashore to snore it off in the resthouse rondavels until the desire for sundowners would summon them aboard again.

On a desolate headland a few miles east of Mpulungu, the ruins of Niamkolo Mission, one of the oldest in Central Africa and the first settlement of the white man on the shores of Lake Tanganyika, lay bleaching in the sun. Built by the London Missionary Society, in about 1880, it was eventually abandoned due to sleeping sickness. All that now remained was a solitary tree sprouting from inside the tumbled down church tower. In the papyrus-fringed Kituta bay, round the promontory from Niamkolo, a missionary pointed out the remains of the *Good News*, the first mission boat to ply these waters. Its hardly recognizable shell lay rotting in the silt and sand near the tree to which Livingstone was supposed to have tied his canoe and which now stood 12 feet above the water line. To the west, where the Lufubu river cascaded down the mountain-side, was the point where that great explorer had first looked upon Lake Tanganyika.

Sometimes at full moon, Piet and I would bundle blankets and beer into the back of the vanette and with a rifle and water sac, would speed down to Mpulungu, slipping through the darkening forest where the great red eyes of bushbabies would flash from the trees in the beam of our headlights.

Backing the vehicle up to the edge of the concrete jetty, we would watch the fishermens' flares rise and fall on the silent water, marvelling at the countless fireflies that danced along the shore. The brilliant tropical moon would silhouette Kambulu Island against the distant, starry sky while the crickets, frogs and many other lakeside dwellers provided a symphony that Stravinsky would have envied.

Dreams formed without effort, fears vanished and hopes became probabilities in this other-world atmosphere. The world of daylight was bustling, unsympathetic and practical, but when the moon rose life became dreamy and timeless. And with the moon, rose all those beings afraid of bright light – spirits, good and evil, of men long dead who found in the moonlit hours stepping stones through time and space to mingle with the living.

We would lie bragging of past loves (there were no present loves in the bush!), our hopes and ambitions. The light breeze from the lake would, we hoped, keep away the mosquitoes, until, ten days later, a bout of fever showed how wrong we had been. Washing in the cool lake water, our torch attracted the inquisitive black water snakes which skimmed towards us and sent us scrambling back to the vanette.

The following day, wakened early by the sun and by the white, moth-like lake flies which filled our eyes and ears, we would canoe across the narrow channel to Kambulu Island, kneeling in a terrifying little dug-out, too small for sitting, too wobbly for standing.

Scrambling up the steep overgrown shore, we would explore the hilly isle, spooring bush-pig, musing over pieces of pottery, visiting the small burial ground still tended by some unknown hand where celebrities, aeons since, had been laid to rest, and photographing the oil palm, the only one in the northern province, which stood aloof just above Kambulu's waterline.

Kambulu was roughly star-shaped, with a hill on each promontory separated by densely undergrowthed valleys. These had to be crossed to gain the far shore, where a pebbled cove and underwater carpet of white rocks provided an ideal background against which to detect the dark forms of approaching crocs.

Sometimes we found the shore already occupied with a score of the monsters – and monsters they were, but a few shots would send them churning into the water, leaving the beach free on which to laze the day away, naked but for our hats, dreaming young men's dreams. When one of us went in to swim the other would stand on a rock, gun in hand, ready to scare off any inquisitive reptiles.

Much later, tired, thirsty and sunburnt, we would pick our way cautiously round the coast and hail a canoe to ferry us back to the vanette.

Tanganyika was a fearsome lake, placid and angry by turns, fascinating and mysterious, its depths still uncharted, forever changing colour and mood. A paradise – if one could have only excluded the crocodiles, the tsetse and the mosquito.

HOW RABID CAN YOU GET?

'Alvays 'e snap at beez. *Bon*, such a vay 'e could 'ave swallow one an' bin stinged.'

Hans, the Belgian Locust Control Director, bent down and patted his fox-terrier as it lay panting on the cool tiles of the verandah, frothy saliva seeping from the corners of its mouth. Now and then a bee would fly past to a nest under the rafters and Timmy, half rising, would lunge at it.

'It's a possibility,' I agreed, 'but a temperature of a hundred and four is a little high for a bee sting.'

I had taken blood slides too, just in case it was biliary, a common tick-borne disease of dogs caused by a similar blood parasite to that causing redwater in cattle. I was sure it wasn't. Dogs with biliary had pale, sometimes white, conjunctiva and gums. Timmy's were, if anything, too red.

'I'll give him a shot of sulphapyridine,' I said (sulpha drugs had just hit the market, penicillin was yet to come), 'just in case he's hatching distemper. It may help. Keep him quiet with plenty to drink and let me know how he gets on. I'll pop in first thing tomorrow.'

There was no doubt that Timmy was sick and a bee sting could not be completely ruled out, but I could find no tenderness or swelling and the high temperature didn't fit. Distemper? Possibly, or a nameless infection that would disappear in a day or two, helped by the sulpha drug. But as I got into my car I knew that something deep down was worrying me, something I didn't like but couldn't identify.

I called early the next day.

''E is very thirsty but 'e won't drink,' Lislotte, Hans' wife, told me.

We watched Timmy swing his head round to the drinking bowl and lower his jaw into the water. Almost immediately he raised it again and began to drool. The poor beast wants to drink but can't, I thought.

CRASH!

With the impact of a klaxon horn inside my skull, that subconscious foreboding suddenly surfaced. RABIES! Oh, please God; not rabies! Blood pounded through my ears – literally pounded. I had never seen a case of rabies before, but I went over the symptoms as I remembered them from college. Unusual behaviour, aggressiveness, tendency to attack anything nearby, animate or inanimate. This was the first, or 'furious' stage. Later, difficulty in swallowing with paralysis of the jaw and other parts – the 'dumb' stage, would set in.

Rabies, or hydrophobia, as it is sometimes called in humans, was common enough further south on the railway, but I had never heard it mentioned in Abercorn. The disease could affect all warm-blooded animals, but because the virus concentrated in the saliva, it was most often seen in those species which used their teeth for attack and defence, such as jackals, wild cats – and dogs.

Man could be infected by a bite or, if he had a cut, simply by contact with a rabid dog's saliva. The previous afternoon while I was pick-a-backing Hans' small daughter, Michon, round the garden, Timmy had jumped up and nipped her heel. Both Hans and Lislotte had fondled Timmy, and I – HELL! I'd had my fingers down his throat half a dozen times!

'I'd better take him to my house,' I said, trying to appear calm. 'I can keep a closer eye on him there. Don't let anyone touch him till I get back.' I wasn't going to air my fears until I had had more time to think, and an opportunity to discuss it with the Medical Officer. I found him in the African hospital. He'd never seen rabies, either, but rather doubted my diagnosis.

'Let's wait a bit before we commit ourselves,' I suggested. 'If it is rabies the dog will be dead in two or three days. Don't let's mention it till we know, for sure.' He agreed.

In normal circumstances, all those in contact with Timmy would have started vaccinations immediately, as a precaution. But there was no vaccine in Abercorn, probably not even in Lusaka. It would have been necessary to order it from Salisbury or Johannesburg or commandeer an aeroplane and fly everyone south for their 'shots'. Furthermore, rabies vaccination in those days was neither a pleasant nor an entirely safe procedure; a small percentage of those vaccinated developed a fatal paralysis. We would have to wait – and pray!

When I returned to collect Timmy I was met by a distraught Lislotte.

''E 'as gone; disappeared.'

My heart missed several beats. Another symptom I now remembered was that rabid dogs sometimes wandered aimlessly for miles.

We searched for hours through the hot humid midday. 'Mad dogs and English vets', I thought, wryly, as I blundered through the bush and swamp, along game tracks and down the small stream which ran below Hans' and Lislotte's garden, splashing through the water for half a mile until I came across the poor little dog standing up to his belly, trying to drink. I was now convinced that Timmy was rabid. So many of the symptoms fitted – my God, how they fitted!

I took him to my house and continued treatment with the sulpha-pyridine and subcutaneous glucose saline, a bottle of which I had borrowed from the doctor in the forlorn hope that Timmy's condition would turn out to be anything but rabies. The following day Timmy developed a severe catarrh. He still couldn't swallow and his jaw hung loose, but he stayed alive, which was a promising sign, and he showed no further paralysis. My confidence returned. It was obviously distemper, or a distemper-like disease.

Five days later, the very sick little dog was still alive on a rug in my spare room. I was quite sure now that it was not rabies, but as I was equally certain that there was little chance of his recovery, I suggested that we put him to sleep. Hans and Lislotte agreed, and I buried him one morning behind the office, greatly relieved to have frightened no-one with my ghastly suspicions.

Later the same day, I set off for Mwenimpanza to sell the last of the quarantine cattle to the butchers, before trekking them across the Laungwa valley to Isoka and other centres, where they would be slaughtered.

Foolishly, I decided to break my journey at Nteko, the lonely, bat-ridden stock inspector's house, instead of going on to the homely atmosphere of Mwenzo mission.

After supper, as I sat ruminating over Timmy, a paralysing fear crept over me. What if it had been rabies after all? Why the blazes hadn't I sent the brain off for laboratory examination? Why hadn't I insisted that the MO sent for vaccine and so put the onus on him? I sat and sweated far into the night, trying to convince myself that if Timmy had been rabid he would have died in convulsions within a few days. It was no use. An entry in my diary, that evening, reads, 'Am still terrified that Timmy did have rabies. My indecision could be responsible for four deaths. Hope my nerves stand up to it.'

That brief comment hardly describes the agony of mind in which I wrote it.

Following a sleepless night, I reached Mwenimpanza early and haggled all day with the wily butchers. At four o'clock, my patience gave out and I sold the last five animals for a nominal sum. I had now made up my mind. I would return to Abercorn as quickly as possible, dig up Timmy and send his brain to South Africa. My chief worry was that it would be too decomposed for diagnosis, and to show how confused I was and to what a low mental ebb I had sunk, I asked Kenaan for his opinion. When he assured me that the brain would not yet be rotten, I felt a great load lift off me.

Abercorn was 140 miles from Mwenimpanza, none of the road was good, and the first five miles of it were probably the worst in the province. I left at half past four and drove like someone possessed – which was true enough – tearing up the hill past my house a little after eight that night. Kenaan, still shaking with nerves from his *bwana's* frenzied dash, dug up the little body. I took out the brain,

70

put a portion of it into glycerine/saline solution and another portion into formalin to preserve it, and sealed them in a tin. The next morning I wrote a report, drove the 120 miles to Kasama and despatched both it and the brain by the weekly air service to the Veterinary Research Laboratories at Onderstepoort in South Africa.

I had done all I could. Gradually I relaxed, once again certain that Timmy had not had rabies, and could even laugh at myself for being a neurotic idiot. I would soon have an answer and, undoubtedly, it would be negative.

'Telegram, *bwana*,' Kenaan handed me the envelope. I tore it open.

'REGRET BRAIN TOO DECOMPOSED FOR DIAGNOSIS'

I was back to square one. I told the doctor, who still thought that there was too little evidence to order vaccine or to fly contacts south for vaccination. We agreed to say nothing or, if asked directly, to say that nothing to suggest rabies had been found, which, of course, was true up to a point. Pop, the postmaster, who had twigged the importance of the message, also promised to remain silent.

The next few weeks were nothing short of purgatory. All the old doubts came surging back, and I fluctuated between the gay certainty that it had been an unusual case of distemper and the terrifying possibility that it had been rabies.

To top it all, I contracted my first dose of malaria. Fever doesn't induce clear thinking, and as I lay in bed, a quinine hum in my ears, I determined that, if the worst happened, I would finish myself. I had heard of a fellow who had carried a lethal dose of a poisonous plant around with him for six months after being bitten by a rabid dog, too far away for treatment. He was still alive. I hoped I'd be as lucky. If not, shooting would be quick – even if rather disfiguring – or I could step over the edge of the Kalambo falls, just north of Abercorn, one of the highest in Africa, and drop 800 feet to a certain death. But that, I knew, I could never do. Perhaps I could go down to the Mafinga mountains and lose myself there, far away from everyone, never to be found.

Finally, I decided that the most practical means would be to inject an overdose of barbiturate into a vein. I had put down many dogs in this way. It was painless and quick. Before doing so, I would get very drunk and then, with a record of Handel's *Water Music* or Mozart's *Eine Kleine Nachtmusik* playing, I would jab it in. There were snags. I didn't possess a gramophone or records, and if I were that drunk I'd probably miss the vein!

71

One horrific night, the crisis came. Still limp from the effects of malaria I lay in the dark, once again mulling over Timmy's case. Suddenly, I found I could no longer swallow. Terrified, I sat up and lit the Tilley lamp beside my bed. God in heaven. Was this it? Had the time really arrived when I would have to carry out one of the methods of self-destruction I had so often thought about? I looked at the rifle by my bed. I tried to swallow, but the saliva stuck in my throat. I fetched a glass of water. This time it went down.

'Nerves, just nerves,' I muttered, almost sobbing with relief. Brandy? There was none. A half tumbler of Van der Hum had little effect, so I followed it with the same of gin. I began to feel better. What I needed was sleeping pills.

I had a few Nembutal capsules in the office, they would calm me down. I hurried up the road with a hurricane lamp, feeling rather light-headed and envying the blissful, carefree sleep of the other inhabitants. As I reached for the packet of Nembutal capsules, I dislodged the bottle of concentrated barbiturate solution next to it; it fell to the floor and shattered. It was the only one I had. For a moment horror gripped me. Now I would no longer be able to give myself that fatal injection. With trembling fingers, I took out three little yellow torpedoes of Nembutal, swallowed them and walked home. Within minutes I was asleep, the lamp still burning.

At ten next morning I fought to wake. When I did, I felt a lot better. It was a beautiful day, with soft, white clouds scudding across a blue sky. The phantoms of the night had completely disappeared. I felt I had a future once more!

From that moment I resolved to forget Timmy and the whole blessed affair, and when Victor, the DC, came fussing into the office later that morning, twiddling his forelock, having somehow heard that Timmy might have had rabies, and demanded in rapid uninterrupted sentences why the hell I had not told him before as his two children had often played with Timmy and were therefore liable to contract the disease and would I send for vaccine immediately otherwise he was going to drive his family to Lusaka and would probably hold me responsible for any costs or consequences..., I told him, quietly and firmly, that the brain had been sent away for diagnosis and that there had been no evidence of rabies, and would he kindly go to hell!

It was easier after that, although at times I still had doubts and carried a syringe and lethal dose of barbiturates with me for the next six months.

Some time later, I confided the whole sorry story to a fellow veterinarian. He smiled.

72

'I had the same experience some years ago in Barotseland.' He told me about it. No-one ever had a more sympathetic listener.

Had I been irresponsible in not pressing for the vaccine and in not telling Hans and Lislotte of my suspicions? As far as it concerned their little daughter, Michon, the answer was definitely yes. She was the only one, apart from myself, who was at real risk. Today, with much safer and more efficient vaccines, every in-contact would be vaccinated automatically. But in 1944, in the bush, things were not quite so cut and dried.

And was it really rabies?

It is much easier, now, for me to doubt it.

NORTH LUANGWA AND THE MAFINGAS

The Nyasaland cattle were still in quarantine at Mwenimpanza. Later they would be trekked to their various slaughter points – Isoka, Mpika, Abercorn and Kasama – all between 100 and 200 miles away. Transport by road was impracticable, so trekking them across country was the only solution.

The shortest and most feasible route lay straight across the northern Luangwa valley, a region full of lions, leopards, deep streams and tsetse fly. I decided to walk across first, and see where to build the kraals for overnighting the cattle *en route*. As we were now well into the dry season, I assumed that the Luangwa would be low enough to cross but that there would still be sufficient grazing all along the way.

I forget for what reason, but I decided to walk the route in reverse, starting from Isoka. Allan, my new Stock Inspector, and I arrived at the Isoka *boma* one evening to find the DC sitting on the verandah steps with a glass of brandy in his hand. Next to him an army officer clutched a bloody tooth in a pair of forceps.

'You've missed the floor show,' the DC greeted us. 'I've just had a couple of teeth out.'

The Dental Corps officer, travelling south with a mobile unit from Kenya, had stopped at Isoka for the night, and as usual had offered his services free of charge. In Lusaka he increased his reputation by extracting a girl's wisdom tooth at a cocktail party, in front of a loudly appreciative audience! I met this redoubtable tooth puller ten years later, quite by chance, when he was practising in Richmond. He had lost none of his former skill.

The DC was enthusiastic about the proposed trekking of cattle from the Nyasaland border, but why, he asked, since I was bringing Nyasaland cattle across, didn't we set up a regular route and include

73

cattle from our own border Zone as well? I told him that this was exactly what I had in mind. The cattle were there and had no outlet, all that was needed was a little organization.

'We could set up a monthly cattle market here at Isoka,' he suggested.

'Good idea,' I agreed. 'Perhaps we could slaughter them here and sell dried meat or biltong, instead of trekking the beasts all over the province. It would reduce the risk of disease and cut the cost of distribution.'

Two days later, the sun hardly above the trees. Barton, a newly acquired African Veterinary Assistant, James, the Zone Guard for the area, my frail but ever-faithful personal boy Kosam, and I, accompanied by three very unwilling carriers which the head *boma* messenger had pressganged into service, set off on the first stage of our Luangwa *ulendo*. Kenaan begged off as he had been sick. He would return to Abercorn with Allan and meet me on the Fort Hill road in ten days. Cephas was on leave.

Ulendos were almost the only compensation for the monotonous life on an outstation, for the lack of cinemas and sports and the restricted social contacts. Perhaps not an adequate compensation for a youngster but, as my Lancashire landlady used to say, 'Better than a slap in the belly with a wet fish.'

I wondered, as I marched through the scratchy grass, listening to the porters chattering, how long it would be before civilization began to get her dirty fingernails into this Stone-Age country, to tear its soul with politics and 'isms'? How long before its happy children became infected with Communism, or joined partisan groups screaming for those social benefits which had taken Europe centuries of education and economic stability to achieve? Developing Africa, I thought, was like cooking a joint; it had to be done slowly, otherwise the outside would burn while the inside would remain raw.

We made a mere ten miles on the first day, quite enough considering the rough terrain and several fast-flowing rivers with sharp stones underfoot. At the first village we passed, the women knelt and gave me a strange half-whistling, half-crooning salute, accompanied by chest-beating and handclapping. Here, the huts were decorated with designs quite different from any I had seen elsewhere, zigzagging lines resolving into triangles or diamonds enclosing dots and circles. Some designs had obviously been copied from Indian prints bought at stores further south, and occasionally a caricature of an aeroplane, motor car or soldier, would denote the home of a returned mineworker or warrior.

74

That evening, I went off to shoot my supper. The ground was alive with spoor but a little brute of a honeybird hovered above me, chattering away and warning all game of my approach. I followed the stream that hastened past our camp until it joined another to form a prettily banked rivulet, just like the trout streams that used to set my heart racing in Somerset. Here, I ran into (literally) the net of a Gold Orb spider, a large gold-and-black arachnid whose web had extremely tough and sticky strands, 15 feet or more in length. Sometimes small birds became entangled in its mesh. These strands were once used for the crosswires of telescopic sights. I noticed that a lot of small silvery spiders had spun their webs within the larger web. 'So on *ad infinitum*', I mused. I saw a duiker but it was already too dark to shoot, so I returned to camp and a skinny *kuku*.

We climbed several ridges and traversed several streams, and one night made camp next to a sizeable river. I wandered down the bank and found some spectacular falls with a shallow pool above, in which I had a swim. Below the falls the river spread out into a large, papyrus-fringed lagoon, doubtless full of crocs. I sat on a rock at the edge of the cascade, letting the cold water numb my weary legs as it swirled over the top, musing that this same water would one day reach the sea via the Luangwa and Zambesi rivers. What other faces, I wondered, would be mirrored in it before it reached the Pacific? What other languages would it hear? Hypnotized by the clear, bubbling water, I felt like Tom in *The Water Babies*.

Screams and laughter brought me back to reality. Some women were crossing a fording upstream. They had come to wash clothes, and one had slipped and was desperately chasing her hamper and spilled clothes as they floated downstream. The taunts, cries of dismay, encouragement of friends and the final 'All's well that ends well' could have happened in Devon, or Russia or Patagonia. Human behaviour, it seemed, conformed to a pattern, no matter what the race.

I sat on, at peace with the world, and suddenly realised that tomorrow would be my birthday. I had little to show for my 26 years, and if I didn't clear out of Africa soon I would have little more to show in another 26. I had sent a plea to the Colonial Office for a transfer or release for military service, but I had small hope. Whatever happened, I was determined to leave Africa at the finish of my tour. Youth needed companionship – of both sexes, there was little enough of one and none of the other in the bush.

Barton complained that he could hardly understand the local dialects, which seemed to change every time we crossed a river.

James, too, although this was his district, said that the accents were quite different from elsewhere and made conversation difficult. It showed how isolated and parochial these people were. Not unlike medieval Europe, I imagined.

Lanky, who had spent many years in the Luangwa valley, insisted it was one of the greatest wildlife sanctuaries in Africa. He was probably right. The exclusion of humans meant that the environment was not being destroyed. Africa had a lot to thank the tsetse for! The ease with which Stone-Age flints, *coups de points* and axe heads could be picked up along certain levels, suggested that these had been the water lines of prehistoric lakes. Perhaps the great river, which was said to have once flowed across Africa to empty into the South Atlantic near Walvis Bay, had originated in this valley.

Quite apart from the tsetse, there was another reason that kept Africans clear of the valley. It was the sacred abode of the spirits of the dead. Why else would there be so many lions?

I refused to camp in or near any African village. In the first place I wanted my privacy, and in the second the mosquitoes would be more likely to be infected with malaria and only too eager to sink their mouthparts into a tender white skin. So I passed through Chief Muyeleka's village, a spacious, almost clean settlement on the banks of the Luangwa river, and waded across to make camp in a clearing a little way upstream, on the other side.

It wasn't long before James informed me that Muyeleka was on his way to see me. Knowing that he was very old, I walked down to the river intending to cross and so save him the trouble, but he was already in the middle of the 50-yard wide current, which the dry season had reduced to no more than two feet deep. Four men, themselves pretty ancient, held him aloft on a bamboo stretcher while the poor old fellow tried desperately to maintain his dignity and keep his balance.

He was very hurt that I had not camped in his village, where he had recently built a new rest house, right in the middle! I thought up a fairly plausible answer involving buffalo and game, not forgetting to promise him a goodly portion of any meat that I should acquire. He said he would have liked to send me presents and food for the carriers, but since I was on the other side of the river, this would be impossible. He crawled into his litter again and I watched him carried back across the current, reflecting that this incident, so little and unimportant to me, would be talked about for weeks ... the passing of the *bwana* doctor *ngombe*, probably the first to have passed that way – and he hadn't even had the decency to stay in the new rest house! Some *bwanas* were the end!

Just after dark, a thin, wiry man in ragged khaki shirt and shorts, a rifle slung over one shoulder, strode into camp. James brought him across to where I was sitting. He sloped his rifle and saluted.

'This *fundi* Cowgen, *bwana*,' he announced. '*Bwana* Piet hunter.'

Cowgen had the most wizened, contorted face that I had ever looked upon. It was not grotesque or unpleasant, it had just been battered and beaten by the elements into a shape and configuration that could better withstand the driving rain, the early morning chill and the blistering heat of midday.

Due to his prowess as a hunter he had gained the prefix *fundi*, a word denoting master craftsmanship in any form. He had been following up the buffalo whose spoor we had seen earlier, and suggested that I might like to accompany him on the following day.

Cowgen was ready before I was awake. Although the sun was up, the valley was shielded by the Mafingas and still in shadow. It was winter south of the equator, and the mornings extremely cold. Johannesburg and Salisbury would experience frost this month, and a little of this bite would still be in the wind when it reached Northern Rhodesia.

With my rifle over my shoulder, collecting bottles (for ticks and spiders), microscope slides (for blood smears of any animals we shot), and my Retina 1 (to record the day's events) swelling the pockets of my bush jacket, and with James carrying a water sac, we set off up the valley. Barton, who unashamedly professed to be no great hunter, I left to strike camp and move it to our next site on the Ntonga river.

A passer-by told us that a buffalo herd was heading for a *cul de sac* in the Ntonga valley. We rushed off at colossal speed; the *fundi's* splayed out scaly feet loosely housed in ill-fitting sandals, covered the ground in great untiring strides while I puffed and panted in the rear, too intent on negotiating potholes and rocks to keep an eye open for game.

Plunging down an escarpment, we found ourselves in tall, thick, *kasanse* grass bordering the river Ntonga. We waded across into more tall grass and rushes, and then up a thickly wooded escarpment. At the top, Cowgen, probably fearing that I might collapse, suggested a rest while his helper went on to locate the herd.

Every species of fly in the area sought refuge under my hat or in my eyes and ears. I gave the *fundi* a cigarette which made him splutter at the first puff, amazing since the mere whiff of his misshapen pipe would knock me sideways.

The helper returned to say that the herd had moved up the Ntonga into thick bush. Cowgen decided that it would be too far for me and, anyway, it would be too late to shoot anything that day. Tracking buffalo in thick bush with a trigger-happy, rubber-legged *bwana* by his side was out. So he pointed the way to our next camp site and strode off after the herd, promising to report that evening. I wasn't too disappointed; another 50 yards at his pace would have killed me. After resting a bit longer, James and I ambled off in the direction Cowgen had indicated, but an hour later we were still in the Ntonga valley, surrounded by tall grass and still with the Ntonga to cross. We managed one formidable torrent with the aid of a fallen tree and some rocks but found, to our dismay, that this was only one arm of the river and that we were now on an island, still in stifling grass and reeds, quite lost and not a little anxious.

I plodded on, vaguely aware of a strange odour. Then it hit me.

'Buffalo,' I shouted.

'*Ndio, bwana*. Buffalo.' James replied, uneasily, as if he had known it all along but had been trying to keep it a secret. '*Bwana* must be careful. Better go back.'

I was reluctant, but when we came to several steaming heaps of dung, I knew that discretion was what it was always said to be. James was obviously pleased; after all, only I had a gun and he had little faith in me as a marksman. Trees were few and running on that soggy, grass-entangled ground was impossible. The only escape would be to shoot and not to miss – but there could be 50 of them all charging at high speed. We retreated, escaping from our reed-covered island by means of a fish dam constructed across a quiet stretch, and found ourselves in thick, so-called *mateshi* forest with long creepers trailing from tall trees, twisting and entwining like a goblins' grotto.

After crawling out, we continued down the edge of the Ntonga until we found the camp site on a piece of higher ground, where lordly trees shaded a carpet of grass, allowing cool air to circulate beneath their lofty branches. I flopped onto my camp bed which Kosam had already put up. You had to be in good training to walk at an African's pace, and Cowgen was a furious walker, even for an African. It wasn't just fatigue that was worrying me. Some cuts and scratches were turning into very painful 'veldt sores'. It was not the first time I had experienced this malady, and it was time I knew better than to wear shorts on *ulendo*. Everytime I did, the same thing happened; every scratch would turn into a smarting, red-rimmed ulcer.

But now, at least, I knew how to treat them. At first I had used the conventional remedies, boracic powder, Germolene ointment and, when sulphanilamide arrived, that too. None helped, the sores grew bigger and more painful, my leg became puffy, and I had to stay in bed. But I had noticed that if I covered them with a dressing, they healed quicker. Then, a visitor mentioned that troops in the desert covered over these sores completely with sticking plaster. I wrapped Elastoplast round them, and within a day the pain had gone, and within three, the sores were well on their way to healing. It was the same principle that Truetta had applied to compound fractures in the Spanish Civil War. You sealed up the wound and let it stew in its own antibody-packed juice until the stench was no longer bearable. But it was a sure cure. I used the same technique some years later in Jamaica, with great success, in the treatment of leg ulcers in mules.

The indefatiguable James went out and shot a couple of guinea-fowl with a muzzle loader. These 'shooti-guns', as they were called, were iron tubes bound onto their stocks with copper and steel wire, without sights and usually a bit bent. They were prized above all else. Having stuffed it full of gunpowder, Billy Bantu would ram down a collection of nails, nuts, screws or anything else that could act as a bullet. Next he would fashion a type of explosive 'cap' from the heads of non-safety matches, insert it under the hammer and set off to stalk his prey.

A broadside from one of these grossly-overloaded cannons carried a tremendous kick – at short range. At longer distances its impact diminished and it was extremely inaccurate, which accounted for the pieces of metal so often found in the hides and flesh of game.

No-one could call Billy Bantu unsporting: there was more than an equal chance that the antique armament would explode and kill him instead of his prey, but with a 'shooti-gun' slung loosely over his shoulder, he would tackle the world.

The next morning James, trading on his success of the day before, begged me to let him 'go shooti buffalo with *bwana* gun.' I wanted a day's rest, so I let him go off, rather apprehensively, with my .303 and my peace of mind. At midday Cowgen loped in, saying he had shot a buffalo. He was very superior about it, inferring that it had been a brilliant piece of spooring and an unbelievable shot, so I was greatly pleased when, shortly afterwards, James marched into camp, gun at the slope, right arm swinging high and clutching a buffalo's tail. The entire camp, except for Barton, who thought it a bit below his dignity, disappeared with Cowgen and James to bring in the meat.

There was much feasting that night. I brought out my accordion and everyone danced. I made up a rather gay tune which, for some reason they called *washyama*, (women), and which they made me play every night for the rest of the trip.

A few days later we began to climb out of the Luangwa valley up the slopes of the Mafingas. I was striding ahead, pleased at last to have a chance to climb these mountains, when James shouted urgently, '*Bwana*, stop. That way dangerous.'

'Rot,' I thought, 'what's wrong with it?' Then I noticed that the path led through a gap in a newly made fence and that the earth in the gap appeared to have been scuffled recently, and the whole thing was obviously a trap. Sure enough, the ground crumbled and gave way under the butt of my rifle, disclosing a six-foot game pit with wicked, razor-sharp stakes at the bottom.

My wrath was loud and sincere as I finished destroying the lattice-work camouflage over the pit. It was the cruelty of the method that upset me. Animals could lie staked for days before they died, but it was the oldest and most favoured method of ensuring a meal, however illegal.

A swift, icy stream now ran beside our track, chuckling over water-falls and flashing back the sun wherever its rays pierced the dense foliage. Some falls were metres high with deep, dark pools beneath, but I saw no fish. Stocked with trout, it would have been a fisher-man's paradise. With the fish, game and incredible views, and not more than 20 miles from the motor road, it would equal any fishing resort in Central Africa.

Our camp at John Sichula lay below a rocky obelisk, like a natural Cleopatra's Needle. I turned in early, the camp fire unable to offset the chilly wind. It was a miserable night, becoming colder and colder as the hours dragged on. Finally, I ran out of sweaters and blankets, so at two, when the wind dropped, I upped and sat over the camp fire. Bodies, half covered in leaves, blankets and grass lay close to the embers. How they withstood the freezing temperatures I don't know, but once asleep, it took a lot to wake an African.

Barton and I started to climb the obelisk peak soon after dawn. He had been reluctant to accompany me, insisting that huge man-eating snakes lived in the Mafingas and we would be bound to meet one, but it was too early in the morning to frighten me with old wives' tales. We looked into each cave and under each rock we passed, but saw nothing more than a few bats and centipedes.

The obelisk rock itself was impossible for a non-climber to attempt, so we went on up the mountain through stretches of grass and shrub, reaching the summit about midday. Here we rested on the edge of a great rock slab looking down over the Luangwa, pointing out places we had passed during the last few days and yelling remembered inci-dents to each other above the strong wind.

I christened it 'Luangwa Look-out' and left my name and the date inside a cigarette tin under a rocky shelf. Maybe, one day, some roving official or inquisitive African might find it, or perhaps the ever hungry non-selective termites might polish it off that week, even before I reached Abercorn.

Buffalo spoor and droppings were all over the place. I had no idea that they could scramble up such steep slopes. I wondered what we would have done if we had met one on the narrow, precipitous and only path. I took a last look over the valley, drinking in the blues, greens, yellows, browns – so many shades within each shade. It was a part of Africa I wanted to remember. Then, singing songs from Gilbert and Sullivan, I almost cantered down the grassy slopes to reach camp before dark. Barton, poor chap, quite convinced I was mad, lumbered in my wake.

The following day we headed for the Fort Hill road. It was extremely hot and the path very hilly, so whenever I came to one of the numerous streams, I would disrobe and lie in it. After a time I dispensed with undressing and lay fully clothed in the chilly water, my damp clothes maintaining a coolth until the next stream. It was a foolish thing to do, the alternate heat and cold sapped, rather than restored my energy, and would almost certainly ensure a bout of fever in a few days time.

It would, I estimated, take seven to ten days to trek the cattle across to Isoka, but there should be no great difficulty in protecting them from lions at the sites we had selected.

Early the following day, Allan drove up, having stayed the night at Tunduma. He had a bundle of mail.

'Thought you'd like to get this as quick as possible,' he laughed. On top was my income tax return!

* * *

On the way home, Kenaan swung round on the seat beside me, his hand already on the door handle. '*Bwana* must help he man.'

Presumably, he meant the old man walking along the side of the road, who had waved to us as we passed. I slowed, but Kenaan was out and running back before I could stop. Much '*mapalene mukwai-ing*' and handclapping ensued and, a moment later, Kenaan opened the passenger door and entreated the old man to enter, telling me that this was Donald Siwale, chief counsellor of Queen Waitweka of the Ainamwange tribe, and a 'too good man'.

Donald was elderly, his hair grey and his face deeply rutted. He had a rather large mouth and prominent, obviously false, teeth. His English was remarkable, and I was to find his general knowledge of world affairs profound. I was impressed. I had never come across an African quite so educated and courteous. We became good friends, and he proved an invaluable help in one of my investigations, the collection of poisonous and medicinal plants used by various tribes. I would let him know anytime I was going near Tunduma, where he lived, and he would meet me with specimens of flowers, roots and shrubs, and give me a list of their African names and their uses.

Before I left Abercorn I sent the collection of 59 specimens to Prof. J.M. Watt in Pretoria, co-author of the standard book on the subject. Several of the plants and their uses were new to him.

I heard from Donald Siwale a couple of times after I had left Northern Rhodesia, but it was not until nearly 40 years later, sitting next to the Zambian Ambassador at a dinner party in Mozambique, that his name came up again. I had been reminiscing about Abercorn to His Excellency, who came from that area, and had mentioned my old friend, whose name I had momentarily forgotten.

'That must have been Donald Siwale, I'm sure,' he said.

He told me that Donald was now over 100 and still active, but when I wrote to him he replied from a hospital bed in Lusaka. Yes, he remembered me well and told me that he still had his home at Nyimbili Garden near Tunduma, but he was too old and sick now to spend much time there. One son was a politician, and a grandson was a doctor in Lusaka. He hoped we would meet again.

It was not to be. Shortly afterwards he died – a 'too good man' if ever there was one.

WHITE FATHERS AND WHITE ANTS

'My son, Africa is a hard country. If the white ants don't get you, the White Fathers certainly will.'

I remembered how the young Irish Father and I had stood at the ship's rail watching Table Mountain creep over the horizon. It had been a tense but untroubled voyage, free from gales and submarines, a fact which he had laughingly attributed to the presence on board of six devout Roman Catholic missionaries, conveniently ignoring the influence of the other twelve, equally devout, but alas, heretically inclined Men of God.

He had also given me his infallible method to avoid sea-sickness, 'Keep your mouth shut and your bowels open!' It hadn't altogether worked, nor, for that matter, did his prophecy prove correct; I was neither devoured by white ants nor converted to the Church of Rome.

From the earliest days, the country had abounded with missionaries: British, German, French – Catholic or Protestant – together with the less orthodox sects like Plymouth Brethren ('Plymouth Rocks'), Seventh Day Adventists ('Saturday Adventurers'), Jehovah's Witnesses ('Watchi Tower'), and others. No wonder a cynical Irish DC referred to missionaries *en masse* as 'God-botherers'. It was as if they had been sprinkled like pellets of fertilizer before the advancing administrators to ensure a fertile ground for Imperialism.

Billy Bantu, tolerably happy in his ignorance and ancestor worship, but eager for White Man's skills, found that the only school in the area was run by a mission. Here, for education's sake, he would conform to their beliefs and drift happily down the particular religious river into which he had fallen. One could easily tell where an African had been educated – by his accent. His pidgin English would carry the intonation of his Scots, French, German, Yorkshire, or other teachers, for life.

Apart from religious instruction, missions taught handicrafts, agriculture, self-discipline and a gradual introduction to European ways, all roles which the Government was only too happy to subsidize.

The most widespread of these missionary groups was the White Fathers, the missionary wing of the Catholic church in central Africa, founded by Archbishop Lavigerie in 1869. Their name was derived from the long, white *kansu*, rather like a nightgown, which was their constant habit. The majority were French, German, Dutch or Belgian, but occasionally a French Canadian, Irishman or Englishman would be found. Almost without exception, they wore long beards, some long enough to hide the crucifix which dangled on their chests.

After a first tour of ten years, they were granted a year's home leave, most of which was spent in Rome. From then on, they remained in Africa until too old or too sick to justify their existence in the mission, when they would sometimes be repatriated. Many never saw their homeland again, dying of malaria, blackwater or old age on some lonely mission station where they had struggled valiantly all their lives.

White Fathers were assisted by White Brothers, who took no permanent vows and were sometimes known to leave the Mission and take a job outside. I was amazed that more didn't do so. Cut off from the normal world and feminine company, working 18 hours a day, every day, in the most austere and dreary surroundings, for a nominal pay of a few shillings a year, it was not surprising that some lost a little of their ardour and opted for domesticity.

Roman Catholics, it seemed to me, with their exaggerated ritual, gaudy effigies and priestly paraphernalia, simply helped to replace one set of mysteries with another, but at least they seemed to get their message across more effectively than the less ostentatious Protestant creeds although one White Father confessed, sadly, that he considered it good going if one in a 1,000 of his congregation understood the rudiments of Christianity. About the same as in many so-called Christian countries, I shouldn't wonder!

Since many of the White Fathers at the beginning of the war were German and, as such, were enemy aliens, they were regarded with a certain amount of distrust. The more so as just before hostilities began, a German Bishopric had established a chain of White Father missions down the Great North Road from Tanganyika into Northern Rhodesia. The rifles, radios, motorcycles and other equipment which the new Fathers and Brothers brought with them, were quickly confiscated when war was declared, and all German Father Superiors were replaced by nationalities friendly to the allied cause. But, as far as I know, no missionary of an enemy nationality was interned.

Although I disagreed with their dogma, I had to acknowledge that the White Fathers were a selfless band of enthusiastic spiritual pioneers whose help and hospitality were always there for the asking. I frequently sought their advice, accepted their hospitality and greatly valued their friendship. I admired them immensely.

In spite of the numerous christian missions, the ancient pagan beliefs of transmigration and lycanthropy (the animation of animals by souls of departed chiefs) were still dominant. Lions seemed especially susceptible to invasion by exalted spirits. Perhaps this was why the King of Beasts was so feared, far more so than any other species except, possibly, the snake into which, so they believed, entered the spirit of the Paramount Chief of the Awemba, the *Chitimukulu*

Paramount Chiefs were buried in a Holy Grove near Chinsali which, appropriately enough, was rumoured to abound with snakes. No-one, black or white, was allowed into the grove except those intimately concerned with the funeral rites at the time of the *Chitimukulu*'s burial. Infringement meant an early death. Three Europeans had, so it was said (and you could always find someone to substantiate the story), been courageous or foolhardy enough to ignore the warning. All three met death within a year.

No matter at what time of the year the Paramount Chief died, his body was required to lie in state until the *malezi*, or millet, was ripe – and so, presumably, was he! I strongly suspect that the timing was to ensure sufficient *malezi* beer for the wake! It had once been customary, during the procession from the deceased chief's village to the

Holy Grove, to slaughter a wife at each stream and, having disposed of most in this way, to bury the others with him. This practice, we were led to believe, had now been abandoned but one bizarre and bloody custom still remained. After the completion of the funeral rites by the undertaker, this privileged gentleman had to defend his title, and his life, in a duel to the death with other aspirants to his post. An exciting floor show, indeed, to end the ceremonies!

In the same way that medicine and religion were entwined in medieval Europe, Bantu therapeutics were inseparable from witchcraft. The name for any medicine was *muti*, literally a tree; but as nearly every tree came to be used as a medicine, the word came to denote any remedy, including those recommended for supernatural interference.

There was a *muti* for every occasion. A wild tuber supplied the *muti* in which to bathe new-born babes. The juice of another plant helped to make the object of one's desire reciprocate, and the red flowering *namuteketa*, when made into a gruel and drunk at the beginning and end of the menstrual period, allegedly prevented pregnancy and was widely used for birth-control. The commonest remedy was *chiwangalume*, a plant considered to be a certain cure for colds, rheumatism, syphilis, indigestion and, like the claims of many proprietary drugs in Europe, was said to make the services of a doctor redundant – in this case, presumably, the witchdoctor.

Some remedies were symbolic. To become strong one drank a *muti* made from a strong tree, such as the *mulombwa*, the African mahogany, or a broth brewed from a strong animal. To run fast, there was nothing better than a concoction from the limbs of swift buck. Inanimate objects, too, could pass on their peculiar qualities, so children would run across the road behind my vanette, believing that they could absorb part of the vehicle's swiftness.

Many *mutis* were well proven, like the fish poison *buba*, or *uwuwa* (*Tephrosia voeglii*), an efficient piscine slayer but harmless to warm-blooded species and used to cure mange. I used *buba* as a parasiticide to keep ticks and fleas off my dogs with great success long before I heard of DDT or BHC. I ground the leaves in a little water and rubbed a handful of the mush over the animal's coat once a week. It had a pleasant, clean odour not unlike freshly mown grass, the only disadvantage being that the dog's coat took on a bilious tinge for a day or two. Unfortunately, its cultivation had been prohibited in order to conserve fish, but Kenaan always knew where to get some.

Numerous charms and lockets of hollow wood filled with powdered leaves, were worn round the neck, or the arm, or the forehead, to ward off evils, cure stomachache or headache and prevent heart ailments. The common elephant hair bracelet worn by so many Europeans, including myself, protected the wearer against diarrhoea, because the elephant's dung was always hard!

Animals played a large part in folklore and religion. According to Awemba tradition, the first animal to which the Gods entrusted a message of good tidings for mankind was the chameleon, but it was so slow and dallied so long that they dispatched the wagtail. This little bird delivered the message promptly, so becoming an avian hero and earning the right to sacred protection. The chameleon, on the other hand, was eternally damned and killed on sight. Unfortunately so, since it made a delightful pet and was an avid fly eater. I tried several times to keep one on the mosquito netting round the verandah, but it would always disappear and although the cook, houseboy or garden boy would flatly deny having touched it, it was safe to bet that one of them had seen to it that the sentence imposed so long ago had been faithfully executed.

Western cultures have modified their fertility rites into tourist attractions and are now content to dance round maypoles and to give picturesque thanks to the Almighty for the harvest, but in Northern Rhodesia orgies still took place to ensure a good crop – even to the extent of human sacrifice.

The *banyama* ('the people who eat you') were a supposedly secret clan who lived in Tanganyika and crossed the border specifically to procure victims for human sacrifice, which usually meant ploughing them into the chief's mealie field to increase his yield of corn. Youths with umbilical hernia, a squint or other defects, were preferred.

I once asked Kenaan what he thought about life after death. It was easy to see how missionary training conflicted with his tribal beliefs. Although he wanted to believe that *Bwana* Jesus made the world and he went to Him after death, he thought it more likely that death was the end, or that big chiefs went to a sort of Valhalla, or were changed into *chisanguka* or were-lions. Poor Kenaan, he had a hard job trying to reach an agreement between the beliefs he was born with and the God by whom he had been educated. I told him that the world was round and that it was possible to tell the time and the direction by the stars. He didn't believe that either.

* * *

If I had to design a logo for Dame Africa, it would be an anthill. The old girl was little more than one huge anthill on which thousands of smaller ones were continually being built, much the same principle as the coral reef. Of the many species that throve on her broad belly, the most destructive and hardest to deal with were the white ants, or termites.

White ants were like little, fat, white maggots with short legs. Their base of operations above ground was the conical mud anthill which sometimes reached 15 feet and which they could erect very quickly, although the story of the DC on *ulendo* awakened by an anthill thrusting up through his camp bed, was probably an exaggeration.

The large, slug-like Queen lived in the centre of the anthill, laying eggs consistently over a period of months or years. White ants were considered a delicacy by the Africans, especially in the flying stage just before the rains, when nets were placed over the termite hills to catch them as they emerged. The wings would then be pulled off and the ants popped into hungry mouths raw, or sometimes fried. They were undoubtedly an acquired taste, but it was the act of popping them into your mouth that really took time to get used to.

All buildings had to have a termite-proof coursing in their walls, usually a strip of zinc sheeting inserted between the bricks slightly above ground level, but below the level of the floor, and jutting out a couple of inches on either side to prevent the ants climbing up. Overhanging branches or anything leaning against the wall above the coursing, was an invitation for them to feast on your rafters. It was wise, too, to stroll round the house each morning and knock down any long, mud-covered tunnels that might have crept up the walls in the night from a hole in the floor or a touching branch. To leave one's trousers on the ground when camping could result in them being too perforated to wear – even in the bush!

Nothing made of vegetable matter was safe. Fence posts, furniture, beams, all had a limited lifespan before supplying a meal for the voracious termite. It was hardly an exaggeration to say that the termite Queen was the ruler of Central Africa, and I am sure that she will still be turning out her voracious brood aeons after our civilization – including the White Fathers – has been forgotten.

CHRISTMAS AT BROKEN HILL

My first Christmas in Africa had been spent in the train from Cape Town. I was certainly not looking forward to spending my second in the bush at Abercorn. But succour was at hand.

Once a year Rodney, a former Irish hockey International, accompanied by his beautiful wife, Lys, would drive north from his dental practice in Broken Hill to fill cavities, extract molars and sort out the troubled jaws in Kasama and Abercorn.

A week was usually sufficient for Abercorn. Numerous teeth were filled and pulled, and many people had more comfortable mouths at the end of it but, to balance the obvious relief from aching jaws was the all-too-common complaint of aching heads. Rodney and Lys became the catalysts for nightly jollification to such an extent that most patients Rodney saw the following day needed no further anaesthesia to protect them from his portable drill or forceps.

Taking pity on the two young bush-bound bachelors she had found languishing in Abercorn (or perhaps she was thinking of her teenage daughters!), Lys invited Ian, who had shared my house but who had since been transferred to Lusaka, and me to spend Christmas with them at Broken Hill. It proved to be the most rollicking Christmas of my life. A year of isolation meant that even the smallest social activity was endowed with almost unbearable excitement – and trepidation. I would walk up and down in front of a store, plucking up courage to go in and face the sales girls, and at my first attempt to use the telephone, I replaced the receiver before the call was answered.

Carol and Margo, our hosts' teenage daughters, and their friends home from school in the Cape, aided by several local swains, ensured non-stop revelry. Ian and I must have fallen in love with half a dozen girls – but Bubbles and Virginia I remember best. Bubbles, an ebony-haired, blue-eyed, slim-limbed lass of 20, took every lad's breath away. Oh, yes, I still loved Patricia, and would have gone anywhere and done almost anything for her – or Bubbles. But the dice were loaded. She was a devout Roman Catholic and I a hereditary Nonconformist of Quaker stock. I could only adore her from a distance as we played tennis, swam or danced in large groups. More intimate contact, physical or emotional, was out. Some years later I heard that she had joined an Order and taken vows. Being human and selfish, I felt relieved. (Fifty years later I gave a lift to a startlingly pretty girl near our house in the Natal Midlands. She turned out to be Bubbles' daughter! So much for the convent tale!) Virginia, small and cuddly, was almost as delectable and more earthy, but again, the competition was too great and I only had a few days.

The other lasting impressions of that year's end were the glass of sparkling burgundy in place of the usual morning cup of tea, and the daily celebrations which started before lunch around the pool at the Mine Club – or private house, and continued into the early hours. A gargantuan spread on someone's farm ended with a capsized boat on a dam, a thrill added to by the transparency of the girls' soaked and clinging cotton dresses. Virginia's panties had large red ants on them!

There was one short interruption to our merry-making, one that nearly cost me my life.

Mac, the Senior Veterinary Officer, rang from Lusaka.

'Sorry to spoil your Xmas, Pat.' He tried to sound apologetic. 'A Mr Carlson at Kashitu is having trouble with his herd. Suspects it's trypanosomiasis. Could you visit him? It'll save me a hell of a long journey.'

Kashitu, I could see, was on a side road about 60 miles north of Broken Hill. I set off early and several hours later, after ploughing through mud and swollen streams, arrived – as near as I could figure – at where Kashitu was marked on the map. There were no signposts and little evidence of a settlement, so I went into the first farm I came to. A grey-haired lady with a bun opened the door.

'I'm looking for a Mr. Carlson who is supposed to farm around here.'

'Well, you've come to the right place. Come and have a cup of tea. My husband should be in soon, he's rounding up some steers for sale.'

We sipped tea in the parlour in front of a large cut stone chimney, which went up through the thatched roof, while she told me that they were selling up and returning to Denmark after 30 years in Northern Rhodesia.

'What's the trouble with the herd? Lusaka said you thought it was tsetse.'

'Yes, some of the cattle were looking a bit thin and anaemic and we wanted them to be in good condition for the sale next month. I don't think it is very serious.'

By lunchtime Mr Carlson hadn't arrived. Cold ham and other goodies left over from Christmas were brought out. By three o'clock there was still no sign of her husband, and dark clouds were piling up in a typical African afternoon storm pattern. I would have to leave soon or risk being stuck on the road, and I had no intention of spending the night in a mud drift fighting mosquitoes, instead of at the Mine Club downing beer with the others.

'Wait and have a cup of tea – I'm sure he'll be back soon. He'd love to have the opportunity of talking to a vet.'

'I couldn't refuse but drank it as quickly as I could, praying that old man Carlson wouldn't show up. I'd never get away if he did.

'We can easily put you up for the night,' my hostess pleaded. Visi-

89

tors were probably few and far between.

'No, I really must go,' I insisted, as the thunder rolled ever nearer. Although I would never admit it, I was terrified of lightning.

I reached Broken Hill ahead of the storm in time to bath and join the others at the Mine Club cinema. Halfway through the programme a message was flashed on the screen. 'If Mr Guilbride is in the audience, please would he contact the Manager.'

What the Hell's all this about, I thought as I left the auditorium.

'Mr Guilbride? There's an Inspector of Police who would like a word with you in my office.'

My hands began to tremble. Police always made me feel guilty. Probably the Irish in me. I hadn't done anything wrong that I could remember.

'Sorry to haul you out of the show. I believe you went up to Kashitu earlier today?' The Inspector asked.

'Yes. Why?'

'There's been a bad accident and we have to send up an ambulance. We're not sure if it will get through after the storm. Can you tell us a bit about the condition of the road?'

I told him that I hadn't seen any accidents but that the road was pretty bad and the storm couldn't have improved it. 'Where did it happen?'

'We only have a name, Carlson. A neighbour phoned in but he didn't seem to know much either and the line was very bad.'

'I was with a Mrs Carlson until about three-thirty,' I told him. 'Her husband was still out when I left. I never saw him. Probably ran into a drift or a tree fell on him in the storm.'

The next morning I rang the Police Inspector and asked for news. Mr Carlson was dead, and his wife in hospital. Both had been struck by lightning. He told me that a bolt had hit their chimney about half an hour after I left. Carlson had just come in and was sipping his tea, presumably in the same chair I had occupied. He had been killed outright and his wife, on the other side of the room, burned and shocked.

I felt my skin prickle. How many lives did one have against lightning?

KALAMBO FALLS

Piet had two friends from South Africa staying with him over Easter – Cloete, a swarthy, lean Afrikaner with a delightful sense of humour, happiest when sketching or playing his guitar, and Hennie, another

Afrikaner, tall, fair and rugged, whose only ambition was to hunt.

Luckily for Hennie, there was probably no better place to hunt than Abercorn. No licences were required along the border and shooting was open, except for elephant, His hunting, however, nearly ended before it began. He, Cloete and Dickie, a tall, muscular 19-year-old trainee Postmaster who had recently arrived to help Pop, were cleaning and oiling their guns in preparation for a few days hunting with Piet, when Cloete's gun went off, putting a 7.5 mm bullet through Hennie's right lung.

Happily, the doctor, whose speciality was surgery, was on the station, and within 15 minutes Hennie was on the operating table in the African Hospital. For three days it was touch and go, but eventually he made such a remarkable recovery that a month later he declared himself fit enough to accompany Piet, Cloete, Dickie and myself on a day's trip to the Kalambo Falls.

The Kalambo was a small, insignificant stream running across the border from Tanganyika. Insignificant except for one feature. Twenty two miles north of Abercorn and half a dozen from Lake Tanganyika, it tumbled over an escarpment to become one of the highest waterfalls in Africa. Not as high, or as large, or as beautiful as the Tugela Falls in Natal, but nevertheless, a spectacular, clear drop of over 700 feet.

'Let's see if we can climb down to the bottom of the Falls,' the ever-eager Dickie suggested.

'OK' we all agreed, somewhat doubtfully.

'We'll have to cross the river first,' Piet pointed out. 'This side is sheer cliff.'

At the end of the dry season, when the Kalambo was very low, it was possible for those unaffected by heights, to straddle the two-foot wide rivulet where it poured over a rocky slab right at the rim of the Falls, and look down to the deep, black pool, far below. Even to think of such a thing, gave me a pain in my crutch! On the day of our visit the Kalambo was far too full to risk crossing anywhere near the Falls, so we stumbled upstream through thick riverine foliage, the trees forming a lofty tunnel over our heads, shutting out the sun and providing a safe lair for bands of babbling monkeys.

By stripping and holding our clothes over our heads, not altogether convinced by Piet's assurance that there were no crocs for miles, and fearful lest the current should sweep us down to the Falls, we waded across in a chain, waist-deep.

On the other side, we found ourselves in a ruined fortification – presumably from the 1914–18 war. Here we lounged about naked, letting the sun dry our bodies. Afterwards, we walked back down stream to the Falls and gazed over the top at the cascading water churning into the pool beneath, almost too far away to hear. We set off along the escarpment to where we could see steep but thickly wooded terraces.

It was easy sliding and slipping from tree to tree through the undergrowth. There was little danger of falling out of control and we were too boisterous to worry about snakes, which must have fled at the sound of our crashing, swearing, singing advance. At the last terrace, we found a 100-foot cliff between us and the river. Lying on our stomachs, we peered down at the Kalambo swirling below us, clear and enticing in the hot sun. Somehow the water seemed cleaner below the Falls, and the sight of it and the fact that it was out of reach immeasurably increased our thirst.

We searched for a way down to the river, but there was nothing. None of us, not even Piet, had been down to the bottom before, but he remembered being told of a path fairly near the Falls. We retraced our steps, the foliage becoming thicker and thicker the nearer we came to the waterfall, with a fine constant spray making everything damp.

There was no way down to the pool that we could find, short of jumping, and after half an hour, thoroughly dispirited and burning with thirst, we admitted defeat. Hennie was all in. Against everyone's advice and in spite of Piet carrying a rifle, Hennie had, with his insatiable desire to pot at anything that moved, insisted on bringing his own gun. Now it was obvious that we would have to carry it all the way back for him. Our spirits sank as we looked up at the towering, almost vertical escarpment above us.

Mechanically, we began to scramble up, pulling ourselves from ridge to ridge by grabbing shrubs, trees or tufts of grass. It hadn't seemed that far going down but climbing up was interminable, and I wondered if any of us, apart from Dickie, would make it.

Frequent rests were called, ostensibly for Hennie's benefit. Eventually we left the wooded part and began to crawl up a very steep grassy slope, Dickie, as usual, way out in front, with the rest of us 30 yards behind. We reached the top utterly exhausted and found to our astonishment and delight that we were alongside the ruined fort, and had succeeded in climbing up the slope which we had earlier considered too precipitous to clamber down. This cheered us, at least we had accomplished something.

Our desire for a drink was now overwhelming, but before we resorted to river water, Piet suggested that we try to find a village he knew of upstream, where we could buy some kaffir beer. Guessing the general direction, we set off through the bush on a short cut. A mile further we hit a large swamp and saw the village on the other side. There was no way we could reach it, so we continued on upstream, hoping to cross the river before it entered the swamp.

A moment later a scream from Dickie, ploughing ahead through the scrub, brought us to a standstill.

'Christ! Buffalo bean!'

Buffalo bean was not to be ignored. When ripe, the pods of this villainous bush are covered with millions of very fine, orange-brown hairs. Anything that disturbs the branches sends a cloud of these filaments into the air, and when they come to rest on bare skin, set up an intense irritation. Shirtless, we were perfect targets.

No sooner had Dickie yelled than Cloete and Piet were clawing at themselves in agony, and soon all five of us were running headlong back to the swamp, cursing loudly. We knew that our only relief would be to reach water or mud as soon as possible. Water would wash away the hairs and mud would pull them off. Trying to dust them off with a handkerchief only spread them and intensified the itch. There was said to be a furry-leafed shrub which would pull the hairs off, but the last thing we wanted to do was to waste time looking for it – even if we had known what it looked like.

We plunged into the marsh, oblivious of crocs, bilharzia or whatever. Piece by piece we removed the rest of our clothing and churned it about in the water to dislodge the little hairs. Then we succumbed to our thirsts and lay wallowing in the murky fluid, gulping large mouthfuls.

Afterwards, sitting around in our soaking clothes, we felt a little fearful of the risk we had taken in drinking the swamp water and decided that we had had enough adventures for one day. After all, we hinted to each other, Hennie was still a semi-invalid. If he felt anything like I did, I thought, that 'semi' could come out!

Our main desire now was to reach Abercorn and a bottle of beer without delay. A couple of hours later we were sitting in the bar of the Abercorn Arms, stinking of marsh mud, sweat dripping onto the polished wood, singing to Cloete's guitar and exaggerating, outrageously, each episode of the day for the benefit of the three or four others we found drinking there.

I went to the Kalambo Falls several times afterwards, but never again tried to reach the bottom of the gorge. For all I know, there may be a hotel there by now, with floodlights and boating on the dark green pool below. God forbid!

93

LIONS AND LYCANTHROPY

Colonel C.R.S. Pitman, for many years the Chief Game Warden of Uganda, and author of several books on wildlife, told me that he considered Northern Rhodesia to be the most lion-infested country in Africa, so it was not surprising that the King of Beasts played a large part in many local legends and old-timers' tales. Some of these tales were grossly exaggerated, but others were tragically true, such as 'Chiengi Charlie', the man-eater responsible for 57 human meals around Lake Mweru, and the man-eaters of Mporokoso, with even more human courses to their credit.

Nearer home was the case of Goddard, a Stock Inspector in the Veterinary Department. One day, while staying at a PWD friend's camp (the same PWD official, incidentally, who had sold me his daughter's piano accordion), Goddard received news that his native 'wife' and two of their children had been killed by a lion. The wife, evidently, had managed to put the youngest girl into a tree and told her to climb as high as possible. It was there that she had been found the next day.

Goddard and his PWD friend set out immediately, intending to hunt down the man-eater. Arriving late that evening, they decided there was little to be done till daybreak so they had a few drinks and turned in. Both their beds were in the same room, the door of which opened onto the verandah. They were tired and must have slept soundly, nevertheless, the PWD friend had a vague recollection of Goddard calling out in the night. He put it down to sleep talking or perhaps a nightmare.

When he awoke at daybreak he knew it had been no nightmare. Goddard's bed was on the verandah, his sheets scattered and blood-stained, but of Goddard himself, there was no sign. A brief search revealed his head (it was rumoured that lions were frightened of human eyes) and a few bones, nearby in the bush. The whole family, save for one child, had now been devoured – almost certainly by the same lion.

Fred, the rancher at Mbesuma, where his 3,000 head of cattle roamed the Chambezi flood plain, inevitably had lion problems. So much tame protein was not something that Mr and Mrs Leo could overlook, and in his 25 years on the farm he had killed well over 450 lions, not to mention leopards, cheetahs, hunting dogs and the like.

Some years previously Fred had had a partner, Thornton. One night Thornton was awakened by a noise in this room. As he raised himself to light the candle, a large paw was placed on his chest.

His right hand, holding the box of matches was, unfortunately, next to the lion – so was his gun, propped against the wall at the bedhead.

To make matters worse, the lion began to lick Thornton's bare forearm. Anyone who has felt a cat's tongue can easily imagine the rasp-like texture of a lion's. The arm was soon raw and the ligaments exposed, but every time Thornton tried to pull it away or shout for help, more pressure was put on his chest and the licking increased in vigour.

By great self-control and dexterity he managed to bring his left arm slowly over his head, pick up the rifle, cock it and shoot his attacker through the brain. Thornton lived, but his arm was useless. Some years later he died of sprue.

Curly, an Agricultural Officer at Lunzua, about 25 miles from Abercorn, often came to town for a drink and supper. One night, he left the Abercorn Arms hotel somewhat gayer than usual, cranked up his very old Model T Ford, which he had reconstructed from an abandoned wreck, and set off for home.

It was a bright moonlight night, and some miles out he was surprised to see what he took to be a shaggy donkey trotting along the road in the same direction. Since there were no donkeys in the Northern Province, he accelerated to his maximum speed of nearly 20 miles an hour and caught up with the creature. It sobered him considerably when he found it was an old lion.

The Ford had no brakes, only two gears and a rough uncovered wooden platform for the driver to sit on. Completely unprotected, there was nothing he could do but sit still and keep going. He soon left the lion behind but, unfortunately, the engine stalled. Once again the lion caught up with him. Unable to start the engine, Curly sat quaking on the driver's perch. He need not have worried. Leo never even glanced at him as he loped past. I wondered if Curly realized how lucky he had been. Old lions usually made the most dangerous man-eaters!

Then there was the dear old Anglican Bishop who was making one of his periodic tours of the Northern Province. One night he arrived at the Luwingu *boma*, where the DC and his wife made him comfortable in their guest house rondavel.

At dawn, a terrified, pyjama-clad figure stumbled up the steps of the DC's verandah. When he had stopped shaking and calmed down, he related how a lion had jumped in through the window in the middle of the night and gone to sleep on top of him.

'Oh, I'm so sorry,' apologized the DC's wife, 'I forgot to tell you to shut the windows. That was Bertie. He sometimes comes in on cold nights. He's really quite friendly.'

'Bless him,' laughed His Lordship. 'At least he taught me how to pray!'

There were stories about hunters, too, such as Charlie Ross, who was reputed to have been one of the greatest elephant hunters north of the Zambesi, and who was said to have once stuck a penny stamp on an elephant before he shot it. But perhaps the most unbelievable of the Charlie Ross tales was when he was killed by a particularly famous rogue elephant near Mpika. The night after he was buried his grave was dug over by elephants. This occurred regularly, so it was no wonder that the Africans insisted that the King of the Elephants was paying tribute to the King of the Elephant Hunters.

The same tales often surfaced in different places attached to different names. But even if many were only half-true and greatly exaggerated, the bottom line was clear – the King of Beasts and his henchman still ruled the bush and were worthy of the greatest respect, even if one disputed lycanthropy.

LAKE MWERU

Two blue patches stared back at me from the wall map behind my desk, as if asking when they might expect me.

'OK,' I kept telling them. 'Don't worry. I'll come. Soon I'll come.'

The map showed the lower patch, Lake Bangweulu, to be surrounded by an enormous swamp. One of the biggest swamps in the world, I was told. The other, Lake Mweru, snuggled up against the Congo, seemed uncertain as to which territory it should adopt, and had compromised by lodging an elbow in each. All I needed was an excuse, any excuse, to look them over. After all, they were part of my district. So when Hans, the ebullient Belgian Director of the International Red Locust Control Centre, mentioned that he had to check the locust breeding grounds around Lake Mweru and suggested I might like to go along, I simply told him to name the day.

There was little justification for my visit. Tsetse fly had been in occupation far too long for any livestock to be of importance in the area, but that, I argued, was no reason for ignoring it. Besides, it was a mysterious, little-known area, and Hans was the only person in Abercorn who had been there. I would be crazy to pass up such an opportunity.

Hans was one of Abercorn's more colourful characters. His dark, wiry hair was greying round the ears, and his eyes, sharp and intelligent, were separated by a large aquiline nose that hovered over the slightly prominent lips of a French speaker.

Although in his early forties and a seasoned scientist, he had the energy and enthusiasm of a schoolboy. It was Hans who had made the swimming pool, who had resurfaced the tennis courts at the club with fine anthill soil, who pestered everyone for specimens to increase his large collections of orchids, snakes and insects, and who entertained Abercorn with his quaint expressions and tall tales of his escapades in the bush. It was at his house, too, that we would automatically gather to celebrate the Allied advances, and had even christened his newly born son Zuki, after the bellicose Russian General, Zukhov. He and his charming golden-haired wife, Lislotte, gave us that flavour of Continental Europe which some po-faced British Colonials were so ready to despise, but so eager to experience.

The Red Locust Control Centre directed all locust operations from Southern Tanganyika in the east to the Congo in the west. There were several kinds of locusts in Africa, Hans told me, but the most important in Central Africa was the red, or 'hairy chested' locust. These gregarious grasshoppers bred in special areas such as around Lake Rukwa, just across the Tanganyika border from Abercorn, and in the swamp near Lake Mweru, the Mweru *wantipa*. Control was by poisoning the 'hopper' or larval stage of the locusts on the ground with arsenic before they grew wings. Campaigns were launched whenever 'hoppers' were reported in large numbers, and a successful

Lake Mweru

baiting operation would save millions of pounds worth of crops in the following months.

Hans carried his life-style into the bush with him. I remember ridiculing his *ulendo* box laden with condiments, sauces, pickles and the like, which he was preparing for the trip.

'Dammit, Hans,' I remonstrated, 'we're going on *ulendo*, not a Sunday School treat.'

'*Oui, mon ami* But we go on a long tour. If we are not *confortable* we shall not like eet. *Bon*, we make ourselfs *confortable* an' we enjoy de bush. We go wit'out tings an' we 'ate de bush, we get ill, we die. *Bon*, such a vay I make myself *confortable*.'

He was right. The essentials for *ulendo* or *safari* were a water sac, emergency food, mosquito net, bedding and a gun. For myself, I added reading and writing material and a camera. My stomach, however, unlike Hans', was still too young and too lacking in the niceties of a Continental education, to be overconcerned with spices.

Hans wished to meet his Belgian counterparts in Pwerto, just inside the Congo in the north-east corner of Lake Mweru, which meant first driving to Chiengi on the Lake's northern shore. Half way there we stopped for the night beside a rocky *kopje* overlooking the proud Kalunguishi river. Certain that no vehicle would disturb us, we camped on the narrow track and stretched a tarpaulin across to trees on either side, so making a shelter with a level floor for our camp-beds. Beside us stood a weather-beaten anthill, 15 feet high, sculptured by wind and rain into a sentinel-like figure against the setting sun.

A hundred feet below, the majestic Kalunguishi executed a graceful curve and snaked away to the horizon over a great yellow flood plain. We scrambled down the rocky, scrub-covered slope to the river bank, and from an overhanging bough peered into its deep dark waters, awed by the irresistible force which propelled the tired mass of water forward, as silently and steadily as time.

Night caught us as we climbed back to camp. It had become chilly with a swiftness characteristic of Africa, and we snuggled close to the camp fire to drink our brandy. A cooking pot thrust between the logs held an aged *kuku* (an apt word, indeed, for our present specimen). Below, fireflies twinkled and hippos kept up a bass accompaniment to the shrill stridation of crickets and the calls of nightbirds.

Chiengi, which we reached the next afternoon, straggled up from the lakeside, a scatter of untidy fishermens' huts, many of which appeared deserted. It had been an important administrative post in the days when Belgium and Britain were squabbling for slices of the African cake, but had been abandoned for many years and no European now lived there.

The utter loneliness of the place, rumour had it, had driven the last two Administrators to suicide. One of these unfortunates was said to have played cricket with himself every evening. Stumps were erected, a boy was trained to bowl, and the Administrator exercised his legs between the stumps until the ball was retrieved. When he was bowled or caught, he put himself in on the other side. Homesickness? The 'Forever England' syndrome – or just a passion for cricket? Who can say? Personally, I thought he showed commendable initiative.

The dilapidated Administrator's house still had a watchman and was serviceable in parts. In front, a grassy slope slipped away to a rocky cliff from which an overgrown path trickled down to the papyrus-lined shore 50 feet below.

We slithered down as eagerly as children on their first day at the seaside. Here, with a cake of soap and to the immense amusement of the local piccanins, we performed our happy ablutions. Venturing a few yards out we snatched a hasty swim in the shallow, murky water, conscious of the caretaker's warning of crocodiles.

We lay chatting far into the night, a warm breeze blowing through the rusty mosquito gauze of the sleeping verandah and flapping the remnants of the ant-eaten bamboo blinds that once had kept the rain at bay. Religion and politics figured prominently in our discussion, so did Belgium versus Britain, and I smiled when Hans, after hotly extolling the numerous advantages of his country over mine, such as the more enlightened social services, the superior architecture and the more comprehensive education, all of which I patriotically challenged, remarked quietly,

'*Hélas*; we are a small country, we must make a big noise if anyone is to 'ear us.'

The war, the future of the African, women and much more were debated that night, and as the intervals between our contributions became longer and the lap, lap, lap of the waves more noticeable, I realized what a wonderfully peaceful spot Chiengi could be to a person free to leave it at any time, but what a frighteningly lonely and monotonous prison it would be to a person whose duties bound him there.

Unconsciously, I began to count the laps ... like a marine clock ticking one's life away ... no wonder those poor chaps committed suicide!

The only 'track' to Pwerto was the sandy strip along the water's edge

Old Boma Chiengi

where the sand was hard enough to support the narrow wheels of our battered bicycles. To veer towards the lake or swerve towards the land meant a certain spill. I did both, repeatedly. It didn't matter, the water was cool and the sand soft.

Runners followed closely behind us to push when we struck a soft patch. No matter how fast we pedalled, the regular 'plat, plat' of their feet was always at hand, and when we had to deviate inland into softer sand, a steady pressure would still be maintained on our saddles. Not many athletes, I felt, even in the peak of condition, would be able to compete with these lean lake-side stalwarts.

We camped at Kipungu, halfway to Pwerto. A more lonely spot would be difficult to imagine. On either side a belt of sand stretched over the horizon with occasional green prongs of papyrus jabbing out as if the jungle wished to dip its fingers in the cool waters of the lake. Behind us were miles of bush: in front, miles of water.

It was in this area that the verbose missionary and writer, Dan Crawford (author of *Thinking Black*, Morgan and Scott, London 1912), had pioneered his faith, 70 years before; and where, not far away, at his mission on the cliffs at Luanza, he had asked his visitor, King Albert of the Belgians, what he thought of the view. 'Oh,' said the King, 'I imagine myself at Folkestone looking over at Calais.' His Highness must have had a lively imagination!

Some time before, I had started to collect spiders. Why, I cannot imagine. Spiders had always given me the creeps, but no-one else appeared to have collected them in these parts. Masochistically brandishing a killing bottle, I stalked my unsuspecting arachnids as they hopped about on the shore or trapped them on papyrus stalks. Soon I had over 20 different species.

We reached Pwerto next morning. It was Sunday. There was a special feeling in the air. Even in the bush, life seemed hushed as Mother Nature paid respects to her Creator.

100

It was my first visit to Belgian territory, and the first thing that caught my attention was a series of leather thongs hanging from the verandah roof outside the agent's office, weighted at the end with large rocks.

'*Chikotis*,' explained Hans. 'Whips.'

The *chikoti* summed up the Belgian attitude towards the African ... 'Look after him and make him work.'

Food growing was compulsory, medical services were good for those in industry or government service. Negley Farson, in his book *Behind God's Back*, regarded the Congo simply as a business concern of the Belgian Government. It was, and it paid better dividends if the African was well looked after and in good health. If he was lazy or obstreperous, well... there was always a supply of *chikotis*. One of Hans' scouts who was caught in the Congo without a pass, told us that he had received nine lashes on his nether end as a routine when arrested, and when his 50 days jail sentence was up, he had been helped back over the border with another nine. He seemed to think it a bit of a joke!

There were no shortages in Pwerto. Everything was imported, mostly from America, which had some kind of wartime exchange agreement with the Congo. Most bizarre were the Canadian Mounted Police uniforms. Many a clothes-conscious African could be seen swaggering around in riding britches, peaked hat and a Mounties' tunic. Tinned Spam, Chesterfield cigarettes, chewing gum and cheap clothing were plentiful. Only the beer was local, a gaseous but admirable light lager called Simba. Compared to Abercorn, Pwerto was paradise.

On the way back to Chiengi my front tyre went flat. Hans was already ahead and out of sight. Enviously, I pictured him on the verandah swigging cool drafts from the water bottle we had left pending our return. He was anything but cool when I arrived, half an hour later.

'Vair haf you bin? I cannot find de vater. Vair you put eet?'

I finally unearthed a bottle and passed two glasses. Hans snatched his and took a gulp.

'Aah! *Merde*! Eet's not vater. Eet's kerosene!'

We never did find the water.

*   *   *

A choking cry from Hans awoke me in the dim morning light.

'*Mon Dieu*! *Au Secours*! 'Ellllp!'

His pants halfway down his legs, he came galloping up the path from the PK, that little house 20 yards to the rear, where one could sit and meditate in silent comfort – usually! There was little about him that suggested silent comfort.

'Quick. Bring de torch.' I followed him down the path. He pointed to the toilet opening.

'Look dair.' I shone the beam down the shaft of the 'dull thump'.

'Vat is dat for an animal? *Mon Dieu!*'

About three feet down, clinging to the damp wall of the pit, were two or three enormous crab-like creatures, black and about the size of a side plate, with huge lobster claws and long trailing antennae.

'But dey vair on de seat. I was joost to sit down!' I understood his concern. They looked terrifying. I tried to catch them in a hastily rigged-up butterfly net, but they disappeared into cracks in the wall. Thereafter, each time we felt the urge, we banged on the seat before daring to sit down. The Africans called them *kalaili* and held them in great respect. I didn't blame them, but I was told by the British Museum of Natural History, to whom I later took a specimen, that they were harmless. They could have fooled me!

The early morning sun bounced off the glassy lake as we left Chiengi and turned onto a new track which Hans had had cut through the bush to the locust guards' checkpoint at Mukupa where we would camp. Tree stumps still spiked through the soft surface; it would take a couple more rainy seasons before they rotted and the road levelled.

Next day Hans rode off to inspect his Scouts, and I left soon after to visit some hot springs which Hans had extolled with his usual Gallic exaggeration. These lay inside a *mushitu* (the lush vegetation surrounding a spring) which I could see three miles away like a blob of green paint dropped onto the roasted grass of the flood plain.

I was mighty glad to reach the cool, deep shade of the towering trees and let the sweat pour off me. The hot springs proved to be real enough but not boiling as Hans had said. I took off my shirt and splashed the hot water over my body. It was surprisingly refreshing. The *mushitu* was full of dark shadows and mysterious, half-audible noises; a stage set for a fairies' grotto, with shafts of bright sunlight probing down inquisitively through the high branches and tropical fronds, sucking up moisture from the clammy, decaying atmosphere.

Africa, I decided, was a land of extremes. Floods followed droughts, mountains dominated plains, tropical forests ended in deserts. Dame Africa's virtues and vices were all superlatives, her moods all manias. It didn't just rain, it poured. It wasn't just hot, it was frying, and when it was cold it was a bitter penetrating cold that defied sweaters and blankets. Rivers either overflowed or were stagnant pools. Blazing heat could turn to biting cold as inky blackness replaced brilliant sunshine. There was no regulating mechanism, no moderation, no compromise. Life-cycles were short-circuited; everything – humans, plants, flies – reproduced faster, replacing quality with quantity. My feet sank deep into the rotting vegetation. Untold civilizations, I mused, had destroyed themselves by thoughtless cultivation and deforestation, leaving behind deserts and dust bowls when all that was needed was a little understanding – and humus. Present civilizations would do the same, unless they put an end to opportunist farming and the destruction of forests. Mother Nature was, in many ways, a delicate old girl. Scratch her back with a plough or cut her with a road, and her skin would peel off leaving a running sore, the only salve for which was vegetation.

I squelched through the thick, humming foliage, expecting at any moment to come upon some lost city with stone embattlements and carved statues, its temples and arenas torn apart by roots of great trees. Unfortunately, there were few such remains in Central Africa since the indigenous races had worked mainly in wood. The only relics I knew of were the mysterious stone ruins at Zimbabwe in Southern Rhodesia, a few cave drawings near Mpika and the numerous *coup de poings* and axe heads in some of the river valleys. White ants had digested the rest.

Spiders were here in their hordes, flocks, creeps or however spiders are referred to *en masse*. I caught some white ones and some with multi-coloured shells, like butterflies, which had spun their webs between the smaller branches. I was amazed at the number of cockroaches, which I had always considered as house pests, waging an unrelenting war against them in Abercorn, trying to keep them in check with a hot solution of Jeyes and a stirrup pump. They were so numerous that one had to stand back after opening a door and let the abominable insects fall down before going through, a habit I maintained long after leaving Abercorn. Many of these in the *mushitu* were almost white from living in that gloomy undergrowth. According to an article I had read, the cockroach was considered the most likely of all living things to survive major climatic or nuclear disasters. I was inclined to agree, although I imagined that the white ant might run it a close second.

Thirst, hunger and restlessness soon got the better of me and just after midday, with the sun dead above in a flaming sky, I ventured out onto the grilling plain. It took over an hour of grim determination, goaded by the thought of a cool drink, to propel me back to camp without dropping. Where the grass had been burned, a warm breeze blew over the black ashes, lessening the agony, but where the grass was still tall and unburnt, the heat was unbearable. I thrust forward, blindly, hoping for a burnt patch before I fainted.

I arrived at camp sun-struck and dizzy. Glasses of cool water and a sleep revived me a little, but I felt light-headed for the rest of the day. Anticipating a dose of fever brought on by the heat and exhaustion, I took 15 grains of quinine and retired. It was a disturbed night. Chief Mukupa's daughter was being wed. The caterwauling and drums, beaten with drunken fervour, lasted till dawn.

Mukupa paid us a call the next day. He was not quite himself. I caricatured him as he argued with Hans. His beady, sullen eyes, protruding underlip and almost absent chin were easy material to ridicule, and the sketch caused considerable merriment amongst the locust Scouts. Mukupa, it seemed, was not a popular chief.

The local schoolchildren, whom the proud teacher paraded outside their mud-walled academy to do lessons in front of us, added one plus one, two plus nought and even such mathematical conundrums as three plus two plus nought, scratching their figures in the sandy soil with a twig while an older student, full of importance, went round tapping daydreamers on the head with his baton. What British schoolchild, I thought, would not have given a term's pocket money to swop places with these abecedarians – if only to escape the ever-

Chief Mukupa

104

present threat of exams. No such barbaric competitions had yet penetrated this isolated hamlet. I fervently hoped they never would.

We abandoned the vanette at Mukupa, the end of the track. Hans' driver would take it back to Mporokoso where we would meet him in a week's time, while we continued by bicycle over the hard rough hummocks of sun-baked mud which made the journey both uncomfortable and hazardous. Towards midday we heard the roar of a waterfall and Hans shouted that we were near Mwasha, our destination for the night.

Of all the falls I had ever seen, Mwasha were the most beautiful. Although not marked on any of my maps, they were one of Dame Africa's hidden jewels, and only lightly wrapped in the discomfort of reaching. The clear torrent of the Mukubwe river appeared suddenly from the forest to plunge 30 feet over a semicircular rock shelf into a deep, crescent-shaped lagoon. From this, it flowed away in a series of rock pools, deep enough to swim in. In the centre of the lagoon a long finger of rock pointed skywards, carved by nature into a massive totem-pole. Surely, I thought, it must have a religious significance.

We spent the afternoon drifting from one rock pool to another, eating paw-law and allowing the cold bubbling river to wash away the heat. This was the Africa I could love. Succulent tropical fruit, crystal water, bright sun and no crocodiles (at least we hoped not), what a riparian paradise! I half-expected a water nymph to pop up, a dryad (or is it naiad?) to bound out of the forest and entertain us with its capers. Only one thing was missing. A girl would have made it perfect. I thought of Patricia. What a time we could have had! Maybe, one day, I would bring her here.

We dared each other to dive into the crescent pool whose dark, turbulent waters seemed to hold a thousand horrors worse than crocodiles. Neither of us was brave enough.

Dragonflies darted and hovered above the water, and the trees along the banks were filled with singing birds. Hans, a knowledgeable ornithologist, began to recount their scientific names, but somehow this wasn't the moment for Latin tags.

Beauty, I felt, should not be classified. It didn't matter whether those divine ripples were the song of *Gypohierax angolensis* or the mating call of *Bycanistes subcylindricus*. It only mattered that they sang. Keats had said it all:

> There was an awful rainbow once in heaven.
> We know her woof, her texture; she is given
> In the dull catalogue of common things.
> Philosophy can clip an angel's wings.

Perhaps, one day, some arrogant atheist would reduce the Almighty to a gas, or measure the difference in altitude between heaven and hell. Till then, I was determined that my angels' wings would remain unclipped.

'Rain spiders', so-called because they often appeared shortly before the rains broke, were everywhere, darting about like small pieces of cotton wool (from long abdominal hairs) as if seeking an elusive treasure. Their two large sabre-like teeth could easily be seen, and many an impulsive pussycat or dog had to have them prized from their lips.

Now that I was constantly on the lookout for spiders, I came across different types each day. Their ingenuity in mimicking other insects always amazed me. One camouflaged itself by carrying pieces of bark on its back, another mimicked and preyed on ants, and others mimicked butterflies. Maybe spiders should join cockroaches and white ants as leaders in the race for survival.

I would much rather have walked then cycled, but Hans, who was 15 years my senior, could not be swayed. I saw little point in cycling ahead, arriving hot and thirsty at the camp site, only to wait hours for the carriers bringing food and water. One also missed a lot *en route* with one's eyes constantly fixed on the track, trying to avoid humps and holes, and I am sure that the porters respected a *bwana* who tramped with them far more than one who cycled ahead and waited impatiently for their arrival. But this was Hans' *ulendo* and he called the tune.

At our next stop I spent the afternoon on my camp bed reading Livingstone's *Missionary Travels*, finding a great deal in common with his descriptions of petty annoyances. Hundreds of tiny *ntulantula* flies (actually bees that had lost the power to sting, although they still made honey) buzzed round my face. They were just as aggravating as the tsetse, crowding into my ears, eyes, mouth and nose, but at least they didn't bite. Horseflies, however, twice the size of Scotland's famous 'clegs', did, so I put up my mosquito net and followed the good Doctor's journeys in the only manner in which tales of adventure and hardship should be read … stretched out in comfort, with a cup of coffee. Zeebruni, Hans' cookboy, produced some of the best coffee I had ever tasted – until we discovered that the sock he strained it through was the one he had been wearing all day! His coffee thereafter was more hygienic, but tasted a lot less satisfying.

The escarpment along which we were cycling was impressive. Running in a mighty curve, it dropped abruptly, like the inside of a frying pan, to the circular *wantipa*, or swamp, 600 feet below. Far

106

away, in the centre of the *wantipa*, simmered the open water of the Chisi pan, around which lechwe in their thousands and game of every sort gathered to spend the dry months of the year, until the rains drove them back to the timber belt.

From the foot of the escarpment a path threaded away across the swamp, like a strand of flaxen hair, to the Locust Scout post at Mpundu. Reports from Mpundu had – thank God! – been favourable and we could now head straight for Mporokoso without trailing through that hot steaming papyrus.

The arid country through which we now frequently pushed our bicycles, once echoed to the lash of the Arab slave dealers. Semiwi, where we camped for the night, and nearby Nsama, had been two of the collecting centres. Victims had been driven in, yoked together in long lines of misery, to be bartered for Arab guns, clothes and alcohol, and then sent on to the slave markets on the east and west coasts.

Centuries-old mango trees provided extensive shade and coolth to the higgledy-piggledy huts of Abdullah Semiwi – to give the village its full name. We made camp beneath a massive specimen on the outskirts. Swarms of piccanins came to stare at us, for many of them the first Europeans they had seen. Chattering delightedly in their high-pitched voices, they scrambled up into the branches, the better to examine us with their big brown eyes. All around jostled evidence of Arab blood. It seemed that old 'hook-nose' had found time to play, as well as to work. The girls, light-skinned and large-eyed, were unusually attractive. (What was it I had been told? Six months north of the Zambesi and they'll all look like Ginger Rogers). When the melee became unbearable, we armed a scout with an empty rifle and told him to keep every youngster out of sight, even to putting the fear of old Abdullah into them once more. I missed Flea, he would have had a great time – until Mrs Tsetse got him. However, I noticed quite a few native dogs about and, although skinny and miserable, the breed had evidently built up some tolerance to trypanosomiasis over the years.

Semiwi's water supply was a stinking ten-foot pit with a porridge of smelly mud at the bottom, so water had to be carried from the Mwambeshi stream half a mile away. We walked out there in the late afternoon to have a wash, smelling it long before we saw it. Semi-stagnant pools with a murky trickle between them, gave off waves of putrefaction. Downstream, at a spot where the water seemed to be actually flowing, we closed our noses to the fetid smell and immersed our briny skins, hoping that the thick lather would protect us form bilharzia and typhoid.

107

A curiously shaped tree in the form of an umbrella reached out from the bank. It seemed to have been placed there specially to shade our ablutions, as if that was the one purpose for its creation. I took its photo, for it would certainly wither away now that its mission had been fulfilled.

The mind picks on weird objects to strengthen the memory. Witness the blot in my medicine notes that helped me to memorize the symptoms of equine influenza, or the doodle in my anatomy book which never allowed me to forget the distinguishing features of the second cervical vertebra of the ox. Now, an oddly shaped tree would fix that evening and the particular odour of the Mwambeshi stream for ever in my memory.

We returned to find that we had no drinking water, which meant fetching a new supply of muddy fluid, straining, boiling and hanging it up in a water sac to cool. Immediately, I felt a raging thirst. Had there been a full sac, I would probably have ignored it, but its mere absence induced unbearable thirst. By bedtime the water was still too hot to drink and I dozed off with agonizing memories of a pub in Cornwall.

Not for long. Someone was raiding our larder.

'Zut! Vat ees dat for a bizziness?'

Hans grabbed the torch and pointed it at the centre of the disturbance. We found a surprised-looking hyena helping itself to our supplies. It was too dark and too near the village for safe shooting, so Hans threw a boot at it and it lolloped off, crashing about in the bush for some time. Next morning we found that it had crunched up four unwashed plates, ripped open a sack of flour and taken both chickens, purchased at the enormous expense of sixpence each.

We were awakened again in the early half-light by the cry of the muezzin from his minaret, calling the faithful to prayer, yet another reminder of the slave trader. Here in the centre of the bush, two isolated villages still kept faith with Islam.

* * *

'Eet ees desairted. Dair ees no-buddy 'ere.' Hans threw his bicycle down in disgust.

We had been cycling for more than two hours. I was exhausted, soaked in sweat and prostrate with heat. Dame Africa's Black Imps had obviously been stoking the furnace extra hard that morning in order to teach these two impertinent white intruders a lesson. We had just passed an open plain covered with hundreds of small white anthills, like tombstones.

'Here,' I imagined the Imps chuckling, 'is where we bury white men!'

Shortly afterwards, Hans had spotted the huts and we had ridden up joyfully. At least we could get a drink or a paw-paw to slake our thirst. Then the moment of truth. All the huts were empty. The village was abandoned.

I was furious, Hans had been adamant that he knew the way and that there was no need for a guide, and had set off like mad thing with myself and Zeebruni, his cook (also on a bicycle and entrusted with the water sac), trying to keep up. Unfortunately, Zeebruni's machine was worse even than ours, and he quickly faded out of sight. Now we had arrived at a collection of burnt-out huts and overgrown gardens. No clapping women, no dogs, no piccanins. Deserted.

'Dey mus' 'ave move de village,' Hans moaned, collapsing on the ground. I could see that, but where to?

We knocked down some small paw-paws, but they were green and bitter and quite uneatable. We looked at each other in silence. Dallying wouldn't help. We had to go on; the sooner we found Kakoma, our night stop, the better.

We chose the largest and most used path. Several times we thought we saw huts but, like oases, they disappeared. I could imagine the Imps fairly chortling at our discomfort. Thirst made it impossible to think clearly and my throat was on fire. I marvelled that there was still enough moisture in me to sweat. Not for much longer, I feared.

A great truth suddenly came to me. it was not love that made the world rotate. It was that gem – water. Plain, unadulterated, sparkling H_2O – the elixir of comfort and life. And beer. What was beer but water in her Sunday dress? The Devil could have bought my soul cheap that day. For one cold beer I would gladly have rendered him eternal service.

A bicycle bell in the distance dispelled my dreams.

'*Eh, la*,' croaked Hans. ''Ere ees de cook. Water.'

Hans could never have been labelled a negrophile, but as Zeebruni unhitched the water sac from his handlebars and unstrapped a rather squashed pawpaw, Hans was within a millimetre of hugging him. The new village of Kakoma, Zeebruni said, lay behind us on the other side of the deserted one. Back we raced, refreshed with fruit and water. Again the path split. As we were debating which way to go, a *kansu-ed* figure hove in sight, riding a bicycle. The good White Father was visiting his flock around the *Wantipa*. He took us half a mile up the track to the new village, where we drank the milky, slightly smelly water offered, without waiting to boil it. Meanwhile goats, chickens and dogs fought for a mouthful of dirty fluid in the gourds lined up for the carriers. It must have been their first drink for days.

The 25 miles we had travelled that day and the crushing heat made us turn in at sunset. Sleep, however, was another matter. The White Father had warned us that there were a couple of lions in the district which were becoming addicted to human flesh. Our tarpaulin shelter, open at both ends, offered scant protection. I lay listening to Hans' snores and envying him his lack of nerves, my ears alert and my hand on the gun beside me. If Leo had put in an appearance, I should probably have blasted Hans in my terror.

I remembered Piet's advice: 'If you want to sleep well in the bush, take a nervous bloke along with you. He'll be certain to stay awake and see that nothing comes near.'

Early morning was bitterly cold, as it often is in Africa, and we had a hard job to unwrap the snoring mummies round the now cold camp fire. Cold seemed to stupify the African, numbing his brain and paralysing his body – as it does mine! After much goading we struck camp and started up the escarpment separating us from Mporokoso, every overhanging bush showering us with icy dew, until, as the sun rose, sweat began to moisten our shirts instead.

Halfway up we found a delicious pool of crystal water covered with a quilt of bees. We rippled the surface and cupped our hands letting the little creatures crawl up our arms and lap our sweat with their long, thin tongues. That evening, tired, dirty and very thirsty, we limped into Mporokoso.

*　*　*

On the way back to Abercorn we called at Chilabula, a White Father mission. The Sisters of St Therese had a seminary close by, a diversely-hued brick bungalow, surrounded by arid gardens.

I was struck by the beauty of these nuns, their faces reflecting the love of their work, their inner tranquillity and absolute unselfishness. Their beauty didn't escape Hans, either.

'An' dey 'af to be nuns,' he sighed. 'Vat a vaste, vat a vaste!'

The schoolgirls, who boarded at the mission, entertained us to an exhibition of songs and dances, and as they sang and skipped, with the Mother Superior clapping out the rhythm in the growing dusk, I felt that few people in this materialistic world had achieved such a pinnacle of spiritual understanding as this hard-working, happy, isolated band of Sisters.

Next day we reached Abercorn and civilization. A hundred and twenty letters on my desk were crying for attention.

LAKE BANGWEULU

I was sweating again.

Alternately hot and cold. I pulled up another blanket. That made the fourth. The chipped wall thermometer (I wondered if they had them in Hell) registered 85 degrees, but I was still shivering. This, I decided was my ninth attack of malaria in 15 months. My eyes hurt too much to read, there was a pain in the back of my neck, and the 15 grains of quinine I had taken the night before, plus another ten grains that morning, made my ears hum.

Just as I was dozing off, the noise in my ears grew louder. I raised my head to the small window, hoping. Yes, up there in the blue, blue sky was a silver bird, probably a Dakota of the South African Ferry Command, humming its way south to Johannesburg, to city lights and civilization.

Lucky blighters, I thought. I tried to imagine what they were saying to each other.

'What's that island, *jong*?'

'Let's have a *kyk* at the map. Here it is; Chilubi island, Lake Bangweulu. The white buildings are probably Santa Maria Mission; it's the only place marked.'

'God forsaken hole, I should think. It's all swamp.'

'Drive me bats. Give me the Cape, any day.'

There was much about Lake Bangweulu that would have surprised my imaginary airmen. The mere size of the swamp, for instance, over 3,000 square miles, one of the largest in the world; the timid swamp dwellers, the Batwa, rarely seen by strangers and described disparagingly, by neighbouring tribes as 'pygmy-like and web-footed'; the teeming game – black lechwe, sitatunga, sable and others thrived along the water's edge; Livingstone's memorial at Old Chitambo to the south of the marsh where, on the night of May 1st 1873, the intrepid explorer and missionary had died, his body and diaries being carried the thousand miles back to Zanzibar by his devoted servants. And the *chimpekwe*, the mythical lake monster which everyone knew about but no one had seen and which, from all accounts, resembled its cousin in Loch Ness. Several authorities declared that it did, or had existed, including Hughes, the author of *Eighteen Years On Lake Bangweulu*. Lanky assured me that he had been shown the burial place of one such beast. But why no bones over the years? I asked. A good old-timer's story, for sure!

Two weeks before, accompanied by Flea (I had left Panda behind

111

with Ian), Kosam and John, my most recent African Veterinary assistant, I had arrived at Momfulwe, on the northern shore of Lake Bangweulu, that lower patch of blue on my wall map. Here we would await the government launch which would take us to the islands. In fact, the map showed that the lake itself was a relatively small patch of open water sprinkled with jigsaw fragments of swamp-encircled islands, three of them large, the rest mere papyrus-smothered sandbanks. The reason for my visit, apart from love of exploring, was to assess the sheep-raising potential of the islands which already possessed more of these animals than the rest of the Northern Province.

Momfulwe was a bonny spot, the road ending on a little promontory beneath an enormous tree, said by early explorers to be capable of shading a whole caravan. Beneath our feet was a dirty, grey sand that made walking tiresome and which, I was soon to discover, teemed with chiggers, those minute skin burrowers which fully earned their scientific name of *Pulex irritans*. On one side, the ground sloped abruptly to a green lawn of papyrus, on the other to a sandy cove. A small island, 50 yards from the beach, provided a safe anchorage for fishing canoes.

As the vanette was being unloaded, I was surprised to see a white man approaching. Although dressed in dirty khaki slacks and shirt, his grey hair, fine features and unkempt George the Fifth beard gave him a distinguished air which, I fear, belied his true character.

Jack had been in the country since the turn of the century. His first job had been on the railway pushing its way up from the south.

'Those were tough times,' he told me between spits, 'men died every day.' If you drank enough you lived to forty, if you didn't you died before thirty. We had no laws, not many anyhow, but they jugged me once – for shooting four of these black bastards. It was worth it, the thieving swine.'

Jack was tough all right. Tough enough to have survived those early days. I invited him for a drink and some food. He strolled over at sundown, hitching up his filthy trousers every few steps. At midnight, having polished off a bottle of brandy, not to mention several forays into my whisky and gin, I guided him back to his tent where he flopped, semi-conscious, onto a camp bed.

We both rose early, Jack a little less talkative but bright enough for me to marvel at his powers of recuperation. His present job was building a rest house on the end of the promontory for the District Commissioner. We leaned against the half-finished walls and admired the view.

What a super place the Yanks would make of it, I reflected. A few bulldozers to clear the papyrus and bush, air-conditioned chalets, swimming pools, yachts – what a delightful holiday resort for the Copperbelt. If only .... But there were many 'if only's' in Africa. Meanwhile mosquitoes, bilharzia and crocodiles, would continue to call the shots at Momfulwe.

A little way along the shore was the isolated Anglican Mission of Samfya which, I was told, owned a herd of cattle. I visited them, and in the absence of the missionary and his wife, who had gone to Fort Roseberry for the day, and of John, whom I had left in camp, co-opted their fair-haired daughter, Beryl, aged five, to interpret for me. She led me, hand in hand, down to the kraal and for half an hour, her head on one side and her face puckered in concentration, relayed questions and answers between me and the herdboy on the health and sex life of her cows.

A messenger from the DC at Fort Roseberry arrived later that day to say that the launch had been held up and I should pick it up at Nsombo, a small port 100 miles to the east. Before leaving, Jack conned me out of a tin of cigarettes and five pounds of flour. His technique was superb.

'Damn. Seem, to 'ave left me cigarettes in me 'ut,' slapping his empty pockets, ostentatiously.

'Here, have one of mine.'

'Thanks very much. English! 'Aven't seen Players for years (nor, incidentally, had I). Used to be me favrit'.

'Well, hang on a sec,' said I, torn between generosity and fear of being made a sucker. 'Maybe I could let you have a few.'

I opened my tin *ulendo* box. Of course, Kosam had placed the three tins of Players right on top under Jack's covetous stare. I settled for one tin. The same process with appropriate variations gained him a goodly ration of flour. Poor old Jack, I didn't really grudge him a fag and a bit of dough, but I had only catered for one on this trip.

Shortly before leaving Abercorn, the doctor had cut a stubborn wart off the knuckle of my forefinger. I had assured him that I could take out the stitches myself. Now it looked as if pus was accumulating beneath them, so I called on the Polish M.O. at Fort Roseberry, on the way to Nsombo.

'It'll be OK,' he said dressing it. 'Any other warts?' I showed him two more. He grinned. 'I'll remove these without the aid of a knife.' he produced an ethyl chloride spray and began to freeze the offending growths.

'It's purely psychological, of course,' he went on. 'the spray has really nothing to do with it, but what you must do is to look at them every day and tell yourself that they're growing smaller. In ten days time they will both have disappeared. It's like the thousand other remedies for warts. It just depends how susceptible the patient is to auto-suggestion.'

'Right,' I agreed. 'I'll examine them daily – Coué method.'

I only half believed him so I was pleasantly surprised when the warts did start to dry up and had disappeared within the promised period. What was even more surprising was that a plantar wart, which I'd had on my heel for several years, swelled up, became very painful, and also disappeared. I was to remember this incident years later when I was deep into an investigation on cattle warts. Curing warts in cows, however, was a little more difficult – they weren't susceptible to auto-suggestion!

Half way to Nsombo I spied a cosy *dambo* through the trees. Navigating the roadside gully I drove through the forest to the *dambo's* edge and found an ideal camp site. A small gurgling brook, born just behind my camp, divided the half mile of yellowing grass that stretched before me in the late afternoon sun.

Leaving Kosam busy with the evening meal, I wandered across to the trees on the far side, and came across a deserted village. Old gardens, circles of mud where the houses had stood, pieces of pottery and a broken tin bowl were all the white ants had left. The sun had almost set as I strolled back, and the last golden rays struck the tips of the small white anthills that dotted the *dambo's* edge, making them flame against the dark background of forest.

Words of *Die Lorelei*, describing the evening sun on the mountain tops, came to me ...

'*Die Gipfel die Berge funkeln
In Abend Sonnenschein.*

The entertainment committee of bush sprites treated me to a fascinating display of massed fireflies, incidental music by courtesy of Messrs Frog, Cricket, Lizard and Nightbird.

Nsombo proved to be a marshy inlet with a few mud huts and a couple of Kimberley brick, tin-roofed stores. The launch had not yet arrived, but there was a message asking me to take the large metal canoe, the *Mary Ann*, which was tied to the jetty, and pick up the launch at Chilubi island.

With the sun peeping over the horizon, we left the muddy quayside and punted cautiously along a shallow channel through the reeds. The smell of decay in the muck stirred up by the canoe's bottom was overpowering, and the heat, although still early, was becoming oppressive. Ten-foot-high papyrus obscured the view which, if I could have seen it, would only have been more papyrus and phragmytes reeds.

The middle section of the *Mary Ann* was shaded by an awning. In front and behind this sat the paddlers, six fore and six aft. These stalwarts, together with myself, John, Kosam and a *boma* messenger from Luwingu and, of course, Flea, constituted the ship's company.

Half-an-hour later we gained open water and found a fresh breeze which inspired the paddlers to renewed efforts. As they swayed together, they sang a lilting ditty. The general meaning, John said, was 'Should we be drowned, our children will come and pick up our bodies.'

I sketched the swarthy oarsmen as they dipped their short paddles into the dirty green water. Flea couldn't make it out at all and divided his time between sniffing the crew and trying to jump overboard.

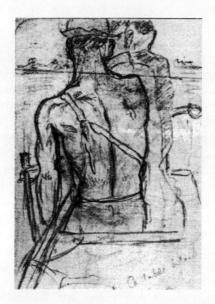

Leaving Nsombo in the Mary Ann

Small islands soon began to separate themselves from the horizon, and an hour later we landed on a typical papyrus islet about three feet above lake level, formed from a sandbank and years of trodden down reeds. Fishing nets hung on a rickety wooden structure in front of a reed hut, from which the fisherman and his family watched us

115

suspiciously. Nearby, a patch of kaffir corn, or millet, struggled unsuccessfully with the elements. Flea was delighted to stretch his legs by chasing the fish eagles that scratched along the strand for piscine entrails.

While 'looking at Africa' behind the patch of kaffir corn, I heard a motorboat 'putt-putting' towards us across the light green water. Moses, the mechanic, had decided to meet us halfway. We transferred our baggage and said farewell to the *Mary Ann*. I unearthed my piano accordion and sitting astride the bows, my feet trailing in the water and Flea howling in protest, we skimmed away over the lake towards our first objective – Chilubi island and Santa Maria mission, the nerve centre of the area.

By mid-morning, Chilubi appeared on the horizon like a dark snake. Moses steered us through the surrounding papyrus to a small jetty, behind which the neat whitewashed buildings of Santa Maria mission reflected the brilliant noonday sun. A fine avenue of *Cidrela tuna* and blue-flowering jacaranda trees ran up to the mission. The few piccanins who had gathered to greet us scattered as Flea bounded ashore.

Music and singing filtered through the open church doors as I strolled up the avenue, and I realized that it was Sunday. In the bush there was little to distinguish Sundays from weekdays, although I often felt an even greater tranquillity on the Sabbath.

The congregation had begun to emerge from the small arched doorways of the church, and I could see the habits of the White Sisters as they stood talking to the *kansu*-ed White Fathers or to native girls. A middle-aged, robust, fair-haired Father spotted me and came hurrying over.

'Father Maestrom. Welcome to Santa Maria' a large smile spread over his chubby red face, which tapered gradually from a broad forehead to a trim, pointed, blond beard, giving the impression of an inverted isosceles triangle with a pair of fiery blue eyes embedded in the centre. He showed me to the vacant doctor's quarters and then took me across for lunch in the refectory.

Here, he told me about his plans for the development of the islands, plans which, according to him, were constantly baulked by the Government. But nothing could daunt his enthusiasm. The authorities, I learned later, who regarded him as a fanatical priest (which he was) and a sharp customer (also with some justification), were unhelpful and suspicious, guessing (correctly, I'm sure) that his ambitious plans for community health centres, playing fields, post offices and agricultural stations, badly needed as they undoubtedly were, were primarily a means of extending the mission's influence.

I felt sorry for him. He was so keen, so energetic, so bubbling with ideas but so hampered by impecuniosity, officialdom, white ants and the apathetic paludal islanders themselves, that I automatically took his side. He had an active precise brain and spoke nine languages. Had he not been a missionary he might have been a successful tycoon or famous politician. Perhaps, one day, he would be a famous missionary.

Candlelight improved the appearance of the doctor's quarters. The roughness was less obvious and the creepy-crawlies less visible. The good doctor, a lady, was on leave recuperating from blackwater fever, the dreaded sequel (some said) of repeated attacks of malaria. She never returned; instead she married Brother Severian, a happy-go-lucky lay brother who had recently quit the mission.

She was undoubtedly, a tough lady. When an RAF Beaufort crash-landed into the swamp, *en route* from Cairo to Johannesburg, she travelled four days by canoe to reach it, only to find that the swamp dwellers, the Batawa, had already taken the crew from the half-submerged, snake-infested plane, to safety.

In gratitude for her brave attempt the RAF presented the Mission with the wreck – there was little else they could have done with it, salvage was out of the question! This handsome windfall with its miles of copper wiring, petrol tanks half-full of aviation spirit, compasses, radio, perspex windows and upholstered seats, had been quickly dismantled by the cheerful Brother Severian, and most of it had already been sold, except for a gun turret which still adorned the mission garden.

Next day, John and I started a tour of inspection on bicycles borrowed from the White Fathers. Early as we were, the Fathers had been up for several hours and presented us, most thoughtfully, with a packet of sandwiches. I could hardly believe that the mornings could have been so nippy, the handles of my bicycle were like sticks of ice.

Chilubi island was in the form of a mishapen starfish, four or five spikes extending out from a cental rib. Wherever we went, we were either heading towards the end of a prong or towards its base. Flea rushed ahead, barking with joy, putting to flight any piccanin or chicken that crossed our path. He was not quite so brave when confronted by the village pack, when he would try to slink between the wheels of my bicycle.

We decided to save ourselves a couple of miles of cycling by canoeing across an estuary between two prongs. We found a roughly scooped-out log in the reeds and John went off to find its owner. Meanwhile a friendly picanin gave me the once-over. His only word of English seemed to be 'motor car', an object he had probably never seen but could ably mimic by actions and noises. I gave him a 'ticky' for his demonstration, which he examined carefully, popped in his mouth and ran off, changing gear loudly as he went.

Just before the village of Chief Chiwanangala, we passed through a large *mushitu* of tall, creeper-covered trees full of monkeys, where Flea spent a wonderful ten minutes challenging them to come down.

John pointed out a small red flowering shrub called *namuteketa*, (*Clerodendron spinescens*) the bantu bid for birth control, but judging from the numbers of picanins which milled around us, it was either ineffective or not used. There was no open water here, the marsh that stretched unbroken to the horizon would continue unbroken over countless more horizons, its reeds swaying gently in the breeze, hiding the shy swamp-dwellers, many of whom would never see a white man.

Flying over the area the following year, the swamp filled the horizon for nearly an hour. Countless canoe-traces scratched the even mat surface, connecting the minute papyrus islets like a gigantic spider's web, with here and there the long zigzag of a fish dam. I was to see similar papyrus islets twenty years later on Lake Titicaca, high up in the Andes. Looking down, I could see the white buildings of Santa Maria mission standing out clearly against the dull browns and greens, and the dark blob at the other end of the island, which I knew to be the *mushitu* where Flea had challenged the monkeys.

It was now past midday and all the villagers were deep in siesta. Siesta time, so the White Fathers told me, started soon after daybreak and lasted till just before sundown! Snoring forms littered the shade beneath mango tress. Even the women who did 90 per cent of the minimum chores, were propped up against hut walls, open-mouthed, heads lolling, waiting for the sun to drop.

We let them sleep on unless we found sheep still locked up in their little stake kraals, when we would shake a somnolent villager back to consciousness.

'Why are the sheep still in the kraal?'

'The owner is away and won't return till evening, *bwana*.'

'What's his name?' taking out my notebook and looking very angry.

'Well, you see, there are many people who own sheep in that kraal.'

'And they have all gone away?'

'Well ...'

'Perhaps YOU own one?'

'Well ...'

So I would tell him how obliged I would be if he would let them all out, but now, Pronto! *BWANGU BWANGU*! John would follow, telling of a man he once knew who was put in prison for such negligence. Sometimes the answer would be that as the sheep fed yesterday there was no need to let them out till tomorrow and, anyway, they ate the crops when the owners were sleeping, so they could only be freed in the early morning or evening.

'What about water?'

'They can wait,' would be the apathetic reply.

Once they were freed, we would chase the thirsty animals out between the cassava mounds. As we cycled away the villagers would gape after us. It was unbelievable. Madmen, for sure. Or was it just a dream? Ah, well – in that case sleep would be the best answer. Never in my life have I come across such sleepy-happy people.

Could you blame them? What with undernourishment and malaria, bilharzia and hookworm, white ants and droughts, the hurdles were just too high. There was enough manure to make excellent gardens, but collecting and digging it in – that was hard work, and their fathers never used manure so why should they? It was far more pleasant to sleep in the deep cool shade of a mango tree. Work only increased your hunger and that meant making a larger garden. Better work less and eat less. Poor Billy Bantu. In the days it was too hot and at night it was too dark, so what was he to do? Why, nothing of course!

We passed through village after village of sleeping forms and kraaled sheep, too weary ourselves to argue with the snoring zombies, simply opening the little kraals and setting free the parched animals as we went.

There were two distinct types of sheep, a fat-tailed, brown-and-white variety and a darker, larger type with a prominent sternum and thinner tail. Estimates put the number on the four main islands of Chilubi, Chisi, Mbawala and Nsumbu, at about 3,000, but whether they were on the increase or decrease, on-one knew.

Father Kohle, a tall, well-proportioned blonde German, took me round the mission hospital, and insisted that I, too, must be of pure Nordic blood.

'*Der Führer* would say you were a true Aryan,' he joked.

'*Der Führer* won't get the chance,' I retorted.

He sold me some drugs and instruments, saying that since the doctor had left and would be difficult to replace, I might as well use them before they went out of date or were stolen. Later, I discovered that most items were free gifts to the mission from the Medical Department!

That afternoon, I loaded a few essentials into the launch and headed for Muchinshi rest camp on the western tip of Chilubi, opposite the large island of Chisi, which I intended to visit the next day.

Below the rest hut a field of long grass swept down to a swampy cove. Some women were fishing in the warm green water, not with nets as one would have expected, but with rod and line, wading up to their knees, four of them in a row, casting their floats, babies slung across their shoulders and a few nicknacks balanced on their heads. As the watery sun sank behind a giant *musukisi* tree into the mist which had begun to creep over the water, I was no longer in Lake Bangweulu, Central Africa, but in the Kentish marshes, in October.

Captain Cook must have felt much the same while exploring the South Sea islands as I did cruising down the Chisi shoreline the next morning, looking for a place to land. There seemed to be a low steep bank all along the water's edge. We called to a woman and child who were hoeing in lakeside garden. They immediately dropped their instruments and fled screaming. A little further on we came to a cove with a jetty. This, we were told was Mbulu, the chief's village. The chief, who strode down to welcome us, dressed in a white shirt and grey flannels, proved to be a well-travelled (i.e. to the mines) and intelligent fellow. He took us on a tour of inspection, pointing out items of interests and – Glory be! – asking questions! Most Africans, I had found, would rather continue in ignorance than go to the trouble of asking 'why?' and many seemed quite incapable of thinking up any questions at all.

The sand-dunes at one end of Chisi curled round like a lion's claw to make a wide bay, luxuriant with water-lilies, the dunes standing out white against a blue sky. Apart from the absence of coconut palms, it was easy to imagine myself on a South Pacific atoll.

The sheep on Chisi were left tethered day and night on the thick grass along the water's edge. This both protected the crops and gave continuous grazing, which was reflected in their excellent condition. Crocodiles occasionally helped themselves, but the real scourge of the island was white ants. On some parts, the Chief said, they had given up planting altogether, the little that the white ants left was taken by the birds.

Back at Mbulu we sat in the shade of a large mango tree, the village elders in a ring around us, nodding from time to time in agreement with the chief's opinions. The islands had once been producers of soap, made from oil of the large, horse chestnut-like, *musukisi* tree, but the process, like so many other native industries, had been forgotten. Could I ask the Agricultural Dept. to send someone to teach them? Could I exchange some of his sheep for cattle? The children needed milk and the manure would be useful. This was the first reference to manure which I had heard from an African. Most certainly I would try to get him cattle. I also promised to try and get him kaffir corn seed before the rains.

As it turned out, my attempts to swop his sheep for cattle came to nothing and I don't think the Agricultural Dept sent his seed in time, or did anything about the soap making. It wasn't surprising, therefore, that the African placed little confidence in the promises of visiting officials. They suspected it was all talk. Alas, how often they were right!

* * *

At the Muchinshi rest camp, once more, I had a late lunch and, feeling suddenly exhausted, lay down on my camp cot. An hour later I woke shivering and yawning profusely, sure signs of a dose of fever. I took my temperature – 102. My face was flushed and I was beginning to sweat. If I was going to have an attack of malaria – my God, it might even be blackwater – it would be best to make tracks for Santa Maria mission, I told Kosam to pack up and informed Moses that we would be leaving in ten minutes.

I lay, burning, on a tarpaulin in the bottom of the launch. Whenever I raised myself to see where we were, the line of trees along the shore danced before my eyes. Everything seemed unreal and it was not I who staggered up the path to the mission and fell into bed, clothes and all, but someone I was watching on a movie screen.

Father Kohle soon put his head round the door, and his deep laughing voice was like music. He heaped on another two blankets, gave me a couple of aspirin, a strong slug of brandy and 15 grains of quinine, and said he'd be back after Vespers to change me – or bury me, it just depended. With a shirt, pullover, lumber jacket, slacks and four blankets, I felt like a bit of bacon in Old Nick's kitchen.

It was now dark and I could hear the chanting in the church across the courtyard. Sweat trickled down my face, my scalp prickled, a mosquito buzzed around but found my skin too wet for landing. Weird thoughts, silly combinations of words and long-forgotten incidents chased through my mind until the welcome reappearance of Father Kohle. I had nick-named him 'Doc' and he certainly lived up to it. He ripped off my clothes sponged me down, brought new sheets and a replacement for my now squelchy mattress. Kosam laid his bamboo sleeping mat beside my bed, in case I should want anything in the night.

121

When I woke, the sun was high and Father Kohle was standing by my bed, tablets in one hand, a glass in the other. I felt indescribably weak, but his cheery voice gave me encouragement. Maybe this time I wouldn't die.

After he had gone, I lay studying the tiled ceiling of the ugly cell which for many hot, frustrating years had been considered 'home' to a succession of mission doctors. The same bare, whitewashed walls must have encompassed many a home-sick soul. The same big, flat wall-spiders must have glowered down on the despair of many days, and the lizards that darted along the rafters were undoubtedly the same ones which had stalked their prey above the sick woman whom blackwater had so nearly pushed through death's door. White ants now, as then, continued their war against the whole edifice, fashioning their mud tunnels higher and higher until, unnoticed, they gained the wooden rafters. How many times, I wondered, had persons stricken with malaria, tossed in this rickety, unsprung bed and studied the bare roof tiles. For how many had it been their last view?

It was high time I considered my future. I had been in Africa 20 months – it seemed like 20 years – with nothing to show for it. Sure, I had gained some experience in dealing with the indigenous inhabitants, buying cattle, writing reports, filling in forms and coping by myself in the bush, but I had learned nothing to advance my professional training or aspirations. I was an outsider. I had to get out before it was too late.

My spider collection and, more recently, a study of the poisonous and medicinal plants used by the various tribes had given me a collector's interest and kept me observant. It was better than nothing, but could hardly be considered research.

The Veterinary Research Laboratories at Onderstepoort had kindly sent me reprints of all their work in tropical diseases and had, most generously, supplied equipment for blood counts which I had proposed (optimistically, they thought) to carry out in wild animals. They were right, even for that you needed basic facilities like electricity, clean water and reference books all of which I lacked – let alone a decent microscope!

Whenever I could I would sketch the people on the station or in the bush, and continue with my cartooning. Most of these drawings were eventually lost during years of changing countries. I sold one cartoon to a wartime South African paper, *Blimey*, for the huge amount of ten shillings and sixpence – except that they never paid me! It depicted a white-clad doctor bending over a patient on an operating table, a hammer in one hand and a sickle in the other, while an intern whispers to a nurse, 'He's a famous Russian surgeon'. I thought it was worth more than half a guinea.

I had also started to collect original cartoons by *Punch* artists – Sillince, Pont, Acanthus, David Langdon, Emmett and others, which I still treasure. There was little else on which to spend my money, and five pounds a drawing (to charity) seemed a pretty good investment for works by such well-known cartoonists.

Most disturbing to my peace of mind were the regular letters from Charlie, my Cambridge colleague, gloating over the life in Jamaica, the girls, swimming, sailing, cocktail parties and the full range of clinical work. I began to dread those envelopes with their Jamaican stamps and neat, sloping hand. Patricia, too. Her letters came regularly, and I would torture myself by reading between the lines. After all, a Fleet Air Arm station was not a nunnery and she must be exposed to all sorts of male dangers. I was due home leave in another year and would seen her then – unless.

Whatever happened, I had to make sure that I didn't come back to Northern Rhodesia. I had already bombarded the Director with requests for a transfer or release for military duties. His reply was always the same: 'How can I let you go when we are only a quarter-staffed?'

As soon as I returned to Abercorn I would draft another appeal, this time to the Colonial Office itself. The Director would be obliged to forward it – even if he did attach some unfavourable comments. I would stress my interest in clinical and research work, my lack of interest in Africa and the type of work I was doing. I would make it clear that if I couldn't get a transfer outside of Africa, preferably to the West Indies, I would resign. Looking back, I can't imagine why they never took me up on it!

It took several days to recover sufficient strength for the journey back. I spent them sitting by the gun turret in the Mission garden, reading the stack of professional journals which I had left piling up for some such opportunity as this, and in discussing life, art and politics with Fathers Maestrom and Kohle. Religion we wisely left alone.

I had swopped four old car tyres for two hefty rams. Car tyres were much prized by the fishermen, who picked hundreds of feet of cotton thread from them, the most durable material that could be found for making nets. The rams I would present to the *boma* flocks at Luwingu and Fort Roseberry, in appreciation for the use of the launch.

Father Maestrom and Father Kohle came down to the jetty to see me off. As I watched Santa Maria fade into the early morning haze, I raised my battered felt hat to those untiring, unselfish men who toiled

18 hours a day, year after year, without material reward, to educate, inspire and save the souls of the sleepy, happy-go-lucky islanders.

I was, as far as I knew, the first veterinary officer to have visited the area, so, at least, it was a start. On my next visit I determined to spend much longer and map out a comprehensive programme for animal production and disease control. But, as nearly always happens, within six months I found myself posted to the railway line, and never visited the islands again.

Bangweulu would, I knew, long remain undisturbed, and perhaps, when civilization reached its ultimate catastrophe, the mosquitoes, water-snakes and crocodiles of this stifling swamp would be a pleasant relief from alphabetical bombs!

MY FUTURE IN A CLEFT STICK

'Want to go chase buffalo?'

Piet slid into my visitor's chair and lit a Cape to Cairo. 'There's a herd moving up the Chozi flats towards the border and they have to be turned back. It'll be our last chance before the rains break.

After a night at Piet's Mukalisi camp, we drove to the large *mulombwa* tree which marked the turn-off for his almost invisible track to the Chozi flats. Recent bush fires had lain a thick carpet of

Chozi Flats

124

grey ash between the blackened trees, which emphasized the tyre marks of previous visits. Fresh blades of grass were already springing up through the blackened soil, and the occasional yellow or red flash of a *veld* flower showed that the rains were not far away. Occasionally, patches of four-foot-high grass that had escaped incineration sprayed us with millions of seeds as we ploughed through them until the radiator's mesh was choked and the water boiling. Now and then we had to cut down a tree which before had been small enough to brush past.

Twenty miles south of the main road we glimpsed the flats, a band of yellow where the grass had been too wet to burn, dotted with huge grey anthills, bushes and small trees sprouting from their tops.

We camped as usual above the Mwanga flat, an oblong field that stretched to the horizon, with gradually rising forest on all sides. Securing a tarpaulin between four trees we drove the vanette beneath it, making an excellent bedroom well out of the range of snakes and creepy-crawlies. Six blankets, four beneath and two on top, would help to keep out the chill of the night.

'Let's have a look-see while we're waiting for scoff,' Piet suggested. 'The *buffels* should be somewhere nearby. Spider reported them near Chasamilo last night. That's about six miles south of here.'

Spider was one of Piet's best hunters. His name was appropriate, he was all spindly arms and legs and stalked his prey, stealthily, as might a tarantula. In World War One, he and Garden, Piet's personal boy and cook, had fought in the East African Campaign, but on which side they had originally enlisted was debatable. It really didn't matter, for in company with many other native scouts they would switch sides depending on the rations offered by the opposing forces. The native patrols would meet in the obscurity of the bush, discuss the conditions in the respective camps and, if necessary, change sides. After all, both sides were *bwanas*, so what was the difference?

It must have been a happy-go-lucky scrap in many ways. There was a story of an unpopular British Officer who was captured by the Jerries and ransomed for six bottles of whisky. The British, however, preferred their Scotch to their officer and refused the exchange. Another note offered to return him for six tins of jam. Again, the British felt they couldn't spare jam at that moment. Finally his release was secured for 12 loaves of bread and some tobacco. One can only imagine the scene on the officer's return to the British lines since, with growing glee, the Germans had made a point of showing him each refusal note!

But I was telling you about Spider. Experienced hunter as he was, a

125

buffalo had nearly finished him the year before. Piet and I were camping in our usual place beside the Mwanga flats. One morning, reports came in that there was a large herd of buffalo approaching the border from the south. Piet sent Spider with other Game Guards to investigate and, if necessary, drive the herd back, away from the game fence. At midday the Game Guards reported that they had contacted the buffalo herd, shot one and that Spider was following them up. Meanwhile help was needed to carry in the meat.

At dusk the men returned with the meat, saying that they had heard shots in the distance, presumably Spider shooting the herd further south. By noon the next day there was still no sign of Spider.

'Don't worry,' Piet assured us, 'Spider is the best hunter of all.'

But by evening even he was worried. We hadn't been asleep long when a rifle shot woke us up. Hurriedly we lit lamps and went to investigate. A few hundred yards from camp we discovered spider, semi-conscious, but still crawling. We carried him into camp and laid him by the fire, gave him some brandy and examined the terrible gashes in his leg. There was little we could do but bundle him into the vanette and head immediately for Abercorn. Later, he told us that he had followed the herd and wounded a young bull which had turned to attack him. He waited until it was only 12 yards away before pressing the trigger, and even though he hit it, the bull kept coming, throwing him into the air and knocking him unconscious. When he came round he saw the buffalo lying beside him – dead. It had been a last desperate charge.

He retrieved his gun, reloaded and fired a couple of shots to attract attention, in case anyone was nearby. When no-one came he started to crawl towards camp, reserving one last round for emergency. It took him 36 hours to cover the seven miles. It said a lot both for the doctor and for Spider's resistance, that within two weeks he was hobbling around again, and continued to limp after buffalo for many more years.

We climbed a nearby anthill and gazed down on the long yellow flood plain that stretched before us. The glaring sun had burned out the bright colours and was making the horizon shiver. We paid particular attention to where peninsulas of low, straggling trees invaded the even carpet of the flats. Some of these, in the shimmering heat, could easily have been mistaken for buffaloes.

'We'll walk across to the other side after some grub and see if we can find any trace of them.' Piet said.

A slight breeze sprang up, rippling the long grass and chilling the sweat on our shirts. We scanned the horizon once more. A group of trees that had caught our attention before, now seemed to be a slightly different shape.

'Probably the heat haze,' I suggested.

'Dunno. Let's watch it or a bit.'

'We had just made up our minds that it was a group of bushes in a small depression, when one of the bushes moved towards another.

Piet let out a yell in the direction of the camp. A moment later, Garden appeared.

'Glasses, Garden. *Fukkala* glasses. *Ndeshya*. Hurry.'

We studied the objects again with the help of the binoculars. They were buffalo right enough, about 40 of them enjoying a midday siesta at the edge of the flats. A couple of young calves were fighting but the others, with the exception of one massive animal that prowled around as if on guard, lay ruminating placidly waiting for the sun to sink a little lower so that they could start their evening graze.

'We'll cross the flat north of them and let them know they are out of bounds,' Piet decided, jumping down from the anthill. 'Come, let's have some scoff.'

After lunch, we filled our pockets with ammunition and, accompanied by Garden and Kenaan, set off across the plain. Kenaan was highly delighted at the prospect of shooting some meat.

'*Bwana* Piet too good shot. Plenty *nyama* tonight,' he cackled, grinning all over his chubby black face.

Our first objective was an anthill in the centre of the flat, about halfway between us and the herd. A convenient elephant track made during the rainy season when the ground was soggy led us diagonally almost right to it. As Jumbo had lolloped along in the rain, his heavy feet had carved a ditch, 18 inches deep, through the soft, black cotton soil, which helped hide our crouching forms below the top of the grass.

The sun was halfway to the horizon and we estimated we had another two hours of daylight to stalk the herd, possibly shoot one and allow for a safe retreat should anything go wrong. There would be little joy in being caught in the middle of an open plain, in the dark, with an angry herd of buffalo at our heels.

In order to drive the herd south we would have to attack them from the north, but unfortunately this would also be upwind. Buffalo have poor sight and indifferent hearing, but their sense of smell is extremely acute. The slightest whiff of our BO would give the game away.

A straggle of trees ran into the plain about half a mile to the north of the herd, and we reckoned they would move towards it. Just then the grand old man of the herd began nudging his harem into activity until the whole herd was on its feet. One by one they strolled over to a small pool to drink and then started to graze, moving slowing northwards, exactly as we had anticipated.

Bent almost double we followed a shallow ditch, keeping one eye on the herd. After a quarter of a mile we came across a patch of fresh game droppings.

'Just what we want,' said Piet, taking a large pat and smearing it over his shirt and slacks. I did the same. Then we rolled in a couple more juicy dollops until game BO had completely replaced our own. I was wearing an old school hockey shirt, half of which was dark blue and the other half light blue. I noticed that it blended in with the surroundings a lot better than Piet's khaki shirt and trousers, which had been bleached almost white from continual washing.

The herd was moving faster now so we hurried on half-crawling, to reach the finger of trees before they did. Once there we hid behind an anthill panting as much as we dared, with the beasts now only a hundred yards away on the other side of the thin belt of trees.

'Better go in a bit further,' Piet whispered. Little by little, we crept towards a tall anthill in the centre of the tree belt. Halfway Piet stopped, rigid. I followed his gaze. Not 20 yards away, grazing happily, was a hartebeste. We sidled from tree to tree until we had passed it and reached the anthill.

'That was lucky,' Piet whispered, 'it could have given the alarm.'

We watched the massive beasts approach. The dung must have been doing its work, for they were no more than 50 yards away, like a squadron of tanks moving in low gear, irresistibly, noiselessly, one, three, ten ...

'Piet, look out. They're coming round behind us.' I had been focusing my camera on the main herd and hadn't noticed a small bunch that had broken off and were now on our other flank.

Piet swung round and took aim at an old cow which was nearest. She had begun to scratch her muscular neck against a branch. Piet steadied his rifle and I sighted my camera and waited, tensely. Up and down went the buffalo's neck and then, getting to the really itchy spot, began to make smaller and smaller movements until the head was almost stationary.

The report, four feet from my left ear, was terrific. Instinctively I clicked the shutter and remember seeing a white splash appear on the bark. The perverse creature had decided to lower its head just as Piet had fired. With a grunt it turned and lumbered back the way it had come.

I looked for the rest of the herd. They had turned and were making for the open plain. Thank God they didn't flee in our direction. The precipitous sides of the anthill under which we crouched would have been impossible to climb .. unless a buffalo was on our tail!

We waited for the stragglers to join the herd, then raced after the fleeing animals, bounding through the long grass, heedless of noise, intent only on keeping them in sight. About half a mile further they stopped running and clustered together. We climbed, panting, onto an anthill and waited. They had no idea where we were or what had happened, but the old bull had the wind up and was prancing around, grunting, pawing and tossing his massive head; his broad-based horns for all the world like a Viking's helmet. I rather wished I were elsewhere.

Piet's rifle cracked again, making the herd come to life and canter away, leaving one on the ground. We paced the distance to the one Piet had dropped. It was 313 yards. A pretty good shot, even for him!

'That's the last we'll see of them' Piet assured me. 'The Guards will pick them up on the other side of the Luchinde and shoot them south. We'll cut this one's throat and leave the carcass till morning. It'll be all right – unless there's a hungry lion or hyena around.'

Just then Piet discovered that he had dropped his spare clip of ammunition and his magazine was empty.

'Have to rely on you if we meet anything, Pat. Man, but there's going to be a hell of a bang when the bush fires catch up with those rounds!'

The sun had now set and the short twilight already giving way to night as we started back to camp. Kenaan was beginning to feel sorry for himself, complaining that he was much too old for these hunting trips.

'OK,' I told him. 'Rest as long as you wish.'

'*Awe*. Too much lion, *bwana*' and on he stumbled, grumbling to himself. I didn't blame him for not wanting to stay behind. Probably he would have been safe in a tree, but I wouldn't have bet on it.

The sweat that had drenched my shirt as we chased the buffalo now felt icy cold in the night breeze. We lost the path and had to depend entirely on Piet's built-in compass. I longed for a sundowner and my bed, but it was over an hour before we saw the camp fire dead ahead. Good old Piet!

A tumbler each of cherry brandy to warm us and some well-cooked reedbuck steaks washed down with beer restored us to normality. Tired, replete and a little muzzy, we stretched out in the back of the vanette, oblivious of the bush noises, the barking dogs and the crackling of the camp fire.

'This is the life,' I mumbled, sleepily.

129

Bwana Piet, snoozing after a day's hunt

'I know one thing that would make it a hell of a lot better,' Piet mumbled back.

'What?'

'Damn it, Pat! Why the hell aren't you a girl?'

At daybreak, we took the vanette across the flats and found the carcass undisturbed. As always, I searched the insides for signs of disease or parasites. The rumen, the first and largest of the four bovine stomachs, was choc-a-bloc with paramphistomes, small blood-sucking flukes, that clung to the rumen wall like clusters of miniature jelly babies.

Chief amongst the worms was the inch-long wire-worm, *Haemonchus contortus*. The females resembled a barber's pole or a stick of candy rock, due to the white, egg-filled uterus which spiralled round the rest of the red, blood-engorged body. This was also one of the most common and potentially dangerous of all worms in young domestic ruminants. Luckily, there existed excellent anthelmithics with which to treat it.

It was nearly midday before we had the animal cut up, the skin flayed and the meat loaded. The sun, which had been devastating, was now shielded by great clouds which were rapidly filling the sky.

'We'd better get the hell out of here,' Piet growled. 'if it doesn't rain today, it will tomorrow.'

Slowly we started back and, of course, now that we no longer needed meat, every buck on the flats popped up to have a look at us.

Halfway to camp, I saw a figure trotting towards us, a long stick in his hand with a piece of paper at one end.

130

'I don't believe it,' I said. 'A runner with the proverbial message in a cleft stick!' But when I thought about it, a cleft stick was the obvious answer. To carry a message in his hand would have crumpled it and exposed it to all sorts of hazards, and to have put it in his pockets would have soaked it in perspiration. Cephas would have put it under his fez, but this gentleman had none and had wisely resorted to the traditional cleft stick.

The envelope, addressed to me, was marked 'Urgent'. I tore it open.

'Urgent messages await you Abercorn. Return immediately – Postmaster'

Dammit, couldn't Pop have said what they were about? They must be highly confidential. Father? Mother? They were both in their seventies. My brother Terry? Unlikely, the war was over and he was about to be demobbed. What else? I was baffled.

'We can make Abercorn in four hours if we pack up at once,' Piet could see my anxiety. 'Anyway, looks like a deluge coming, and then we'll be stuck. So let's move.'

An hour later, with the vanette springs flattened by the weight of the meat and camping equipment, we bumped slowly back towards the main road. We didn't quite make it. As we were crossing a, till then, dry *dambo*, the heavens opened. Wheels spun, mud flew and everyone except Piet who was at the wheel, jumped out to help push. Gradually, we gained harder ground. The main road was already a river when we reached it. I took off my shirt and stood in the torrential shower trying to clean the sticky black mud off my body and clothes. We stayed at the Mukalisi camp only long enough to unload the meat and skins, change our clothes and drink a coffee laced with brandy.

There were no messages in my house or at the office, so I went straight up to Pop's house. He wasn't in. I was becoming desperate. But there weren't more than half a dozen places he could be, it was a matter of spotting his car. I found it with several others at Westy's house. There was a loud clamour as I entered.

'Lucky bugger. So you did it at last,' 'Take me with you,' and many more such enjoinders greeted me.

'OK, fine' I yelled above the noise. 'But what's it all about?' Everyone seemed to know except me.

You've been transferred to Jamaica and you are to take over Lusaka till you sail,' Pop raised his glass. 'Happy landings.'

BLUE-EYED BUREAUCRATS

Jamaica! At last! I was two feet off the ground, bouncing on a rum-scented cloud of ecstasy. Good old Colonial Office! At last they'd got the message!

Now I could get back into the clinical picture, be a proper vet again – not a frustrated *bundu*-bashing *bwana*. Perhaps even do some real research, and – I'd almost forgotten! – I could start digging for some of those doubloons which ringed the Caribbean islands like golden bangles. I could hardly wait to write to Charlie.

During my treasure-hunting fantasies at Cambridge, I had bought a large map of the West Indies, drawn by an early eighteenth-century cartographer, Herman Moll. Nothing could have enraptured a vicarious treasure hunter more than this 200-year-old chart of New World Eldorados, laced with dotted lines depicting the paths of the 'Spanish Flota from Vera Cruz to Havana', or 'The Gallions (sic) from Cartagena to Spain', with detailed diagrams of the Spanish forts at Darien and Cartagena and the French fort of St Augustine on the coast of Florida, in case some card-carrying buccaneer wanted to lay them siege.

The map had cost me two pounds, picked off a heap of old prints in a secondhand bookshop in Old Bond Street. I had also selected a map of Jamaica, dated 1755, for five shillings. From time to time, when life in Abercorn became too depressing, I would study these two fascinating documents. More than anything else they had kept alive my adventurous spirit and once fanatic fixation on buccaneers and buried treasure. Now, as I brought them out again and studied the notes I had made in the Cambridge University Library on possible treasure sites, I felt the old excitement surging back.

It was still a fantasy, I knew, and I suspected that if I ever did discover a hidden cache, it would hardly provide as much of a thrill as poring over these old charts.

Apart from the delightful prospect of Jamaica, I also had two months home leave to look forward to. A longing to see Patricia had dominated much of my last two years, but her letters had not been quite so regular of late and names of pilot officers (even one Squadron Leader) had been creeping in. It was possible that her affections had altered course. Even if they hadn't, now that the moment of truth was at hand, I had a niggling fear that I would still be unwilling to take the final plunge, especially as Jamaica opened up a whole new garden of delectable blossoms for the plucking.

The thought of Lusaka, even temporarily, was a little daunting. There would be no more escaping into the bush for a few weeks *ulendo*, and what I had seen of those blue-eyed bureaucrats on my fleeting visits was not encouraging. Neither were the other trappings of civilization, such as the telephone and the official parties with their cliques and small talk. Nor could I any longer use distance as an excuse for delay in sending reports. And official etiquette – heavens! I'd probably have to shake the mothballs out of my dress suit. I'd not looked at it since I had arrived.

I hoped it wouldn't be too long before I was given a passage, but there was a backlog of officials with long-overdue leaves to satisfy first. No matter, old Ian was working in the Secretariat, he'd soon fix me a passage. I would only be in Lusaka for a month or two.

Now that my days in Abercorn were numbered, I began to realize how much life in the bush had enveloped me, like a thick, comfy overcoat, protecting me from the anxieties and tensions of gregarious living. Would palm-fringed shores and coral reefs compensate for the thrill of exploring mountains and wandering down riverbeds, for the constant expectancy of the hunt, and for the camp fires when no dream seemed impossible? I had a feeling they would!

I was due in Lusaka on December 1st, and since it was already November 15th, I had little time to brood. Allan, my Stock Inspector, would look after things for the time being, but he was shortly leaving the service. So what? The Northern Province had existed happily for thousands of years without veterinary interference; I was sure it could do it again for a few months.

Accompanied by Kosam, Flea and Panda, and with exaggerated farewell salutes from Kenaan and Cephas, and carrying a large hamper of home-baked goodies which Sylvia, the Nursing Sister, pressed on me for the journey, I drove out of Abercorn into the rising sun. The bush was at its best. The patches of new grass that thrust through the ashes of recent fires were poster green and the shadows under the trees deep purple. Veldt flowers were sprinkled everywhere, washed bright by overnight rain. Above me, small foamy clouds hung in a cerulean sky.

At the Ningi pans, a small duiker stood grazing by the roadside. Normally, I would have grabbed for my gun, but I had no need of meat and this little creature had obviously come to wish me farewell. It stood there, golden red, its nose twitching, watching with great brown eyes. I blew the horn and watched it scamper into the bush. 'Run, little friend,' I called, 'and a long and happy life to you.'

I had decided to go the long way round and pass Piet's Mukalizi camp on the off-chance that he was there, say goodbye to the Zone Guards at Nteko, pass through Tunduma to bid farewell to Donald

Siwale and the Mwenzo missionaries, and call in at Mbesuma to wish Fred all the best.

Piet had left a message at his Mukalisi camp suggesting I follow him down the Chozi for a last hunt. But the truck was too overloaded to attempt the track, now soft from the first rains, and I couldn't afford to get stuck. I pinned a note to the *mulombwa* tree where the Chozi track began. It would reach him sooner or later ... unless the white ants ate it first.

The Mwenzo missionaries forced more culinary delights on me and I promised Donald Siwale, who was waiting for me at Tunduma, to let him know the results of the poisonous and medicinal plants he had helped me collect, and which I had sent to Witwatersrand University in South Africa.

Fred had a few more lion trophies to show me at Mbesuma, and at Kanona I found that 'Skipper' Mills had been seriously ill. Nevertheless, his frail, pyjama-clad figure appeared at supper to make sure everything was in order. Six months later he was dead, but whenever stories of elephants are told in Northern Rhodesia, his name will be amongst the first to be honoured.

* * *

Lusaka in 1946 was really two towns, the old town built along the railway line, and the new Lusaka, the official capital, only a few years old, which had erupted like a wart on a hill three miles away. Here Government offices and civil servant residences formed a community of their own. In the centre of this growth, rising above the blocks of apartments and 'semi-permanent' cottages, was the yellow brick temple of bureaucracy, the Secretariat, popularly known as the 'Biscuit Factory'.

Inevitably, the views of the commercial and official Lusakas were at odds. The traders and farmers of old Lusaka referred to the pampered expatriate civil servants on the hill as 'H.U's and B's' ('Highups and Bloodies') whose only delight, they were convinced, was to put a spoke in the trading wheels and who always backed the African against the settler. To the Government officials, old Lusaka existed solely as a shopping centre or for a night out at the cinema.

I occupied a wattle-and-daub-thatched 'semi-permanent' next to Ian, one of many that had been put up during the war to house the expanding civil service. The windows had no glass, only wooden shutters, and there was no ceiling, but it had a bedroom, dining room and sitting room, electric light and water, and an inside toilet. What more could anyone want?

The Veterinary Department's offices, between the main street and the railway, opposite Kee's store, were in the same building as the District Commissioner and the Magistrate's court. There were four rooms, my office, the Stock Inspector's office, a general office and a dispensary. There was also a telephone and outside PK, but no running water.

Odie, my Stock Inspector, was a short but burly Afrikaner, efficient and energetic, the essence of self confidence and determination. He looked after the routine matters, leaving me to attend to clinical cases on the European-owned farms. I treated more animals in one day than in two years in Abercorn.

Most of the European farmers were of South African origin, hard-working and hospitable, but there were a few who were not quite so serious or well-organized. One of these, an English settler, rang me to look at his bull. I found the gentleman banging away under his car. I introduced myself and asked where I could find his bull.

'Bull, bull, bull, bull? What bull?'

'Didn't you telephone about a sick bull?' I asked, a bit put out.

'Oh, the BULL. Yes, of course. Let's see if we can find it.'

I offered him a cigarette as we strolled down the bougainvillea-lined drive to his kraal. He hesitated, like a schoolboy, one eye open for authority.

'Did you see my wife about?'

'No,' I replied.

'That's good. You see, she stopped me smoking last month.'

He thrust the cigarette into his pocket until we reached the seclusion of the kraal, when he lit up and puffed at it frantically. I asked him where the bull was.

'Ah, the bull. We must ask the herdboy to bring in the cattle.' This he did by yelling at the top of his voice until a youth appeared. It proved to be the gardener who was despatched to find the herdboy. I became impatient.

'What's wrong with the bull, anyway?' I asked.

'Don't really know. The herdboy told my wife it was looking sick and she told me to ring you.' he shrugged apologetically.

Half an hour later, when no-one had appeared, I went on to another farm, promising to call on my way back. When I returned, the herdboy had already brought the animals, including the bull, into the kraal. There was some confusion as to just what was wrong with it. The boy thought the foot was hurt, but I could see nothing wrong. So much for the wasted hour, I thought. Back at the house I met the wife, an immense domineering woman, who never ceased to extol the virtues of the Aryan race and to describe exactly what she would do

135

with the Africans if she had her way. I could well see why he was so frightened of her. One slug from those massive arms would have knocked him through the wall. On all subsequent visits to that farm, I carried an extra pack of cigarettes.

Several Afrikaners ran their farms by the moon. One asked me to lend him an instrument to castrate his calves; then, taking out his diary exclaimed, '*Ag*, not dis week, *jong*. Not till efter de new moon. Ef dey castrated ven de moon rise, is *goed*, ef ven de moon go down, den dey will die. Ef I plant mealies ven de moon down, dey die, but potatoes, dey vill grow. Sure ding, *jong*, I tell you.'

This was new to me and I regarded him as a 'nut-case', but moon-cultivation I found had a large following, especially amongst the older Afrikaners.

* * *

I was disappointed to find that those obnoxious bureaucrats in the Secretariat and Accountant General's Department, to whom I had written such rude letters from the seclusion of the bush, and with whom I was itching to do battle, were not at all the ogres I had imagined. Most were charming, long-suffering and efficient. I blushed in many an office when I remembered my outrageous correspondence.

The secretaries in the 'Biscuit Factory', due to wartime conditions, were mostly wives or daughters of officials or traders, with an occasional professional secretary for the more senior members. Overall, the secretariat seemed a happy place with the atmosphere of a club, the Chief Secretary being the club chairman.

The Head of Government and the King's Representative, His Excellency the Governor, was a popular personality with both civil servants and traders and nearly everyone, at sometime or other, found himself invited to dinner at Government House. My visit was embarrassing.

The invitation was for eight o'clock. At seven forty-five I was ready, dressed in my tuxedo and draining a bolstering glass prior to setting off. My route passed Judy's house, a senior Administrative Officer, intimate with the Governor and his wife, so I stopped to say 'hello' and pick up any tips on etiquette that I might need, – after all, it was nearly three years since I left Cambridge! A sundowner party was in progress, Everyone exclaimed at my evening dress and asked where I was going. I told them.

'What time have you to be there?' asked Judy.

'Eight o'clock.'

136

'Good God, man! You're much too early. Nobody who IS anybody will be there before half-past.'

'Fine, let's have a wee sniffer, then.' I settled down to a gin and ginger. At ten past I said I'd better be off.

'Don't be an idiot, there's scads of time.'

Another ginger square went the way it should but at twenty past I insisted and followed by further offers of sustenance, departed, dawdling along so as not to be too early.

I had a shock in store. John, the Governor's son was pacing up and down the portico.

'Where the blazes have you been? Everyone's waiting. I rang you house, your boy said you'd left before eight.'

'Damn sorry, old man. Had a puncture and had to go in to Judy's to clean up,' I lied, making a mental note to tell Judy to back me up.

'Okay. I'll explain to dad.'

No-one was rude, but the silence said everything. I was never late again ... I was never invited again!

There was plenty in Lusaka to keep me busy, professionally. The most important single cause of all ill heath in cattle was ticks, both from the amount of blood they sucked and from the diseases they transmitted – heartwater, redwater, and gallsickness.

Heartwater or rickettsiosis, took the heaviest toll. Unlike the others which were due to blood protozoa, heartwater was caused by a rickettsia, an organism halfway between the viruses and the bacteria. Death was often so swift that it was the only symptom. At autopsy, the sac around the heart was found to be very enlarged and filled with fluid – giving the disease its name.

Redwater or piroplasmosis, was easily diagnosed by the dark urine and the severe anaemia. Gallsickness or anaplasmosis was recognised by the marked constipation, jaundice and a tendency to aggression. At autopsy, animals dying of gallsickness had an enlarged gall bladder distended with thick semi-coagulated bile. Both the redwater and gallsickness parasites could usually be seen in blood smears under the microscope. Luckily, East Coast fever did not occur in the Lusaka area.

The principal method of controlling all tick-borne diseases was by dipping – making the cattle plunge into and swim through a long, narrow, concrete bath filled with tick-killing chemicals. In those days the usual tick killer was arsenic. Dipping was highly efficient if the concentration of arsenic was to strength and the dip fluid kept clean and free from mud and dung. A simple dip-side test showed whether the dip was satisfactory, or needed topping up.

The drawback to arsenical dips was that they were poisonous to cattle as well as to the tick, and cases of poisoning were frequent. If cattle were left near a badly fenced dip, they might break through and lick the concrete sides or the ground onto which the dip had splashed. The dip tasted salty and a cow could consume a fatal dose within a few minutes. Treatment had to be given fast. Sodium thio-sulphate, known to photographers as the fixative, 'hypo', was the most effective, if given immediately by mouth or into a vein.

For the first time I had horses to deal with – colics, lamenesses, foalings, and African horse sickness, a mosquito-borne virus disease, which had prevented equines from being raised in much of the country. The out-of-date brochure which the Colonial Office had sent me on my appointment concerning living conditions in Northern Rhodesia had noted, a little facetiously, I thought, that 'saddlery should not be brought as there are no horses.'

Dogs had their troubles, too. The most common and deadly disease was biliary fever, caused by a tick-transmitted organism almost identical to that which caused redwater in cattle. Treatment was not always easy. In early cases before the anaemia was severe, recovery was usual, but later, when the dog was prostrate with chalk-white gums, there was little to be done. The curative drug, acaprin, would just as likely kill the dog as the parasite. Sometimes I injected methylene blue into these advanced cases, it gave less reaction and was often effective. Anyway, a blue pet was better than a dead one. Today there are several safe and very effective drugs.

Then there were always vaccinations, the occasional cat to spay, cow to calve, simple surgery and a sprinkling of accident cases.

I was driving to office one morning when a cat ran across the road, closely pursued by a dog which hit my front fender. I stopped, but it ran off squealing into a nearby garden. The owner appeared, a middle-aged, buxom *haus-frau*, and told me what she thought of me, ending with 'and you can damn well pay the vet's bill!'

'OK,' I agreed, 'I'll do that.'

Sure enough, half an hour later she popped into the office with her cowering animal. I probably looked different behind a desk and without my wide-brimmed, felt hat, for she gave me a long tale how some reckless young *boer* was speeding through town and ran over her pet. Not a word about the cat or the dog being to blame.

'Anyway, he's going to pay the bill,' she said.

'Oh, what's his name?'

'Damn. I never asked.'

'Well, there's nothing broken. A couple of days quiet should see him right. There's no charge. You know what these young Dutch lads are like, very harum-scarum. Tell him you'll have him up for speeding next time.'

'Next time I'll use my *sjamok* on him.'

And out she went, thanking me profusely.

Squash was popular with the younger members of the club, as were tennis and hockey, but it was the odd game of rugger that showed us in our true colours. Rugger could only be played in the rainy season when the ground was soft and the grass long and succulent enough to form a cushion. We let the grass grow to a foot or more before each game, so that for the first ten minutes it was easy to follow the run of play from the corridors of mulched herbage. Later, the whole field would become a soft squelchy mass and the 30 'blown' participants, whatever their original colours, would end up in various shades of brown and green. I suppose we enjoyed it, it was one way of generating a thirst, and there was no dearth of beer in Lusaka. Ian, in spite of a marked limp and considerable pain in his knee, often took part in these battles, playing many an outstanding game at full-back.

The Lusaka bioscope changed its programmes often enough to keep everyone happy, and then there were the Saturday night dances at the Lusaka club. They were formal black-tie affairs patronized by everyone from His Excellency to the Veterinary Officer. Nevertheless, we grumbled at having to dress up, at the same unchanging repertoire of records, at the same boring cliques and drunks and at the same individuals so obviously infatuated with someone else's wife or husband and so confident that no one else knew about it. These dances were, in effect, office parties with a family atmosphere, and many a sticky problem caused by an officious minute was solved over a beer at the bar.

One cloud continually hung over me; my hopes of an early passage home were fading fast. I was now fearful that the Colonial Office might suddenly change its mind, as it had done before. I even contemplated trying to motor home across the Congo and the Sahara, but there were too many pitfalls, not the least of which was the expense. I would just have to wait it out as patiently as I could.

Meanwhile, life had its compensations, of which Nan, the daughter of a local businessman, was by far the most attractive. We played tennis, went on picnics, swam at the public pool and patronized the Saturday night dances until she left for a Scottish university, where the following year she was chosen as the Rag Beauty Queen.

139

OF FOOT AND MOUTH AND OTHER ANT-TICKS

The manager of Chelsea Estates looked glum.

'We have a problem. Several animals are lame and drooling.'

A brief examination of the tongues and feet of his cattle confirmed my worst gears. Foot and mouth disease!

Odie, my Stock Inspector, and I looked at each other in silence. A foot and mouth disease control campaign meant weeks of indescribably hot, hard work, dust, ticks and the antagonism of farmers. It could go on for months. Gone were my hopes of an early passage home. Foot and mouth was top priority. The little Black Imps, which I had hoped I'd left behind in Abercorn, had obviously thought up this one.

We drew out quarantine boundaries on the office map. It wasn't easy, other farms adjoined Chelsea and there were African-owned cattle scattered around. We decided to close an area bounded by an untenanted road, a marshy flood plain, a river and a belt of uninhabited tsetse fly bush, in all about 50 square miles. All farms and villages were ordered to keep their animals within the quarantine area and to have them ready for inoculation.

In England, outbreaks of foot and mouth disease were controlled by slaughter of diseased and in-contact animals. This stamped out the focus and prevented further spread. It was costly but essential to keep the country free of the disease and maintain the export trade. Other countries vaccinated, but because of the fragility of the vaccine and various strains of virus, they never seemed to stamp out the disease altogether.

Contacts with game animals, enormous distances and the difficulty of controlling animal movement off individual farms, made both these control methods impractical in Northern Rhodesia. The most effective method and one which John, the Director, had pioneered, was to quarantine the infected area and spread the disease as fast as possible inside it, so that all animals would become infected and recover at the same time, acquiring a temporary immunity which would allow the area to be opened up within weeks.

Success depended on infecting all animals within a few days, ensuring that none left the quarantine area, and praying that no wild game carried the disease outside.

I returned to Chelsea later that day and arranged to start inoculations the following morning. Odie had to finish another job before joining me. I decided to use the small dairy herd, whose animals were easier to handle, as a virus 'bank' for producing the inoculation material. This I made by grinding up some of the broken blisters from the tongues of infected animals in a mixture of glycerine and saline and injecting a few drops under the surface membrane on the tongues of three healthy dairy cows. Within hours, these would develop into large blisters from which I could again collect and dilute a further batch of infective fluid for the day's 'vaccinations', and infect another three cows for the following day.

The handling kraal, a large circular stockade, built of stakes lashed together with bark rope and wire, was new and appeared strong; nevertheless, poles were now being lashed horizontally onto the inside.

'It doesn't seem to need any more strengthening,' I remarked to the farmer.

'That's not for strengthening, man. That's to help us jump up and over quickly.' I was soon to appreciate the importance of these footholds.

The first group of six-year old, long-horned Afrikander steers had been on range all their lives, and had no intention of being friendly. I wondered how the blazes I was going to carry out the delicate procedure of inoculating the tongues.

From the start it was chaos. Inside the oval kraal, some 30 by 40 yards in size, were 100 head of wild, Afrikander steers with razor-sharp horns of which any bullfighter would have been justifiably scared. I addition, 40 Africans in two teams of 20 each, two Europeans (myself and, later, Odie), two Veterinary Messengers and a Veterinary Assistant were in constant danger of being horned or trampled on. Outside, a boy heated branding irons in a wood-fire, while another was ready to hand them into the kraal to mark each animal after inoculation. On the outside, also, sat the farmer who, being rather portly, I had suggested should guard the 'vaccine' and fill the syringes. Another rather aggressive farmer joined us and spent his time roaming round the outside of the kraal with a *sjambok*, threatening to use it on anyone he thought was slacking.

Each team of catchers was equipped with a long hide rope, or *riem*. Success depended on the dexterity of the team leader. This worthy gentleman ran along behind his victim with the noose end of his *riem* looped over a long stick, waiting his chance to thrust it under an uplifted hind leg. As soon as the noose was in place, he yelled to his team, following closely in tug-of-war formation, who braced themselves to take the strain, thus throwing the animal violently onto the ground. Immediately it was down, the team was on top of the frightened beast, pulling out its tongue and yelling to the '*bwana* doctor *ngombe*' to come and inject it.

Approaching the prostrate animal across the arena was hazardous

141

since the other team, half-obscured in a cloud of dust, would be in the process of chasing another victim, or perhaps those oxen which had already been injected and branded and were now thoroughly annoyed, would be careering round the kraal looking for someone on whom they could vent their wrath. Once I had reached the prone animal, I would try to ignore everything and concentrate on slipping the long needle underneath the surface membrane of the tongue – not easy when you knew that at any moment you might be charged by a ton of infuriated beef. The risk to the animals was also high. Two beasts had to be slaughtered that first day, one from a dislocated hip and the other from a broken femur. But there was no other practical way of throwing them.

Once the injection was given, a yell went up for the branding iron, which was passed over the top of the stockade. Branding was done just below the left shoulder joint, so as not to damage the better parts of the hide. As the animal was released, everyone would scatter keeping a wary eye on the berserk creature until it had disappeared into the rest of the herd.

We managed to inject only 200 or so that first day, but by nightfall I was dead beat. We distributed the two slaughtered steers for the boys *posho* or rations, knowing that meat was the best investment for a good day's work.

I had been accommodated in the farmer's guesthouse. After a bath and supper I rolled into bed assured, I felt, of a good night's rest. It was not to be. No sooner was I warm, for the nights were pretty cold, than it felt as if armies of insects were attacking me. I fought this sensation until the itching forced me to investigate. Minute brown and black specks covered my ankles and waist, and some were moving – 'seed ticks'!

TICKS! TICKS! TICKS! The little larval forms, known as 'seed ticks', dominated every excruciating moment of that tortured night, digging in around my ankles, around my waist, and more intimate sites, until scratching was the only activity I could think about. A scrubbing brush, soap and water made my ankles and waist even sorer. Bravely, I applied a little formalin (that cure-all for nearly every animal malady, external or internal, in Northern Rhodesia), and was soon hopping round the room in agony, the brutes still *in situ*. I thought that Iodovas (a mixture of iodoform powder and Vaseline) might make the little blighters relax their hold. It didn't, but by this time I was so sore that the itching was almost a comfort. I fell asleep scratching.

It was the same the next night. Kerosene, on the advice of my messenger, took some of the little brutes off, but a subsequent bath only spread the smell all over me, making supper barely eatable and the bedclothes reek. I went to sleep with the ticks indisputably victors once more.

Inoculation became slower as the catchers' hands became raw from constantly tugging on leather thongs, and several stalwarts 'retired hurt'. On the fifth day I called a halt, sent messengers to recruit more helpers, and returned to Lusaka for a night to recuperate.

A bath, drinks and sulphanilamide ointment on the tick bites improved life. I slept well and was back at the kraal, with Odie, just as the catchers were stirring. Another 20 catchers had been recruited, so we now had three teams. It sped up the inoculations, but room for evading collisions was greatly reduced.

Each day was the same. We worked from sun-up till sundown, injecting, branding, yelling, wiping sweat and dust from our eyes, trying to keep the needles clean and dodge the rampaging animals. At midday there was an hour's break while the boys ate and we slept. After the first hour our hats, alone, distinguished us from the catchers.

Odie had a near shave when a steer charged him, but he managed to jump over the side of the kraal, head first, helped by a thrust from the angry animal's horns. A little later a steer had him on the ground, but he kept calm and lay flat, covering his head with his arms so that all the animal could do was to push him along with its nose, until we distracted it.

The high point of the day, however, was when two catchers, jumping out of the kraal to escape a charging beast, had landed, together, on top of the *sjambok*-wielding farmer, breaking his leg. Wisely, they took off, and we never saw them again!

On another memorable occasion, the Chelsea Estates headman, rather a cocky individual, had seated himself on the stockade, from where he shouted wise cracks at the catchers and chortled at their predicaments. Unfortunately for him, he had seated himself on the temporary barricade across the exit from the kraal into the dipping bath. It was not long before one of the steers, still smarting from his brand and charging around, looking for someone to attack, spotted the joker. Whether it was the irritating lad's face or whether it realized he was seated on the weakest part of the stockade and a possible way out, or whatever, the steer decided that that was the way it was going. The unfortunate fellow had barely time to turn round when the steer crashed into the barrier and both went headlong into the dip-bath.

Convinced that we would have a corpse on our hands, we rushed to fish him out and to stop any other animals breaking through. We found him clinging to a ledge at the side, screaming in terror, but apparently unhurt. The old army grey coat he had been wearing had prevented major bruising, and although well and truly ducked, he was none the worse for his bath – in fact, probably a good deal less lousy!

I didn't escape either. While bending over, intent on an inoculation, something smote me hard on the south end. I ploughed into the dust with a couple of catchers on top. When the offending animals had quietened, I noticed that my syringe needle was missing. As I jumped down to fetch another, a pain shot up my arm and I found it hurt to bend my wrist or move my thumb.

'I've sprained my wrist,' I yelled to Odie.

'What's this?' He pointed to a small black puncture wound on the inside of my forearm, close to the wrist. I looked closer.

'It's the goddam needle,' I swore. 'Must have broken it off in my arm.' Feeling for the end with my grimy fingernails, I tried to pull it out.

'Try your teeth,' Odie suggested.

I did, but it was no use. It hurt like hell. In the end Odie fetched the pliers from the vanette. I gave one or two half-hearted pulls, but it hurt so much I asked Odie to try. I wanted to yell, but in front of an audience who regarded the white man as super-human, I could hardly do so.

Odie soon had it out, the end of the needle bent into a hook where it had hit the bone. No wonder it was hard to shift! I remember thinking how lucky it was that no artery had been cut or tendon torn. It was impossible for me to continue injecting, my arm ached and it hurt to move my fingers. I thought of going into Lusaka for a anti-tetanus shot as my arm was black with dust and dung, and the wound was deep and ragged. Instead, I sucked it well and decided to wait till the weekend. By then my arm was less painful and I forgot. I suppose I was lucky that time.

To keep the 'vaccine' cool in the absence of ice and refrigerators, we hung the bottles in a wet sock under a tree, letting the breeze cool the contents by evaporation. I had often used this method to cool beer in the bush on those occasions when I was lucky enough to have any.

We boiled the syringes and needles each evening, but had no time for such niceties during the day. If a syringe dropped in the dust, we unblocked the needle by blowing through it and wiping it with alcohol. Asepsis was almost a fad.

We had now moved to an adjoining farm and were camping near

144

the inoculation kraal. The pre-prandial, *al fresco* bath each evening, notwithstanding the scent of kerosene from attempts at tick removal, was the most pleasant time of the day. Odie and I would lie, as far as it was possible to lie in our four-foot tin tubs, discussing the day's events and letting bottle after bottle of beer course slowly down our parched throats. Constant decisions had to be made as to whether to sit up and submerge one's knees or lie down and leave one's knees to brave the evening breeze.

It was bliss to lie under that twinkling canopy – 'the wondrous glory of the everlasting stars', as the Australian poet, Banjo Paterson, put it, and watch the shadows thrown by the industrious Kosam's fire dance up the tree trunks, calling to him now and then for more *akawa menshi* to warm the bath and put off the moment when we should have to face the cold night air.

Once abed, elephants could have walked through the camp. Elephants, perhaps ... but not ants!

I was woken one night by Odie's yelling and swearing.

'You having nightmares?' I called over, facetiously, to the other tent.

'The whole bloody place is covered in ants!' He yelled back.

'Wait. I'll come over,' I shouted, grabbing my torch from under the pillow. Luckily, I shone it before getting out of bed. The whole ground was moving, and ants were all over the outside of the mosquito net. We both started to yell for help, but after a day of inoculating the boys might was well have been dead. Eventually a sleepy messenger appeared.

'Yes, *bwana*'

'*Serui* ants. *Fukkala* fire *ndeshya*.

The lad must have walked right into them, for he suddenly came to life, hopping about, cursing and slapping his legs. The camp was soon seething with boys carrying faggots soaked in kerosene with which they drove back the moving millions. I stayed in bed. One didn't fool about with *serui* ants.

It took three weeks to finish inoculating the 5,000 European-owned and the few hundred village cattle in the quarantine area. I returned to Lusaka and kept my fingers crossed. Amongst the heap of correspondence waiting for me were two letters with bad news.

One was from Patricia, the first for some months – she was engaged! When I had recovered from the shock and hurt pride, I had to admit that no-one could blame her. Her fiancé, a Flight Commander in the Fleet Air Arm, was obviously an outstanding fellow, even after discounting her biased opinion, and she was very much in love. There was nothing for it but to send my congratulations and wallow in self-pity. I felt like Sir Lancelot (I think it was him) after his loss of Lady Guinevere:

> Who riding ever through a lonely world,
> Whene'er on adverse shield or helm he came,
> Into the danger desperately hurled,
> Crying her name.

Of course, my hurt pride and self-pity didn't last too long; I was young and headed for the female delights of the Caribbean. But it was great while it did!

The other letter was from Cyprus – from Charlie. He had been transferred. This was totally unexpected and a severe blow. I had looked forward so much to our working and sailing together. He did not yet know that I had also been transferred.

Things rarely work out the way you want them to, and often it's just as well. In moments of self-honesty I had to admit that I wasn't really ready for marriage, and apart from sailing, I doubted whether Charlie and I could have done very much for each other,

It looked as if I had come to the end of a phase in my life. There would be a new beginning in Jamaica, free of past ties, in which underwater adventure and scientific research, to say nothing of the girls, would be powerful ingredients.

AU REVOIR AFRICA

'What about a game of squash, Pat?'

I recognized the voice of a friend in the Secretariat.'If you win, I promise you a passage home.'

Thus encouraged, I trounced him in all three games. Willingly, I bought the beers.

'*Winchester Castle*. Tomorrow fortnight – from Durban.' He raised his glass. 'Good luck.'

I was really on my way!

It was dusk as our train crossed the Victoria Falls bridge, but just light enough to make out the billowing clouds of spray that rose above the dark canopy of forest. Dame Africa was ringing down her curtain. I lifted my glass of 'dop' in salute. She had been a trying old girl, but I had come to respect her and, in a nostalgic way, even love her – at least in parts.

A middle-aged administrator on his third home leave sat opposite, puffing on an old pipe, narcoticized by a paperback detective. No nostalgia there. He would be back again in five or six months. Thank God I wouldn't, nostalgia or no.

But three years of Dame Africa's companionship was not so easy to shrug off. Three years of trying to hate her, grumbling at her, resisting her, coping with her whims, admiring her and now perhaps a little fearful of missing her. Her cauldron of Northern Rhodesia had helped to forge me into a more self-confident, even arrogant young man, although the process had often been frightening, frustrating and lonely. But loneliness, I had long discovered, was more often due to the presence of strangers than the absence of people. London could be a lot more lonely than the bush, and many of my most treasured memories were of times when I had been alone.

I began to recall the actors who had held the stage with me over the last few years. The most important of all, Billy Bantu himself. Uninhibited except by fear of witchcraft, generally happy in his ignorance of Western ways but thirsting for the material benefits to which the white man had exposed him. Craving a foundation to replace the crumbling platform on which his ancestral Gods had stood, he had turned eagerly to the missions who had obligingly distilled the Great Creator and His universe into a few simple beliefs and promises. Fatalistic, apathetic, improvident to the point of exasperation, trusting – but often untrustworthy by European standards – he remained in his practical world of food, beer, women and tobacco, a loveable, laughing, uncomplicated child capable of great depths of loyalty to those he respected. There were few signs of patriotism or philanthropy, these would come with education and when his stomach was more easily filled and when politics were included in his diet. But I suspected that they would make him no happier.

He had a long way to go to catch up with Western technology. Everything seemed to break in his hands. Like the bicycle for which he had waited so long and which he rode so proudly round and round the village until, carried away by self-importance and the envious faces of his friends, he failed to notice the tree. Now the bicycle stands outside his hut, still a prized possession, but he will have to walk until he has saved enough to replace the fork and front wheel! An almost unbelievable story was told me by a missionary who taught iron work. He left his class on their own one afternoon, and on his return found that they had broken the anvil!

So what future had this child of nature whom Western civilization was embracing so avidly? Could he take his place with other students of technology, or would he only excel on the playing field? West

Africa and America had proved that he was in no way inferior to any other race – as long as he was given time, that was the crucial factor. As Chirupula Stevenson said – and Chirupula was as near an African as a white man had ever become – 'Speed can bring hell to Africa.'

Patronizing? Certainly. But in 1946 the Third World was only beginning to awake, and Central Africa still had her eyes shut. Those countries in Europe who watched her, watched through the avaricious spectacles of commerce, unable or too uncaring to penetrate her soul.

As the train jerked south to Salisbury, I remembered the smells of the rain-soaked bush, the cry of the ground doves, the loneliness of the great Bangweulu swamp, the evenings on the Chosi flood plain and the taste of Van der Hum, Old Brown Sherry and Limousin brandy round the camp fire; the anthills, the heat of the long grass at noon and the chill of the early morning mists, the winding bush paths crossed by the spoor of game and the columns of ants; the wild thoughts and sweats during bouts of malaria and the hum of quinine in my ears; the beat of drums and the songs of mission children in the setting sun, the red earth of Abercorn and the beauty of the Mwasha Falls; sundowners and peanuts, the fishermen's flares on Lake Tanganyika, the grinding sound of my old vanette, the earthy smell of the outside PKs with their huge spider webs and hornet's nests, and the lunchtime swims in Hans' pool. All these memories and many more came crowding in, begging not to be forgotten.

Lastly, my friends, black and white. Kenaan, old *Nsofu*, the father figure of livestock in the Northern Province, and Cephas his brother, Kosam, my ever-faithful, ever cheerful and competent cook, houseboy, seamstress, laundryman and companion. Donald Siwale, surely the epitome of a gentleman. The counsels of all of them I held in high regard and was deeply grateful; for their help. I only hoped that I had been worthy of their friendship.

With special affection I remembered my European neighbours and colleagues, who had made life bearable. Ian, Hans and Lislotte, Rodney and Lys at Broken Hill, with whom I had spent my first Christmas; my neighbour Sylvia, the Nursing Sister, the Westys, Tim and Daphne at Lusaka, Rum Mum, Lanky, and *Bwana* Piet. Mike and Allan my stock inspectors. Father Maestrom, Father Kohle, the Abels at Kawimbe and numerous other missionaries of all denominations who, like the DCs, always had a bed and a meal to offer.

And my dogs. Flea, an irreplaceable companion, and Panda – plucky little Panda. I had left them both at Piet's family farm near Lusaka. They had often been there at weekends. I hoped they would be happy – it was impossible to take them with me, and I hadn't had the courage to put them down.

All these people, places and pets were woven into my personal tapestry of Northern Rhodesia, a tapestry different for each beholder and one that I knew I could never adequately reproduce, nor ever forget.

PART TWO

JAMAICA

(1946–1957)

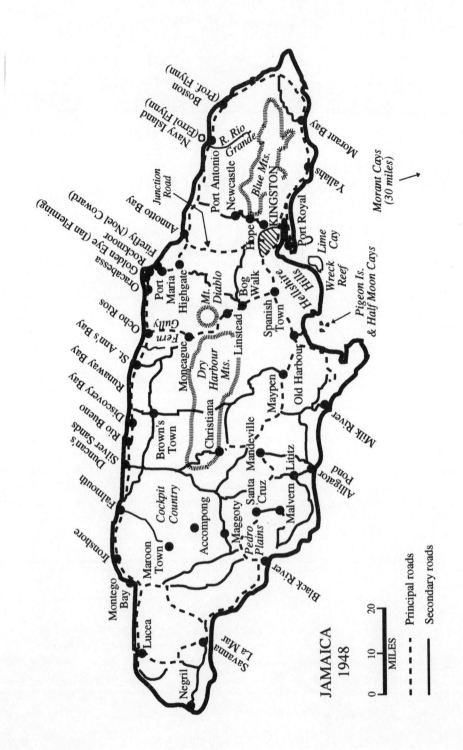

JAMAICA
1948

MILES

0   10   20

- - - - Principal roads
———— Secondary roads

Boston (Prof. Flynn)
Navy Island (Errol Flynn)
R. Rio Grande
Port Antonio
Newcastle
Blue Mts.
Junction Road
Annotto Bay
Firefly (Noel Coward)
Rochmoor
Golden Eye (Ian Fleming)
Oracabessa
Port Maria
Highgate
Mt. Diablo
Bog Walk
Linstead
Hope
KINGSTON
Port Royal
Lime Cay
Wreck Reef
Pigeon Is. & Half Moon Cays
Hellshire Hills
Spanish Town
Morant Bay
Yallahs
Morant Cays (30 miles)
Ocho Rios
St. Ann's Bay
Runaway Bay
Discovery Bay
Rio Bueno
Silver Sands
Duncan's
Falmouth
Ironshore
Montego Bay
Lucea
Negril
Savanna La Mar
Fern Gully
Moneague
Dry Harbour Mts.
Christiana
Brown's Town
Cockpit Country
Accompong
Maroon Town
Maggoty
Pedro Plains
Santa Cruz
Mandeville
Lititz
Malvern
Maypen
Old Harbour
Milk River
Alligator Pond
Black River

MAGIC ISLE

Cloud-tipped peaks rose from the sea like the spine of some marine monster in the first rays of a palaeozoic dawn.

The Blue Mountains! Jamaica!

* * *

Storms had followed our little banana boat with its 12 helpless passengers across the Atlantic buffeting us without cease until the Turks and Caicos Islands hove insight.

Now, approaching Jamaica's shoreline, we passed low scrub-covered islets ringed with yellow and green coral reefs, swung round a beacon light and some old fortifications clustered at the end of a long flat tongue of land, and entered a huge harbour.

'That finger of land is called the Palisadoes,' explained a Jamaican couple beside me at the rail, 'and this is Port Royal we're passing now. Most of the old town sank years ago in an earthquake.'

I nodded. I knew a lot about Port Royal from months wallowing in books on sunken treasure in the Cambridge University Library, and about Captain Morgan and his fellow buccaneers who used Port Royal as their base until it was swallowed up in the earthquake of 1692.

Little gripes of excitement curdled inside me. We were actually sailing over the sunken remains of that 'wickedest city in the world' … over the bars and brothels of the buccaneers.

A stocky, broad shouldered young fellow came on board to welcome me. I took an immediate liking to his craggy, intelligent face and quizzical eyes.

'Roger, Veterinary Investigation Officer,' he announced, crushing my fingers. Carrying a case apiece, we walked down the gangplank – and into pandemonium!

The tempo of life was unlike anything I had seen in Africa. Every movement was carried out with as much gusto and noise as possible, singing, yelling, arguing, laughing; no-one seemed capable of doing anything quietly. Shrieking, bare-bottomed piccanins of all shades dived off the pier for coins. Fat, black mammies, their gaudy dresses strained across vast bosoms and rolling bellies, squatted in front of baskets laden with fruit or cakes. Even at this early hour all the bars were open, blaring raucous music. No colour consciousness here. Negro, Indian, European, Chinese and their mixtures surged around me, apparently on terms of equality. Girls, bra-less in flimsy, low-cut frocks, men in shorts or in slacks shredded by hard wear into ragged knee-length breeches, and children, most of them naked, made up a

153

happy-go-lucky, devil-may-care kaleidoscope of humanity. It struck me that the sooner the races of the world intermingled and produced a khaki-coloured population like this, the better it would be for everyone. Here was a pulsing, dynamic, joyously uninhibited romp, unrestrained by the British *bwana's* stiff, upper lip. A new land, new behaviour, new standards. This was for me!

A brief word with Customs and Roger whisked me away through hordes of bicycles, donkey-driven drays and handcarts bearing palm fronds above their green mounds of coconuts or 'jellies'. 'Waaa-ta jeddy doe!' their owners chanted; 'Feee-ish, fresh feee-ish', or 'Ackee, buy me ripe ackee.'

We climbed through residential suburbs, the gardens ablaze with multi-coloured bougainvillea, dark red poinsettias and 'Barbados Pride'. Tufts of grey-green aerial fungus hung from the telephone wires like Christmas decorations. 'Cross Roads – Halfway Tree – Matilda's Corner Liguanea,' Roger sang out as we climbed higher. Exotic names, I thought, exactly right for this magical new world. At the top of a long, straight hill, we turned in through a cut stone arch.

'This is Hope Botanical Gardens, headquarters of the Agricultural Department, which includes the Veterinary Division,' Roger informed me. 'I'll introduce you to the Director of Agriculture right away and get it over with.'

Passing banks of bright blossoms and spacious lawns where peacocks strutted, we pulled up at a two storey, shingle-roofed, wooden building. After my experience in Africa I could hardly believe my eyes.

'Don't you have white ants here?' I asked incrediously.

'Oh yes, but they don't seem to be such a problem. In fact, if you were to clean them out, I think most of the wooden buildings would fall down.' I was to hear this theory many times.

An upstairs verandah ran right round under the eaves, enclosed here and there with shutters to make more office space. The whole edifice shook as we mounted the stairs to the Director's office, where I found it impossible to concentrate on what he was saying because my ankles were under a frenzied attack from hordes of ravenous mosquitoes.

'Good God! How can anyone work in such gloomy mosquito-ridden offices?' I asked as we left.

'New blood. They hardly worry me now.'

Roger shared one of the two veterinary residences at Hope with Tom, the Senior Veterinary Officer in charge of the Division, a slim, earnest young man with a high forehead and serious eyes.

'Sorry I couldn't meet you,' he apologized as he poured me a Red Stripe beer. 'Another bloody meeting with the JAS.'

'JAS?'

'The Jamaican Agricultural Society. It's like a privately run agricultural and livestock service for small farmers, subsidized by Government. There is also the Jamaica Livestock Association, completely autonomous and patronized mainly by the larger livestock breeders and estates. Both do a good job. You'll find that Jamaica probably has the best agricultural and livestock service in the tropics – better than most European countries.'

Over further Red Stripes, Tom and Roger gave me an idea of what to expect. How different from Africa! There were no dangerous epizootics or plagues such as rinderpest or East Coast fever, and no wild animals – except the mongoose. But ticks were plentiful and both redwater and anaplasmosis were common in cattle, otherwise the diseases were much the same as those found in Europe. Thankfully, foot and mouth disease and rabies had been kept out by strict quarantine regulations.

Livestock breeding was advanced, and in tropical dairy cattle, Tom assured me proudly, Jamaica led the world. Unlike Northern Rhodesia, there were a great many horses, mules and donkeys and, of course, pets.

The beer was pouring out of me. The temperature was probably in the mid-eighties but it was the humidity, helped by the ominous black clouds I could see piling up in the direction of the Blue Mountains, that was doing the damage. On Roger's advice I showered and changed into one of his shirts, but within ten minutes it was as wet as the one I had discarded.

After lunch, Tom walked me across a paddock to the Veterinary Division's buildings, a hundred yards behind the residences. The path led beneath huge, densely-leaved mango trees, their branches thickly hung with hornets' nests.

'Hope has about ten thousand mango trees – nearly all Bombays.'

'Is that good or bad?' I asked; the name meant nothing.

'Bombays are the best of all. They're not stringy and you can eat them with a spoon, like a peach. There are other excellent varieties, Julie for example, or No. 11, but they can't compare with Bombays. By the way, avoid walking across this way with Roger.'

'Why?'

'He has a habit of swatting hornets' nests then dashing for the labs before the angry brutes can catch him!'

Roger, I found, was usually successful in reaching sanctuary ahead of the enraged *Vespidae* – except on one occasion. Unfortunately, it happened to be his wedding morning, so perhaps his mind was else-where. The wedding photos show the groom with a wide but grotesquely lopsided grin, proving that that particular round had gone to the Hope Hornets!

The single-storey Veterinary Division building had a dispensary and clinic at one end, laboratories at the other, and offices in between. In front, across a wide-gravelled driveway, were stables and loose boxes. All around were paddocks liberally sprinkled with mango trees, through which could be seen other buildings of the Agricultural Dept.

A car drove in as we were talking, From it emerged a neatly dressed, almost dapper young man with slicked-down dark hair and that well-laundered look so common in North Americans. Even in that heat, I noticed, he wore slacks, a long-sleeved shirt with a red-spotted bow tie, and showed no sign of perspiration.

'Meet Bob, from Toronto. He's my deputy. Not at all a bad lad for a Canadian. He and Margo live in the other veterinary residence.'

Later, Roger dropped me at a boarding house below Liguanea. Like most other residential houses it was a wooden two-storey affair, smothered in bougainvillea and creepers and surrounded by massive trees. Everything about this place, I decided, was pure magic.

* * *

'You'll be stationed at Montego Bay, and take charge of the western end of the island,' Tom told me that evening over rum and gingers. 'It's on the north coast and becoming quite a tourist resort for rich Americans. Nick, the present VO, will be leaving soon. Roger's going up there tomorrow. You'd better tag along.'

Tourist resort! Just up my street. A fair proportion of the fat, rich, American tourists would be bound to bring along their slim, bikini-clad daughters (bikinis were just coming into fashion). Oh yes; after the she-less wilds of Northern Rhodesia, Montego Bay would suit me very nicely, thank you.

Humming birds were already at breakfast, probing the bright red hibiscus with their long, thin beaks as we nudged through streets swarming with bicycles, handcarts and mule-drawn drays. There were donkeys, too, in their hundreds, staggering under the weight of their overloaded panniers and the voluptuous market women astride their sagging spines.

We passed fields of sugar cane, and lush pastures dotted with white, humped Zebu cattle.

'Caymanas Estates. Those are some of their Nellore herd. Jamaica has some of the best Zebu cattle in the West Indies. We export quite a few to South America.'

A little further on we passed an old ruin beside a small river.

'Ferry Inn,' Roger told me. 'The halfway house between port Royal and Spanish Town. Recently, they've discovered hundreds of wine and brandy bottles in the river, dating from buccaneer days.'

Spanish Town, the original capital of Jamaica, 30 miles west of Kingston, had seen better days. The former Governor's house, now a hollow shell with chunks of blue sky showing through the boarded-up windows, made a façade to one side of the central square. The sculptured memorial to admiral Rodney on another side, however, was still impressive.

From Spanish Town we followed a river up a long winding valley to Bog Walk and Linstead.

'Carry me ackee go a Linstead Market. Not a quattie wo'th sell,' Roger carolled. 'Probably Jamaica's most famous folk song. I'll point out the next ackee tree I see. It has a red fruit the size of a pear. Ackee is the staple food of the peasant for most of the year. They eat it with salt fish. It was brought here from West Africa as a food for slaves by Captain Bligh about the same time as he brought the breadfruit.'

'What's a quattie?'

'The local name for a penny ha'penny. It's going out of use.'

Another five miles of winding road brought us over Mount Diablo to the rolling pastures of Moneague and Walker's Wood. Here we dropped into a steep-sided gorge, like an exaggerated Devonshire lane or a fairy tunnel over-grown with ferns under a canopy of trees.

'Fern Gully. It takes us down to Ocho Rios on the coast.'

I was not prepared for the Kodachrome brilliance of the north coast. Through the coconut palms I could see dazzling yellow beaches lapped by a green ocean which gradually turned to dark ultramarine as it stretched away to the horizon. This was the tropics I had hankered after – coral reefs, palm trees – an explosion of youthful fantasies!

We breakfasted at Shaw Park, an old family farm and hotel in the hills above Ocho Rios. Our arrival was opportune. Robin, the son, heir and manager, told us that one of his recently calved milking cows was down and looked like dying. It was an easy diagnosis – milk fever. A bottle of calcium borogluconate solution, extricated from the boot of Roger's car and injected under the skin, soon had her on her feet. The physiology of milk fever is complicated but the end point is clear, a lowering of the calcium ions in the blood, usually in cows which have just calved. The treatment is one of the most spectacular in veterinary medicine. Robin gaped in awe as his

157

cow – seemingly comatose and about to expire – rose to her feet and within a few minutes was looking for her feed. Many a vet has built his reputation with this simple physic!

The coast road west from Ocho Rios, sometimes macadamized, sometimes dirt, ran within inches of sandy beaches and clear, coral-spangled water. Now and then we dived into great carpets of sugar cane. Coconut trees were everywhere, in large plantations or in small groves, or scattered singly along the shore. Sea almond trees and the shrub-like sea grape covered much of the inner shore-line, making an impenetrable barrier between us and the water. Here and there a poinciana tree or a poinsettia bush flashed scarlet against the dark blue of the Caribbean.

Near St Ann's Bay was the site of Sevilla Nueva, the first Spanish settlement in Jamaica, built in 1509. A little further on at Runaway Bay, a gorgeous strip of sand where the British finally chased the Spaniards into the sea, we stopped for a swim.

On through more cane fields to Dry Harbour (later changed to Discovery Bay to please the tourist board) where Columbus had first landed on 4 May 1494; then to Rio Bueno, a once-thriving sugar port, now a collection of slate-roofed, cut-stone warehouses, and a 300-year-old church sparkling white against the ocean where, one day, I would be married. Through more cane fields to Falmouth, still engulfed in mangrove swamps, and once the busiest post on the north coast, but where, because of yellow fever and malaria, life expectancy had been less than 30 years.

We entered a large shed-like store in the central square, the walls hung with shirts and dresses of the most outlandish patterns – outlandish, that is, to grey-minded Europeans after five bleak years of war. Antonio's in 1946 was the only shop in Jamaica selling these far out 'calypso' designs. I was told that during the war a consignment of glaring cottons bound for West Africa had been diverted to Jamaica due to submarine activities. It was unloaded at Falmouth and the far-sighted Antonio collared the lot. Since then, an Antonio or Falmouth shirt had been the hallmark of a Jamaican.

We called at Good Hope just inland from Falmouth, where Roger was conducting some tick control experiments. Once a cane property, it was now being run as a dude ranch for American tourists. I was fascinated by the ancient overgrown ruins of the sugar mill with its water wheel and 'factory' and enormous chutes, and the old slave houses and 'hospital, all built of cut stone. Invading vegetation had made little impression on their solid piles. Similar ruins were to be found all over Jamaica, proof of her once having been the world's largest producer of sugar.

'Twenty miles inland from here,' Roger told me, 'is Cockpit Country.'

Cockpit Country, or the 'Land of Look Behind', was a 500-square-mile patch of limestone which had been eroded into circular depressions and sink holes, with huge underground caves and river courses. The surface, razor-sharp honeycomb rock, was covered by thorny scrub and cactus except for the bottom of some larger 'cockpits', where an area the size of a football pitch might be covered with fertile soil. It was into this daunting terrain that the runaway slaves had fled in the early eighteenth century, and had been united into a separate society, later known as the Maroons, by the Cudjoe brothers, Jimmy and Accompong. After a long and usually successful guerilla-type war with the British, they were granted their own land and laws, and were still living under a leader called 'The Colonel' in the almost inaccessible settlements of Maroon Town and Accompong. We lunched with the newly appointed Rector of the University of the West Indies, a noted London surgeon, who lived in a barrack-like cut stone building halfway up the hillside near Falmouth, once the Jamaica home of the Barretts of Wimpole Street.

Approaching Montego Bay we passed beneath Rose Hall, a gaunt, square, three-storey ruin, a tropical 'bleak house', floating on rolling hills of sugar cane. Here, the hated mistress, Annie Palmer, 'The White Witch' as she was called, had bedeviled the slaves until they rebelled and killed her.

Something suddenly struck me as we drove along.

'It always seems to be high tide,' I commented. 'It's like driving beside a lake.'

'That's because there are no tides,' Roger said.

'No tides! I thought tides were universal.'

'They are, actually we have four tides a day, but being in the Gulf of Mexico which is enclosed on three sides, they rebound into each other so that each is of only a few inches.'

The closer we came to Montego Bay, the more excited I became. Past the newly built airport, along a curve of sandy shore and we were in a jumble of houses and hotels strung along the water's edge.

We went through the town and up to the Agricultural station a few miles inland to meet Nick, the Veterinary Officer. The station buildings were modern, and there was an excellent office and lab. Nick was all enthusiasm for the place, but he had made up his mind to take a PhD in the USA.

'Watch it,' he warned, 'you get some pretty highly pressured girls coming down here. You'll probably be married within a year. I only just escaped. Glad I'm off while I'm still free.'

159

'Don't worry,' I told him. 'I'll watch it.'

Doctor's Cave, the main beach and principal attraction, was like an enormous natural swimming pool. A crescent of white beach curved out from a group of hotels to a sandy point, enclosing a crystal-clear, peridot-green basin. Girls, clad in scanty two-piece swim suits, scampered along the sands while fat elderly men and women in vast straw hats and Bermuda shorts with 'American tourist' written all over their sagging, sunburnt bellies, waddled in and out of the calm, warm water. In one place an enormous thermometer had been fixed in the sea so that the more fastidious could see the temperature before testing it with their toes. 'I never go in if it is below seventy-eight,' a resident told me.

The fact that the low-lying area immediately behind this magnificent beach was an abandoned cemetery worried no-one.

'What are the chances of doing some research?' I asked Roger offhandedly, as if I had just thought of it.

'There's always something that wants investigating,' he replied, 'if you can find the time. Clinical work, disease control and husbandry advice can keep you pretty busy.'

I'd find time all right! Never in my wildest dreams had I imagined that I should ever work in such a tropical paradise. Hot sun, cool sea breezes, a sparkling ocean, heart-stopping girls and later in the day, or sometimes earlier, the ever-reviving, joyous rum punch. A tropical paradise for which tourists paid hundreds of dollars a day ... and I was going to be paid to work here!

This, I thought, as I walked down to the water's edge, is as near

Christmas Card, 1946

160

heaven as I'll ever get! My bum had really landed in the butter!

But I was in for a shock. Those little Black Imps in Africa must have sent a messenger ahead of me to advise their Jamaican cousins.

'COW SICK, COME QUICK'

'You're to take over Highgate, not Montego Bay.'

My heart almost stopped. An influential dairy farmer and Member of Parliament, who owned a property near Highgate in the Parish of St Mary, had twisted the Director's arm and had had me posted to his constituency instead.

I ached with disappointment. I hadn't yet seen Highgate, but I knew it couldn't be anything like Montego Bay. To start with it was at least 15 miles from the sea, a nondescript village, so everyone said, with nothing to recommend it. It was a new station, there were no proper buildings, everything was makeshift awaiting the next year's budget. Worse still, there were no tourist attractions in the vicinity, although Kingston was only 40 miles away, albeit over a tortuous thoroughfare called Junction Road.

Teddy, the Livestock Officer at Hope, took me up to have a look around. Highgate dribbled along a road ('street' was too grandiose a word for a narrow strip of disintegrating tarmac) on top of a ridge smothered in banana and coconut trees. Most of the half-dozen wooden stores were roofed with tin or with wooden shingles, including the boardinghouse, the garage and a twice-weekly cinema.

My base would be at the Orange River Agricultural Station, a mile below the village in a hot steamy valley full of banana trees, tall elephant grass – and ticks! My office – that's what they had the audacity to call it – was the partitioned-off end of the implement shed, with one glassless, shuttered window looking out onto a scum-covered pond, and only a low, rough, unplaned shelf for a desk. Tractors and their implements roared in and out on the other side of the partition; the smell of petrol and oil was all-pervading. I guessed that as soon as the rainy season finished the whole place would be smothered in dust. There was no electricity or running water.

'Sorry about the primitive conditions,' Tubby, the globular, jovial Senior Agricultural Officer, apologized in a broad Scots accent. 'The new buildings should begin next year.'

Meanwhile I was supposed to share a barn with tractors and ploughs! Not bloody likely! And research? How the hell could I do any research under such conditions?

I bought a car, a streamlined, maroon Chevrolet coupé. It was the first car I had ever owned – really owned. I'd never seen anything so slick, and Government had even given me an interest-free loan to buy it and would also reimburse me for all mileage I did on official duty.

Those first weeks in Highgate were perhaps more depressing than my first weeks in Abercorn. There, I had expected little but here, after my glimpse of Montego Bay, I had expected everything. At times I even found myself longing for Africa! The 'new boy syndrome' I had experienced in Northern Rhodesia was just as irritating in Jamaica. 'I hope you like bridge – Oh, we must teach you'; 'There's an excellent golf course at – '; 'You'll love it here; I expect you play polo.' I hated bridge, I despised golf, I had no wish to play polo. I wanted to do research – preferably on animal diseases transmissible to man, and in my spare time to play tennis, swim, sketch, hunt for treasure and, of course, chase girls. I considered resigning and emigrating to the USA, or going to help with the massive foot and mouth campaign being carried out in Mexico. Luckily, I did neither.

The gloomy, bat-ridden guesthouse, Earnsdale, gave me a room with windows so overgrown with creepers that I found it too dark to read, even at midday, and since Highgate had no electricity, it was back to the kerosene lamp once more. The owner, poor woman, lay tossing on her bed in a back room, in the last throes of cancer, her occasional groans adding to the overall misery of the place. Just before she died, her niece, a vivacious, intelligent 40-year-old, came to help her out, but it was Glen, the local doctor and fellow resident, who saved my sanity. Recently graduated in the UK, he had taken the job of Medical Officer in Highgate while he awaited the arrival of his English wife before setting up practice on his own. His elfish humour saw me through many a long evening.

It was impossible to read intelligently or do any kind of office work in my noisy, dusty tractor shed, or the gloomy guest house. Such activities I carried out in my car, parked along the sea-shore.

Obviously, things would not improve till I found myself a house, so when a newly-constructed, two-bedroom dwelling on the outskirts of the town became available, I moved in immediately. Stella, a middle-aged matron who lived next door, cooked and cleaned and her teenage son helped me in the garden until I acquired a full-time yard boy. Within a week I had also moved my office from the tractor shed into my house.

I missed Flea and Panda, left behind in Northern Rhodesia, but there was no way I could have brought them to Jamaica. Apart from difficulty and cost, quarantine regulations only permitted dogs and cats to enter from the British Isles or New Zealand, due to the possibility of bringing rabies, so I put the word around and was soon the

162

proud owner of a female Alsatian cross Airedale puppy. Poppet was adorable and when Jack, an Alsatian cross Golden Retriever, joined our family a couple of months later, he thought so too. They had over a dozen shaggy puppies before I spayed her.

Their temperaments could not have been more different. Poppet, a loving, motherly type, would certainly chase away intruders, but only with a half-apologetic bark. Jack was much less accommodating. He had been brought to me to be put down as dangerous, but he was such a beauty, I said I would keep him.

Warned that he was likely to attack children, I kept him on a long rope for the first week. Then one Sunday, as I sat sketching on the seashore, I looked up to see Jack by some small Indian children a hundred yards away. My stomach cramped as one of the kids, perhaps four or five years old, put both arms round Jack's neck and hugged him. Jack licked his face.

I never worried about him after that and he never let me down in the four years I had him. Still, to be one the safe side, I placed a large notice on my front gate, in broad Jamaican:

'BEWARE HANGRY DARG'.

* * *

I was still devastated at having been denied the fleshpots of Montego Bay, but once I had moved out of the drab, claustrophobic guest-house and the tractor-infested office, I had to admit that there was a certain excitement in my new job.

There was a thrill of romance each time I picked my way up a barely passable road to an eighteenth-century property house, perched amongst pimento groves and concrete barbecues. Perhaps the owner would have a beautiful daughter ready to fall into my arms. Anything could happen in this sunbright, magic country. And as I wound down again, having only encountered the overseer and struggled for an hour with an overdue calf – the only thing that fell into my arms! – I would be stunned by a sudden vista of a blue ocean through coconut palms at a bend of a chalky lane. Wizened crones, breaking stones on the roadside, would pull clay pipes from their toothless faces and sing traditional folk songs as they hammered their rocks. Old digging songs like 'Sammy Dead-o', or 'Hill and Gully Rider', or 'Iron Bar' – later made famous as 'Jamaica Farewell' by a local boy, Harry Bela-fonte, whose mother I was told still lived above St Ann's Bay.

Many estate houses, although badly in need of repair, contained the most fabulous antiques. Old four-posters, massive dining tables and dressers, winding staircases, all carved from Jamaican mahogany or from that incredibly hard wood once used for propeller shafts, lignum vitae. Ancestral portraits, suffocated by decades of smoky candles and untrimmed wicks, their features barely discernable, looked down at me from the walls of shadowy living rooms and dark panelled corridors. This was another pleasing aspect of Jamaica in sharp contrast to the Africa I had left. Jamaica had a past recorded in print and stone – old estate houses and churches, ruins of sugar mills and battlements, heroic tales of buccaneers and the Spanish Main. Northern Rhodesia's past was restricted to vague records by missionary explorers and some cave drawings, but no cairns or columns or citadels. White ants had devoured the rest.

Although beer or rum and ginger were the usual pre-prandial drinks, I was frequently offered a home-made Jamaican liqueur, Pimento Dram, after the dessert. The basic ingredient for this tangy elixir was pimento berries steeped in rum, but it was the jealously guarded additions that gave each its distinctive flavour. Nearly every pantry contained a large flagon in which the proud owner was brewing his particular variety of Pimento Dram. Pimento was a small native tree, the berries of which were dried on concrete barbecues and exported to produce allspice.

Cinnamon, cloves, pepper, ginger, other fruits like guinep or star apple, or the dregs of liqueur bottles and sometimes, we joked, even a dead mouse or cockcroach were added to the concoction during its 12 to 18 months maturation. No wonder each had its own, particular flavour, unlike that other famous Jamaican liqueur, Tia Maria (first made by the Government pathologist in his bathtub), which had only coffee added to the rum.

At first, I had only the three north-east Parishes (similar to English counties) of Portland, St Mary and St Ann to contend with, but within two months, Nick had left Montego Bay and I added the Western parishes to my domain, including my cherished Montego Bay. Work doubled, but so did the opportunities for swimming, exploring and romance, and it was pure bliss after battling with a difficult calving and covered in 'cowsh', to pull off the coast road, slip on a pair of trunks and wade into the gorgeous green water. If there was a lot of work to do in the west end of the island, I would spend a couple of nights in Montego Bay, and chat up a sympathetic tourist. Charlie's accounts of Jamaica had been well founded.

Apart from the large estates there were countless small holdings and peasants with their cows, goats, pigs, chickens and donkeys constantly in need of assistance. Nearly everyone had a cow tethered on the 'long pasture', the grassy verge of the roadside. As I had no telephone, calls for help from the small farmers usually came by telegram, and the message was nearly always the same, 'Cow sick, come quick'. No hint as to the ailment. A cow could be calving, have fallen into a gully, have mastitis or just be off its feed, but the message rarely differed, 'cow/hog/donkey sick. Come quick.'

'Come quick', however, was often easier demanded than accomplished. Directions were usually confined to a name and a district – 'Jones, Pear Tree Grove'. I would find Pear Tree Grove on the map, and off I would go. Sometimes the road was good, sometimes impassable. If I was careful, I usually got there.

At the approaches to the village I would begin asking for Mr Jones. Inevitably there were several, so I would go to the Post Office, if there was one, and ask which Mr Jones had sent me a telegram, to be told that it was 'Massa Jones of Long Tree Bottom'. Long Tree Bottom, of course, was over the next hill and across a stream, about a mile from where I could leave the car. Well, it was pleasant to stroll through the countryside and I could usually find a 'piccny' to carry my bag. Arriving at Long Tree Bottom, I would find that this particular Mr Jones had sent the telegram on behalf of his brother, who was over the next hill at Fruitful Vale!

Off I'd go again to arrive at a scatter of huts called Fruitful Vale.

'Yessah. Dis Massa Jones' yard, but 'im gaan a Ginger Hill.'

'When will he return?'

'Dunno, Sah.'

'He sent me a telegram that his cow was sick.'

'Yessah. She down de pasture.'

A walk through the long elephant grass and thorn bushes or 'makka' would reveal a case of worms and semi-starvation.

'Massa did give she a Red Drench, yesaday, but she too mawga.' Red Drench was the panacea for all ills. A proprietary medicine company had collared the market some years before with their Red Drench, Black Drench and Gaseous Fluid, and now there was not a livestock owner in the whole country who didn't use them regularly, no matter what the ailment. 'Mawga' was the local *patois* for 'thin', probably derived from the Spanish 'magro', meaning lean.

Sometimes the animal was already dead, the telegram having been given to a friend, who would be passing a Post Office later that week. Each case was played by ear, the treatment aimed as much at the owner as at the animal. Most farmers showed their gratitude by offering me a pawpaw, a 'hand' of bananas, some yampi (a potato-like crop), or a 'jelly' (coconut in the unripe, water stage), which his young son would scramble 20 feet up a coconut palm to obtain. When I'd finished drinking the sweet water through a hole in the

165

shell, – no drink is more refreshing than coconut water – the farmer would slice off a piece of the husk to use as a spoon and split the nut in half with his 'cutlass' (panga) so that I could scoop out the jelly-like fruit.

Sometimes, after walking half a morning I failed to find the owner or his animal and had to wait till I returned to the car to replace my sweat from a, by now, warmish bottle of Coca Cola.

The large estates were more rewarding, the animals easier to restrain, and I could usually look forward to a couple of rum punches before a bountiful property lunch.

While the first priority of the Government Veterinary Officer was the investigation and control of dangerous infectious diseases, it was the clinical cases and simple surgery that took up most of his time.

I had done so little clinical work since I graduated that I found myself almost in the situation of learning a new trade. Unlike my previous posts in Africa, however, I did have an excellent set of reference books and most of the equipment I needed, and if I was completely stumped, I could always send a telegram to Tom, Bob or Roger at Hope, for support.

Theoretically, there was a scale of charges, but in practice this only applied to the larger private farmers and estates. There was no way a peasant could have been sent a bill, so attention to such cases was always recorded as 'investigation', which was free. After all, who could tell whether a 'Cow sick come quick' call might not turn out to be the start of some deadly epizootic?

One thing I found most agreeable to my ego – I was now 'Dr'. Britain called its veterinarians plain 'Mr', while all other countries, including US-dominated Jamaica, called their vets and dentists 'Dr'. Rightly so, I felt. Hadn't we studied the same subjects as our medical cousins for the same number of years? The only difference was that our patients were animals.

BUSH SURGERY

One of my first cases was a particularly difficult calving. The cow, a Jersey, had been covered by a Holstein bull and the calf was abnormally large. After nearly an hour of pushing, turning and pulling, I realized that I would never be able to get it out alive in the normal way. A caesarean was the obvious answer. The problem was that I had never done a caesarean on a cow, nor for that matter, even seen one done! But I certainly wasn't going to let that stop me.

166

Telling the farmer to wait, I returned to the station to collect the extra instruments I would need and steal a quick glance at my text book of surgery.

Outside my house, I found an agitated old man waiting for me. In barely intelligible Jamaican he told me that his cow, heavily in calf, had fallen into a gully and hurt herself. As his 'yard' was on the same road as my projected Caesarian, I agreed to look at his cow on the way. His name, he said, was 'Mr Simmit', the Jamaican pronunciation of Smith.

His 'yard' was up a rocky side road which soon became impassable, so I abandoned my car and set off on foot. A half-mile later and several hundred feet higher, we came to the site of the mishap. The cow, however, was still in the gully, a fact that 'Mr Simmit' had felt it wiser not to mention. Moreover, it was jammed six feet down, on its side, bloated and without a hope in hell of getting out.

'Is there anyone who can help?' I asked.

'No, Sah. Me son 'im gaan a Port Maria an' me neighba' 'im sick a bed.

'It'll take at least four men with ropes to get her out and she might die even if we do. When was she due to calve?'

'H'I h'expectin' her a kyalve dis week.'

'There's only one thing I can do – try and save the calf. There's no hope for the mother. I'm afraid I'll have to shoot her and take the calf out afterwards.'

Reluctantly he agreed. I prepared the humane killer (a pistol-like instrument from which a blank .22 cartridge thrusts out a four-inch metal rod), placed the muzzle on the cow's forehead just above the point where the diagonal lines from each eye to the opposite ear crossed each other, and pulled the trigger.

I always felt sick after killing an animal, but there was no alternative. I gave 'Mr Simmit' a large specimen jar and told him to milk as much out of her as he could, then I grabbed my post mortem knife – no need for asepsis here – and knelt on the cow's chest.

Just as I was going to slice through the skin, it struck me that here was the ideal practice run for the Caesarian I had to do later. I cut carefully through the skin and the muscles of the flank and tried to follow the exact procedures which I had just read up at home. It was a bit cramped but I reached the uterus, hauled out the calf and cut the cord. We struggled with it to the top of the ravine, slapped it about and dried it off. It was a lovely little heifer.

'What about the old girl?' I asked, pointing into the gully.

'Me haf-a lef her fe John Crow,' he answered, sadly. I was sure, however, that there would be quite a few two-legged 'John Crows' with sharp knives to help themselves to a juicy steak before the winged ones arrived!

'Mr Simmit' managed to milk out about a pint of colostrum – the first milk of the mother which is so important for the new-born's survival. I left him with instructions for feeding the calf and hastened on to my genuine Caesarean.

She was justifiably nervous when she saw me approaching, she hadn't forgotten that I had already groped around inside her for the best part of an hour. I gave her a spinal anaesthetic and for the second time that day cut into a bovine abdomen. All went well – almost text-book, and a few minutes later, with her still standing, I hauled out a strapping bullkin. It was enormous. No wonder it had jammed!

I wish I could record that both calves did well. Unfortunately, 'Mr Simmit's' heifer died a few days later. It was expecting too much for him to have raised it under those conditions. The bull calf and its mother, however, prospered. So perhaps the trial run had helped, and 'Mr Simmits' cow and calf hadn't died in vain.

* * *

The first West Indian Veterinary Conference took place in Kingston soon after I arrived. Delegates came from as far north as Bermuda and from British Guiana in the south, as well as from most of the other Caribbean islands, British, Dutch and American. It was opened by the Chief Secretary, Hugh Foot who, ten years later, as Governor of Jamaica, would open the second West Indian Veterinary Conference.

Each morning, I wove my way over Junction Road, from Highgate, to the meetings at Hope, sometimes fitting in a case or two on the way, to stagger home later at night after an evening of social festivities. At the end of a week I was ragged, but the conference did more than anything else to help me settle into my new life. I no longer felt an isolated, forgotten civil servant in a small town on a small island, but a valued member of a large team of friendly colleagues from all over the Caribbean, all with similar problems and all dependent on one another for the improvement of animal health in the area. Already, after only three months, I was beginning to feel that Jamaica was my home.

One of the things I appreciated most was that, unlike Africa, nobody seemed to have feelings of inferiority on account of skin colour. It was not true to say that there was no racial discrimination, there was, but it had been largely superseded by class. Prejudice was a private preference, not a group obsession or an official decree. No matter what shade, or how lowly a person might be, he was still a Jamaican with jealously defended dignity, a feature that was soon brought home to me.

My 'yard boy', Clarence, a youth of some 18 years and, incidentally, the image of Victor Mature, a rising film star of the forties, was about as dim and as lazy as it was possible to be. I reacted to Clarence's idle habits as I had done to his far-off cousins in Northern Rhodesia.

'Why the bloody hell don't you bloody well take your bloody finger out and do so-and-so,' I would yell, to the consternation of a respectable Jamaican family who lived opposite.

The first time I let loose at him, he said nothing. The second time he stood perfectly still, regarding me as a disappointed schoolmaster might regard a recalcitrant child; then, in a quiet, sorrowful voice, he admonished me:

'Musn' you don' taak a me dat way, sah. Dat hurt me feelin's.'

I never spoke to him – nor to anyone else – 'dat way' again, even under grievous provocation. I owed a lot to Clarence.

DIPPING PROBLEMS

It wasn't long before the politician farmer who had scotched my posting to Montego Bay telegraphed me from Kingston.

'OVERSEER BALLARDS VALLEY REPORTS TEN COWS SICK STOP VISIT IMMEDIATELY'

This seemed a genuine emergency, but a 'please' or 'grateful if' would have been nice, and he could certainly have afforded the extra expense. Ballard's Valley was only 12 miles distant, a dairy farm on the flat coastal strip near Port Maria. I was greeted by the overseer or 'busha', a tall, well-built black man with greying hair and smiling face. Taking off his battered trilby, he extended a massive paw.

'Baugh. Glad to meet you, daacta. Big trouble, man.'

We walked across to a large paddock on the other side of the milking sheds. Three cows were lying on the ground grunting, and two of these had severe diarrhoea. Several more were standing dejectedly with their heads down, making no attempt to chew the cud.

Poison, I thought. Must be. Then Baugh gave me the clue.

'Dem bin a dip dis marning'

Of course. Bang on. Arsenic. I'd seen a lot of dip poisoning in the

169

farms around Lusaka, my last post in Northern Rhodesia. Although the newer, relatively non-toxic dips were coming on to the market, most dip tanks in Jamaica were still filled with the old arsenical solution. As a killer of ticks it was certainly effective. Unfortunately, it could be just as efficient as a killer of cattle! The most common cause of poisoning was from the splashings made by the animals as they plunged into the dip, which then dried on the walls of the bath and on the grass alongside, providing a salty and appetising lick. Protective fencing around the dip to keep animals at a safe distance was essential. Most cattle enjoyed leaping into the narrow, 20-foot long tank and swimming in the cool fluid to the other end where a sloping ramp allowed them to walk out and dry off in a concrete-floored chute.

Sometimes, if the day was very hot and the animals were thirsty, they might try and drink the dip or lick it off the coats of others. It had certainly been a hot day, but that was not the cause of the poisoning this time. We found a loose wire in the security fence around the dip. It was evident that some animals had got through and had had a good lick at the encrusted arsenic-laden splashings on the wall of the tank.

There is a fairly reliable remedy for arsenic poisoning – if given early. I had some of it in my car, but not nearly enough for that number of sick animals.

'What time does the chemist in Port Maria shut?' I asked.

'N 'bout fifteen minutes,' 'busha' answered.

I jumped into the car and sped the three miles into the little town.

'Three pounds of Sodium thiosulphate, please,' I panted, my foot in the door.

'Must be doing a lot of photography,' he commented. Sodium thiosulphate, or 'hypo' as it is commonly called, is used as a fixative for photographic films and prints.

'No, but I hope it will fix some cows with dip poisoning.'

Back at the farm, I gave each animal four ounces of the white crystals as a drench in a whisky bottle of water. Then I dissolved some more of the drug in sterile water and injected it into the recumbent ones. I left 'busha' with the remainder of the crystals and told him to give all the cows another dose the following day.

We were, I think, extremely lucky. Two of the three lying the ground – those with diarrhoea – died a few hours later and another three took some days to recover, but the others were back to normal the next day.

Some weeks later the owner invited me to a cocktail party in his luxurious Kingston mansion and was profuse in his thanks. I wasn't

170

quite sure whether this was an appreciation for past services or an insurance to cover future favours, but the amount of time I spent on his wretched property in the following months soon dispelled any such doubts!

* * *

Near Ballard's Valley was another large estate, Llanrumney. John, the flamboyant owner, had emigrated from Italy between the wars and had had the misfortune to have been incarcerated as an enemy alien in 1939. Now, rising 50 and a confirmed bachelor (well – not quite, as it turned out), he was making up for his years in captivity. His large, dark, protuberant eyes twinkling under coal-black brows, would open wide and dart from side to side (like Eddie Cantor's had done on pre-war screens) as he described his latest womanizing escapades.

John was proud of Llanrumney, a he had every right to be. From the verandah of the spacious house, built on a hump in the middle of the estate, he could survey his acres of bananas, coconuts and sugar cane and expound at length on the breeding of each of his valuable dairy cows which grazed just below.

It had been Captain Morgan himself, that renowned buccaneer and later Governor of Jamaica, who had built Llanrumney. There was nothing left of the original house, which had stood on the same mound as the present estate house, but about a mile away the thoughtful captain had constructed a residence for his paramour. What was left of this abode had, by some administrative blunder or through pure ignorance, been desecrated still further by the Public Works Department, who had knocked down the remaining walls to provide stone for their road construction. Before the vandalism was stopped, a large part of this priceless ruin had disappeared beneath tarmac.

John worked hard and played hard, and often his verandah would be alive with the famous and the beautiful. Many well-known film-stars and politicians holidaying in Jamaica would drop in to share his wit and hospitality.

But wedlock couldn't be put off for ever. One of the more beautiful visitors from the north finally made an honest man of him and later presented him with a little girl. I was in England, struggling with a post-graduate degree, when I 'heard. Passing through Rome a few months later, I bought a typical Italian doll to take back for his little daughter. I never gave it.

'John's dead,' Roger told me when I showed him what I had

171

brought. 'Fell off his horse one morning while he was riding round the property. Probably a heart attack.'

The widow had already left for her home in the States. I never saw his bambina.

Years later, passing through Jamaica on holiday, I was driving from Highgate to Port Maria. On a bank beside the road that skirted Llanrumney estate, looking down towards the sea, I came across John's last resting place. So many cheerful memories surged through me, it was almost as if John had been waiting to share them. At the head of the engraved slab there was an urn. I removed the lid, wrote a message on my card and dropped it inside.

'I'll come and see you again, John, one day,' I murmured as I left.

I still hope to keep my promise.

THE WIDOW OF WOODFIELD

Each evening I returned from the field to a sheaf of pink telegraph forms and scribbled notes. Some needed immediate attention and I had to hit the road again, but more often I would pour a rum and ginger and sort the messages into priorities and areas for the next day.

It was no chore to set off before six. The air was cool, the countryside dew-laden, the sea sparkling, and I was young and in love with everything. Nearly always, between cases, I was able to swim somewhere along the magnificent coast and snooze or read a book for an hour in the soft warm sand. My two dogs – Jack, and when she was old enough, Poppet – I took with me. They loved the sea as much as their master. Only once did I – and they – regret their outing. Fifteen minutes after leaving the house, my eyes began to sting and the dogs to howl. I looked over my shoulder. The cork had worked loose from a bottle of formalin I had foolishly left on the back seat. Formalin is a most noxious and irritant chemical and as suffocating as ammonia. Just ahead was a small bridge. I braked alongside it, opened the door and hurled my two yelping hounds over the parapet into the stream some 12 feet below. Then I re-stoppered the bottle, placed it upright in my medicine box in the boot and drove straight home, my two soggy pets beside me on the front seat. It took a week of scrubbing and airing to get rid of those pungent fumes.

I never bothered to carry food with me. The large estates usually offered some kind of a meal, and if I spent the day with peasants I would be just as content with their simple, but equally generous, offers of a 'jelly' or a glass of milk laced with white rum.

172

Cries for assistance came at all hours. Most were justifiable, the owners having come long distances to fetch me, so although I would often set out moaning and grumbling, I would usually find that my services had really been necessary and would return home feeling especially virtuous, the farmer's praises ringing in my ears. But there *were* cases when I would gladly have given the owner a lethal injection. Such a person was the lady I came to know as the 'Widow of Woodfield'.

I was awakened by an urgent knocking. It took me a moment to surface and find my torch and yell that I was coming. Padding through the lounge to the front door in my underpants, I was more than taken aback to find a large woman standing outside, especially as she appeared to be on crutches. Just behind her hovered a figure in a chauffeur's uniform.

'My little dog.' her ladyship quavered. 'You must come immediately.' My nakedness seemed to have escaped her notice, although the headlights of the car outside the gate were sufficient to show me that she had grey hair and small eyes sunk in a puffy face.

'What's wrong with it?' I asked.

She adjusted one crutch and raised a battered tin listening trumpet to her ear.

'What?'

'I said what's wrong with your dog?'

'It's going mad. '

'Well, give me your address and I'll come and see you first thing in the morning.' Visions of rabies, still unknown in Jamaica, came to my mind.

'No. You must come at once,' she roared, in an authoritative voice. 'follow us.' With that she dropped her trumpet, which I now saw was attached to a cord round her neck, wheeled about and hobbled back to her car on her crutches. 'I'll give you breakfast,' she called as she heaved her bulk in through the car door.

I looked at my watch. It was just after three. Still in my underpants, I went out to the car.

'Where do you live?' I asked.

'At Woodfield, near Walkers Wood, in St Ann's.'

That was some 40 miles away.

'Wait a moment.' I told her. 'I've other cases in that direction tomorrow. Let me pack my bag, then I needn't come back.'

I packed my tuberculin testing syringes, took the tuberculin out of the kerosene Electrolux, placed a box of blood sampling bottles in the boot, backed my coupé into the road and followed my strange, visitor's tail lights into the night. This time, both Jack and Poppet remained behind.

I had expected to find a dog frothing at the mouth, attacking objects and showing other symptoms generally associated with fits. Nothing of the sort. Reclining on an old four-poster in madam's boudoir and scratching frantically at its ear, was a small, brown mongrel. Its coat was long and matted except at the base of the tail, where the hair had been torn away to leave a weeping sore. It greeted me with a suspicious growl.

'Don't touch him, he'll bite you. Disraeli is a little devil.'

Fine, I thought. So now what?

She sank her large body into the bed and tried to cuddle her beloved as it scratched and circled.

'Do you think you could hold it while I make an examination?' I asked.

It was no good. Each time I approached the little fiend it would wriggle free of her voluptuous arms and come for me across the bed. The only way to calm it would be to give it an anaesthetic, but if I couldn't get near it, how the devil could I?

'Is he particularly fond of anything in the food line?' I ventured, shouting at the top of my voice as she was unable to use her trumpet and hold Disraeli at the same time.

'Cheese,' she replied. 'Disraeli would sell his soul for a piece of cheese.'

To suggest that the wretched animal, even with a name like that, had a soul was, I thought, carrying things a bit far, but I was encouraged by its taste for cheese.

'You'll find some in the refrigerator in the kitchen,' she continued, giving me directions as to how to get there. I lit a candle (she had no electricity either) and found the Electrolux in the corner of a kitchen the size of a tennis court. Cockcroaches scuttled across the benches and floor like dried leaves in an autumn wind. I cut small chunks from the lump of cheddar and buried a capsule of nembutal (a powerful soporific) in each. Disraeli gulped down four chunks as if he hadn't eaten for a week.

'Now we wait,' I told her, relieved that I had been able to administer the drug so easily.

The scratching soon began to ease and in half an hour there was only a regular breathing from the tangle of hair on her lap. Although not surgically anaesthetized, Disraeli was 'out' for all practical purposes.

The first thing was to get rid of most of the matted coat. It was hard work, even with sharp scissors. I was so engrossed in this shearing operation that it was some time before I became aware of a common sequel to anaesthesia – its effect on ectoparasites. Whether from the taste of the drug or the drop in body temperature of the anaesthetized animal, their reaction was similar to that of rats on a sinking ship. The counterpane, I suddenly discovered, was hopping with fleas and crawling with ticks. Hurriedly, I dusted the whole area including myself, with a mixture of DDT and BHC powder.

Obviously, the fleas had been the main cause of the poor beast's agony, but I discovered two other problems. Dogs possess a pair of glands underneath the tail, the ducts of which empty into the bowel just inside the anus. Their purpose is obscure but often, especially if the animal is inclined to constipation, they become impacted with a thick, evil-smelling fluid. This leads to severe irritation, ill-health and makes the animal constantly rub its back end underneath furniture or scrape its bottom along the ground.

Disraeli's glands were large and impacted, so I squeezed them out with a lump of cottonwool, a procedure which has to be done with caution. It takes a great deal of soap and aftershave to eliminate the disgusting odour from an accidental squirt in the face.

He also had a severe canker of both ears. I cleaned them out and put in some drops, hoping that he would allow his doting mistress to keep up the treatment for a few days. Then I gave her all the flea powder I could spare and a lotion for the sore on his back. By now the sun was up and we sat down to an enormous breakfast.

As I wound down the chalky road from Woodfield towards Moneague and my next case, I felt that my early morning outing had, after all, been worthwhile. The dog was a lot more comfortable, the old lady a little happier, and I had made a new friend.

I came to know the 'Widow of Woodfield' well, and soon discovered, to my cost, why her trumpet was so dented. Whenever she disagreed or became annoyed with the person speaking into it, she used to hit the offender over the head! Nevertheless we remained good friends until she died.

A HOUSE BY THE SEA

The sea was an azure magnet. I spent every spare moment in it or by it, swimming, exploring, or lazing on the sand, sketching the sea, the palms and the white Indian cattle that grazed beneath them almost to the water's edge.

In Africa, I had dreamed of a tropical paradise. Now I had it – and for free!

One of my favourite spots was Robin's Bay, a small, shingly cove between Port Maria and Annotto Bay. At one end of the inlet a grassy promontory commanded an uninterrupted view of the spray-swept coastland and its numerous small bays and headlands, clustered with coconut palms. Behind these, through a scree of mist, rose the purple and green backdrop of the cloud-capped Blue Mountains.

Once there had been a polo club on the flat, grassy land behind Robin's Bay, and the small club house still had a caretaker and a bar. Now and again on a Sunday it would spring to life with picnickers, but for most of the time it slept peacefully, fanned by the warm north wind which gusted across the deep channel from Cuba.

Here, one afternoon, I met Phyllis, a daughter of a local farmer, who had ridden down on a mule to have a swim. We made it a regular rendezvous, meeting in the late afternoon or evening and taking a dip before repairing to the tiny club bar, where her twin brother who managed an adjoining property, would sometimes join us to end the day in a haze of rum and ginger.

At night, when the surf flashed in the light of the full moon, the beauty was agonizing. We would stroll over the headland and lie on the warm turf, the waves pounding the rocks below while the whole range of tropical forces surged within us.

Sometimes I would bring my accordion, but the damp salt breeze had an unfortunate effect on the notes. At a crucial or moving phrase, a key would jam and the instrument become a bagpipes.

*   *   *

View from roof verandah, Rockmoor

176

There was nothing wrong with my house in Highgate. It was new, clean and airy, but it was in Highgate, and Highgate was a drab community 20 miles by road from the sea, so when a house which I passed frequently on the coastal road near Gallina Point between Port Maria and Oracabessa appeared unoccupied, I felt that luck was on my side. The next time I went that way I pulled in through the brick gateposts, past a large slab-topped tomb, the size of a kitchen table, and onto an unkempt lawn.

Rockmoor house lay about 50 yards back from the road. It was a solid, whitewashed cut-stone bungalow with a red roof made of some synthetic material which was peeling off in places. Wooden steps led up on one side of the front door to a small roof verandah. Behind the house, thick vegetation stretched back to a 100-foot-high cliff that continued on both sides as far as I could see. The nearest house was a mile away. Patches of honeycomb rock erupted like sores through the short grass lawn surrounding the house.

My first concern was water. I found the remnants of a well and, behind the house, two massive stone tanks. The newer tank was low enough for me to peek over the side. It was empty, a carpet of dried slime covering the bottom. The older one had high walls but there were stone steps on the outside. It was about a third full, a thick crust of algae floating on the surface.

This was a great disappointment, for water would be crucial. Then I saw the cause. The guttering around the roof was broken in several places so that any rain, which was the only means of filling the tanks, was immediately lost onto the ground. Well, that would be easy to fix.

I peered through the windows. It should be cool, I thought, with its three-foot-thick walls and cement floors. I learned later that it was over 200 years old and had once been a sugar store. I climbed up the wooden steps to the roof verandah. It was rickety, and the salt wind had scalded much of the paintwork.

A surge of seagrapes and other coastal vegetation separated the road from a hundred yards of jagged honeycomb rock that ran down to a glistening sea. I crossed the road and stumbled over the razor-like honeycombs until, near the water's edge, I came across a lovely pool with all sorts and colours of coral growing on its sides. Scores of little fish in iridescent blues and greens, 'sergeants' with their black and yellow stripes, and 'butterfly fish' and 'four-eyes' swam busily in and out of holes in the coral.

An ideal spot in which to cool off if I was careful to avoid coral scratches and the black, pincushion-like sea eggs, whose long, waving, needle-sharp spines would pierce and break off in any part of me they touched. They could easily be removed from the pool either with thick gloves or by knocking them off with a stick and collecting them in a net. They made excellent bait, and on some of the islands were considered a great delicacy.

The sea, like a glass-topped table, was only a few inches lower than the rocky shelf. I lay down and peered over the edge into the still water. Although crystal clear, it was deep and dark, and I could probably see no more than ten or fifteen feet into the terrifying depths. Now and then a large fish swam near the surface. It was eerie, not a place to swim. Odds were that a shark or two wouldn't be far away.

I slipped and stumbled back to the road over the honeycomb rock and was annoyed to see another car parked in the front yard. Hell, I thought, I hope no-one else is thinking of occupying it.

A small, elderly man approached me.

'Henriquez.' He smiled as he stretched out a hand. He turned out to be the owner and had seen my car in passing. Yes, 'Rockmoor; was for rent. He had to do a few things to it first but yes, it was available.

I tried to hide my joy, in case he upped his price. He took me inside. Screwed to the wall by the front door was a small metal phylactery.

'We're a good Jewish family – and we've paid for it.' he walked over to a steel plate in the wall.

'My son was in the RAF. The last thing he did on his last leave was to put in this wall safe for me. Soon afterwards he was shot down over Germany. He landed safely by parachute and was interned in a POW camp. As soon as they found out he was a Jew, they shot him.

There were tears in his eyes as we wandered outside in silence.

'Could you hold the house for a week?' I asked.

Tubby would first have to approve my living so far from Highgate. Using my Highgate house as an office instead of the tractor shed was one thing, moving 25 miles away would need some fast talking.

I tackled him one evening over drinks. I pointed out that since I was now in charge of the whole of the north coast, it would be sensible to move nearer to the centre of my activities; that my present house was up for sale (true) and might go at any moment (highly unlikely, as the owner hadn't had a nibble in six months); and that since the buildings at the Orange River station would not be ready for at least 18 months, there was really nothing to hold me to Highgate. All of which arguments Tubby could have easily squashed. Instead, he gave a couple of snorts, informed me that in his opinion all vets were a thoroughly undisciplined, independent lot of rascals, told me to be sure to keep plenty of beer in my refrigerator at all times, so that he could refresh himself in passing, and poured me another rum and ginger.

Stella refused to budge from Highgate – I didn't even ask Clarence. Then I heard of a lady with a school-age child who was looking for a job. Vin Jones turned out to be a tall lightish-skinned, good-looking woman of about 35, with an educated manner. I couldn't have found a more perfect servant. She had been working as a seamstress, and in addition to cooking and washing would, she said, be only too delighted to make the curtains, cushion covers, my bush shirts and anything else that was needed.

Vin's cooking, although basic, was good, and she had a most economic mind. On Saturday mornings just after sun-up, I would take her to Port Maria market, give her the 12 shillings she required for the week's groceries, and leave her to haggle while I sat in the car sketching the local inhabitants as they passed, or reading the latest copy of *Horizon*.

Her daughter, an extremely well brought-up girl of 12, only appeared in the holidays. I never discovered where Vin's husband was, or indeed if she had ever been married. I feared that she might be lonely, as we were too far away from Port Maria or Oracabessa

Salt Gut near Oracabessa

for her to have causal visitors, but she appeared content without them.

Social activities were limited to Port Maria's tin-roofed tennis club where, on Saturday afternoons, the more prosperous or ambitious local citizens would parade their teenage daughters, neatly attired in short pleated tennis skirts, for the younger aristocracy (farmers' sons, bank clerks, business representatives – and the Veterinary Officer) to inspect and, hopefully, pursue. Although the shades of these attractive damsels ran from white to burnt sienna, I do not remember a single black face. Racial tolerance in the country districts, it seemed, still had some way to go. After tennis I might invite a couple of the local lads and some girls back to Rockmoor, and we would sit on the roof verandah, drinking rum and ginger and listening to the sea pound over the honeycomb shelf, the moonlight flashing off its dark surface.

I was young, healthy, the owner of a shiny maroon Chevrolet coupé, constantly smothered by beautiful girls and doing a job I thoroughly enjoyed in one of the most gorgeous places in the world. Life was idyllic.

TB AND BANG'S

Tuberculosis and brucellosis (or contagious abortion) were the two cattle diseases that occupied me most. Both could cause severe economic loss, but as there was no practical treatment for either, efforts were directed purely at eradication.

Tuberculosis was slow in onset, the animals becoming thin and developing a spasmodic cough. The disease was passed from cow to cow mainly by droplet infection due to coughing and spitting up infected sputum. The most reliable way to diagnose the disease was to carry out a 'tuberculin test'. A small amount of tuberculin (an extract made from the tubercle bacillus itself) was injected into the skin. If the animal had TB, an allergic type of reaction caused the skin at the injection site to swell, the so-called 'positive' reaction.

The site we used for the injection was one of the folds of skin formed beneath the tail when it was held up high, a procedure known as the 'caudal fold test'. It was rapid and simple to perform and the 'reading' quick and easy, since the injected fold could be compared at a glance with the non-injected one on the other side of the tail. If animals were well handled, it was possible to inject 60 an hour and to read the results three days later at the rate of five to ten a minute.

Nearly always we combined the test for tuberculosis with that for contagious abortion or 'Bang's disease', more scientifically known as brucellosis. The importance of brucellosis in cattle was that apart from causing abortion it led to chronic ill-health and a decrease in the milk yield. It could also infect man, causing 'undulant fever', a 'flu-like disease, from which it took a long time to recuperate. Another closely related strain of the same organism which infected goats was responsible for Malta fever, and another strain was the cause of brucellosis in pigs. Both these strains could cause severe disease in man but, luckily, neither occurred in Jamaica.

The test for brucellosis in cattle consisted of taking blood from the jugular vein of each animal and carrying out a serological test on it in the laboratory,

The usual procedure was to crowd the cattle into a long, narrow chute made of poles or bricks called a 'crush' or 'race'. Two assistants would precede me along the outside, the first raising the tail of each animal and the second wiping away the accumulated dung beneath it with a cloth and soapy water. I would follow with my tuberculin syringe, injecting the caudal fold on the right side of each tail. The right one was always used, so that if anyone else read the test, they would know which side to look at.

Having injected all the animals with tuberculin, I, or an assistant, would go along the crush once more, jabbing a wide-bore hypodermic needle into the right jugular vein and collecting samples of blood for brucellosis testing in the lab. Three days later I would return to read the reactions to the tuberculin test, bringing the results of the brucellosis test with me. Any animals that reacted 'positive' or 'suspicious' to either of these tests would be isolated and then, depending on the circumstances, either destroyed or re-tested two months later.

I hated TB and 'Bang's' testing, especially if the farmer had poor facilities for handling his animals. Once, on a smallholding, it took me from seven in the morning till five in the afternoon to test 20 head! I was remembering this when I set out for Mr Walker's property near Darling Spring, where I had arranged to do a test. I was not looking forward to it; Mr Walker was inclined to be unreliable and his cattle to be on the wild side.

Parking my car in the narrow lane below I struggled up a rough path to his yard, noting as I went that there were no cows in the pen. A buxom, barefoot lady was hanging out some faded clothes on a wire stretched from the tin-roofed cottage to a coconut tree. A couple of naked piccanins clutched at her thick legs.

'Marnin' missus,' I called. 'Me com fe test de keeows dem.'

'Massa Walker gaan a bush. Me kyall 'im.' She let out a penetrating screech which was answered faintly from somewhere below. 'Him a-com now-now,' she told me confidently.

Sure enough, a few minutes later a Panama-hatted perspiring, lightly coloured man of 50-odd, followed by a skinny youth, appeared through the banana trees.

I explained my presence.

'Lard, sah. Te day Wensd'y, no? Me feget. Bwuoy, tell Amos fetch de keeows.'

The young lad disappeared and Mr Walker offered me a chair in the shade of a mango tree. It was a typical start of a frustrating day. Time meant little to the Jamaican small farmer, one day was as good as the next; Monday or Friday, it was all the same. A bit like the Irish, I thought. His only deadline was to put his milk cans on the road in time for the factory truck to collect them.

The sun rose higher, the flies were more persistent and my tolerance wore thinner. After an hour I was thinking of leaving when yells and curses from below indicated that the cows had been collected, and soon a shout told us that Amos had them in the pen. About 30 cows and a malicious looking Jersey bull were milling around inside the uneven, rocky kraal, already sensing that they had been brought there for no good and anxious to return to their breakfast.

Amos proved typical of many peasant herdsmen – he was scared of the cows, and they of him. His shouts and frequent sallies with a stout stick only succeeded in angering them more, so that after trying to drive them into the milking stanchions without success, I confiscated his weapon and told him not to utter another word or I would use it on him. It was quite easy, with a few cajoles and low whistles and a handful of meal, to get five animals at a time into the stanchions and put the halter chains round their necks.

Mr Walker elected to lift the tails while the youth, whom he now introduced as his son, washed beneath them with a dirty rag dipped in a tin of murky water. The cows had as little love for Mr Walker as they had for Amos. One caught its master a neat blow on his upper leg as he tried to lift its tail. Thereafter he insisted we tie the back legs together which, it transpired, was Amos's usual practice at milking time.

We struggled on through the morning, some cows objecting so strongly to our manipulations that they ended up on the ground. At least it was easier to keep them still in this position and certainly safer for the operator. The young heifers had to be caught separately with a lasso round their necks and hauled up to a post. We never did catch the bull, he took off as soon as he saw what we were doing to his harem. I was delighted to see him go, he would probably have got our blood long before we got his. After dropping a few bottles in the mud, recording half a dozen kicks on my shins, seeing my tuberculin syringe flung ten feet through the air and getting a face full of 'cowsh', we released the last one and Mr Walker sent Amos up a coconut tree for a few 'jellies'.

It was the pattern for many future tests tiring, hot, dirty and frustrating. But with the prospect of a swim on the way home and a siesta beneath a sea almond tree with a Red Stripe and a book, it was eminently bearable.

PROLAPSES AND PARASITES

Jamaica is a hilly island. Save for the coastal plain and the bottom of the wider valleys, there is little level land. So it was not uncommon to see a peasant farmer standing on the hillside, planting his yams, bananas and corn with his hands working the soil in front of him at waist level.

This existence on a permanent tilt had an unfortunate effect on a proportion of pregnant cows which grazed the steep slopes. The condition was known as 'bed down', and was most common in those breeds with large, roomy pelvic cavities, such as Holstein-Friesians. In the advanced stages of pregnancy the ligaments supporting the uterus became stretched, and after birth took place they remained a little loose. Further grazing on steep slopes with the head end some three feet higher than the tail end put an extra strain on these moorings and often led the cow to prolapse her womb.

A 'bed down' was a daunting sight. Like the sleeve of a coat pulled inside out, the inner lining of the uterus would now be on the outside and the muscular wall on the inside, giving the appearance of an elongated, glistening, dark red sack hanging from the cow's back end. The sheer size and weight of this grotesque appendage, filled with blood which was being pumped in faster than it could escape because of the tourniquet effect of the eversion, was truly awesome.

Correction was not too difficult, but needed a degree of persistence and energy. Provided the prolapse had occurred within the last four hours or so, it could usually be put back without much trouble, but the longer it was left the more difficult it became to replace.

Almost a *sine qua non* was to give the cow a spinal anaesthetic near the tail-head. This paralysed those muscles which strained against my attempts to push the womb back. After this epidural injection, I would ask the owner to bring a large towel or a sheet or even a 'crocus bag', the local name for any kind of sack. With a helper on each side, this was placed under the prolapse and then wrapped around it and twisted so that the mass of blood in the prolapse was gradually squeezed and pummelled back into the body.

An easy case could be replaced in minutes, but often, by the time the request for help had reached me, the 'bed' had been out for most of the day, and it was a slow, exhausting business to push back the now hard, dry lump to where it belonged and hear that delightful final gurgle and slurp as the last bit was sucked into the abdominal cavity.

There was the possibility that the cow might prolapse again so, as a precaution, I always inserted some sutures of heavy tape across the exit. For this, I used the legendary office 'red tape'. It was better than the thickest catgut and cost nothing. Anyway, the back end of a cow was a fitting place for red tape!

* * *

'Adam had 'em' – so goes the adage. I didn't doubt it! Worms were much older than man.

The warm, humid conditions and luxuriant vegetation in much of the island were ideal for the propagation of all types of parasites, both internal and external. Horses, dogs, poultry, man and every other living creature played host to a score or more. Jamaica was indeed a parasite's paradise.

I saw their ravages everyday. Soon after weaning, at between two and six months old, calves became thin, stopped growing, hung their oversized heads and showed a rough coat and pale, almost white, conjunctiva and gums. The worm responsible in 90 per cent of the cases was a thin, inch-long, blood-sucking nematode, known as the 'wire-worm', or to give it its scientific name, *Haemonchus contortus*; the same worm, incidentally, that I had found in buffalo on the Chozi flats in Northern Rhodesia. These little horrors attached themselves to the wall of the calf's fourth stomach (abomasum) and sucked blood. They were easy to identify: the females were striped like a candy stick or barber's pole due to the white egg-bearing uterus which spiralled round the blood-filled digestive system. They would lay hundreds of thousands of eggs which would be dropped onto the pasture in the dung, developing within hours into infectious larvae to be eaten again by a grazing animal.

When calves were kept in small paddocks, the grass soon became so loaded with worm larvae that the calf's natural resistance was swamped, resulting in a fatal anaemia. *Haemonchus* probably caused more ill-health and calf deaths than any other worm in Jamaica – perhaps in the world. Regular dosing with an anthelmintic – in those days phenothiazine – and frequent rotation between large, 'clean' pastures, usually solved the problem.

184

Haemonchus was not the only parasitic enemy of calves. The large, white roundworm – a relation of the earthworm, could also cause problems. Then there was the liver fluke, a small, grey, leaf-shaped parasite which lived in the bile ducts of the liver, causing digestive upsets, anaemia and frequently death. Liver fluke depended on a certain snail to complete its life-cycle, so the draining of land to eradicate the snail was just as important as dosing with the only available drug – carbon tetrachloride.

Yet another nasty little intruder was the 'lung worm', the larvae of which swam up the film of dew which covered the blades of grass in the early morning. Once at the top they would await a breakfasting calf, in whose bronchi and lungs they developed. Calves were most affected and although treatment was often useless, the infestation could be controlled by preventing young stock from grazing until the sun had dried the grass and the larvae had retreated.

In dogs, hookworm was the commonest and most devastating of the internal parasites. These slim, half-inch-long bloodsuckers would attach themselves to the lining of the intestines and drain the animal until its gums were white, its guts full of strawberry jam and it was too weak to walk. If treated soon enough the animal responded well, but all too often in would be to late, the treatment killing both the parasite and the weakened host.

Another worm and one which was new to me, was a type of heart worm, very rarely diagnosed when the dog was alive.

'My dog's been poisoned, doctor. My neighbour doesn't like me and now he's poisoned my dog. I want to know what poison he used then I'm taking him to court.'

I don't know how many times I heard variations on this theme as a distressed owner laid his pet's corpse on the table. The first time I autopsied one of these 'poison' cases I was quite unprepared for the large tumour-like mass surrounding the aorta, which had ruptured to fill the chest cavity with blood. Whatever it was, it was obviously not poison. Roger was also baffled until we found a tangle of worms in the centre of the growth. The worm, *Spirocerca lupi*, lived in the walls of the aorta, stomach and oesophagus, forming large nodules which sometimes ruptured – in the case of the aorta, with fatal results. A dung-eating beetle had been incriminated in its life history.

A true heartworm – since it lived free in the ventricles of the dog's heart – was the mosquito-transmitted *Dirofilaria immitis*. It could be diagnosed on a blood slide and treatment was possible. Dirofilaria was very similar to worm that caused elephantiasis in humans, *Wucheria bancrofti*.

Then there was the external group of parasites living on the animals' skin, especially ticks. As in Africa, they carried two potentially fatal diseases in cattle, redwater or babesiosis, and gall sickness or anaplasmosis. Luckily, Jamaica had no East Coast fever and no heartwater, those devastating tick-borne disease of east, central and southern Africa. Dipping was the proven control for all tick-related diseases and, if done regularly and properly, was highly effective.

'Seed ticks', the larvae of cattle ticks, known in Jamaica as 'grass lice', made it almost impossible to walk through some pastures. As in Africa, they would congregate round the ankles, waist, and crutch, dig in their mouth-parts and start their lunch. But by now, superior insecticides were reaching the market and it was easier to get rid of them, although after one application of a new tickicide to my stomach and legs, I contracted a severe headache and spent the night vomiting.

Amazingly, the tick-transmitted 'biliary' so disastrous to dogs in Africa, was almost unknown.

A lady colleague found that the best way to rid herself of 'grass lice' was to use a razor and shave them off! I wondered how Adam had tackled the problem!

DR BILLY

I was sick. Very sick. I had returned to Rockmoor after a day in the sun without a hat. My forehead was burning, I had a pain behind my eyes and I felt nauseous. Too much sun, I thought. I went straight to bed, asking Vin to bring me some soup later.

She found me sweating and feeling very sorry for myself. My temperature was 105, I felt weak and shaky, and before long had a classical rigor. It was obviously a relapse of fever from the year before in Africa. Malaria was now rare in Jamaica.

'Bring the bottle of quinine from the bathroom shelf and fetch me some more blankets.' I told Vin. 'I have to sweat it out.'

'Lard, darcta. Wen yo' finish, me haf fe give yo' bushy bath.'

After my sweat, she returned with a cauldron from which were sticking out a variety of twigs and leaves. A 'bushy bath', evidently, was a fairly common remedy as she had the ingredients to hand. In any case, I was too weak to argue.

She sponged me down and then began to apply her witches' brew to the soles of my feet. An important part of the cure, judging by the time it took.

In the morning, after a fitful sleep, my temperature had dropped but I felt mangled. I scribbled a telegram to the Kingston office, telling them that I probably had malaria and would be out of action for a few days, and told Elias, my yardboy, to send it from the Oracabessa post office.

Not long afterwards, I heard a car drive in through the gate. My bed was on the gauzed-in sleeping verandah so that the front door was almost at my feet. There was a knock, and a rather stocky, dark haired young man loomed up at the foot of the bed.

'Billy,' he said, a large grin pushing his chubby cheeks apart. 'Local quack at Port Maria.'

Elias had flagged down his car at the gate and begged a lift to Oracabessa. Billy had read the telegram and thought he would call on me on the way back to Port Maria to see if he could be of help. I was certainly glad to see him.

'I've a spare room, man. I'll pick you up this afternoon.' I was too grateful to make much of an objection and so was able to spend the next two or three days in caring luxury. It as the start of a life-long friendship.

Billy and Jan were a striking couple. Billy was dark, Portuguese-looking, with large brown eyes, vertical forehead, cheeks beginning to droop a little and a rather too prominent paunch for his five feet eight inches and his 30 years. Jan was a petite blonde with a strong Aberdeenshire accent, who had long golden hair piled on top of her head, like a lady from the court of Louis XIV.

Billy's chief interest was surgery, and I would sometimes spend a morning with him in the operating theatre of the Port Maria hospital watching his dexterous fingers enucleate tumours, remove appendices, pin bones, repair ruptures and resolve all the other surgical problems. Sometimes I acted as anaesthetist – chloroform was the only general anaesthetic available. Six drops on the mask, count to twelve, slowly. Another six, count, then four drops, count, and so on.

Occasionally, there would be a row. Billy was an explosive character and couldn't abide inefficiency. One morning, after I had the patient well under, Billy strode in from the robing alcove, shouting, 'Stop the anaesthetic. Take her away.'

'What's wrong?' I demanded.

'Bloody idiot nurses. All the surgical gloves are too small or have holes.'

It would have only delayed the hysterectomy a few minutes to sterilize new ones from the store, but no, it was to be a lesson to the 'idiots' not to let it happen again.

There was a strange sequel. The middle-aged lady in question decided not to go ahead with her hysterectomy after all. The interruption had, she was convinced, been a divine intervention. She left the hospital the next day, feeling on top of the world. Three years later, when I last heard of her, she was still in good health. Perhaps it *had* been divine intervention – who can say?

FIGHTING COCKS

There was a telegram in my mail.

'GRATEFUL EARLIEST ASSISTANCE SICK DONKEYS
JSPCA BROWNS TOWN'

I found the local branch of the Jamaica Society for the Prevention of Cruelty to Animals on the outskirts of a small rural community tucked away into the hills between St Ann's Bay and Falmouth.

As I parked in the small yard between two white-washed buildings, a short, dowdily dressed ball of fire bustled out to meet me. Half of her grey hair was pulled back into an untidy bun, leaving the other half to blow around her purposeful, but smiling face.

Mrs Anderson-Cocks, or Mrs A-C (the abbreviation of her name could well have referred to a type of electrical current) was, undoubtedly, the most energetic, courageous, caring, single-minded, as well as the most inflexible, pig-headed lady I have ever known. She was the founder and had been the fund-raiser, driving force and caretaker of the St Ann's Branch of the JSPCA for two decades or more. There was, literally, nothing she would not do for the overloaded, beaten donkeys and the starving, parasite-ridden dogs which abounded in the lanes and villages. Peasants, police and magistrates were terrified of her.

'Why don't you come and work here?' she demanded as soon as I had dealt with her donkeys and dogs. 'I'll give you a hundred pounds more a year than the government.'

I decided to ward off this takeover attempt, although for the next nine years I was on her management committee and observed, with some sympathy, a succession of imported veterinarians trying to live up to her impossible standards of devotion and hard work. Several resigned and joined the less taxing Government service.

I would arrange to call at Brown's Town on market days so that I could attend to the collection of ill-treated mules, donkeys and horses which Mrs A-C had persuaded the local constable to impound in the clinics paddock, and to the never-ending accumulation of half-starved, sore-dappled dogs and cats that awaited me.

Although it took the tolerance of a saint to keep up with her demands and often lacerating temperament, there was no doubt that she was doing more for animal welfare than anyone else on the island, and I felt sure that many animals, if they could have spoken, would have said 'God bless you, Mrs A-C.'

Mrs A-C, like so many other idealists, sometimes let her distended sympathies overrule common sense. She once accompanied a consignment of horses to Kingston, where I had agreed to put them up in the Veterinary stables for the night, before they were exported. I arranged for her to sleep at my house, a hundred yards away. Not on your life. She spent the night with her gee-gees, in the stable, sleeping in the hay! She was the stuff that martyrs were made of – in her case martyrs spelt with a 'T'!

* * *

If Mrs A-C could have seen me the following week-end, she would have bust every single one of the stays I suspected she wore.

Cockfighting, like dog fighting or any other forced combat between animals for the amusement of their masters, is one of man's sickest traits. Moreover, in Jamaica it was illegal. It was, in fact, the illicit aspect with its hint of danger (six strokes of the tamarind birch, if convicted) that challenged me to accept an invitation by one of the JAS field staff to the following Sunday's 'meet'.

The 'meet' took place in a bamboo-shaded depression in the hills near Bonnygate, a few miles inland from Oracabessa. Here, a 'pit' had been made by driving stakes into the ground to make a knee-high circle, around which hessian was stretched to form a boundary wall. Small groups of punters were laying bets in loud boastful voices, and the master of ceremonies, or whatever he was called, was shouting instructions and urging the owners to get their birds ready for the next fight. An aroma of curried goat, Jamaica's equivalent of the barbecue, hung amongst the bamboos. A great deal of rum seemed to be finding its way down a great many throats.

I was surprised at the compete lack of secrecy. The noise could have been heard a mile away. I soon saw why. The local sergeant of police and one or two of his constables from the Oracabessa police station were in attendance, in plain clothes. My constant dealings with cruelty to animal cases and stock theft problems had acquainted me with them all.

'Glad fe see yo', darc,' grinned the corpulent officer. 'Put yo' money on Massa Virtue's bud.'

Some fights never started, others petered out after the first brush between the protagonists, but some only ended when a bloody fowl gasped its last on the sandy floor of the arena, or when it took off

189

At the cockfight, 1948

over the heads of the spectators, to be pursued by the humiliated owner and the boos of disappointed punters.

Amongst several important people in the audience I noticed a titled English gentleman on holiday at Ocho Rios, whom I had met at a cocktail party. He was placing bets with great gusto while his two lady companions, white-faced and glassy-eyed, tried to appear fascinated in spite of the heat, dust, smell, blood and noise.

I wandered round, sketching the various types and their birds. Half-way through the afternoon, my friend decided he had lost enough on the feathered combatants and took me home, but I understood that the 'meet' would go on till dusk.

The next time I saw the porky sergeant, he smiled at me slyly.

'How much yo' mek, darc?' he asked. 'Sarry h'about Massa Virtue bud.'

'I did all right,' I replied. I reckoned that since I hadn't placed a single bet, and so had lost nothing, I had come out a winner! It had been an experience, although not one that I enjoyed. One thing was certain – I could never discuss it with Mrs A-C!

CALYPSOS AND CRICKET

I was becoming more Jamaican by the day. No longer did I tell the farmer that I was going to inject his animal. I replaced it with 'me gwine fe jook 'im.' 'Jook' covered everything that pricked. 'Macka (thornbush) jook me!' I would exclaim, sucking my finger. 'Better jook him na cook him, no?' – general laughter at my wit!

A man's house was his yard. 'Him gaan-a him yard,' meant he had gone home, or 'Him gaan-a bush,' that he was somewhere on the property. An animal was never hit or struck – it was 'bounced'. 'De haan bounce-a me keeow h'odder,' told me that a horn had bruised or cut the cow's udder. 'H's were usual before all commencing vowels and were just as frequently dropped at the beginning of a word – as in Cockney, but there were no hard-and-fast rules.

An Indian was a 'coolie-man', a peasant a 'quashie'. Many words had been distorted from the English, 'asked' became 'aksed', and there were some words that had come from Africa like 'nyam', to eat, from the bantu 'nyama', meat. Swear words varied from 'Coo-yer' to 'R'ass' (Your ass), still punishable by a ten-shilling fine for uttering it in public!

There was a host of sayings and proverbs, many adapted from their English originals with a Jamaican slant. 'Play wid puppy; puppy lik yo' mout.' (Familiarity breeds contempt). 'Wen yo' t'row stone a pig-sty, him wat holler "kwee-kwee", him yo' hit.' (If the cap fits). 'Swap black darg fe monkey.' (Out of the frying pan into the fire), and a thousand more.

I learnt many a folk song, too, popularly but inaccurately called calypsos, calypsos being the product of Trinidad. Some, as 'Ten pun ten fe te cut manoo', which I picked up on the wharf at Oracabessa, were extremely bawdy. Others, such as 'Linstead Market', 'Wata come a me y'Eye', 'Day dah Light', 'Chi-chi Bud Oh' and 'Rookumbine', were as beautiful and haunting as any folk song I knew.

I spent many hours banging out these tunes on my accordion, accompanied always by Poppet's loud wails, which began as soon as she saw me take it out of its case. The accordion is a marvellous instrument, it makes the maximum noise for the minimum effort, it can be easily transported and it can reproduce almost anything a piano can – even music! And top accordionists now play with philharmonic orchestras. But, in my opinion, the accordion should be kept for gay or nostalgic dance music or group singing. The 'musette' tuning, especially, can evoke romance like no other instrument.

Folklore was as common and as important as in Africa, in fact much of it had come across with the slaves. Like Brer Rabbit, who came to the Southern States with slaves from Lower Guinea, Jamaica's legendary spider, Anancy, had arrived in the same way from Upper Guinea. Anancy's exploits in outwitting other more powerful and pompous animals, formed the basis of many Jamaican folk tales.

The mongoose, another favourite folk character was more recent, the animal having only been introduced to Jamaica in 1872, to try and eradicate the cane rat. For a time it was effective, but it soon found that chicken eggs and field crops tasted better. By 1890 it was declared a pest. Tales of its cunning were incorporated into many folktales and ditties, such as the famous folk song 'Sly Mongoose'.

Any 'ghoulie or ghostie or long legitty beastie, or whatever went bump in the night', was called a 'duppy'.

But in spite of all the strange words, distinctive accent and different mannerisms, and the rioting tropical vegetation, the more I travelled my district, the more I felt that I had been there before. Then one day, I gave a lift to a schoolboy near Gayle who politely raised his cap as he asked me to drop him at the Rectory at Lucky Hill. Suddenly, I understood my feeling of belonging, of doing all this before.

This was England! A bit hotter, admittedly, with different flora and, if I ever thought about it, a mainly black population. But the Jamaican countryside had the indisputable calm and closeted atmosphere and the friendliness of rural England. The small villages, the parish church and rectory, the village blacksmith on the village green where the sheep and cattle would be shoo-ed to one end to allow for a game of cricket and the manor or 'Great House' on the hill, were just like the English villages in which I had grown up. Even the speech, although often difficult to understand, had a Welsh lilt to it, which could have been mistaken for a county accent.

When, in my first year, the cricket Test Matches began, I was still British enough to hope that England would win. A few years later, I was rooting solidly for Jamaica.

Oh yes, I was still proud to be British, but there was no doubt that Jamaica was rapidly becoming my home.

IAN FLEMING'S GOLDEN EYE

Three miles further along the coast road towards Oracabessa overlooking a secluded cove, stood the beach house, Golden Eye. The estate agent who looked after it for the writer, Ian Fleming, took me to see it.

In 1947, no-one new much about Fleming, except that he worked for a London newspaper and was the brother of Peter Fleming. Peter was already well known for his book, *Brazilian Adventure*, describing his search for Colonel Fawcett, an explorer who had gone missing in the Amazon jungle while trying to locate the legendary city of El Dorado. That first visit to Golden Eye was a day I won't forget. It was my first introduction to the underwater world and to spear-fishing. Fleming, who was to arrive the following week, had several harpoon guns, including a large, metal one made in France and a small, very inefficient, bow-and-arrow type of weapon. I was comple-tely unsuccessful with both, but the memorable thing was my first look underwater with goggles. I was enraptured. Here was a new and delightful world, silent and mysterious, and painted in pastel shades of green, yellow and pink. Perhaps I thought this was the treasure I had been seeking all along – the underwater world of Nature's treasures, not man's crudely made doubloons and trinkets.

Jaques Cousteau and Hans Haas had just published their books on this underwater wonderland and their adventures with a camera and speargun, a sport almost unknown in Jamaica. Fleming must have been one of the first to 'goggle' in the Caribbean. I vowed to make my own gun as soon as possible.

The only piece of Fleming's writing that I had read had been an article in *Horizon*, 'Where Shall John Go; Jamaica?', one of a series of escape travelogues for war-weary Brits seeking sunnier skies. It would be another five years before he hurled James Bond onto the espionage front to do battle with SMERSH in *Casino Royale*. Fleming's wartime exploits in the Naval Intelligence Division, his organization of the evacuations of hundreds of refugees, including King Zog of Albania, from Point Verdon near Bordeaux and his part in drafting the manifesto of the US Information Service, later to become the CIA, were quite unknown to me. He was merely Peter Fleming's brother, working for the Kemsley Press and holidaying each year on the north coast.

My second visit to Golden Eye was with John, the police inspector in Port Maria, who had recently arrived from Palestine and took me along to meet him. John's hobby was drawing in pastels, and Fleming had already acquired two of his pictures.

We found Fleming attired in a short-sleeved silk dressing gown, open over a Falmouth shirt and dark blue shorts. A brightly coloured square, or choker, was tied neatly round his neck. We sipped our drinks in the long lounge looking over his private, rock-bound cove, with its head of coral rising like a mushroom from the centre of the sandy bed.

Fleming was an impressive host, charming, cultured, good-looking, with a high forehead and a friendly, open manner. Only his eyes seemed to betray something – uncertainty perhaps. To me, nearly 15 years his junior, he epitomized the successful, debonair man of the world, but lurking behind the façade I seemed to detect another, less mature personality – a sophisticated sixth-former?

I sat fascinated while he told us of people and places I had only read about. Then he turned to me, probably in kindness as I hadn't said a word, and asked me about my profession and interests. He was mildly surprised that I read *Horizon* and had seen his article, and showed keen interest when I told him of my special interest – the diseases of animals that could be transmitted to man, the so-called zoonoses. I had begun a series of articles (later published in the *West Indian Medical Journal*) dealing with those of importance in the West Indies. Why I remember this conversation so vividly was because a few years later I happened to read a collection of his short stories, one of which was based (rather inaccurately) on an animal disease introduced by the villain to wipe out the population of Jamaica. Whether that evening's conversation had contributed to this 'who-done-it' I do not know, but I like to think so.

Golden Eye was to be occupied by two other famous personalities. Prime Minister Anthony Eden, at Ian's invitation, endured a ten-day holiday there after the Suez crisis, coping with a surprising lack of conveniences and home comforts which the eccentric owner had over-looked. Much later, Bob Marley bought Golden Eye and lived there until his death.

About the same distance on the other side of my house, perched on the last bluff before Port Maria, another famous personality and close friend of Fleming since his Intelligence days, had set up house – Nöel Coward. I never met him, but I did contribute, indirectly, to his wardrobe. One day when Coward was visiting John at Llanrumney, he commented favourably on his host's bush jacket, which John had copied from one of mine made in Northern Rhodesia. Coward borrowed John's and had several made for himself. Nöel Coward, incidentally, still rests at Firefly, his house on the cliffs above Port Maria in a simple grave overlooking the blue Caribbean.

Fleming and Coward were only two of the scores of the rich and famous who flocked to Jamaica each year between December and March, when the icy winds of Europe or North America started to penetrate the thickest of fur collars. Passenger lists read like *Debrett*. In fact there were so many Earls, Lords, Counts and Countesses splashing in the sea along the north coast, that had the water not already been blue, I am sure it would rapidly have become so.

PROMOTION AND POLITICS

It was inevitable. Tom, the Senior Veterinary Officer, had been transferred to Swaziland, and Ivan, another colleague, had returned to
England. Then Bob, who had been running the division after Tom's
transfer, decided to go into private practice in Ontario, leaving only
Roger and me to cope with disease control, clinical cases, research
and administrative work for the whole island. I was ordered to Kingston to act as Senior Veterinary Officer.

I left Rockmoor with mixed feelings. There was much that I would
miss. The wild terrain that isolated my house on all sides, the little
rock-pool which, when a norther was blowing, would be inundated
with huge waves, surging in over the honeycomb table, effervescing
like a deluge of gin and tonic. The small, cozy tennis club at Port
Maria and afterwards the evenings on the roof verandah with a rum
and ginger and a sympathetic companion, listening to the pounding
of the waves and to the wind teasing the coconut palms. But more
than anything, I knew I would miss the friendly life amongst the
small farmers, the peasants, the shop keepers, and the Estate owners
– some of whom I had almost come to regard as family – indeed,
some did become so!

Life in Kingston, I suspected, would cease to be carefree and independent. Although I would be living next to Roger in Bob's old house at
Hope, away from down-town smells, noise and heat, I would be on
the end of a telephone, surrounded by civil servants, harassed by
bureaucracy and no longer my own boss. My duties as Acting Senior
Veterinary Officer would include the administration of the Veterinary
Division and all its programmes, attendance on endless committees
and, when time allowed, dealing with urgent clinical cases – anywhere
on the island.

Well, I was used to hard work and just a little excited at the
prospect of promotion, and there would certainly be tangible compensations. I knew several extremely attractive girls in Kingston who
would be much more permanent than the package-holiday tourists of
the north coast, and I would certainly meet others. Since I would
have the whole island as my hunting ground, I could always find an
excuse for a night or two at Ocho Rios or Montego Bay.

Another lure of the metropolis was the University of the West
Indies, then being built at Mona, almost across the road from Hope.
Contacts I had with the young enthusiastic staff of the medical
faculty assured me that I would receive every support in my work on
zoonoses. I had been imprisoned too long in academic isolation –

195

here was the escape, and I was raring to go.

On the last night at Rockmoor, Roger came across from Kingston to help me pack up. Afterwards we took the Tilley lamp and some bottles of beer down to the little rock-pool. Scores of brightly coloured fish, attracted by the light of our lamp, darted back and forth between our legs as we sat sipping our drinks in the warm water. The stars were brilliant and a soft breeze blew up gently off the ocean where lights of passing ships added to the romance of the night.

I had intended to enlarge my rock-pool and had had holes made to take the dynamite, but the owner decided that it was too risky and might destroy the pool altogether. The fellow who drilled out the holes for me wore a tracheotomy tube in his throat, so that his efforts produced a low whistle as the air rushed in and out. He was the only person I have known who could truthfully be said to whistle while he worked!

Rockmoor remained empty for as long as I was in the island. Returning for a family holiday, 15 years later, I made a sentimental journey to Oracabessa and Port Maria. Rockmoor was still empty, but Elias, the yard boy whom I had taken on the day I moved in, was still there, as caretaker. The holes around the rock pool for the dynamite were still there, too. One day, I thought, I might return and finish the job.

Office work I found bearable if not taken too seriously, and it was exciting to trace back through old files and learn about early tribulations in the field of animal health. Like the time in the twenties, when foot and mouth disease was introduced with some cattle from India. The herculean efforts made by a former veterinary giant, Stephen Lockett, and his colleague Rushie Grey, to combat this and other epizootics, made fascinating reading.

Visits to the docks and airport at all hours to enforce the island's strict quarantine measures, together with the demands of pet owners, backyard poultry keepers and the peasant's cow, pig or donkey, kept me on the run. Then I had to deliver my weighty (but ignorant) opinion at numerous meetings, give lectures at the Agricultural Assistants Training School and try to add a little salt to my diet by doing some investigating. I was well into my survey of 'Animal Diseases of Importance to Human Health in the Caribbean', and soon added two more studies: an investigation of cattle warts, a serious problem in some herds, and 'farcy,' the local name for the large ulcers which erupted periodically on the legs of mules working on sugar estates.

Roger curtailed much of his research to help me out. His investigations included a peculiar debilitating condition which affected cattle grazing the red, bauxite soils in the central parish of Manchester, called Manchester Wasting Disease. Autopsy showed the main artery, the aorta, to be lined with a hard, white, calcified crust, resembling bleached crocodile skin. The heart, lungs and other vessels were sometimes affected as well. Roger suspected a mineral imbalance related to the high calcium and aluminium and low phosphorus levels in the soil, a theory which his phosphorous feeding experiments seemed to support. Later, he heard of a condition in Argentina, *enteque seco*, closely resembling the Jamaican malady, except that it seemed to be triggered off by eating a plant of the potato family. This weed didn't grow in Jamaica and the condition in Argentina, apparently, was unrelated to bauxite soils. Clinically, however, it was identical.*

I also acted as veterinary surgeon to the Knutsford Park racetrack. Races took place on a Saturday afternoon about twice a month. I took routine saliva samples from the first two horses in each race, but the Government Chemist who did the tests never came up with a 'positive' while I was there. Either his technique was faulty, or the trainers and jockeys had a dope he didn't know about. My suggestion to the Jockey Club, that the obvious solution was for the veterinarian in charge to give each horse a routine shot of dope before each race, so that none had an unfair advantage, was not approved!

I only once placed a bet. I had been treating a filly, Sunspider, from trainer Grannum's stable for a badly cut fetlock, using the Elastoplast technique so successful in treating my veldt sores in Africa. She was a beautiful animal, her coat a shimmer of gold and purple, but she was very small, and the odds against her were 20 to 1. I put five shillings on her to back my treatment – and she came in first!

The two private vets in Kingston gave little help. One was about to retire, and the other admitted that he hadn't read a veterinary text-book or journal since leaving college 30 years before. His one compe-tency was to pass a catheter into a mare's bladder, which was 'showy' and usually quite unnecessary, but which he never failed to perform, no matter the ailment. The only other active practitioner in the field

---

*Further work in other countries suggested that the condition might be due to a pasture grass of which 'crab grass' (*Stenotaphrum secundatum*), common in the Manchester area, was a prime suspect. Nearly forty-five years later, Roger conducted more analyses and showed that this grass contained high levels of vitamin D, suffi-cient to account for the pathological changes in Manchester Wasting Disease.

of animal medicine was a quack who kept his name before the public by arranging frequent testimonials to his skill in the personal column of the *Daily Gleaner*, from supposedly grateful clients – before they had to call us in!

It was Mrs A-C and her irascibility who indirectly helped us with our staffing problem. Her first contribution was a retired Indian Army Veterinary Corps major, who she had contracted to look after the clinic at Brown's Town. After struggling manfully for a few months, he capitulated and asked us to give him a job in the more predictable Government service. Within 18 months two more vets had joined us from the same source, proving that she was a far more efficient recruiting agent than the Colonial Office!

Then Dougie, a skeletal, humorous, chain-smoking Canadian, arrived from British Guiana, making a total of six Government vets, while we awaited the return of the five Jamaicans whom the Government had sent abroad to study.

As they began to trickle back, I felt that for its size, the island had as competent and up-to-date veterinary service as any country in the world.

Unfortunately, not all returnees, however willing, were allowed to help. Gerry, for instance, flourishing his diploma and eager to get to grips with animal health in his island home, found that his prowess with bat and ball had more clout than his professional skills. We established an office for him at May Pen and advised the farmers of Clarendon Parish that they would now have a resident veterinary officer to attend to their problems. They did – for about three days. No sooner had I returned from installing him, that I was informed that Gerry would be required immediately to practice for the Jamaican cricket team and would, therefore, be unable to carry out his veterinary duties in the foreseeable future.

Gerry never did go back to May Pen, or any other station, while I was in Jamaica. First it was the national team which collared him, then the West Indian side – he went onto captain both. And when it wasn't cricket, it was football.

Cricket was a religion, an incontestable symbol of national pride. It superseded all other priorities. By unwritten law, all persons, whether in government or in private employ, were automatically excused unessential duties to watch test matches. Every office had a radio (TV hadn't reached Jamaica), blaring the ball-by-ball commentary while secretaries pretended to type and technicians peered unseeingly down the microscope. Test match time was not a period of accurate or productive work.

I had always despised the game and had once written a poem,

'Odium to Cricket', for the school magazine, but within a day or so I, too, was caught up in the hysteria of test match fever and became just as enthusiastic and vociferous as anyone else. I still am.

* * *

Complaints were a regular part of my bureaucratic diet, and I answered them as frankly and helpfully as I could. After all, if people take the trouble to complain they are usually hurting. But my philanthropy couldn't save me from one embarrassing situation. The young Jamaican veterinarian at Mandeville had run foul of the local Jamaica Agricultural Society.

'He only diagnoses disease through the windshield. He never gets out of the car', complained the letter from the JAS Secretary. I knew this to be totally untrue. Peter was a very competent and conscientious young man. Such accusations always got my back up.

'If you could give me more details of the specific instances,' I wrote back, 'I will investigate the matter thoroughly, but I'm sure you'll agree that vague and unsupported allegations are not worth the paper they are written on.'

No further details were sent me, but shortly afterwards I noticed a headline in the *Daily Gleaner*. 'RUDE LETTER ANGERS JAS'

Unsuspecting, and chuckling to think that someone had probably told them a few well-deserved home truths, I read further – and was staggered to find that I was the culprit. My reply to the JAS had been considered insolent and insulting at their Annual General Meeting. I had been severely criticized. Some sly personal remarks had also been made by one of the less lovable politicians on the platform. My letter was quoted in full and certainly appeared very abrupt.

I flew to the file and examined the copy. It was identical to the *Gleaner's*. It made no sense. I rang for my secretary who, I now saw, had signed the letter in my absence.

'Have you still got the shorthand notes of my reply to the JAS complaint?' I asked.

I followed the typed script as she read from her notes. Two lines were missing in the typed version, so that in place of my reasonable reply asking for details, the letter gave the impression that I considered the complaint unworthy of the paper it was written on. I sent a corrected copy to the JAS immediately, explaining the circumstances and apologizing. I never received an answer.

What really really annoyed me was that I had sat on the platform during the morning session of the meeting next to Tom, the JAS Secretary, whom I'd always regarded as a good friend. He never gave the slightest clue that they would be discussing my letter that afternoon, which we could have resolved in a couple of minutes. I felt very hurt and angry.

But such incidents were few, and the Veterinary Division was highly respected.

Politics rarely interrupted our lives, unless one of the farmer politicians – like my friend at Highgate – demanded our services when, of course, we had to jump. After independence and the first General Election, when Bustamante, leader of the Labour Party (Conservative), defeated his own cousin, Norman Manley, leader of the People's National Party (Socialist), more and more legislators felt it their duty to wallow in 'cowsh' or 'pigsh' at the weekends, so instead of swimming or playing tennis, I often found myself on a Saturday or Sunday struggling up a country road to a case that could easily have waited till Monday but which my political master, home for the weekend, insisted I come and treat; or to a corpse three days old, which he wished me to autopsy! The politicians did do us one service. The roads connecting Kingston to their farms were usually macadamized within months of their taking office!

Bustamante, when Prime Minister, visited me in the office several times. He was a tall, broad, dark-skinned fellow in his late sixties, with a shock of untidy, near-white hair and coarse, rather jovial features. He was relaxed and friendly, and when not in a flowery open neck shirt (usually unbuttoned) which showed tufts of grey belly hair, he always sported a bow tie. I came to know his pig farm in St Thomas well.

Sir Hugh Foot, the Governor, always ready to tickle his political colleagues in the ribs, declared in an after-dinner speech at a Veterinary Association Conference that he was amazed at how swiftly people came to resemble their animals. 'Take Busta, for example ...' he grinned. Sir Hugh could get away with anything!

Poppet, who usually lay at my feet in the office and took no notice of anything or anybody, took a violent dislike to Busta and would walk round him, sniffing and growling, her hair bristling. I assumed that it was unlikely to be political prejudice more likely the smell of pigs!

I had a great respect for Allen, Busta's Minister of Agriculture. I first met him in a meeting where a farmer was trying to obtain some compensation from the Government, and I had been called as expert adviser. Halfway through, a small, emaciated man wearing a gaudy Falmouth shirt sticking to his chest with sweat, wandered in. I thought it was the cleaning boy and was most surprised at his auda-

200

city when he sat himself at one end of the conference table. After a few moments he rapped the table and pointed at the claimant.

'You're a liar, Sir ...' and in two minutes he had got to the bottom of problem which had been debated for half an hour. Many times I was to see him bring sense and order to exasperating meetings. His only training for the job of Minister of Agriculture had been as a sidesman on a fruit truck!

CORAL KINGDOMS

I had not been in Kingston long when an envelope with a St Kitts-Nevis stamp appeared on my desk. The writing seemed familiar, but I knew no-one on that small Leeward Island. I ripped it open.

Charlie! Excitedly, I read it through. 'Thought I'd surprise you. Just arrived. Cyprus became rather boring. Am working on an excuse to visit Jamaica.'

Shortly afterwards, he cabled me to meet his plane. In his hand was a peculiar looking instrument like a crossbow.

'Home-made speargun. I've come to show you how it's done,' he bragged.

Charlie and I had been colleagues on the Colonial Fellowship year at Cambridge, and it had been the accident to his eye that had persuaded the Colonial Office to swap our original postings, switching me to Northern Rhodesia and Charlie to the Caribbean where specialised treatment was available. Just before I was posted to Jamaica, Charlie was transferred to Cyprus. Now he was back in the West Indies again.

His justification for the visit, at Government expense, was the pretence that he needed our advice on setting up a veterinary diagnostic laboratory in St Kitts.

'Your advice,' he told me firmly, 'will be that such a step is neither feasible nor economic and that I shouldn't even think about it. I have no intention of setting up anything. Damn it, there's only a couple of dozen cows in the whole island.'

It seemed that Charlie had achieved an ambition he had often aired – to become a Veterinary Officer in a country where there were almost no animals. St Kitts was his Shangri-La!

I arranged work along the north shore, where we could spear-fish between cases. Charlie's home-made gun was not a success. A metal tube with a slit running along its upper length was set into a wooden stock. Thick rubber bands cut from the inner tubes of truck tyre were attached to a crossbar at the front of the stock and stretched back to

201

a hook on the harpoon. When the harpoon was released, the bands propelled it up the tube. The trigger mechanism was temperamental, at any moment the heavy, quarter-inch-thick metal harpoon might hurtle through the air. Once it narrowly missed a passer-by, who ran off convinced we were after his blood.

Charlie persuaded me to take local leave and accompany him back to St Kitts. I spent a glorious two weeks goggling along the reefs and lagoons that ringed the island, and visiting the sister isle of Nevis, where Nelson was married. My holiday, however, nearly ended in tragedy.

A local fisherman, Boraine, invited me to spear-fish a large reef which extended out from the north-west of St Kitts towards the island of St Eustatius. We pushed off in a small dinghy and were soon swept out over the submerged reef by a fierce current.

Half a mile off shore, Boraine flung the anchor overboard. He and his brother followed. Beneath us was a deep sandy floored canyon with coral sides rising to a few feet below the surface. I grabbed my mask and gun and jumped in. When I surfaced, I found myself 20 yards from the boat and drifting fast.

I managed to place a foot onto a shallow bit of reef and hang onto a coral head. If I had been wearing flippers I would have felt a lot more confident, but with only tennis shoes I realized that it would take me all my energy to swim back to the boat – let alone spear-fish. I couldn't see my companions anywhere. By swimming down into the ravines where the current was less strong and by pulling myself along on the coral, I finally made it back to where the boat was straining against the anchor rope. The others arrived a moment later. Even with flippers, they had had to keep to the canyons.

'Spring tides,' Boraine grumbled. 'No good. Let's go.'

They each took an oar. I sat in the stern, where I soon noticed that instead of nearing the shore, we were drifting rapidly towards the outer reef, where enormous rollers thundered down onto the ring of exposed coral separating us from the ocean. It was terrifying. I took over the oar from Boraine's brother, who was tiring, but with too much energy and too little skill only succeeded in snapping it. My God, I thought, we really are up the proverbial creek – and paddleless!

I could see no-one on the shore. I don't know what good they would have been, anyway. Prayer seemed the only recourse, but before I could put it to the test, Boraine spied a motorized fishing canoe coming our way. I could have cried with relief. I had been certain that we were all for a watery grave.

* * *

Spear-fishing soon became an obsession. Both Roger and I had graduated from our former erratic, home-made guns to which Charlie had introduced us, and now slipped into the water to face the monsters of the deep armed with more powerful and much more reliable, commercially produced weapons, although still based on the same principle of rubber cords to propel the harpoon. Later I procured a gun with a powerful internal spring, and later still a light, easily handled and devastatingly accurate compressed-air gun, made in Spain.

Although I always carried my gun, mask and snorkel, so that I could stop and fish whenever I had an opportunity, it was the long holiday weekends on the cays, those small coral islets which dotted the south coast, where we had our real adventures.

To get to the cays, we hired Carl's six-berth, 35-foot cabin cruiser, *Invader*. With Carl on the bridge and 10 to 15 of us (more if you counted the children) littering the deck, we sang and drank our way to Pigeon Island or Half Moon Cay, a few miles off the coast at Old Harbour.

After Roger married, Pru took over the organization of these trips and saw to it that crates of beer and soft drinks filled the ice-lockers together with vegetables and fruit. On a point of honour we took no meat apart from emergency eggs and bacon, relying on our skill as gogglers to provide our daily protein. The halo of multicoloured reefs that surrounded these wooded, waterless and uninhabited islets, were sliced by sandy-floored channels through which we could enter and anchor in large, quiet lagoons.

Each morning saw us in the water by sun-up clothed in T-shirts or, if one was particularly susceptible to sunburn, in long sleeves. I usually added long trousers and tennis shoes to protect against coral scratches and sea-eggs. Some of the more relaxed and less committed gogglers even wore wide-brimmed hats. An inflated inner tube with a bucket tied inside was towed by one of us as a repository for speared fish and to prevent their blood from attracting sharks.

If the reef was shallow enough, we walked on it till we came to a crevasse or gully. Some of these were deep, twelve to twenty feet. By gliding slowly along the side of the coral cliffs, one could creep up on an unsuspecting snapper or grouper as it grazed seaweed, or fed on the small reef life which crawled or swam between the staghorn fronds and domes of brain coral.

There were hazards. The most dangerous, theoretically, was the Moray eel. Morays lived in holes in the coral, snapping up unsuspecting prey that swam past. Sometimes a hand or foot might be mistaken for food, or perhaps considered aggressive, with serious consequences for its owner. A Canadian marine biology student had her Achilles tendon severed while walking on a shallow reef. Sea-eggs, too, always had their long black spines waving in the water, ready to prick the unwary. The local 'infallible' remedy was to urinate on the hand or foot containing the pieces of embedded spines – not an easy operation on a reef! Stinging coral, although not dangerous, was best avoided.

The least harmful of the reef occupants, but certainly the most frightening, were the 'sand sharks' and grey 'reef' sharks, which were often as frightened of us as we of them.

The water was so warm that we could fish all day without feeling chilled, but usually by early afternoon we'd had enough. Depositing our catch on board with those in charge of catering, we would swim to the cay with a few bottles of beer and spend the rest of the after-noon snoozing in the shade. At dusk, around a fire of driftwood, with beer and rum punch flowing freely, we would cook and demolish the day's takings. Afterwards, the less adventurous would return on board to sleep in bunks or on deck, while the rest of us dug holes for our hips in the soft, warm sand and lay gazing at the silhouette of the Blue Mountains, dark against a moonlit sky.

Once we went out to the Morant Cays, 50 miles south-east of Jamaica. For this trip we had the 18-foot sloop, *Mystic*, belonging to Abe (later Sir Abe, the builder and owner of the famous Tower Isle hotel near Ocho Rios), with Laurie, a local businessman, at the helm. It had been stormy all day. At ten in the evening, after a debate on the verandah of the yacht club, we final decided to brave it. It was a rough passage and neither Roger nor I were good sailors, but enough water swooshed over the gunwales to clean up the mess.

The Morant Cays, like the other cays, were uninhabited, but unlike Pigeon Island and Half Moon Cay, they were treeless and it was no easy feat for Laurie to find the half-mile long, five-foot-high bank in the early morning haze and rolling sea after eight hours of dead-reck-oning. A small shed on the larger cay saved the day. It was the only object above the horizon.

The reefs around the two cays were like underwater gardens. Avenues of staghorn coral rose from a sandy floor six feet below the surface, between which glided all kinds of fish, like birds in a sub-aquatic, Cocteau-created orchard. Now and then a light grey shape would materialize at the edge of our underwater world and fear would drain blood from our limbs until it disappeared or was identi-fied as harmless – a huge grouper, perhaps. Sharks were far more common here than on the Cays nearer land and some were enormous, but although they would come within 20 feet, they would veer away

Reef garden

again with a sudden swish of their tails. I imagine that there were too many tasty fish for them to bother about bony, two-legged unknowns.

We were less sure of the barracuda. They would hang in the water a few feet below the surface, too far away to shoot at but too near for comfort, their long snouts displaying villainous teeth as they rhythmically opened and closed their horrible jaws. If we moved away they followed, if we approached they retreated, always the same distance. It was eerie and unnerving.

At night we went lobstering, wading chest-deep with one of us carrying a Tilley pressure lamp on his head. The light was enough to illuminate the sea floor for 15 feet around and made it easy to pick out our prey as they crawled over the sandy bottom. A good evening's catch would be two sacks full. The Morant Cays were also the breeding ground of the 'Booby' bird, whose eggs were considered a great delicacy. 'Boobies' did not suffer intruders lightly. To walk across the cay where Boobies nested on the ground, meant warding off determined attacks by screeching and irate hens, flying at you like dive-bombers.

For some reason, the more I skin-dived, the more frightened I became of that dull green apron that surrounded the underwater world. I would imagine all sorts of terrifying monsters lurking there, ready to hurl themselves into view. It was like my childhood fear of the dark or tigers under the bed.

The only time I had real cause to be frightened was one day while fishing an off-shore reef near Morant Bay. I had shot a large grunt and swam ashore with it, a distance of perhaps a hundred yards. As I walked out of the water, a fin followed me. The blood must have attracted a shark, I thought. After a beer, my courage returned and I decided to try my luck again, boldly swimming back to the reef. A little later I missed a large moon fish and my harpoon, which was not attached to a cord, sank to the bottom. As I was coming up, a submarine-like object coasted over my head. Roger and a friend who were standing on the only square foot of jagged coral above water, had also seen it.

'Shark. Get out!' they yelled as I broke surface.

For the next 20 minutes, until we were rescued one at a time by canoe, we balanced on our precarious perch, while the long grey torpedo circled round us.

Another time I met a shark almost head-on while swimming round a cliff of coral on the north shore. We were both so intent on our own private searches that we nearly bumped into each other. I don't know which was the most terrified, but I can offer a pretty good guess!

I was anxious to try and capture this underwater extravaganza on film and tried to build an underwater housing for my camera. It was not a success but, unfortunately, the only one on the market was way above my means. Ten years later they were two-a-penny, but by then I was elsewhere.

A HOT AND DIRTY JOB

Vaccination campaigns were a bore – dusty, monotonous and hot. I dreaded them all – save one. In the south-west of the island, in the Parish of St Elizabeth, was a low-lying, flat area unlike any other part of Jamaica. The rainfall was low and the area sparsely covered in scrub. There were few streams, and well water was inclined to be salty. Thorn trees predominated and the blue-flowered lignum vitae, one of the hardest woods in the world, grew wild, as did the yellow-flowered logwood tree, the source of the common laboratory stain, haematoxylin. Jamaican mahogany, the favourite wood of Messrs Chippendale and Heppelwhite, was once common here, too, but had now almost disappeared. Grazing was scant and people joked that

206

the cattle, which always seemed sleek and healthy, lived on the minerals in the soil. This was the Pedro Plains.

There were two diseases in this area which popped up now and then and against which cattle had to be vaccinated annually. The more serious was anthrax, a cause of sudden death in cattle and other animals. The organism responsible, a very resistant bacillus, could live in the soil for many years, probably over a hundred. In humans, anthrax could cause a severe bloody dysentery if eaten in infected meat, or produce a nasty sore called a 'malignant pustule' if the skin was infected, for instance by shaving brushes made of contaminated goat hair. Or it could cause a severe infection of the lungs, called 'wool-sorters disease', once common in the people sorting imported wool in Liverpool warehouses. All these could be fatal if not treated.

In cattle, deaths from anthrax were sudden with thick, tarry blood exuding from the anus and nostrils. If, by mistake, an autopsy was made – a most dangerous occurrence – the spleen was usually found to be very enlarged. The standard procedure in a case of sudden, unexplained death was to cut into an ear and take blood smears. These were then examined under the microscope for the presence of the anthrax bacillus. If found, the carcase was burnt immediately.

The other disease, 'blackleg' or 'blackquarter', could also live for long periods in the soil and was equally fatal to young cattle. The organism, one of the 'gasgrene' group of bacilli, entered through the skin of the legs and produced large swellings in the muscles beneath, full of gas and decomposing flesh. Unlike anthrax which could affect nearly all warm-blooded animals, blackleg confined its ravages mainly to cattle under 18 months old. Death was often sudden, but occasionally an animal might be seen to be lame a few hours before it died.

It took about a week to vaccinate the 5,000 or so head of small farmers' cattle against these two diseases. Vaccination points were set up, usually on small holdings where good 'crushes' were available.

Vaccinations were done by the JAS field staff. The job of the veterinary officer – which when there was no-one else meant me – was to see that each vaccination point had a refrigerated box with sufficient ice and vaccine for the day, an adequate supply of syringes and needles and, to ensure that the campaign went smoothly, a regular supply of cool drinks from the nearest 'Chinaman store'. By mid-afternoon I would collect the unused vaccine, see that the syringes and needles were sterilized in a saucepan over an open fire in readiness for the next day, check that the following day's vaccination sites were ready, and then drive up the winding dirt road away from the heat and dust to the haven of Malvern, a small town tucked into the

207

cool misty Santa Cruz Hills. An evening on the old pimento property with Dinah, whose son, Trevor, was at Veterinary College, and whose daughter, Valerie, was a close friend in Kingston, was worth every bit of the dusty day's toil and would amply rejuvenate me to face another day's sweat and thirst.

Pedro Plains differed from the rest of Jamaica in another way. In the middle of the last century, a German vessel had been shipwrecked nearby. The survivors had settled there and intermarried with the locals, producing an olive-skinned, green-eyed colony. A few miles inland, the little settlement of Lititz bore witness to their German origin. But although the girls of Lititz were reputed to be the prettiest in the island, I never considered – as did a friend of mine – taking a teenager to Kingston, educating her at a private school and marrying her. Undoubtedly a courageous act, but one that brought unusual happiness to both. Just before I left Jamaica, I passed them and their two kids sailing paper boats on the goldfish pond in Hope Gardens, as happy a family as one could wish to see.

Swine fever (hog cholera, if you are an American), was a serious infectious disease of pigs which smouldered mainly in the almost inaccessible lush foothills of the Blue Mountains at the east end of the island. Here, the rainfall was high and the vegetation thick. Bananas, cocoa, yams, and every sort of vegetable and fruit choked the fertile valleys and steep slopes, and because of this abundance of root crops and fruit, nearly every peasant owned a pig.

For long, sweaty days we would scramble up hillsides or slide down muddy paths, shouting to the occupant of each thatched hut we approached to 'Bring yo' haag fe jook.' Their 'haags' often turned out to be 300-pound sows with wills of their own, which didn't include being 'jooked'.

We could have left the whole campaign to the JAS field staff and the Agricultural Department's Parish Instructors to carry out, but swine fever vaccine was delicate and needed careful handling and constant refrigeration. To ensure that these conditions were met, a veterinarian always accompanied a vaccination team. It was frustrating work. A whole day could be spent trudging up and down steep paths through incredibly hot humid vegetation, cajoling, charming or threatening the owners, understandably reluctant to expose their prize sow to the whims of some passing Government officials, often ending the day having 'jooked' less than a dozen screeching porcines. But it was worth it. Swine fever disappeared from Jamaica in the early 1950s.

One of the biggest vaccination campaigns we organized was against

208

Newcastle disease, a fatal, influenza-like disease of poultry, which broke out for the first time in 1956. It took us completely by surprise, and although there was a very good commercial vaccine on the market, there was a panzootic of Newcastle disease occurring throughout North and South America and no supplies would be available for several weeks. We had a firm policy never to produce our own vaccines – it was too expensive and time-consuming a process and commercial firms could do it much better and far cheaper – but this was an emergency. This time we had to.

By lucky chance, I had an ampoule of freeze-dried Newcastle disease vaccine-virus in the deep freeze. We decided to start production right way. The procedure was simple enough. Fertile eggs were inoculated with the vaccine-virus, incubated for two days, the contents harvested and ground up in a liquidizer with antibiotics to kill any contaminating bacteria, filtered, diluted and distributed in conveniently sized bottles.

Production may have been easy, but there were several other problems. First, having made the vaccine we had to test it, a process that would normally take at least three weeks. But poultry farmers were clamouring for immediate action, and we couldn't wait that long. I decided to take a chance. Instead of testing its efficacy as a vaccine, I would only ensure that it didn't actually cause Newcastle or any other disease when administered. This I did by inoculating chickens with the vaccine and observing them for one week. If they were still healthy, I would know that even if the vaccine wouldn't prevent Newcastle, at least, it wouldn't cause it.

Our next problem was how to package and distribute it. This particular vaccine was administered by instilling one drop into the nostril of each chick. We needed bottles which would hold varying amounts of vaccine, say from 50 to 500 doses, and an easy method by which the farmer could apply it, such as droppers. At that moment we had no bottles, no corks and no droppers.

Our first breakthrough was with the Government Pathology laboratory.

'No, we've no spare vaccine bottles,' said the pathologist (the same gentleman in whose bath the delectable Tia Maria was born), 'but we have five thousand rubber vaccine corks which have been sitting around here since before Port Royal sank. You can have those.'

I accepted them gratefully, but they were no good to us without bottles. I contacted the local glass works. Yes, they could make us bottles to fit the corks.

Now we had only to find droppers. My two lab technicians, Smithy and Trewick, found some bundles of thin glass laboratory tubing in our store, enough to make several thousand droppers. But we still needed the little rubber bulbs to go on the end to make the dropper work. Smithy soon solved this one. He found that an inch of rubber tubing, stapled at one end to seal it, made a perfect substitute for a rubber bulb.

Within a week we were ready to distribute. It was here that the Jamaica Agricultural Society proved its worth. We asked the Parish Agricultural Instructors to telegraph their needs to the headquarters of the JAS in Kingston, whom we supplied daily with the required amounts. They, in turn, dispatched bottles of vaccine to the JAS seed stores throughout the island, all of which had refrigerators, where the Instructors could pick them up.

The charge was a penny a dose, with a sixpence refund for the bottle and dropper. In a few days the campaign was in full swing throughout the island. It must have been one of the cheapest vaccines ever produced and distributed, and I doubt very much whether, in the circumstances, any other country in the world could have given a quicker or more efficient service, especially as we were allocated no extra funds to launch it.

By the time commercial vaccine became available once more, the epizootic was already under control. We were all very proud of ourselves.

Only the unfortunate Poultry Officer was unhappy. While he had generously supplied us with eggs for vaccine production and so helped to halt the spread of this dangerous poultry disease, he had to cancel his breeding programme for the next two months as we had used up his entire production of fertile eggs!

FILM STARS AND ROAST PORK

Jamaica, like Britain, had a head start in disease control. Both were islands.

Top of the list of dangerous epizootics were foot and mouth disease in cattle and rabies in dogs and cats. These animals were barred entry from any country where there was the slightest suspicion of the plagues existing. A nasty disease in horses, equine infectious encephalitis, also put the whole of the new world out of bounds for the importation of equines. The virus could be carried by birds and then be spread from birds to horses by mosquitoes. Man could also be infected, but if he recovered, often remained a cabbage.

How Jamaica had escaped its ravages was a wonder. Cuba had it, so did Haiti and Puerto Rico. It was common both in South America and in the southern United States, and even though most of the 'flyways' along which the birds migrated between North and South America passed through Jamaica we still remained free. There was no way we could keep birds out, but horses we could.

It was dogs and cats, however, that gave us the most trouble. Many an irate visitor on the dockside or at the airport who proudly displayed their immaculately groomed pet, was astounded that I could consider them capable of carrying a disease and furious that, despite health certificates from their local veterinarian, I refused it entry. Most had been misled by ill-informed and uncaring travel agents who had told them that if objections were raised, a ten-dollar bill slipped surreptitiously to the customs official would be more than enough to sort things out in a 'Banana Republic'. Usually we could persuade the owner to send back the animal, but sometimes there would be a heart-rending scene as I had to put it to sleep. We had no kennels for long-term quarantine and no money to build or maintain them. Very occasionally, we agreed to hold an animal in quarantine for a limited period at Hope. Such was the case of sailor-man Yeo.

This shabbily dressed young fellow in a battered Panama hat, dirty T-shirt and oily slacks stopped me as I drove out of the labs one Saturday midday. He looked awfully hot.

'Is this the Veterinary Office?' he asked. I said it was.

'I think you have my dog. I got shipwrecked near Port Antonio and the police said they had to send my dog to Kingston for quarantine.' His accent was American.

'A small fox-terrier?'

'Yes.'

'It's in a stable. We were beginning to wonder what to do with it. Look, I'm just going for lunch, care to join me? We can sort out your dog afterwards.

We went to my house and had a beer.

'What's all this about being shipwrecked? People don't get ship-wrecked these days, not on large islands like Jamaica.'

He looked a bit shame-faced.

'I ran into Jamaica one night when I was asleep. It made a big hole – in my yacht, that is. It took two weeks to repair, and it has taken two days to sail round to Kingston. I would like to leave as soon as possible.'

His name was Yeo, he told me, and he came from the Mid-west where his father, coincidentally, was also a veterinarian. He was going to enter the same profession, but wanted to sail round the

211

world first. Heavy seas between Cuba and Jamaica had kept him awake for two days and nights, and when it had calmed a bit he had fallen into an exhausted sleep and had, quite literally, run into the north coast of the island. He now hoped to head for the Panama Canal and the Pacific.

The dog was as delighted at the reunion as his master, but the latter's face fell when I mentioned the quarantine fee.

'I'm supposed to charge you five shillings a day, so that will be a total of just under four pounds – about ten dollars.'

He screwed up his face. 'I don't have any money, I really don't, except for about five dollars. I had to pay for repairs to the boat and I'm just about broke. I walked up from the docks.'

It was over six miles, uphill all the way from the waterfront. No wonder he looked hot.

'Don't worry,' I said. 'We'll put it down to investigation.' he looked greatly relieved. 'I'll run you back to your yacht. I've got to go into Kingston anyway,' I lied.

'Thanks. I still have a couple of beers on board. Come and have a Schlitz.'

We pulled up at one of the smaller wharves. I was expecting to see a reasonably sized sailing vessel; after all, he was sailing around the world in his 'yacht'. I looked seawards. Nothing. I was about to ask him where it was, when I saw a mast waving just above the edge of the dock, and looking down, spied a small craft hardly bigger than a sailing dinghy, bobbing about 12 feet below us.

Yeo scrambled down the rusty iron quayside hoops, his dog in one arm. I followed. The 'yacht' was possibly 17 feet long, with a well half-covered by tarpaulin.

My host unearthed some cans of beer from a pile of junk in the well deck, and we sat on the sides and toasted each other. Even in the comparative calm of the dock, the little vessel was rolling uncomfortably. I refused another beer, making the excuse of a tennis match.

'I'll be off in half an hour,' Yeo said as I climbed up the hoop ladder. 'Thanks for everything.'

'Drop me a line,' I told him and he wrote down my address. The 'yacht' looked mighty small, far too tiny to tackle the high seas. But there was nothing I could do but wish him luck.

'I'll be hearing from you,' I called.

'Sure thing,' he replied.

I never heard from my intrepid adventurer and his canine mate. Perhaps they were shipwrecked again, or gave up. Or perhaps he made it and is now practising veterinary medicine somewhere in the

Self at desk, Abercorn 1944.

Abercorn veterinary office and messengers.

Nyasaland border road 1944.

Ian 1945.

Self, Flea and Panda (in front) Lusaka, 1946.

Myself and my father, Durban 1955

Bwana Piet, Abercorn 1944.

Lanky, Abercorn 1944.

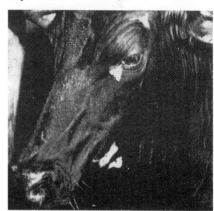

Moth feeding on tears of cow.
Uganda 1959.

L. Bangweulu Swamp Taxi.

Manuel, Self and Peter (project 'Godfather' from Rome).

VITAR High Altitude Veterinary Research Station. Huancayo (11,300ft. : 3,300m).

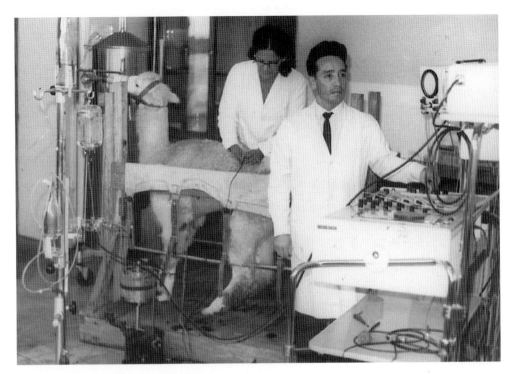

Cardio-vascular lab. Huancayo. Dr. Cueva.

Llama and *cria* grazing near Ticlio.
(15,000ft).

Huancayo High Altitude Station.
L-R back row: Jim, Hank, Self,
Manuel with VITAR staff 1966.

Prof Augusto, Prof Saul, Self and Anzac Ian, Cuzco 1965.

Jim and Prof Jack (Armidale Univ. Australia) 1967.

Llamas and *Huarizos* (*Llama* x Alpaca) near La Raya.

L. Titicaca. Canoe made from water rush *tortora* with cattle grazing water weed *llacho*. Similar canoes made from *tortora* are found on Easter Island.

'El ultimo golpe' Mary with twins... Shivy (left) and Coro. Just before Shivy's heart op. Lima 1969.

The Family in Recife, Brazil 1975.

Midwest, dining out on tales of his adventures and of how, once, he had run into Jamaica!

* * *

Another Saturday, again as I as leaving the office, the telephone rang. I was becoming a bit wary of calls at this hour. Crises always seemed to happen at weekends. Eventually I picked up the receiver. It was the local agent for the Coca-Cola company. He was almost incoherent.

'I'm in a hell of a fix, Pat. You've got to help me.'

'What's up?'

'Joan Crawford's arrived, and she's brought her dog with her. The bloody customs won't let her land it, and she's threatening to leave. It's as much as my job's worth. She's married to the President of Coca Cola!'

'There's absolutely nothing I can do,' I said. 'The quarantine laws are very strict, and it's my duty to enforce them. Sorry.'

'Oh, Lord. Can't you come down here and talk to them? Maybe we can work something out.'

'I've told you, there's nothing I can do, but I'll come and hold your hand of you like. Where are you?'

'Pier No. 2.'

I found my sweating friend pacing up and down in front of the Customs Office, where they were holding her frightened little animal. Joan Crawford had injured her back on the trip and had already left with her husband to consult the orthopaedic specialist at the University Hospital.

'The law,' I again insisted pompously, 'is the law. Only the Governor can change it, and he certainly won't.'

'Ring him, Pat, please; it's a chance.'

'I refused, but he was so insistent that I thought it would be the best way to terminate the matter. I rang his ADC. A moment later I had Frank on the other end and explained the position.

'I know Joan Crawford's visit means a lot to the tourist trade and Jamaica's image, but the law can't be changed for one person, especially *this* law. It would be used as a precedent, and every American tourist will be bringing their wretched pets with them, and we'll have rabies in the island before we know where we are.'

As I was talking, the Governor rang through to his ADC on the intercom. Frank, in a moment of impaired judgement, said he had me on the line and explained the position. Sir Hugh asked to speak to me. I told him the story again, pointing out the importance of the regulations and insisting that we had no option but to keep the dog

213

on board the cruise ship and return it to the USA.

To my surprise, instead of agreeing he told me to stay near the phone and he would ring me back within five minutes. Then, as an afterthought, he added, 'Tell me the real danger of this dog bringing in rabies.'

'Infinitesimal,' I told him. 'It's a small apricot miniature poodle, a lap dog, very friendly and obviously pampered. It also has vaccination certificates. But that's not the point. Once we let ...'

I know, I know,' Sir Hugh replied, and rang off.

It was a long five minutes. My friend was walking back and forth, full of hope and tossing cigarette after half-smoked cigarette through the customs office door while I assured him that there was no way the dog could land. We were still arguing when the phone rang. It was Frank.

'Pat? HE wants to speak to you.'

Sir Hugh's voice was terse, commanding and final.

'I've noted your objections, Guilbride, but I am going to overrule the regulations on this occasion. Joan Crawford's visit has had too much publicity. I've already spoken to the press. There will be no mention of the dog, nor any photos of it. You are to deliver it personally to Joan Crawford. Understood?'

'Yes, sir.'

'I will send you a letter, exonerating you from all responsibility in the matter. This is entirely my decision.'

I was flabbergasted. I had the greatest admiration for Sir Hugh. He was an administrator without equal and a courageous diplomat, but it seemed to me at that moment that all our past efforts to stop the introduction of rabies might suddenly have flown out of the window. To how many entreaties had I turned a deaf ear in upholding the law, including an American only the week before, who was completing the purchase of a large estate. When I told him that he could not bring his dogs and cats with him, he had decided to retire elsewhere. The estate agent arranging the deal, a tennis partner of mine, was a lot less friendly thereafter.

I took the fluffy little dog (I forget its name) to my house at Hope. My elated Coca Cola friend went to the University Hospital to tell Joan C. the good news. He rang soon afterwards to say she was about to leave. I told him to bring her past my house and I would deliver her pet into her hands. A few minutes later, the car carrying her and the president of the Coca Cola Company stopped outside my gate.

'With the compliments of His Excellency,' I told her sarcastically. I am sure she had no idea what I was talking about or of the battle fought on her behalf by Coca Cola's worthy agent!

Ten days later, I went down to the Myrtle Bank Hotel, where Joan Crawford and her husband were to rest after motoring from Montego Bay, prior to flying back to the States that night. There was an expectant crush of fans and reporters round the hotel entrance.

The little poodle was full of bounce, jumping from Joan to her husband and back, hardly leaving their arms. I was quite satisfied that the fluffy little bundle would never introduce anything except love into Jamaica. Not even a flea!

Some years previously, Elizabeth Taylor had been less lucky. After remonstrating with Roger for half an hour, she rang the Governor (not Sir Hugh), who upheld Roger's decision that the dog should remain aboard the Burton yacht.

Joan Crawford was not the last film star to tweak our disease-control regulations. I had barely sat down at my desk one morning, when a socialite with whom I was acquainted rang me.

'Could you come down to my house as soon as possible. Errol Flynn wants to ask your advice.'

I certainly could. I'd love to meet the illustrious film star whose stirring adventures I had long admired on the screen.

Flynn appeared on his hostess's verandah in a dressing gown, his face still pouched with sleep. Beside him was a bouncy ten-year-old boy.

'Errol's son wants to take a mongoose back to the States. Can you tell him how he can do it?'

'A mongoose? There's no way the US authorities will let a mongoose into the States. There's a twenty thousand dollar fine, minimum, for anyone importing a dangerous rodent.'

'Dad, you can pay that, can't you?' piped up the young lad, by his side.

'The hell I can,' declared his father, and toddled off back to bed. It was my one and only interview with the great Errol.

Flynn owned the small Navy Island off Port Antonio in the north-east of Jamaica, to which he would pay short visits in *Sirocco*, his graceful schooner. There were always plenty of females on board, and sometimes he sailed away with more than he had brought.

Flynn's father, 'Professor' Flynn (I never discovered exactly what he was professor of, or where), had bought a cattle property, Boston, on the coast a little east of his son's island. Occasionally I would be summoned to minister to the 'prof's' animals and, on one occasion, found I would have to return another day to finish the work and probably stay overnight.

I looked at my diary. 'What about the fifteenth?' I suggested.

'Too late." The 'Prof' shook his head. 'The Old Lady comes back that day, and she don't like us putting rum in our coffee. Make it the twelfth.'

The 'Old Lady' proved to be the exact opposite of her spouse. He was tall, jagged of face and rather arrogant. She was small, round and shy. But she must have had considerable clout hidden somewhere within if she could prevent her mate from lacing his coffee!

* * *

Other importation regulations gave us just as much of a headache.

A sudden outbreak of a particularly virulent virus disease in pigs in the United States compelled us to ban the importation of all fresh or frozen pork products from that country. A serious enough decision at any time, but to make matters worse, it happened to be only a month before Christmas.

The reaction was alarming. My office was soon packed with irate, vociferous and gesticulating importers, thumping my desk and demanding to know what the hell was going on.

I explained that we had to protect the pig industry in Jamaica – 'What pig industry?' they retaliated, with some justification. I told them I was sorry but was sure that the American authorities would soon bring the outbreak under control. It did little to pacify the worthy men of commerce who could see large Yuletide profits disappearing into the frothing jaws of bureaucracy. Who could blame them?

Even more heart-rending was the effect on the private citizens of Jamaica, many of whom had relatives in the States who had scraped together a few dollars to send Christmas fare to their old folks at home. What better Xmas present could a son or daughter who had emigrated to the north, send to their dear ones in Jamaica than a large juicy ham? As Christmas approached these delicacies began to arrive in their hundreds, by post, by airfreight and in the luggage of visiting friends and relatives.

At first we put the confiscated articles in our cold room, awaiting a decision from the owners as to whether they wished to send them back. None did, it was too costly. Soon our cold room was full. Customs said they had no place to store them. We piled them in a stable but within a few days, in that heat, the in-patients of neighbouring stalls began to appear uneasy. We had no option but to destroy the decomposing delicacies.

With a policeman from the Liguanea station looking on, to make it more official and protect us from accusations of stealing, we fed the

216

sticky parcels, six at a time, into our open brick incinerator. It was enough to make the strongest weep.

I felt immensely sorry for the hundreds of families who lost their Xmas dinner in our incinerator, and for their generous friends and relatives whose spirit of Christmas wafted away each day over the mango trees at Hope in a delicious aroma of roast pork. Those who have read Charles Lamb's 'Dissertation upon Roast Pig' in his *Essays of Elia*, will know what I am talking about.

Had we over-reacted? Perhaps a recent outbreak of foot and mouth disease in Canada which had been caused by the meat in an immigrant's sandwich and another in Martinique from imported meat had made us extra careful, but some years later when Jamaica was one of the few, if not the only country in the Caribbean free of this virus, I knew we had been right.

* * *

Clinical cases sometimes had their dramatic moments. A ragged, barefoot fellow awaited me one morning. I listened to his tale of woe. His cow had been trying to calve since the previous day, but as he was walking it along to our clinic at Hope she had lain down, two hundred yards up the road towards Papine. Could I help him?

I sent Fred, the stable attendant, to see what he could do to bring her in. He soon returned to say he was unable to budge her and that it would probably be best to attend to her where she was.

I found a Jersey-type cow lying on its side, straining. Not only had the old girl seen fit to collapse on the roadside, she had done it right next to a bus stop. Examination showed that a foreleg of the calf was twisted backwards and was preventing delivery.

I gave the cow a spinal and thrust my arm into the uterus. The calf was very tightly enclosed and my hand was squeezed numb against the pelvic bones. A bus stopped and a number of inquisitive passengers descended – including the driver. They were all full of advice and encouragement but couldn't stay long.

Ten minutes later, the same bus, returning from Papine, stopped on the other side of the road. Several passengers came across to see how things were going and add their suggestions. The driver, having been there before, acted as a compère.

Other buses stopped, with repeated performances until, three-quarters of an hour later, a hefty tug, aided by several passengers, brought forth a large and lively calf. There were clappings and congratulations all round. It was, probably, the most exciting event that had ever happened on the Papine route!

217

Another time, late one Saturday morning (of course), I was called to the King George Vth TB Sanatorium, just below us at Liguanea. Beside a two-storey wing of that imposing establishment I found a cow tied to a post, trying desperately to give birth. The butter-coloured tips of two baby hooves were just visible.

After the usual spinal anaesthesia, I found that the calf was coming out backwards, a typical breech presentation. It was a difficult case and I seriously considered doing a caesarian, but I struggled on throughout the lunch hour and into the afternoon, cursing the waste of a Saturday, until, at last, I had it turned around with the head coming first. I put a rope on its feet and head and asked a couple of lads to help me haul.

It came out, finally, rather dried up and dead, but as it hit the ground there was a spontaneous round of applause, with cries of 'Dat right, daakta, dat right. Good man, good.'

I turned to see the balconies of the sanatorium lined with pyjama-clad patients who, unknown to me, had been following the whole procedure.

I took a bow amidst further cheers. No longer did I consider my Saturday afternoon wasted.

* * *

In general, I had been wrong about Kingston. Life could hardly have been more delightful.

I had a job I loved and which divided my activities between office and field; I played tennis and hockey regularly and spear-fished at weekends or whenever my work took me near the coast. Girls were rapturous – if anything, too desirable and too many – perhaps that was why I had only two serious involvements, both with American lasses, one from Boston, the other from New Orleans.

Night life in Kingston was gay and varied, and hardly a week passed without at least one visit to a nightclub – the Glass Bucket, Colony Club, Wickie-Wackie, or Morgan's Cove – usually in a party but sometimes alone in the hopes of meeting a pretty American hieress.

I spent many hours at the university, in the library or at meetings of the journal club, or discussing problems with the medical staff. I was desperately trying to make up, both professionally and socially, for those three barren years in Northern Rhodesia. I was now 30, carefree, confident and ambitious, and I loved everything about Jamaica.

Photography had been a passion from my teens and had earned me tidy sums from time to time. I found Jamaica to be a treasure chest

Members of the 'Car Spring Trio' band
The Glass Bucket Nightclub, 1949

full of spectacular scenery, and made the most of it with my small, light and very scarred pre-war Retina 1. The poster-yellow sands onto which tumbled clear cascades from rocky clefts half-hidden in a riot of ferns, the dark ultramarine line which marked the horizon, the light green waters over the inshore sand and corals, and the mangrove-cuddled inlets, the sunsets flaming behind windswept palms and, far from least, the heart-demolishing maidens, ran me through film after film. Even the pipe-smoking, prune-faced old hags astride long-suffering donkeys plodding their way to market, their panniers piled high with bananas, pineapples, grapefruit, ackee, pawpaw, star appels and a hundred other vegetable delights provided a photographic extravaganza entirely new to me.

I wooed the Tourist Board, and within weeks was selling them Kodachrome transparencies at five pounds a piece – a royal sum in 1949. Often after leaving Jàmaica, I would come across one of my pictures on a tourist pamphlet exhorting the New York vacationer to consider Jamaica for his next getaway, and ten years later, my Boston girl wrote that she had seen herself in one of my photos while

219

she and her husband were sifting through brochures for their next holiday.

'I still have that dress!' she added.

POCOMANIA

'There's a pocomania meeting on the next property tonight,' said my host as we wound up the dusty road to Malvern after a day's vaccinating on the Pedro Plains.

Pocomania, often confused with *obeah* or witchcraft, resembled revivalist cults in other countries. It involved a mixture of hymns and chants, frenetic dancing and rapid respiration, which hyperventilated the tissues and led to dizziness, mouth-frothing, eye-rolling, mass hysteria, and loss of consciousness.

Soon after dark, we strolled down a rough path to where a bamboo-and-rush meeting hall had been constructed.

'We can only watch from outside, they don't like us to go in.'

Gaps in the rough construction allowed us to see nearly everything that was going on inside. The hut was crammed, mainly with women. At the open-door end, sitting at a crude desk on which hissed a Tilley pressure lamp with moths and other insects flying around it, was the 'elder' in charge of the proceedings. Behind him sat two or three young lads with home-made drums. The elder was talking and the congregation responding. From time to time a hymn or religious chant was offered up in high-pitched grating voices. It was rather boring, but a bottle of rum punch helped to bolster our impatience. Several of the women began to dance by themselves, swaying and chanting. Others joined in, the drums beating furiously until the whole hut was jumping. A young girl began to foam at the mouth and collapsed on the floor. No-one took any notice. Others followed. It seemed to be only the women that were affected.

'This will go on all night,' my host whispered. 'Let's go.'

I was only too happy to agree. 15 minutes and you had seen it all. Anyway, the mosquitoes seemed to be starting their own party.

Years later, I was to witness exactly the same frenetic twirlings and stampings at the *mucumba* ceremonies in Brazil. Jamaica or Brazil – there was little difference, they'd all arrived from the West Coast of Africa.

Jamaica had many odd religious doctrines. Every other shack in the countryside had a placard proclaiming that it was the centre of some strange sect. 'CHURCH OF JEHOVAH', 'CHURCH OF THE

220

RISEN CHRIST', 'ASSEMBLY OF THE HOLY GHOST', 'BLACK BROTHERS IN CHRIST', the list was endless. Whether they were offshoots of parent churches in the Southern States from which they received funds, or a whim of the artful occupant who would doubtless pass the plate around, I never discovered.

The names in many cases, I suspected, were to give their pocomania-orientated activities a semblance of respectability.

Rastafarians were another cult, political rather than religious. Rastas, with their beards and long straggly plaited locks, were common enough. They had nothing to do with pocomania. One friendly Rasta used to wander up and down Duke Street, begging sixpence to guard my car when I visited the dentist or went shopping. He assured me that before long, he and the other Rastafarians would be on their way back to Africa, where the Ras Tafari, the Messiah and King of Kings, the Emperor of Ethiopia, had granted them land. I would assure him with equal confidence that he would only be 'swapping black dog for monkey'.

It was then 20 years, or more, since the prime movers of the cult, Marcus Garvey, Leonard Howell, Joseph Hibbert and Archibald Dunkley, had preached this strange doctrine, but there had been little progress towards the exodus to Africa. A shipping company, the Black Star Line, had been formed in Liberia, for the purpose of conveying the faithful back to the dark continent (it didn't seem to matter that Ethiopia was on the other side of Africa), but it had gone bust.

Rastas had occupied a succession of sites, from an overgrown rubbish dump, the Dungle, to a property near Kingston, called Pinnacle. The authorities looked on them as dangerous subversives and had put several of their leaders in jail. The more solid citizens no longer regarded them as a semi-religious cult, but as ganja-smoking, antisocial vagrants, and blamed them for most of the crimes that were committed, which was probably unfair, as some were both abstemious and devout Christians. There was no doubt, however, that the sect shielded many criminal opportunists, and it was not until the arrival of Bob Marley, a reggae musician of world renown, that Rastas acquired a smattering of respectability. Today, the cult exists in many other countries, associated with reggae music, rather than the smoking of cannabis.

Apart from strange religious cults, Jamaica also had its quota of queer characters. The one I remember best, probably because we saw him so often, was Woody. Soon after I arrived in Jamaica, we were drinking tea on Roger's verandah when a bicycle pulled up, from which descended a thick-legged, bronzed, unshaven man of late middle age, dressed in shabby khaki shirt and shorts with a khaki beret on his head. He called a greeting, lumbered up onto the verandah and sat down as if he was expected – which, in a way, he was.

Woody was a beachcomber in every respect except that he lived in a shack at Papine in the foothills above Hope and never went near the sea. He was a Yorkshire man, he said, but had lived in Bermuda and the West Indies for most of his life. He was full of queer ideas and told us of a recurring dream in which a bearded gentleman in olden days attire – a Spanish Grandee, he thought – said that he had buried his treasure near Woody's shack, but always the dream ended before he could find out the exact spot. Everything about Woody was makeshift. His shirts, trousers and shoes he made himself, and it showed. Until her death, a few years previously, he had lived with his English wife in a small cottage near his present shack. One could only sympathize with the poor woman, closed in by forests of coconut trees at the foot of a gorge, her only view that of a coconut smothered church and with no-one approaching her social or educational level anywhere near. She must have been desperately lonely. People that had known her told me that she had married beneath her. She had, they said, been well educated and a very competent artist.

Woody's story ended, for us, one Sunday afternoon. A stranger drove in and parked under the mango tree on the drive way.

'Did you know Joseph Woods?' he asked.

'Woody? Yes, of course.'

'He's dead. Died yesterday in hospital. Pneumonia. Funeral's tomorrow at Gordon Town. The Masons will arrange everything. Woody was once grandmaster of the Kingston lodge. He often mentioned you chaps at Hope.'

I said how sorry I was and that I would tell the others, and that we would certainly be there.

'By the way,' he added, 'there are some paintings in his hut, done by his wife. Any interest to you?'

The paintings were mainly views from the cottage in which she and Woody lived. Two or three were of the church across the valley from their house, with its small graveyard and encroaching coconuts. In each there was an identical smudgy area, as if the artist had tried to rub something out. That afternoon, as we laid Woody to rest next to his wife, I realized that their graves were in the exact spot where the paintings had been smudged. Woody had always said that his wife had been psychic.

I kept two small paintings, one of a seashore in the moonlight and the other of a waterfall along the road to Morant Bay. The others were huge and the endless coconut trees were too depressing, but they were undoubtedly works of art. Where they are now, I've no idea.

PROFESSIONAL UP-DATE

I couldn't sleep. I was far too excited – and uncomfortable. Fifty silver dollars in a chamois money belt were sticking into my ribs. The bank had asked if I would mind taking them instead of notes since bullion was too heavy and expensive to transfer from Jamaica to the States. Home leave in June, 1950, had given me the opportunity to travel back to Britain via the USA and Canada and visit a number of scientific institutions en route.

That afternoon, the twin propellered DC3 of British West Indian Airways had dropped me in Miami. I remember looking down at the white-crested waves as we flew over the dark blue ocean where, two days earlier, a similar plane had crashed on its way from Havana to Miami. I had crossed my fingers against a repetition.

From Miami I had taken a Trailways bus northwards into the hot summer night, in order to meet 'Big Jim', the chief of the United States' Veterinary Public Health Service, in Atlanta, with whom I had been corresponding about my zoonoses survey.

All I knew of the USA was from films and Americans I had met. I had no idea that the country was so huge, or the traffic so fast. The roads stretched into the distance like nylon ribbons along which our bus sped at eighty miles an hour. I was fascinated by the neatness of the towns and villages, their streets lined with trees in full leaf, at the brightly painted houses set well back behind close cropped lawns, undivided by hedges. The whole country had an air of wealth and superiority. Every male smelled of exotic after-shave and every lady seemed dressed for a fashion show.

'Big Jim', a huge teddy-bear of a man, with a prodigious mental capacity, introduced me to Bob, the young Veterinarian in charge of the rabies research at the Communicable Disease Research Center at Montgomery. Bob and Martha, his technician, later to become his wife, and Ernie, a hard living bachelor and roving rabies ambassador for the Center, made it a memorable week, both socially and professionally.

The country was booming. America led the world in everything from juke-boxes (on which you could even buy silence) to veterinary science, and from T-bone steaks to toilets, or 'Rest Rooms' as they were now called. Everyone appeared content. There were no protest marches, no radicals rampaging through campuses. Black Power was

223

emerging but still in a non-violent stage. Then, without warning, the first of several sharp spikes were thrust into Uncle Sam's well covered rump – North Korea invaded the South.

There was an immediate reaction. World War Two had finished only five years before. People were terrified, it was if a plague had broken out. Everyone was careful to distance themselves from the public enemy No. 1, the Communists. My favourite tie, unfortunately, was predominantly red. I hid it at the bottom of my suitcase as if it was evidence of terrible crime I had committed. I no longer emphasized my English accent as I had done till then, it only led to – 'When is your Mr Churchill going to wake up and help us fight these goddamn Communists?' I would reply that as I had been travelling, I was out of touch with our Prime Minister. Only occasionally would this evoke a smile. Korea was serious business. So began the hysteria which would end in McCarthy-ism.

I visited several Veterinary Schools and attended several conferences before crossing into Canada, to talk over old times with Bob and Margo, who had left Hope two years before. A two-week refresher course at Guelph Veterinary College, which touched on everything from parasites to physiology, and surgery to genetics, gave me a much needed academic update. The theories and techniques of those far off days seem crude and naive forty years later, but at the time they were the forefront of veterinary thought.

At Guelph, I ran across Alan, who had been one of the Jamaican laboratory assistants at the Hope Veterinary labs. and had just completed his first year of veterinary science. He went on to become Professor of veterinary surgery.

Before leaving the USA, I spent a magnificent week on the whaling island of Nantucket with my very special girlfriend from Boston. The friendliness of the New Englanders and the air of quiet contentment along the Cape Cod coast convinced me that if I were to emigrate to the States, it would be here that I would settle.

Two crowded months after I had first landed in Miami, fitted out with American T-shirts, several gaily coloured bow ties, a washable, nylon Trilby hat (for God's sake!), over-awed by the calm dexterity of the New York bus drivers and a little frightened at the speed with which wheels turned in that fascinating country, I boarded the *Queen Elizabeth* for Southampton.

On my return from leave, I found Roger in the new post of Director of Livestock Services and myself in his old post as Veterinary Investigation Officer. This was exactly what I had hoped for. Now I could concentrate on those investigations at which I had been nibbling in the few moments left to me between clinical cases and administration.

Mac D, the first of the Jamaican students to return, took over my responsibilities for the clinical and administrative work at Hope, a stocky, humorous, down to earth, no-nonsense 40-year old. He and Pansy, his bubbling, buxom wife, added a new dimension. Until then all the vets in the Department had been expatriates – British, Canadian or American. Mac D was the first Jamaican veterinarian in Government service. Full of humour, hard working and helpful, he was one of the most honest men I have ever known.

The bad news was that there was now no longer any room for me in the Hope residences, Mac D and his family having precedence over a mere bachelor. I soon found a perch with Greta, a statuesque 50-year old who divided her time between her teenage son and daughter, good works, the arts and her paying guests. Her massive double-storey house at 72 Hope Road was typical of the later-Victorian Kingston residences. Almost entirely made of wood, roofed with wooden shingles, verandahed above and below, onto which opened large casement windows that rattled in the slightest breeze, it was surrounded by lawns and enormous guango (*Pithecolobium guayanensis*) and poinciana trees. The whole rickety edifice, she assured me, was safely held together by white ants!

It was a lively household. Greta was the leading impresario of amateur dramatics, and soon had me in a production of Shaw's *St Joan*. Her son, at Oxford, was to be president of the Union in two years time, and her daughter, a gorgeous russet-head, was with the Young Vic Players and would soon marry one of the most promising young English Shakespearean actors and rising film star, Robert Shaw. At one time or another, nearly every local and many visiting artistes, graced Greta's verandah at sundown.

One of the paying guests was Captain Lindsay, the retired founder of one of the largest ocean salvage companies in the world. The captain had endeared himself to the citizens of Kingston by donating the Bournemouth Swimming Club, which he owned, to the city. Over an after-dinner Benedictine, he would delight us with his experiences.

'I was with some friends on my salvage pier at the east end of the harbour,' he told us once, 'when one of the ladies said that as a young girl she had lost a gold bracelet there. For the fun of it, I said I would dredge it up for her. We put down a hose and sucked off the top layer of sand through a sieve, and – blow me down – there it was, a bit tarnished but none the worse for forty years in salt water.'

The old gentleman told us that until he was nearly 60, he suffered from sea-sickness, yet was at sea more days than not. Anyone with that determination deserved to succeed.

One thing worried me about Greta's rickety old house. What would happen if a hurricane struck? I was soon to find out!

A CURE FOR 'CAULIFLOWERS'

'Buckthorn, Celandine, Figwort, Mugwort, Nailwort, Black Poplar, Sun Dew and Turnsole,' says Culpepper, the seventeenth-century astrologer-physician, 'will all cure warts.' I could well believe him, although I had tried none of them.

My textbooks assured me that cattle warts were a transient affliction of calves and of no consequence. My experience was otherwise. Instead the occasional case described by the authorities, I found they would often occur in small outbreaks, and instead of erupting in ones and twos and disappearing in a few weeks, as my learned texts would have me believe, they would grow into large 'cauliflower' clusters sometimes covering the whole body, occasionally persisting to adulthood.

Apart from the common, soft, mushroom-like 'cauliflower' wart, usually occurring on the face, ears and neck of calves, there was another type, a hard, dry 'villiform' or 'flat' wart, more often seen in adult cattle, and occurring anywhere on the skin including the teats, about which text-books said nothing.

Unlike the common 'cauliflower' wart, which grew rapidly and eventually disappeared, the less frequently encountered 'villiform' wart grew very slowly and remained for life. It consisted of a cluster of usually short bristle-like projections occasionally reaching an inch in length. A cow at Yallahs, a dry, thorn-bush area, had a crop on her forehead resembling some bizarre sort of hat. The 'villiform' wart seemed more frequent in thorn-bush country, and as the most common site was around the mouth, I presumed that they were transmitted by thorns pricking the lips and face while the animals browsed.

An interesting observation was that farmers had only recognized warts as a problem in recent years, about the same time that they had switched from arsenic-based dips to those based on organo-phosphates. Arsenic was known to have a beneficial effect on the skin. Sufficient, I wondered, to keep warts in check?

As with human warts, there were numerous cures for cattle warts, although I drew the line at taking an infected animal out to a crossroads at full moon and rubbing decayed meat on its protuberances!

226

That was pure auto-suggestion, and I doubted my ability to bend a cow's mind! Injections of arsenic and antimony preparations were widely advocated in veterinary books, as were applications of petrol and sump oil, or the tying of a hair or rubber band round the neck of the wart, or crushing it with a pair of Burdizzos – the instrument used for castrating calves.

I started with the arsenic and antimony injections in animals with cauliflower warts. True enough, some calves cleared up after a few weeks, but so did many of my untreated 'controls'. I would have to think of something else. Nothing shifted the villiform variety.

In the meantime, in addition to trying to treat warts, I started to investigate their cause. I knew they could be transmitted by scratching wart material into the skin of a healthy calf. But was this due to a virus, like the verruca, which had led to such elaborate precautions in our school changing rooms? There was no direct evidence (in those days) that the same applied to cattle warts.

If it was a virus, how was it spread? Or if not, did some of the actual wart cells have to be transmitted from animal to animal? I noticed that when young animals were cut with barbed wire or thorns, warts would often spring up along the wound. This certainly pointed to the cut becoming infected from another animal – but how? Direct contact? Flies? Or perhaps the virus was circulating in the body, waiting for a suitable site in the epidermis, such as a scratch or cut, in which to proliferate? Flies appeared to be the most likely transmitter.

House flies, stable flies and horse flies were common enough in Jamaica, so was another very interesting little diptera, *Hippelates hippelates*, which I called the 'hippy fly'. A third the size of a house fly, rather like a fruit fly, this little fellow seemed unable to actually pierce the skin but would settle beside fresh blood, extend its proboscis and suck up its dinner, its belly swelling visibly until, a minute later, dark red and replete, it would stagger away.

Here, I thought, might be the answer. I took a calf, generously decorated with 'cauliflower' warts, scarified some till they bled, and tied it next to another, wart-free calf, small areas of whose skin I had scratched until blood appeared. 'Hippy flies' soon covered the raw areas on both calves. Every now and then I would wave my hands over the animals so the flies would resettle on the other calf. I repeated this experiment several times for periods of half an hour each, but never obtained a transfer of warts.

It was the chance occurrence of the hurricane that gave me my first evidence that warts might be due to a virus. I had injected the skin of

227

four calves with varying dilutions of ground-up and filtered wart material, both 'cauliflower' and 'villiform'. The filter I used prevented any cells or bacteria going through. This meant that if any warts appeared on the calves, they would be due to a very small infective agent probably a virus.

I inspected the calves twice a week for five weeks. No growths appeared and I told Fred, the stockman, that if nothing had come up by the following week, we should sell them. A few days later, hurricane 'Charlie' hit us. In the chaos that followed, the calves were forgotten until, one day, I spotted them grazing next to a fence. A series of small bumps had appeared at the inoculation sites over the ribs, showing that some injections had 'taken'. In great excitement, I told Fred to bring them into the stables while I ran off to fetch my research protocols.

This was encouraging. If there was an infectious agent involved such as a virus, then perhaps the calf could produce antibodies against the infection, or in other words, it might be feasible to make a vaccine against warts. I started with the 'cauliflower' wart, grinding up wart material, adding a small amount of formalin to destroy any tissue cells or infective virus, and then injecting it into my long-suffering patients. The results were much the same as with the arsenic and antimony drugs, marginally better than with the untreated controls.

About this time I saw an advertisement in one of the veterinary journals for a wart vaccine made in hens' eggs by a well-known firm in the States. Damn it, if they could make it, so could I. I wrote them. Their reply flabbergasted me. In essence, what they did was to inoculate fertile hens' eggs with ground-up wart tissue which had passed through a bacterial filter, incubate the eggs for 24 hours, and without testing for virus growth, grind up the whole egg in an antibiotic fluid and dispense it in bottles as a vaccine. This was a hit-and-miss method if ever I heard of one. I felt I could do a lot better.

There are several different parts of the fertile egg in which viruses are known to grow – the yolk sac, the chorio-allantoic membrane, the amniotic sac, and so forth. I inoculated each of these sites with ground-up 'cauliflower' wart material in an antibiotic solution, incubated the eggs for five days, harvested the various organs and stored them in my deep freeze. When I had enough, I injected groups of warty calves with the different potions. I decided on six weeks as a cut-off period for a cure. Warts would have to disappear or be well on the way to disappearing by that time, for the treatment to be classified as effective.

Again the results were only a little better than the untreated control group. The thought then occurred to me that perhaps this 'vaccine' was not, in effect, a vaccine at all, but that the protein in the egg material was merely giving a non-specific 'shock' reaction and stimulating the body's natural immune mechanism, so in my next trial I used non-infected egg material as a control. The results were the same as with the 'vaccine' egg material.

If the results were due to protein shock, I thought, then perhaps if I increased the dose and used another protein such as sterilized milk, it should be just as effective, less messy and a lot easier to prepare. The results were much better; 'cures' were between 20 and 40 per cent higher than in the controls injected with sterile saline.

From then on I used injections of sterile milk as a regular treatment for 'cauliflower' warts, sometimes with spectacular results, at other times only slightly better than the untreated controls. Statistically, I still could not prove that the milk treatment was definitely superior to any other treatment. I would have to do several hundred more before I could say so with certainty.

My treatments were challenged from an unexpected quarter. Joe, a farmer near Highgate, had long been troubled with warts in his herd, so I arranged to visit him and see what I could do. On arrival, I was rather surprised to be introduced to a scruffy, dark-skinned, white-haired old man, whom Joe told me was the local *obeah*-man, or witch doctor. He had been told him that the 'h'animal daakta' was coming to treat the cattle for warts and insisted that his cure was infallible, so Joe suggested he meet me. I didn't mind, I was anxious to see what he would do. Maybe he had the answer.

We divided the infected animals into three groups, one for him, one for me, and one group for the untreated controls. I watched the *obeah*-man do his anti-wart magic on his group, which seemed to be a series of incantations delivered in a voice like a parson, while he flicked some powder over them. I inoculated my group, recorded the brand numbers of each animal in each group so there would be no arguments, and departed.

Six weeks later I returned to see the results. The obeah-man didn't turn up, but his treatment was about the same as the controls, mine was definitely better. Hypnotism or suggestion, so it seemed, might work in his human patients, but he still had to perfect it in cattle.

In the end, as so often happens in research, I was left with far more questions than I could cope with. Did breed difference play a part? Holsteins seemed to be far more resistant to the 'flat' wart than Jerseys, although they were very susceptible to the 'cauliflower' type. Why were 'flat' warts so rare in males? Maybe there was a sexual preference, or perhaps it was because I saw fewer males. Were the two types caused by the same virus, the type of skin dictating the difference in appearance? Unlikely, I thought, as both types transmitted true to type. Did the virus circulate in the blood and simply latch on to a site where the epithelium was damaged? I could have spent the next ten years locked into all these fascinating possibilities, but shortly afterwards I left Jamaica for a year to study for a postgraduate degree, and when I returned I found myself saddled with administrative duties. My results, as far as they went, were reported at the Second West Indian Veterinary Conference, the proceedings of which, due to lack of funds, were never published.

I still follow reports of others in this field, and it is now known that there are several strains of virus causing warts in cattle, but treatment still seems to be as unpredictable as my hit-and-miss procedures of 40 years ago!

I had hoped to write up my work for an external PhD through the University College of the West Indies, but there was a snag. The UCWI was a branch of London University and London wouldn't agree to offering me a PhD since my original degree was from Edinburgh. Edinburgh, however, was quite happy to let me do the work at the UCWI if it was surpervised by a PhD graduate from Edinburgh. There were none. Catch 22.

I have two little reminders of those days. A small wart on the right side of my scalp and another on the palm on my hand, both of which started at the time I was grinding up wart material. Presumably, I must have scratched some infective tissue into my skin – so perhaps I have added another condition to the long list of zoonoses – cattle warts!

ILL-TREATED MULES

I watched the old mule limp painfully out of the stone-walled 'pen' and be led down to a piece of barren ground. I followed, a humane killer in one hand and my post-mortem case in the other.

It was a job I detested, but it had to be done. Suppurating abscesses covered three of its legs and it hadn't worked in the last two years. This was another condition I was starting to investigate.

Marjorie, the dark-haired, attractive daughter of an old Jamaican family, who recently had returned from Glasgow with her clergyman husband and been appointed Veterinary Officer to Trelawney Parish, unpacked the autopsy instruments and helped me dissect out the affected parts of the animal I had just shot.

The condition was known locally as 'farcy', a word more correctly applied to the ulcerative skin form of glanders, a very dangerous but now rare disease of horses (and sometimes man). We knew this was not glanders, nor was it epizootic lymphangitis, another very nasty disease of horses, for which it had been mistaken for many years.

Throughout Jamaica, hundreds of mules were used each cane harvest to draw the carts full of sugar cane to the factories for processing into sugar and rum. The life of these 'animal tractors' was unenviable; the Jamaican muleteer was not noted for his sympathetic handling. Whips, sticks, ill-fitting harness, kicks, jostling in the shafts, rope burns, sharp stones whenever they fell, all caused cuts and bruises which later might turn to abscesses and ulcers. Treatment, if any, given by the handlers was to wash the wound in Jeyes. If it was deep, it might be plugged with horse dung mixed with Jeyes – in my opinion, one of the causes of the high incidence of tetanus cases we saw in these animals. Equine manure is a source of the very resistant tetanus organism.

At the end of the cane season the mules were rested, the weight they had lost was gradually regained, and the wounds in the younger animals usually healed, leaving only scars. Even so, they would often break out again into ulcers during the following cane season, while the old chronic cases would certainly do so, making them too lame to work. The Long Pond Sugar Estate, where Majorie and I were working, had some 15 such mules in different stages of 'farcy', but today's was the first case I had autopsied.

I collected pus from the abscesses and nodules and then cut into some of the old scars. The underlying tissue was fibrous and beneath it, almost on the shin bone, I found deposits of a hard, white, chalky material. I cut these out and placed them into sterile sample bottles. There were numerous such foci in each leg.

When we had finished, the carcass was covered with dried sugar cane, sticks and logs and then set alight. It was impossible to bury carcasses in that rocky ground. We walked back to the stone pen in which the other cases had been collected together.

'Let's give them massive doses of terramycin,' I suggested. 'I doubt if it will do much for the old chronic cases, but it might help the more recent ones. We'll spray the ulcers with antibiotic at the same time.'

I wrote down the name of each mule, its age, history and description of the lesions, as well as details of treatment.

'Give them all another shot each day for a week, and let me know how they get on.'

'Come and have a beer and something to eat,' Majorie invited.

The rectory at Whitehall, a rambling stone bungalow four miles from the sea above Duncans, looked out over rocky pastures and cane fields, almost a Derbyshire landscape – if you forgot the sugar cane! I little realized, as we sat on the verandah sipping beer, that a few years later her husband would marry me and my wife and this garden would be the scene of our wedding celebrations.

In the laboratory, I ground up the hard, caseous material I had taken at autopsy and spread it onto Petri dishes of blood agar. After 24 hours in the incubator, small dewdrops of streptococci appeared on the surface and the blood in the agar around them became haemolysed and colourless. Because of their ability to rupture blood cells they were termed 'beta-haemolytic' streptococci and probably disease-causing. They occurred in every case I examined.

Sometimes, if I left the Petri dishes in the incubator for a further 24 hours, I might find other minute, pearl-like colonies mixed with the dew drops of the streptococci. Under the microscope the organisms appeared to be corynebacteria, a group known to cause abscesses in sheep, and which included the group of bacteria responsible for diphtheria in humans. The antibiotic treatment of the younger, more recently infected, cases was nothing less than spectacular. Even some of the old cases had improved.

Long Pond was only one of several sugar estates on which I had started to investigate 'farcy', or ulcerative lymphangitis, as we now knew it to be. Another was Golden Grove, near Duckenfield in St Thomas, where I had over 20 mules under treatment. I could divide my cases into 'hopeful' and 'hopeless' categories. First-time sufferers would respond dramatically to antibiotics, especially if I applied anti-biotics to the leg sore as well and bound it up with Elastoplast – like I had done to my own 'veld sores' in Africa. But the older and more chronic a case became, the less likelihood there was of a cure, and those with multiple scars, nodules and swollen lymphatics of several years standing, I simply shot. It was kinder and removed possible foci of infection.

One day, while treating mules on Golden Grove, the overseer complained that he suffered from a similar condition. He showed me his leg, covered with scars where abscesses had broken out and healed.

'You're in my "hopeless" category,' I told him. 'I think we'd better shoot you.'

Relenting, I gave him a note to a friend in the University Medical School, pointing out that I had been treating mules for a similar condition on the estate where he worked, and mentioning the organ-

232

isms I had isolated. I lost contact with the overseer, but I remember that his initial treatment with surgery and antibiotics was successful. Whether it was a permanent cure, I do not know. At any rate, I'm sure he wasn't shot!

As with so many other diseases the cure was only half the battle, the really important part was the prevention of the cause. Only dedicated and stubborn persons like Mrs A-C, committed to animal rights and willing to fight for them, would be able to banish the whips and sticks which caused many of the wounds, and to persuade the estate managers, overseers and drivers that it was in their own economic interest, as well as their moral duty, to ease the lot of their grossly overworked, underfed and maltreated mules.

Unfortunately, there was only one 'Mrs A-C' but, thankfully, other help was at hand. Mules were soon superseded by mechanised transport and 'farcy' today, I am told, is a rarity.

A VERY HIGH WIND

'June – too soon,
July – stand by,
August – must,
September – remember,
October – all over.'

So went the rule of thumb for predicting tropical storms.

'Hurricane!' Carl loud-hailed us from *Invader*.

'When?' we yelled back from the reef.

'Tomorrow or day after, if it comes this way. Get everyone in, we're leaving at once.'

It was a three-hour cruise to Kingston, and although Carl was anxious to get back, we persuaded him to stop for a while off Wreck Reef, a large, totally submerged coral jungle under the Hellshire Hills, near Port Royal. It was not a nice reef, the waters were rough, and the currents strong and it was too exposed to shark and barracuda, but we had been told that the fish were larger there than anywhere else.

Only Roger and I jumped overboard. I got nothing, but Roger shot the biggest fish of his career – a 17-pound snapper. We had no time for more, the weather was already changing, the sky had a milky haze and the breeze was freshening. Carl, his head close to the radio, gave us details of the hurricane's progress. It was still a long way off but 'Charlie', the serial name given it by the American weather

233

bureau, had now definitely turned towards Jamaica. It would probably arrive or, if we were lucky, pass us the following evening.

We glided in past Port Royal. People were pulling small boats out of the water, and the sound of hammers could be heard everywhere, as they secured shutters and roofing. As soon as we had off-loaded at the Yacht Club, Carl took his boat out into the harbour and secured it in deep water with several anchors. It was too large to haul onto land, and to have moored it near a jetty would have been asking for disaster.

The weather deteriorated gradually during the night, and the next day was overcast and gusty. In the middle of the afternoon, showers began.

Everywhere, people scuttled about, bringing in the verandah furniture, boarding up ventilation panels, nailing down loose shingles, shouting encouragement to their neighbours. Food shops were crowded, memory of the 1941 hurricane, just ten years before, was still strong in many minds. Shoppers joked with nervous good humour and were unusually polite as they jostled through the turnstiles of the supermarkets. There was an air of Christmas Eve about the town. I remember wondering as I drove up the rain lashed road from Half-Way Tree, my car filled with tinned food and other non-perishables, whether people would be as polite and merry on the morrow. That afternoon, Roger, Mac and I toured the labs and stables, locking all the filing cabinets and doors, closing windows, removing canvas awnings and seeing that the animals had plenty of food and water. All the staff had left early in the day to secure their own houses.

Greta's old wooden house, with its numerous louvre ventilation panels and loosely fitting verandah doors, was almost impossible to make hurricane-proof, but we did what we could with what was available. None of us had experienced a hurricane before and had little idea of what to expect.

'Charlie' was due at eight that evening. The radio cancelled all other programmes save messages and warnings to evacuate certain low-lying areas along the south coast. Just before darkness fell, a queer greenish glow seeped over the sky, the gusty squalls disappeared and an eerie calm took over. At seven o'clock, the Governor, Sir Hugh Foot, began broadcasting to the island, giving last instructions regarding emergency services, and wishing us well. We heard later that the poor fellow only just made it back to King's House through a gauntlet of crashing trees, soaked and half-stripped of his clothing by the gale. Lady Foot remained at her post in downtown Kingston all night, organizing the Red Cross relief service.

234

We stood on the verandah, waiting and wondering. Nothing moved, and there was only the occasional sound of a car, usually at full speed. It was like waiting for an air raid after the sirens had gone – or the end of the world. At precisely three minutes to eight, we noticed a leaf on the oleander bush next to the verandah move slightly. Then another and another. There had been flashes of lightning for some time but no sound of thunder. Now we heard a growing roar.

At five minutes after eight, 'Charlie' arrived. He didn't do so gracefully. He flung himself at us amidst roaring trumpets and wildly flailing limbs. As he did so, the lights went out.

The whole house shook and swayed in the raging wind. We bolted the doors and walked around with flashlights. Even inside, the wind was appreciable and the rain, driving horizontally, made short work of the ventilation panels we had tried to board up.

The roar was continuous, and the water which had been dripping though the roof was now pouring in. Nothing was dry – except my bed, which I had taken the precaution of covering with a ground sheet.

For a time we crouched under the heavy mahogany dining table, as much for protection as to keep dry, but the floor soon flooded and drove us out. Ominous creaks and groans convinced us that the house was going to collapse at any moment. I remember Greta's quip that it was held together by white ants. I prayed that they would hold hands and stay put!

After 40 minutes, there was an unbelievable calm. We went outside, all was still, the only sound a far-off roar. The garden was a tangle of branches and fallen trees.

'Thank God that's over,' I said.

'What's over?' Greta was scornful. 'This is half-time. We have another hour of it to come. This is only the eye.'

True enough, a few minutes later, 'Charlie' was waltzing in the other direction, even more fiercely, it seemed. I went upstairs but couldn't open the door of my bedroom. Then a door onto the upstairs verandah crashed inwards. There was no way we could get it shut, it was like three ants pushing against an elephant. We retired to the kitchen, which seemed almost untouched and sat drinking rum and ginger in the dark till our uninvited visitor moved on. As the last gust disappeared and the noise died away, we began to take stock.

No wonder I hadn't been able to open my bedroom door – the window had blown in. Twigs, leaves and papers plastered walls and ceiling. My ground sheet had now disappeared off my bed, so had the sheets. The rest of the night was not comfortable, but we were alive and uninjured. We learnt that 54 persons had died in Kingston alone, and 50,000 were homeless.

Dawn presented an extraordinary sight. Greta's house was surrounded by other houses I had never seen before. Not that they, or we had moved, but every tree for miles around was down, one large one blocking the entrance to our driveway. There were no telephones, no electricity and no water. Power was restored within the week, water in ten days, but, blessedly, it was more than a month before the telephone began to pester us again.

As soon as I could get the car out of the gate, I went up to Hope. The roads were covered in fallen trees, telegraph poles and tangled wires, but with care it was possible to circumnavigate them on the verges. Roger and Pru were fine, so were Mac and Pansy. The labs had leaked a bit but had no extensive damage. The mango trees had all been well pruned – not a hornet's nest was left!

Head-office of the Dept of Agriculture in Hope Gardens was a different matter. The enormous guango tree which had shaded it for 50 years had fallen, but unfortunately, as everyone proclaimed, had missed the dilapidated building by inches. No-one had seen fit to batten down the offices, which were littered with ruptured filing cabinets and chairs, and the walls and ceilings papered with decades of official memos, letters and confidential reports. A top-secret docket lay empty in the doorway.

Smithy, my senior lab technician, provided the only amusing anecdote. When the roof blew off his shack he decided to join a friend higher up the hill and above possible flooding.

'Me start de climb wid coat, shirt h'an' trousers, but me finish 'olding h'onto me h'underpants!'

He was more fortunate than one of the Agricultural Instructors in St Thomas, who ended by tying himself to a coconut stump with fencing wire to stop being blown away.

The destruction throughout Jamaica was enormous. Nearly every banana tree had been blown down, and the lopped-off stumps of coconut trees reminded us of 'Charlie' for years afterwards.

The following day, we went down to Port Royal, which had borne the brunt of the storm. Mountainous seas had rolled over the Palisadoes peninsula, halfway along which we came upon a tramp steamer, high and dry in the middle of the road. Carlos' motor launch, *Invader* pulled her three anchors and ended up cushioned in a mangrove swamp three miles away on the other side of the harbour.

Only the old stone buildings at Port Royal were still standing. They'd gone through it all before, several times. They had stood firm, but had been unable to prevent a foreign family holidaying in one from being drowned.

In his book, *A Start In Freedom*, Sir Hugh Foot says that 'the worst thing about a hurricane is waiting for it.' I disagree, the worst thing is trying to clear up afterwards.

A NEAR MISS

'Wait a couple of weeks, then we can take you up on the inaugural flight of our Lodestars.' Bobbie, a lean, well groomed ex-RAF pilot, took another sip from his gin and tonic. 'They're a great improvement on our Catalinas and I've just offered this young lady a job as air hostess.' He turned to a pretty, fair-haired girl, sitting beside him at the circular bar of the Courtley Manor hotel. She's from New Zealand, working her way round the world.'

'Can't,' I replied. 'I've got to be in Montgomery next week for a symposium. But your return flight will fit in nicely.'

Bobbie's airline, Caribbean International Airways, was run on a shoestring. Repairs and servicing were carried out by arrangement with mechanics of other airlines. Until now, there had been no air hostesses.

The main attraction of CIA was that it was the only airline that stopped at the Cayman Islands on the way to the States. I'd never been to the Caymans. So, instead of taking the more direct and much more reliable British West Indian Airways flight to Miami, I opted for CIA's slow, cumbersome Catalina flying boat to Tampa, with a night stop on Grand Cayman.

For me it was an ideal flight. At never more than two thousand feet, the bulky crate lumbered across to the north coast near Port Maria, and then turned west to plod along the coastline at a steady hundred and twenty miles an hour, for a landing at Montego Bay. It gave me an excellent view of my old haunts, the house at Rockmoor, with its thread-like path chipped through the honeycomb rock to the little pool, Robin's Bay with the small club house sprinkled about with coconut palms, the small cove at Golden Eye, Ian Fleming's property and the magnificent reefs around Ocho Rios and St Ann's Bay. Other airlines whizzed over at ten thousand feet.

The Caymans were a group of coral islands rising only a few feet above sea level, protected somewhat by extensive reefs. The land was honeycomb rock covered with scrub and low pasture, a breeding ground to billions upon billions of mosquitoes which rose like clouds of smoke each dusk to harass man and beast. Houses had to have double doors, one closing before the other opened, and mosquito netting on the windows was constantly inspected and renewed. Malaria and other mosquito-borne diseases were not a problem, but it had been known for mosquitoes to suffocate cattle and goats by clogging their nasal passages. During the day the sea breezes and hot sun kept the little brutes at bay, but dusk was a time to head for home.

The Caymans, however, had one enviable advantage! There were no taxes. The islands had been given exemption from all taxation by George III for their heroic rescue of the crews when ten British ships went aground there during a storm in 1788.

I took an old, beaten-up taxi from St Georges along the sandy shore road towards West Bay Town. The driver, a genial grandfather with skin the colour of well-ripened corn and the accent of a Penzance pirate, provided a running commentary as we went, but there was little enough to comment on save shacks, sand and sea.

Next morning, it was brought home to me just what a shoe-string airline CIA was. I was last to board and found that the almost empty cabin of the day before had been well over-booked by the happy-go-lucky Cayman Islanders. Several of us had to sit on the steps which led down into the cabin from the rear door. 'Don't worry,' Ron, the pilot, assured us, cheerfully. 'These crates can carry double this number of passengers.'

Two weeks later I was waiting in Tampa, for Ron and the inaugural flight of the Lodestar fleet, which was to take me back to Jamaica. The plane was due to arrive at midday and return to Jamaica the following morning.

To pass the time, my hostess suggested we took in a film. We returned home later that afternoon. Almost immediately, the telephone rang. My friend answered it.

'My God. You'd better speak to him personally.' She handed me the telephone.

'This is the Caribbean International Airways Office,' said a very shaky voice. 'I'm very sorry to tell you that the flight from Kingston crashed on take-off, so tomorrow's flight to Jamaica is cancelled. We have arranged for you to fly to Miami tomorrow and booked you on a BWIA flight the following morning.'

'What happened?' I asked.

'That's all we know, ' she sobbed.

Jamaica was stunned. Parties were cancelled, tennis courts were empty, official engagements postponed. Only one of the fourteen people aboard the ill-fated Lodestar, Bobbie's brother-in-law, had managed to escape. Bobbie himself and his sister, both directors of the airline, and eleven others perished, including the young New Zealand air hostess to whom Bobbie had offered the job two weeks before in the bar of the Courtley Manor, partly out of kindness and partly because on an inaugural flight there should be someone to hand round the champagne.

The official enquiry showed that the cam-shaft of one engine had snapped at take off, causing the plane to lose height and plunge into the sea a hundred yards off the Palisadoes. The landing gear was still down when it hit the water, making it flip onto its back. Doubt was expressed at the plane's soundness, the 'airworthy certificate', having been signed by the mechanic of another airline, in haste and under pressure, less than an hour before take-off.

It was the end of CIA. Half their fleet, two of their three pilots and two directors had been lost on that flight.

Distress at the diaster went even deeper in the Cayman Islands where the airfield at St Georges was renamed Bobbie Roberts Field, in memory of the very popular man whose airline had put their islands on the map.

As I stood in the large crowd at St Andrew's parish Church at Halfway Tree and paid my last respects to Ron and the passengers in a multiple funeral, I thanked my lucky stars that I had been unable to delay my visit to co-incide with CIA's inaugural Lodestar flight.

JAMAICA-HOPES

There was quite a gathering at Bodles Livestock Experimental Station that afternoon in June 1952. The cattle had been groomed till they shone and their stanchions scrubbed clean. VIPs in gleaming cars were directed to the special car park behind the rows of chairs. White-coated herdsmen, new rope halters in hand, stood together, talking importantly.

Dr Phil, the Senior Livestock Officer, almost unrecognizable in coat and tie, had it not been for his height, girth and large mop of grey hair, was on the dias talking to Roger, also dressed in his Sunday-go-to-Meeting best. Before them stood Nymbrook 4th, the highest producing cow in the herd, having just completed a lactation of 9363 lbs of milk in 305 days, almost entirely on grass.

This was a great day for both Dr Phil and Roger. The former for his far-sighted breeding and selection programme, and the latter for his drive and organization in putting the final crown on 40 years of herd improvement – the opening of a provisional herd book and the naming of a new breed.

239

In 1910, the then Director of Agriculture, H.H. Cousins, started to improve the local milk breeds with imported bulls. His sole aim was milk production, and in order to achieve this, he knew that his animals had to be resistant to the heat and high humidity, be fertile, and be able to live off poor grazing. Of the bulls he imported to upgrade his herd, he found the Indian milk breed, the Sahiwal, to be the best for hardiness and the Jerseys to be the best for improving the quality of the milk. Over the years, a smattering of Brown Swiss, Ayrshire and Holstein blood had been included, but the breed type in the 1950s was predominantly Jersey.

Phil, in his thesis for his doctorate at Edinburgh, had shown that it was feasible to improve milk production by selection within the animals already in the country without importing more new blood, so it was decided to collect all these Jersey-Sahiwal type cattle together, register them in a provisional herd book, and carry out a very strict selection and breeding programme.

A spontaneous burst of applause greeted the Governor as he pulled up in front of the assembled audience, the Union Jack flying proudly from the sleek black Austin Princess. Sir Hugh was as popular a Governor as Jamaica had ever had the good fortune to be captained by. Instead of his uniform of plumes and sword, he wore a soft grey suit and trilby. Official State gear might have upset the cows! There was an expectant silence as he mounted the dias and was presented to Tubby (now Director of Agriculture), Dr Phil, Roger and other dignitaries.

Sir Hugh outlined the progress which had been achieved in animal breeding in Jamaica, paying tribute to Mr Cousins, who had started it all, going on to point out the benefits for the island in the future, then, turning to Dr. Phil, who had directed the breeding for the last 20 years, he told the crowd, '... and I have no doubt, whatever, that he is one of Jamaica's most important sons.' While Dr Phil squirmed with embarrassment and tried to hide behind the other VIPs, the assembly gave him a great ovation. Sir Hugh knew the right thing to say at the right time; Dr Phil was already a legend in livestock circles.

When the clapping finished, the Governor took a step towards the cow which stood on the dias, covered with an embroidered blanket. The attendant pulled off the blanket and Sir Hugh, in a voice warmed by emotion, declared. 'It gives me great pleasure to name this breed the "Jamaica-Hope".'

It was a happy choice of name. The work had been carried out where Cousins had started it, at Hope, 40 years before, and the name hinted at great prospects for the dairy industry in the future.

240

A provisional herd book for the new breed would be opened immediately. After five years of careful selection and culling, it would be closed and the final herd book come into force. Already, milk production in this new breed had outstripped all other breeds of dairy cattle in the tropics. The future was exciting.

It was not only the Jamaica-Hope that was dignified with a herd book. Provisional registration for the Jamaican-Brahman, a Zebu animal with predominantly Nellore blood, had been started the previous year in affiliation with the American Brahman Breeders Association in Texas. As a member of the local appraisal team, I looked forward to the twice yearly visits of inspection by officials from ABBA in Houston. I had always loved these graceful, humped Zebus with their pendulous dewlaps and long ears, their short-haired, sleek bodies and arrogant air. No wonder that in India they were considered sacred.

Two other herd books followed. One for the Jamaica-Reds, essentially a red poll type, the other for the Jamaica-Blacks a breed based on heat-adapted Aberdeen Angus.

Exports to South America, already high for these breeds, rose still further. It looked as if Tom's statement on my first day, that Jamaica led the world in tropical cattle development, had been no idle boast!

IRONSHORE DISEASE

Lyndon, the veterinary officer from Westmoreland, dumped some bottles on the lab bench.

'Got a real mystery for you, Pat. What would you call a condition where cattle just lie down and won't get up?'

'Laziness?' I joked. 'Any other symptoms?'

'None. They look fine, you wouldn't think there was anything wrong with them except that two died on the first day. The others seem normal.'

'How many are we talking about?'

'Five.'

'So, two out of five have died and the other three are lying down, apparently normal, but won't get up? Where is this?'

'Ironshore Estate, near Rosehall, about eight miles from Montego Bay. I autopsied the two that died, the only lesion was inflammation of the small intestine just before it joins the colon. I've brought you some specimens.'

'Poison?' I suggested.

'Probably, but which one?'

Cases of poisoning, unless caused by a simple inorganic chemical, are notoriously difficult to investigate. Plant poisons often defy investigators for years. I hoped it wouldn't prove to be one of those. I sent the specimens over to the Government Chemist, asked Smithy, my head technician, to try and isolate what he could in the way of pathogenic bacteria from the lesions, and told Lyndon I would go back with him that afternoon.

Next morning we found three cows lying down in a weed-invaded paddock on Ironshore Estate, munching some Napier grass that had been cut and placed in front of each. They seemed perfectly normal. I prodded one, urging it to get up. No response. It was the same with the other two. They just looked at me with their disdainful Jersey eyes, as if to ask what the hell I thought I was doing, and went on chewing.

All reflexes seemed normal at the front end but they had no power in their tails and seemed insensible to pricks on their hind legs.

'So what poison only affects the hind end?' Lyndon teased.

'God knows. Can't be entero-toxaemia, or botulism, they look too bright – and anyway they're alive!'

We tried to find out everything that had happened on the farm in recent months – treatments with new medicines, change of dip fluid, opening up new pastures and so on. Nothing had been done that hadn't been done each year for years.

'Maybe it's linked to the "X" disease of coconuts,' remarked Lyndon facetiously. A mysterious disease had been killing coconut trees along the north coast. The last expert brought into investigate it had suggested that it was due to an unidentified toxin, stirred up from the depths of the sea by earthquakes and blown landwards in the spray. No-one believed him, and the theory was considered to be a bit of a joke.

We were about to leave when the overseer mentioned something which changed the whole picture.

'We cut back the dogwood last year. First time in years.' He pointed out the profusion of light green leaves which were sprouting in the hedges from stumps of dogwood trees.

Neither Lyndon nor I knew anything about Jamaican dogwood, although I remembered that somebody had mentioned something about its being poisonous. It was a fragile lead, but dogwood poisoning should be easy to prove. All we had to do was to feed it to animals and see their reaction.

Before we could start, another property, Norwood, next but one to Ironshore and further inland, reported cases of the same mysterious condition. The cattle at Norwood were mainly beef-type animals with

242

a high percentage of Indian blood, and were kept on free range.

'Have you dogwood?' we asked.

'Plenty.'

'Have you been cutting it?'

'No.'

'Well, do the cattle eat it?'

'Don't think so. It's rather bitter.'

Seven animals of the herd of about a hundred were lying down, just like those at Ironshore. I felt I should do something, so I gave one an enormous dose of Vitamin B complex, intra-muscularly. Two days later, it was reported to be up and walking. It was the only animal in the entire investigation that recovered. Emboldened by the success of this *ad hoc* remedy, I treated several more, but none showed signs of improvement. Meanwhile, another two properties reported cases.

I rang the Botany Dept of the University. Yes, they knew of Jamaican dogwood. Yes, it had a neuro-toxin, but why didn't we speak to the professor himself, he had written several papers on it even before he came to Jamaica. This was almost too good to be true! From his work it was evident that Jamaican dogwood contained a dangerous agent theoretically capable of causing neurologic symptoms. We seemed to be almost home and dry. Now all we needed was to reproduce the disease experimentally by feeding dogwood to a number of animals. We had no other leads, the chemists could detect no known poisons, and nothing pathogenic was growing in our cultures.

I placed one goat (they were cheaper and easier to handle than cattle) in a pen and fed it dogwood leaves. Another goat I tethered on the rough pastureland at Ironshore, where the original cases had occurred. We kept a 12-hour watch in one-hour shifts, with binoculars, recording all the grasses, shrubs and plants the animal ate throughout the day. It was monotonous, uncomfortable and extremely hot, but we thought it all worth the trouble when it died during the third night. Unfortunately, although it had nibbled at about 30 different species, as far as we could determine, it had never touched dogwood. The stabled goat seemed to relish its dogwood diet, and only showed a transient diarrhoea.

Autopsy of the grazing goat showed slight inflammation of the intestine as well as severe congestion of the meninges of the brain, neither of which helped in the least. I took samples for pathological examination as well as samples to freeze for possible virus isolation.

A few days later, the Pathology Dept at the university came up with a possible clue. Every year cases of so-called 'vomiting sickness' occurred in the poorer children throughout the island. Many people

243

thought it was due to eating unripe ackee, a staple food used much as potatoes were used by the more affluent population. Others blamed the medicinal 'bush-teas', suggesting that with the loss of bush-lore in modern times, the peasants were losing the art of identifying herbs and were selecting poisonous ones by mistake.

Whatever the cause, the main pathological lesion of 'vomiting sickness' under the microscope was a blocking of certain blood vessels in the liver, giving rise to the term 'veno-occlusive disease'. Sections of cattle livers from our cases at Ironshore and other properties gave a similar picture.

As a last resort, in case it was some sort of virus, I inoculated mice and guinea-pigs with brain and other material from the autopsies. Just possibly, I thought, if it was a virus it might show up. It didn't.

If a plant was responsible, why had cases suddenly occurred this year? Records of rainfall and temperature had been average and dogwood had been cut on only one property. If it was infectious, why were so few animals affected, and why hadn't it spread to adjoining properties instead of jumping several before showing itself again?

We started a systematic survey of all trees, plants and shrubs on the half-dozen properties where the condition had occurred and compared them with those on properties which had not reported the condition. It was a very long shot, and we were ill-equipped. The only botanists available were in the University, and they could only spare the odd day to help us classify the hundreds of specimens.

We did, however, come across a dozen or so potentially poisonous plants, including several species of the so-called 'nightshade' (*Echites spp*), which had long been associated with sudden deaths in cattle; and a Crotalaria or 'rattleweed', which had also been incriminated in human 'vomiting sickness'. Again, we ground up the leaves and fed them to goats and rabbits. Again, without success.

Inevitably, the investigation wound down. We couldn't reproduce the condition, we couldn't find any difference in the flora of those properties that had the disease and those that hadn't, we couldn't detect any poisons or isolate any pathogens, we ran out of steam. Moreover, no more cases had occurred after the first few weeks, so we had nothing new to work on. Whatever had caused the condition had gone, anyway for the present.

Cases did occur in the following years and were investigated by others, with as little success.

The condition is still remembered as 'Ironshore disease' or 'Dogwood poisoning'. But was it dogwood? Possibly. Or another plant? Who knows? An infection seems unlikely.

Why do I take the trouble to mention this investigation at all? After all, it was a failure, except that we learned a lot about the flora of the area. It's because this one was typical of so many others, starting with enthusiasm and confidence, plodding on through hot tiring days in the field, with interest kept alive by flashes of luck or inspiration, only to fizzle out and be superseded by something more urgent.

But it is only through knowledge gained in this way, from apparently unsuccessful operations, that a platform of data can be built up from which to launch the successful attack when the time is ripe.

Recently, an exhaustive analysis of the blood from cases of 'Dogwood or Ironshore disease' has revealed toxic levels of tin! So perhaps it will now be known as 'Tinshore disease'!

The file is still open.

'TISSIC' AND TYPHUS

I knew Linda's cat well; it often sat on my lap while we talked. Poor Mish! She had been the apple of her mistress's eye, until she had a litter of kittens – the cat, that is. They were lovely little things, although possibly a little thin-haired around the eyes and ears. Within two weeks, Linda noticed red, irritant circles between her bosoms. Ringworm, said the doctor – probably from the kittens. Linda rang me in distress.

'Probably Mish is a symptomless carrier,' I explained, 'and the kittens became infected from her. It's quite common. Unfortunately, there's little I can do. I think you should put down the kittens at once and consider putting Mish to sleep as well. Treatment is unreliable.'

'There's another problem,' she moaned, 'Mish has tissic.'

Tissic was a Jamaican word to describe a peculiar sneezing condition in cats. The animal would have spasms of 'a-tishoooing' several times an hour, and after a time it would exhibit a nasal discharge. Rarely would such animals recover.

'I have no idea how to treat tissic,' I told her. 'I don't even know what causes it.'

'They say it's from eating lizards,' she told me.

'I've heard that too, it's an old wives' tale. But I still don't know what to do about it, and Mish is still a carrier of ringworm, which I don't recommend treating.'

'I think you had better put her to sleep then,' she decided tearfully.

I collected the cat and the kittens and put them to sleep. Then I did a thorough autopsy on Mish. She was like a parasite museum.

Her liver was full of tiny, flat, oblong flukes, like the cattle ones but very much smaller. Until that moment I hadn't even realized that cats suffered from liver fluke. But there was more. In her stomach were two different types of roundworms, neither of which I could identify immediately, but the really exciting discovery was a couple of worms attached to the lining of her pharynx. No wonder she coughed and sneezed and had a nasal discharge. I could find no description of such a worm in cats in any of my reference books, although members of this group of worms, *Syngamus*, were sometimes seen in the throats of chickens and occasionally in cattle. This was thrilling. A new species, perhaps?

I sent specimens to a parasitologist friend at the London School of Hygiene and Tropical Medicine. The liver fluke and the stomach worms, he told me, were well-known in some tropical countries, although they had not been recorded in Jamaica before. The worm from the pharynx, while not common, was not a new species, not quite. 'Sorry, old man,' he wrote. 'I got there first. I described it for the first time, some years ago, in Trinidad. Better luck next time.'

The life cycle of the cat liver fluke was not known to me then, but a report I read later said that it passed through a snail (as did the cattle fluke), which was then eaten by lizards. Cats became infected by eating lizards. The life cycle of the throat worm was also still a mystery, but I wondered whether it too passed through the lizard.

Old wives' tales are often worth listening to!

* * *

I woke with a bursting head. Nothing would relieve it. This was the father and mother of all hangovers – except I had only drunk one beer the night before.

By evening, it was too painful to lie down. I rang Billy, who had left the Government service in Port Maria and was now in private practice in Kingston.

'You've probably got typhus,' he told me cheerfully.

'Oh, God. Am I going to die? I certainly feel like it.'

'You might have done some years ago, but a few days of chloromycetin should put you right. This is only the murine type.' Preserve me from other types, I thought.

Some weeks before I had begun a survey of a rat-borne zoonosis called Weil's disease or leptospirosis. It had been Billy who had first drawn my attention to the disease after diagnosing two human cases near Port Maria, both fatal, the first cases, he believed, to have been recorded in Jamaica. I had never seen it in dogs in Jamaica, but I knew that the dog strain could also infect humans.

Although leptospirosis seemed rare in Jamaica, it had long been a scourge amongst cane cutters in Barbados, the sugar island halfway to Trinidad. One of the symptoms was severe jaundice, and at first this had misled the Barbadian medical authorities into thinking it was yellow fever, a mosquito-borne virus disease which had decimated populations in the area for hundreds of years. In 1907, a Royal Commission from Britain had concurred with the yellow fever diagnosis, and it was not until the 1930s, when a perspicacious young doctor in Bridgetown, Harry Bayley, re-examined the evidence and conducted his own investigations, that the true cause of these seasonal outbreaks of jaundice were elucidated. He confirmed that it was the rat-borne spirochaete of leptospirosis, not the mosquito-borne virus of yellow fever, that was the culprit.

One of the aspects of the disease that fascinated me was its prevalence in countries that had alkaline soil. The organism, it seemed, was highly susceptible to an acid environment below pH 7.0. I divided the Caribbean islands into those which had volcanic (acid) and those which had coral (alkaline) origins. From questionnaires I sent to medical and veterinary personnel, I found that only one of the six volcanic islands that replied had recorded leptospirosis, but that three of the four coral islands had recorded outbreaks. Barbados, of course, was highly alkaline. Fuzzy evidence perhaps, but it tended to confirm my theory.

I also made a soil map of Jamaica and predicted where outbreaks might occur. The first two cases had been in an alkaline area near Port Maria. Next, I began to survey rats from wherever I could get them, which was mainly Kingston, by courtesy of the municipality's rat catchers. I found the leptospira bug in 4 of 38 rats – all from Kingston, an alkaline area. It was interesting but not enough upon which to draw conclusions.

There was nothing inconclusive about my present headache, however, the main symptom of murine typhus. The rickettsia organisms which caused the disease are present in the intestines of the fleas feeding on infected rodents, so I must have picked some up from flea excreta while autopsying the rats. I felt very sorry for myself for a week, but at least it wasn't leptospirosis or – for that matter – plague, another flea-borne disease!

CARIBBEAN CONFERENCES

There must be a mistake. The programme stated clearly that the Regional Conference on Zoonoses would be opened by His Excellency, Presidente Batista, in the auditorium of the Capitolio, Havana at ten a.m.

There was no doubt that this was the Capitolio, the seat of Government; no-one could miss the enormous white building with its impressive dome. The date was right, too, and the time by my watch was nine-thirty. Surely someone should have put in an appearance by now, after all it was the president of Cuba who was opening the proceedings. At about ten minutes to the hour, the few workmen who had been sitting on benches in the lofty corridor stumbled, reluctantly, to their feet and started to hang up some very tatty decorations. They had better hurry, I thought, the big boss will be here any moment.

Half an hour later, some sleepy military bandsmen in scruffy, braided uniforms wandered in and sat down near the door to smoke and chat. They were soon followed by a group of well-dressed individuals with briefcases, whom I assumed to be delegates. After a quick glance around, they departed. I followed and was delighted to see them stop at a coffee stall in a corridor behind the auditorium.

Flaunting almost my total Spanish vocabulary, I ordered a *cafecito, por favor*, in a drawling British accent. The delegates turned to examine me, decided I was an unimportant *gringo* and returned to discussing their own affairs.

Back in the conference hall I found several more delegates seated singly or in groups. Two, whom I passed, were speaking in English. I introduced myself and asked if they knew when the proceedings would start.

'Ten o'clock, old boy. *Hora Cubana.*'

Ten o'clock, in Cuba, they told me, could mean anything from eleven to three in the afternoon, but that between twelve and one would be a pretty good estimate.

I wandered about for another hour or so and then settled myself behind a placard marked Jamaica on one of the long circular benches reserved for delegates. Gradually the hall began to fill, the participants squashing in from the end so that I was shoved along past placards that proclaimed Haiti, Venezuela and Curacao, until my inescapably *gringo* features came to rest behind the placard for Costa Rica, and it was as a delegate from that country that I appeared in the press photo the following morning!

I spotted several friends in the growing crowd. Big Jim, head of the US Veterinary Public Health Service from Atlanta, appeared with some of his colleagues. Several of the staff of the PanAmerican Sanitary Bureau in Washington, under whose aegis the conference was being held, turned up, as did a veterinary colleague from Barbados.

248

It was nearly one o'clock when a blast of trumpets from the semi-organized bandsmen heralded a massive, dark-skinned, negroid-countenanced dignitary in a flashy white tunic covered with decorations.

'Hermann Goering,' I whispered to my neighbour, a doctor from St Lucia.

'Just as bad,' he whispered back. 'His Excellentissimo, Fulgencio Batista.'

As the bull-like head of State led his retinue down the central aisle, a great burst of clapping and cheering erupted from a group of youths in the gallery. Some of the delegates turned and stared, but they were mostly from Latin America and used to such displays by hired groups of applauders. His Excellency bowed, waved to the youths and gave a lengthy impassioned speech, none of which I could understand as the translation system was not yet functioning. Then he left to the cheers of *les claques* in the gallery and another discordant fanfare from the sloppy bandsmen.

I had every hope that the conference would now start, but I hadn't reckoned with the flamboyancy of Latin American opening ceremonies. They dragged on until nearly eleven that night and appeared to me to be more a series of theatrical performances by the speakers than the opening of an international conference. Squashed in, as I was, there was nothing I could do but sit and listen to the elaborate speeches and poems delivered with the most extravagant gestures.

Television cameras (Cuba was one of the first Caribbean Islands to have TV) constantly swept the auditorium, concentrating on the solid block of swarthy Cuban delegates, recognisable immediately by their white starched *guayaberos*, a type of linen tunic or bush jacket, with long sleeves and pleats down the front. The advantage of this garment was that it could be worn open-necked in the day, but could be buttoned at the neck at night when the addition of a black bow tie, carried in the pocket made it formal evening dress.

Cuba was the first Latin American country I had visited. As a visitor, I thoroughly enjoyed my week, but it seemed to me a dreadfully disorganized and selfish place. Everyone did exactly as he wanted to without thought for anyone else. I would be glad to return to the less individualistic and more stable life of Jamaica.

The veterinary meetings of the Caribbean Commission, the first organization to attempt the unification of the British West Indies, provided me with opportunities to visit several of the smaller islands. Barbados, a green raft of sugar cane halfway between Jamaica and Trinidad, had probably the finest rum in the world, best drunk with soda or water, and which left no hangover as did the cruder Jamaican rum, which needed to be mixed with ginger ale or Coca-Cola or in a rum punch, to disguise its taste.

St Vincent, another conference site, was a mountainous isle, 200 miles north of Trinidad. We flew from Port of Spain in a Gruman Goose, which must be the noisiest seaplane in the world, especially one as old as this, with its two radial engines battling to get us into the air and keep us there. The pilot an American and the 'co-pilot', his teenage son, were both dressed in beach clothes. As we took off, the lad began to wind up something on the floor with a crank handle, for all the world like a centre board of a yacht. It turned out to be the undercarriage.

It was memorable flight. After passing Grenada at about 5,000 feet, we flew over the Grenadines, a necklace of emerald isles set in rings of amethyst and gold. The pilot yelled out their names as we passed, but neither I nor the other five passengers could hear above the noise of the engines.

The approach to St Vincent was nothing less than terrifying. Skirting a high, rocky island near the shore, we headed straight for a cliff. Just as I was certain that we were going to crash into it, the sea-plane swung to the right and landed alongside the beach. Spray blotted out everything as we hit the water, but as soon as it cleared, I found that we were entering a small dock from which we ran up a ramp onto the land.

Customs were very informal. The pilot and his young assistant went unchallenged as they unloaded crates of beer and other supplies, and with the help of friends, humped them down the shore to a beach cottage. Before we left the airport, both father and son were in the water, spear-fishing. If one ever had to be an airline pilot, I thought, this would be the airline to choose.

All these conferences were basically the same. Old friends slapped each other on the back, bragged to each other, presented rather inferior papers and got thoroughly drunk in the evening. But they had their use. We found out exactly what was happening in the other islands, who was working on what, and we could pool our technical problems for all to consider.

The farthest afield that I managed was Brazil. Three weeks at the Regional Foot and Mouth Research Centre near Rio de Janeiro introduced me to the extremes of Latin American luxury – and squalor. Rio had one of the most impressive views in the world. On the top of a 2,000-foot hill overlooking the city, a 135-foot-high statue of Christ had been erected, with arms outstretched in permanent benediction. Just as well I thought if ever a city needed constant spiritual succour, it was Rio.

From this statue, the Corcovado, one could look down on the whole vista of Rio and Guanabaro Bay, from the lagoons and hills that divided up the suburbs, to the dormitory town of Niteroi which lay across the bay opposite the Sugar Loaf, a conical granite hill at the entrance to the harbour. The yellow strands of Copacabana and Ipanema were packed with sun-worshippers who emerged daily, like lice, from the wall of high-rise apartment blocks that separated the ocean from the commercial area. Further inland, around the lagoons, sprawled the luxury homes of the ultra-rich with their clubs ($10,000 entrance fee, thank you very much!), the race track and parks. Further inland still, were the barren hills up which straggled the higgledy-piggeldy *favelos*, or slums, made up of thousands of shacks, without roads, water supply or sanitation, pushed higher and higher up the barren slopes like scum, away from the abodes of the elite.

The Research Institute, to which we bussed daily, was some 20 miles outside the city near the small town of Caxias. After leaving the highway we wound along a secondary road past several small villages with their hilltop churches and graveyards. Every day we would pass at least one procession bearing a small white coffin to its final resting place amongst the other crosses on the hill. These processions were usually made up of children who waved and smiled at us, apparently not in the least sad that one of their number had left them for ever.

The reason for most of these infant deaths, we were told, was the filthy water, a problem which could have been solved very simply by a little conscientious organization. Half-covered by foliage along the roadside lay the concrete pipes which would have brought in pure water if the municipality could have scraped together sufficient funds from its annual outlay on bribes and corruption to connect them to the reservoir. They had lain there for over five years. Five years of enteritis, deaths and daily excursions to the graveyards. But that was Brazil. I was to find out much more about Brazil in the years ahead.

Memories of Rio that I still hold after 35 years are the poverty of the *favelos*, the uncontrollable traffic scorching along the boulevards and the terrifying feeling of suffocation when held up bumper to bumper in the middle of one of the long, six-lane road tunnels; the fascinating beauty of the girls and the rhythmic music which pervaded everything, and the excruciating tummy upsets, 'Rio-itis', to which we all succumbed. Football was a religion and its followers as fanatic as any *conquistador*, but matches seemed always to end in a fight, started of course by the losing team.

It was in Rio that I first heard the expression '*Amigo da onça*' – 'friend of the onça', a large jungle cat. Two friends, it seems, were discussing what would happen if they met an *onça*.

251

'I'd shoot it,' said the first.

'Your gun misfires,' retorts his friend.

'I'd use my revolver.'

'You've dropped it.'

'I'd attack it with my hunting knife.'

'The knife breaks.'

'I'd run.'

'The *onça* runs faster.'

'I'd climb a tree.'

'There aren't any trees.'

'Hey,' expostulates the first. 'Are you my friend or the friend of the *onça*?'

An *Amigo da onça* was someone who made problems for others. Twenty years later when I worked in Brazil, I found no shortage of *amigos da onça*!

'SEEK AND YE SHALL FIND'

Scientific investigation, I realized, had now replaced my earlier passion for buried treasure – not that there was much difference between the two.

Nothing gave me more delight than having a problem to solve. I hung a placard in my office:

'SEEK AND YE SHALL FIND'

There was nothing irreverent in this, it simply expressed my new attitude and complemented another notice which I put in the lab:

'MANNERS MAKETH MAN – TECHNIQUE TECHNICIANS'

Without doubt, these were the happiest years of my career. I could follow up my field investigations in the lab, thus developing both sides of my research. Spear-fishing, tennis and hockey kept me in trim, and later in the day a seemingly endless bevy of beauty was at my beck and call. I should have been spilling over with contentment. I was, although two things worried me. I was largely self-taught in research, picking up tips here and there from the University and from visiting scientists, reading scientific articles and books, and attending short courses and symposiums. All of which were creditable enough,

252

but at 33 I was still only on the first rung of the research ladder. Most serious investigators of my age had a string of papers to their name. All I had published were the first two parts of my zoonoses survey and an article on tissic. I desperately needed a sound academic grounding if I was to make it as an investigator.

The other worry was that I was still single. As an unmarried uncle once told me, 'If you can't make up your mind between two girls, neither is the right one.' Well, it was difficult with so many around, but I wasn't going to end up a bachelor like him. The Jamaicans were more cynical, 'Why bodder wi' a cook in de mango season?' they'd say. I was still in my mango season, but I knew it wouldn't last.

It was Louis, the bacteriologist at the University, who helped me to solve my first problem – that of postgraduate specialization. Louis had recently returned from London, where he had taken the Diploma in bacteriology at the London School of Hygiene and Tropical Medicine, the most prestigious one-year course in medical microbiology in Britain.

'Why don't you try for it, man,' he suggested.

'Good God,' I replied, 'they only take twelve students a year. I haven't a hope.'

'Yes, but they like two of those twelve to be vets. I doubt if the competition will be that great.'

Roger wrote an exaggerated and moving plea to Government for my release, and Tubby, the Director of Agriculture, added his quite unwarranted recommendations. I was given leave to apply, and in due course London accepted me.

It was a year of absolute hell, but worth every agonizing minute. The 'Dip. Bact.' was the most coveted of diplomas for those engaged in microbiological research. Six of our number were from overseas, and there was one other vet. The course was restricted to those working in microbiology between the ages of 27 (to allow for a certain previous experience), and 35 (the arbitrary upper age limit for absorbing knowledge quickly).

I found a cheap basement flat in Warwick Road, Earl's Court, but it was not until I had signed the lease and moved in, well pleased with my bargain, that I discovered that the 'loo' was outside in the garden! I didn't think that such things still existed in London.

At the end of the first term our small band scattered for Christmas holidays, pale of face and shaking with nerves. There was not one of us who considered, even remotely, that he or she would ever stay the course. In addition to lectures and practicals, we were given long lists of articles each day to read and assimilate. We divided the journals

253

and gave each other resumés over coffee. It was the only way.

I took every Friday evening off, the only break of the week, and played squash with Jeanette, a dark-haired, grey-eyed, petite secretary who remained a lifelong friend and became godmother to my fifth child.

On my return to Jamaica, I found that Roger had accepted the job of Chief Veterinary Research Officer in Tanganyika (Tanzania); he and Pru would be leaving within a month. Not only would I lose two of my best friends, I would now be saddled once more with the administration of the Division. Gone were my visions of erudite research, armed with the skills and techniques so painfuliy acquired in London. It looked as if pen-pushing was to be my only reward!

I soon found myself out of the lab, banished to a gloomy, mosquito-infested, 10 by 12 foot cell which opened onto the upstairs verandah of Head Office in Hope Gardens, the same building to which Roger had taken me to meet the Director the day I had arrived, eight years before. The mosquitoes had lost none of their voracity.

As for my bachelorhood, I had suspected for some time that it was in danger of toppling.

A few months before leaving for study in London, I had been sitting in the University library, checking references for the last of my articles on zoonoses in the Caribbean. Above and behind me was a balcony from which came some low voices. Idly, I turned and looked up. A gorgeous girl, tall, slim, with a bright merry face and hair the colour of meerschaum, leant against the railing talking to the Head Librarian. What a creation, I thought. I wonder who she is.

It would have been too blatant to rush up and ask for an introduction. I would have to be more subtle. So every day thereafter, morning and afternoon, I would pop into the library, hoping to see her again. Maybe she was a new assistant librarian, or a junior lecturer, or something. Obviously she was no ordinary female!

After an unsuccessful week of pretending to look up references and trying at the same time to keep one eye on all visitors that came in, I plucked up sufficient courage to enquire at the desk as to who it was that the Librarian had been escorting.

'Some visitor from an English University, I think,' was all they could tell me.

Blast! If that were so, she would have probably left the island by now. Just my luck. I chalked up another 'might have been.'

It was Ken and Marjorie, a few weeks later, who put me out of my misery – or into it, as they joked later! Marjorie had come in from Trelawney for a Veterinary Officers' meeting, and Ken had come with her. That evening we sat sipping rum and gingers on my verandah at Hope.

'Have you met cousin Mary yet?' Ken asked.

'No, don't know any Marys,' I replied. 'I've a Susan, a Joan, a Monica and a Valerie, but no Mary.'

'Oh boy, she'll fix your business. I'll see if she's free.' he went inside to phone. 'Yes, she'd love to come up. I'll just go and fetch her. Your bachelor days are over, laddie.'

Well, it was about time. I was growing a little desperate for the right one to come along.

No prizes, of course, for guessing who Mary turned out to be. A cousin of Marjorie's, she had just returned from St Andrew's University in Scotland where, as Jamaica Scholar for 1948, she had been studying for her MA.

We began to see a lot of each other, and it certainly looked as if my bachelor and her spinster days were numbered, but two interruptions cropped up. The day she had arrived back in Jamaica, Mary had slipped a disc and was now rapidly losing power in her left leg. Eventually, she convinced the young orthopaedic surgeon at the University Hospital to operate. It was early days for disc surgery, but John (later Sir John) Golding did an excellent job, and ten days after the operation she was out of hospital and spear-fishing. Then my imminent departure for postgraduate study in London provided another obstacle. I would find it difficult enough to cope with a 'Dip. Bact.' without other distractions, and it would be pointless to marry

St. Mark's, Rio Bueno

255

and leave her behind. So we decided to see how we felt when I returned, and for another year, linked only by letters, we went our separate ways in separate countries.

After my return, we took up where we had left off, but another snag arose. Mary, was offered a Government scholarship – to Oxford University. This was not something one turned down without good reason. However, barely two weeks before she was to depart and nearly two years after we had first met, Mary cabled Oxford that she had more important business, to attend to, and I was able to tell Ken he could now complete the job he had started on the verandah at Hope.

Three weeks later he married us in the ancient stone church at Rio Bueno, a few yards from the deep blue Caribbean. The stench of bats and the acute bronchial attacks of the organ in no way lessened that momentous occasion. Bob, a young English vet who had arrived the previous year, was Best Man, and Danny, who had come with him, the Chief Usher.

Frankly, I never thought we would ever get that far – not because of incompatibilities, but because Mary had purchased a Vespa motor scooter. She rode it to work and even as far as the North Coast, but contrived to spend as much time beneath it as in the saddle. It was the same after she graduated to a motorcycle. Any oil slick or gravel patch acted like a magnet, and Mary would return from her trips with scarified knees and elbows and covered in grease; nevertheless, she arrived at the church three minutes early and temporally unblemished by oil or scarred elbows.

The reception was held in Ken and Marjorie's garden at Whitehall, where Mary's Mum and Dad from Vancouver and the family's many relations and connections in Jamaica wished us a long and happy life together. Sadly, my parents were too far away, in Kenya, to attend.

The first night of our honeymoon we spent in the Queen's Cottage at the nearby Silver Sands Beach Club, the cottage in which Queen Elizabeth had stayed during her visit to Jamaica some years previously. At seven-thirty the following morning we were wakened from a solid sleep by someone whistling 'Lazy Bones' under our bedroom window, I peered out to find the cheery face of Bill (later, Sir William) Weipers, the then Dean of the Glasgow Veterinary College, smiling up at me.

Bill and his wife had been spending a few weeks holiday with their old friends, Marjorie and Ken, after attending the Second West Indian Veterinary Conference in Kingston. On the evening of the wedding, Bill and I had taken over Marjorie's duties, traipsing up

256

hills and down gullies in pursuit of sick pigs, cows and dogs, while she prepared the wedding reception. After lunch, Bill had helped me with a paper I was writing before I went off to change.

'I've brought your article back,' Bill grinned, handing a sheaf of papers. 'I've made some notes and thought I'd get them to you before we leave later this morning.'

Inspite of his uncivilized early morning reveille and his unmelodious serenade, Bill remained a valued friend.

Thirty-five years and eight kids later, Mary is still the same bright, gorgeous girl she was when I first saw her in the UCWI library.

ZOO QUEST

It was a hot, steamy afternoon. I wiped the perspiration off my brow and took a thin file from the top of my in tray. 'PROPOSALS FOR THE ESTABLISHMENT OF A ZOOLOGICAL GARDEN' was printed across the cover.

Fine. I had always been interested in zoos – proper zoos, with animals free to roam large enclosures resembling their natural habitat. While in Northern Rhodesia I had written to Whipsnade Zoo, asking them to put me on their list for possible future appointments. I had also spent a day at the New Bronx Zoo in New York, with the veterinarian in charge, and had been much impressed by the way an illusion of both space and close association of different species had been created by constructing deep canyons between the free-ranging animal groups.

The immediate reason for the file appearing on my desk was a letter from a member of the public, addressed to the Minister of Agriculture, asking why Jamaica had no zoo and proposing that one be established forthwith for the education and entertainment of the good citizens of the island. Being an animal matter, it had been passed on to me to answer.

I agreed. Jamaica *should* have a zoo. Why not? But there was little chance of laying out a Bronx or Whipsnade type of operation. It would have to be small and rely on cages. No, I decided immediately. No cages. Better no zoo than cages. We would have to think of something else. Any type of cage was abomination.

The file had only a dozen pages in it. The first entry, 12 years before, was a letter from another anxious citizen, a certain N.N. Nethersole, who had strongly advocated that a zoo be established in the Hope Botanical Gardens. My interest soared. Nethersole, eh? Well, well. 12 years ago N.N. Nethersole might have been no more

257

than a respected member of the public, but today the honourable N.N. ('Crab') Nethersole was no less than Minister of Finance in Norman Manley's government. Ho, ho! I thought, let's see if he'll put his money where his mouth is.

Later that week, I met with the Professor of Zoology in the University, the Director of the Jamaica Institute and the Town Planner. We decided that a zoo would benefit the island and that we should form ourselves into an *ad hoc* Zoo Committee to further the cause. We wrote down a few basic principles, suggestions and costs and I forwarded them to the Hon. Minister 'Crab' Nethersole. (The nickname 'Crab' was a hangover from his school days and referred to his small and cramped handwriting.)

The national budget had already been approved, so I was all the more delighted to receive a minute from the Financial Secretary, informing me that the Minister had agreed to the sum of £500 in the Supplementary Estimates for the planning of a zoo. It wasn't much, but that we had received anything at all at so short a notice, from such a tight-fisted Ministry, showed that we had at least a modicum of backing in high places.

The Jamaica Institute unearthed a dear old retired architect who produced a layout and buildings better suited to an early Victorian prison, the exact opposite of the open-plan, minimum-restraint, concept we had in mind. These were tactfully rejected, but I left Jamaica before a final decision was reached, my last plea being that the job be given to a professional architect with experience of zoos, and that the Director of the Trinidad Zoo should also be consulted. I had been very much impressed with the way he had handled the extremely difficult task of setting up a zoological garden in Port of Spain with little funds and minimal space. His experience could save us a lot of headaches. The success of the project, I knew, would not be the animals, *per se*, but the attitude and foresight of those in charge.

After I had written this, I heard that the zoo was flourishing under a dynamic and realistic group of administrators who were developing it as a conservation park rather than a conventional zoo.

Even hot sticky afternoons in the office can sometimes kindle worthwhile flames.

BIG SYD

He loped into my office unannounced – that's if I could have ignored the heavy strides which shook the ant-eaten wooden stairs. It would be a big man, I thought, as I heard him approach, and a tall one.

258

And I was right. The figure now filling the doorway was both tall and broad, blotting out half the late afternoon light and making my gloomy cubby hole even darker. His stance, his thrusting jaw and disdainful expression – in fact everything about him – spelt trouble. 'Yee-oo the vet?' he enquired in a deep Southern drawl.

The way he said 'yee-oo' together with the ten-gallon hat with which he fanned his slightly pockmarked face, and his high-heeled, ornate leather boots, suggested a Texan cowboy – a 'baddie' rather than a 'goodie'. Though broad and tall, he was lean and hard. His short hair was just turning grey, his wide mouth never stopped chewing, whether on gum or plug I couldn't tell. His words shot out between chomps without disturbing the rhythm of his jaw.

'I'm Director of Veterinary Services,' I replied. 'If you want the clinic, it's just down the road ...'

'I got a Ro-dee-o,' he interrupted, 'should be here any day. They tell me I gotta get a permit from yee-oo. Christ, it's hot.'

'A rodeo? You mean horses?'

'Yep.' His spiky-heeled shoes hammered the rotting floor boards as he crossed to my desk and flopped his lanky frame onto my visitor's chair.

'Where are you bringing them from?' I asked, at once suspicious.

He ignored the question and went on, 'They tell me you've never had a Ro-dee-o in Jamaica before. This is a good one. You'll love it.'

'Probably, but where is the rodeo now?' I insisted.

'Dunno, exactly, we play all over the place. Last time I heard they were in Ireland. My pardner will know,' he offered, looking at the ceiling.

'Well, that's OK. If they come direct from Ireland we'll let them in, but our regulations specifically prohibit any equine entering from North or South America or the other Caribbean islands.'

He stood up and strode over to the map of the world hanging on the wall in front of my desk. So far, he had not once looked at me direct. Always his eyes were on the ceiling or floor or on the photos on the walls. I knew I shouldn't believe a word he said.

'Reckon they'll come through the Bahamas or Puerto Rico,' he said, studying the map. 'They got their own plane, takes the lot. I'll tell my pardner to let you know.'

I gave him a copy of the Importation Regulations and made out a permit to allow his animal troupe to enter by direct flight from Ireland.

Then – I'll call him Sam Huckster, it sort of fits – picked up his ten-gallon hat from where he'd placed it on top of my out tray and stomped through the door without looking at me again or saying goodbye. The building shook for the second time.

I heard nothing more of the affair for several weeks until my secretary asked me, one morning, whether I was going to the rodeo.

'Rodeo? When?'

'Next week. They've got posters all over town.'

I was due to leave for St Vincent in the Windward Islands the following day, to attend the annual conference of the Caribbean Commission. I decided to go down town, collect my tickets from the travel agent and have a look at the posters at the same time.

I soon found one and it did nothing to reassure me. 'GRAND AMERICAN RODEO', it yelled. 'COWBOYS BRONCO-BUSTERS' – and many other attractions were listed. Last, but not least, was 'Big Syd', billed as a bucking Brahman bull, with offers of $1000 to anyone who could stay on him for half a minute or longer. It was all very exciting, but there was a distinct odour of trouble.

Back in the office, a telephone message from the local agent said that the rodeo would be arriving within the next day or two. I rang Allan, who would deputize for me while I was away.

'They're a bum lot,' I told him. 'Don't trust them an inch. I've given them a permit provided they come direct from Ireland and do not offload anywhere in the Americas.'

The following morning I left for St Vincent and forgot all about Sam Huckster and his rodeo for the next glorious week.

Allan met me at the airport on my return, Mary was with him.

'How did it go?' I asked.

The rodeo had arrived late in the evening of the day I had left. The scene had been chaotic. The rusty transport plane was on its last legs and had only just made the runway. The airport authorities, as if ashamed of it, had parked it in an ill-lit area near the workshops. Allan had arrived to find the customs officials overwhelmed by the Spanish and Portuguese-speaking crew and handlers, who ignored every regulation as they tried to unload their cargo of terrified creatures. The lone policeman who should have reinforced the customs officials seemed to have been trampled underfoot.

As soon as Allan could find the pilot, who was the only person who had the vaguest sense of responsibility, he asked where the plane had come from.

'Puerto Rico,' was the reply.

'How long were you there?'

'About two weeks.'

'And before that?'

'Cuba, Venezuela, Brazil, Colombia. You name it.'

'Didn't you come from Ireland?'

'No, never been near Europe.'

'Well, you'll have to take the horses away; they can't land.'

'Sorry, no can do,' the pilot replied. 'This bloody crate will need an overhaul before it can take off. Lucky we're not feeding the sharks right now.'

In order to bring some kind of order out of the chaos, Allan told them to off load the horses and take them directly to the rodeo site on a sports ground. This he immediately placed under guard, and later fiddled the regulations to make the rodeo site a temporary quarantine area with a permanent police guard. In addition, the tent in which the horses were kept was draped with mosquito gauze and sprayed regularly with insecticides.

Allan took me to see them. Big Syd, a mean-natured Brahman, with a colossal hump, was paddocked nearby. I suspected that his mean nature was man-made and constantly topped up. Already there had been several performances, and they were booked for another ten days. The rodeo appeared to be a great success – especially Big Syd, who never failed to rid himself of any over-confident jockey within seconds of mounting.

'Anyway,' chuckled Allan, 'if you want specialized information on Big Syd, ask Mary.'

'So what have you and Big Syd been doing?' I asked her jokingly.

Mary was immediately serious. 'Damn man wouldn't let me ride it.'

'What, you weren't going to ride Big Syd?'

'Certainly. A thousand dollars is a thousand dollars.'

'You're crazy. What happened?'

'I volunteered, but the ringmaster refused. I insisted, so he put it to the vote of the spectators. They were obviously for me but he said they were shouting no.'

'Bully, for him,' I said. 'You're damn lucky to have escaped.'

I was used to Mary's escapades on her motorcycle, but broncho-bucking was something else.

As the final days of the rodeo approached, we tried to make sure that nothing would prevent them leaving on schedule. They were due to fly out on a Sunday Morning. On the Friday, Allan went down on his daily inspection. He was back very quickly.

'Guess what?' he spluttered. 'Old Sam Huckster has disappeared with all the takings. The personnel aren't paid and say they will abandon the animals.'

'Oh, God. Isn't there anyone in charge?'

'Only the local agent, but he doesn't know where Huckster has

261

gone. Evidently he flew out last night after the show and took all the proceeds with him. The rodeo is supposed to appear in Mexico next week.' After some prodding by the local sponsors, the performers were persuaded to carry on, so that the Friday and Saturday performances went ahead. The pilot agreed to fly them to Mexico, where the local agent was certain that Sam Huckster would meet them. A rendezvous, I considered, highly unlikely to be kept. But just as long as they left the island, I didn't care what happened to them.

Both Allan and I were at the airport to see the menagerie take off. It was mid-morning before they had all the animals loaded, including Big Syd. A few minutes later, the antique transport shuddered down the airstrip and disappeared into the blue over the sea.

We smote each other lustily. 'Come and have a beer,' I told Allan. 'You've earned it.' We sang and joked all the way back to my house.

As we finished the first bottle of Red Stripe, the telephone rang.

'I'll take it,' said Allan. 'Probably a cow calving or a dog run over. Always is on a Sunday.' How easy if it had been.

'Shit, the plane's back! Engine trouble.'

We tore down to the Palisadoes airport. The plane was back where it had been for the last two weeks. Several animals, including Big Syd, had already been unloaded. They wanted to redistribute the weight while they looked at the engine, they said.

After a couple of hours the resident engineer for an American airline signed a note to say that the plane was sufficiently repaired to fly. Once again we watched the animals being loaded, all prepared to wave another farewell. But Big Syd had other ideas. He liked Jamaica. It was a climate he understood, besides, he didn't hold with all this flying. He put his head down, charged his handlers and took off.

The runway was surrounded by miles of mangrove swamp and low bushes. Big Syd was soon out of sight. It was now mid-afternoon. The plane had either to take off within minutes or stay till the next day, which meant more unloading and exposure of the horses to millions of mosquitoes. We decided to let them leave Big Syd, just as long as the rest went. We could find him at our leisure and he was no danger to our disease position.

A second time we watched the plane disappear, this time into stormy clouds. We never heard what happened. Presumably they reached Mexico but whether Sam Huckster turned up to meet them, or whether the rodeo survived, none of us ever knew.

Big Syd, of course, was still with us – and for keeps. Early next day he was found grazing contentedly on the edge of the runway, and allowed himself to be roped and trucked up to the paddocks of the JSPCA – almost as if he had planned it all.

Immediately, Big Syd became news. Letters to the press recommended that he should form part of the national stud, that he should be exhibited in a special enclosure in the Hope Zoo when it was built, or be incorporated into the island's artificial insemination service. He was mentioned in the House of Representatives and became the subject of cartoons by the *Daily Gleaner's* artist, Leandro.

Eventually, when all the furore had died down and test matches had taken over the front page once more, Big Syd was given a retirement paddock by courtesy of a sugar company and, as far as I know, lived a happy life free from interference by people such as Sam Huckster, grazing happily, like Ferdinand, on his guinea grass pasture amongst the cane fields of Moneymusk Estate.

For Big Syd, at any rate, the rodeo had been an outstanding success.

JAMAICA FAREWELL

'Of course you must go.'

I looked at the man across the wide leather-topped desk, his eyes shaded from the low lamp by a green plastic visor, like a Hollywood newspaper editor. The rest of the large room was in shadow, heavy curtains blocking out the mid-morning sunlight.

I'd often seen Sir Hugh at close quarters, but the proximity of the reading lamp emphasized the thinning of the dark brown hair, the intelligent face and the sensitive mouth with its almost camel-like upper lip, so beloved of cartoonists.

'You've committed yourself to the Colonial Service,' he went on, 'and if they want to transfer you, it is your duty to accept, especially as it is on promotion.'

Sir Hugh was everyone's hero, everyone's aloof but friendly uncle. His advice was always worth listening to. A month earlier, when Tubby had summoned me to his office and presented me with a bulky envelope, and said that he hoped I would like my new job in Uganda, I had just laughed.

'Better read what it says,' he suggested. 'It's a good promotion.'

'There's no promotion outside Jamaica', I replied. 'I'm here to stay. Why swop black dog for monkey? Tell the Colonial Office to stuff it.'

'Well, at least read it. You don't have to accept.'

I took the envelope back to my office and pulled out the contents. There was along pompous letter with attachments. The post offered was that of Deputy Chief Veterinary Research Officer, Uganda, at double my Jamaica salary. Enticing certainly, but how could I possibly stomach the stiff, dull colonial attitudes of East Africa after ten years of vibrant, dynamic living in Jamaica? They had to be joking. I threw the letter and attachment into my pending tray.

Two weeks later when Tubby rang and asked whether I had made up my mind, it was still at the bottom. I took it home and talked it over with Mary. She was non-committal. Jamaica was her country, she loved it as much as I. She also enjoyed her job in the Ministry of Planning and had a great respect for her boss, the new Prime Minister, Norman Manley, as well as for George Cadbury, the UN head of the Planning Unit in which she worked. But she was now pregnant. Perhaps it was time to start a new life. It depended entirely on me.

Another week passed. The Chief Secretary was pressing for a reply.

Attached to the offer from the Colonial Office had been a note from the Governor's Secretary, through whose office the correspondence had passed, saying that His Excellency would be happy to discuss this transfer, if I wished. I decided to take him up on it. He might have some angles I hadn't thought of. Now I found myself, like a schoolboy in front of the headmaster, knowing that my fate was going to be sealed, one way or another, within the next few minutes.

Sir Hugh made it clear that times were changing fast. The Old Colonial Empire was on its way out but technical staff, especially those with wide experience, would still be needed to advise the former colonies. It was time I saw a bit more of the world. I had been in Jamaica ten years, to stay longer would no doubt be pleasant, but I was a servant of the Crown. It was my duty to accept higher responsibility when it was offered. I had no option. I must go.

I left Government House feeling much the same as a murderer must feel leaving the dock after seeing the judge don the black cap!

One thing made acceptance a little easier. My family had been connected with Uganda since the turn of the century, although my parents had now retired to neighbouring Kenya. They were in their late seventies and would adore to have their son and new daughter-in-law, not to mention their expected grandchild, within visiting distance. I made this my private excuse – it helped.

Mary, who was expecting in three months, left immediately for Vancouver, where her parents were living. I made arrangements to follow later, taking the opportunity to visit several research centres in the United States well before B-day.

Two weeks after I had written my letter of acceptance, it was announced that His Excellency, Sir Hugh Foot, had been appointed Governor of the troubled island of Cyprus, and would be leaving within days. I wondered if he had had the same doubts about his own transfer, and had used the same arguments on himself!

* * *

Ken and Marjorie, Bob (my Best Man), Mac D (who would take over from me as Director of Veterinary Services), and several others without whom I knew life would never be quite the same, were at Palisadoes airport to see me off.

Conversation was an effort. What more could possibly be said that hadn't been aired a thousand times before. 'Remember when...'; 'If you see...'; 'Don't forget to...'

At last I was off, barely able to grasp the wrenching finality of leaving Jamaica for good!

As we banked over the tiny, coral-fringed Lime and Drunken Man Cays and swung back over Kingston towards the green spine of the island, a host of memories clamoured for priority. Clouds had not yet gathered over Jack's Hill, and I could make out Hope Gardens, Head Office and the Veterinary Division Laboratories, the centre of my life for the last ten years.

I saw my house and searched for signs of the grave where I had buried Poppet the night before. Poor Poppet. There had been no alternative. I had placed capsules of Nembutal in chunks of cheese and thrown them for her to catch and swallow at a single gulp. Then we had lain together on my bed, a special treat for her, while I told her how much she had meant to me during the last ten years – over a quarter of my life. When she had drifted into a deep sleep, I gave her a final injection and carried her lifeless body into the back garden where, with fireflies dancing beneath the mango trees, I laid her in the grave I had dug beside the rose bushes. Afterwards, because one does strange and unpredictable things under emotional stress, I had poured myself a rum and ginger, drunk half of it as a toast, and tipped the rest over the mound, with my blessings.

Jack, my beautiful Alsatian and Poppet's lover, had died of hepatitis three years before and was buried close by. I hoped he would be waiting for her.

We passed over Linstead, Moneague and Walker's Wood, and suddenly there was Ocho Rios, dangling in the blue Caribbean like a gleaming bauble at the end of the twisting dark green cord of Fern Gully. Huge hotels – Tower Isle and others – now dotted the once pristine coastline, and ugly red ulcers marked the sites of bauxite excavations. Over to the right, Oracabessa and Port Maria were plainly visible but too far away for me to make out my bachelor's haven at Rockmoor.

The cane fields of Drax Hall and Llandovery (from which came the pick of Jamaican rum), and the white buildings of St Ann's Bay, near where the first Spanish settlement had been built 450 years before, passed below.

As my eyes tried desperately to capture it all for one last time, Jamaica slipped into the sparkling waves, only a cap of white cloud remaining for a moment on the horizon to mark Blue Mountain peak and the island which had fulfilled all my dreams, where I had certainly found my buried treasure and where I had spent the happiest decade of my life.

That evening, in a small cafe in Miami, a juke box started to play 'Jamaica Farewell'. It wasn't the last time that Harry Belafonte's haunting version of the old digging song, 'Iron Bar', would bring me close to tears.

PART THREE

UGANDA

(1957–1963)

SUDAN

White Nile

Moyo

Albert Nile

KARAMOJA

KARASUK

Gulu

Moroto

Lira

CONGOLESE
REPUBLIC
(Zaire)

Victoria Nile

Soroti

Namalu

Mt. Kadam

Lake Albert

Makinde

L. Kyoga

Mbale

Hoima

Victoria Nile

Kamuli

Mt. Elgon

Tororo

Ruwenzori Mts

Fort
Portal

BUGANDA

Kampala Jinja

Mubende

KENYA

Mweya

L. George

Masaka

Entebbe

Q.E.
*National
Park*

ANKOLE

Lake Victoria

Mbarara

Kabale

RUANDA
URUNDI

TANGANYIKA
(Tanzania)

0 10 20 30 40 50
MILES

UGANDA
1962

THE LAND OF *BADO KIDOGO*

'What a superb view!'

We strolled across the spacious lawn beneath blue frothing jacarandas, and looked down over lush paddocks to the placid waters of Lake Victoria.

'We'll pretend that the lake is the Caribbean,' Mary murmured.

Denys, the Chief Research Officer, lean, in his mid-thirties, had met us that morning at the Entebbe airport. Neatly dressed in khaki shorts and white open-necked shirt which exposed a prominent Adam's apple, he seemed to exude energy and efficiency. His wife, shorter and equally well groomed, spoke with a soft hint of the Highlands.

They had driven us – Mary, myself and six-week-old Shannon – up a winding dirt road over a promontory flanking Entebbe airport, past the buildings of the Animal Health Research Centre to a group of sleepy, tree-shaded residences.

'This whole area is known as Old Entebbe,' Denys told us. 'Here's your house.'

We entered an overgrown gateway and followed a short gravelled driveway lined with shrubs to the front of the house where a large '5' was painted in black on the whitewashed wall. Notwithstanding this incontestable enumeration, the house was known as 'Number 14' for the entire six years that we occupied it. No-one could ever explain why. Number 14 (or 5), was a tin-roofed bungalow closely cuddled

View of Lake Victoria from our house

269

by hedges of hibiscus and tall stately trees, amongst which myriads of mosquitoes seemed to be dancing.

'Lake flies,' said Denys. 'Damn nuisance, but at least they don't bite. We'll leave you to settle in. We've arranged for lunch to be sent over and you'll find your larder stocked with essentials – including beer If there's anything you want, give us a shout. We live right next door through that gap in the hedge. We'll pop in later. Tomorrow will be soon enough to look round the labs. By the way,' he added with a laugh, 'if you look carefully, you can see the Equator running across the lake just this side of the horizon.'

The house itself was disappointing. It was old, and the inside was dark and gloomy. the floors were of polished green concrete and uneven. The kitchen, with its wood-burning stove, was at the back of the house between cockroach-infested pantries and begrimed servants' quarters. Furniture was basic and identical to the PWD issue which I recognized from Northern Rhodesia. But on the whole, it looked friendly.

'Whatever happens, we have super neighbours,' Mary commented after they had left.

* * *

Shannon, our first-born, had arrived while we were in Canada, reluctantly and not without a certain flurry and confusion, which was to characterize much of her early life.

B-day had passed without result. I became anxious.

'You'll have to hurry it up, darling,' I told Mary. 'We're due in Uganda in just over a month.'

On the doctor's advice, Mary took castor oil in enormous capsules, starting at midnight, to try and induce some activity. Her parents' small, wooden, clinker-built house reverberated to gasps and regurgitations as she forced down the bulky torpedoes at regular intervals, at times bringing them up again. But it was not until four the next afternoon before something stirred.

'Better get going,' Mary's mother advised. 'Our family is noted for rapid arrivals. I'll ring the gynaecologist as soon as you've left.'

'First baby?' asked the reception nurse. 'Don't worry, it'll be hours yet.'

Mary was given the flimsiest of unbuttonable gowns and provided with a camp cot in the corridor as maternity was full. I went off to ring her mother and report progress. Luckily, as it turned out, it was visiting hour.

'Is your name Guilbride?'

'Yes.' I looked at the young man, a total stranger.

'Your wife asked me to find you. She needs you urgently. The baby...' I didn't stay to hear more.

'Get a nurse – it's coming,' Mary gasped.

I rushed to the glass cubicle at the end of the corridor where several nurses sat chatting.

'My baby's coming,' I shouted, 'get the doctor.'

When I returned, Mary had been taken away. I paced up and down the waiting room in typical 'desperate father' fashion. Outside the sun was still shining, the maple trees were in full leaf, and away in the distance I could make out the hazy outline of Lions Gate Bridge and Vancouver City.

The calm of the evening was suddenly interrupted by the growing wail of sirens. Just outside the hospital gates, they switched off and the gynaecologist's car swept in, flanked by two police outriders. (She told us later that she had been on the other side of the town and had rung the Mounties for help.)

Minutes later, Shannon was announced. She had a shock of coal-black hair, quite unlike either Mary or myself or any other member of our families. I wondered if they hadn't mixed her up with a Red Indian. At times, I still do!

'Hospitals!' Mary fumed. 'Lot of nonsense. They held the baby in till the doctor arrived. You've delivered plenty of calves, haven't you? We'll have the next one at home.'

We did.

A few weeks later, the three of us had glided down over the placid grey waters and the dark green, forested islands of Lake Victoria, to land at Entebbe, the lakeside capital of Uganda.

We had placed the carrycot on the ground at the foot of the plane's gangway to rearrange our hand luggage. As we picked it up again, the handle on my side broke and our month-old daughter was tipped, bawling, onto the tarmac, to bite the dust of Africa for the first, but far from last, time.

In a way, I was home. I had spent my first five years in Kampala, and our family had been connected with business and administration in Uganda since the end of the last century. But even if my folk had still lived here, and not retired to Kenya, I knew that Uganda could never be home. If we had a home at all, it was the island we had just left, Jamaica.

* * *

The research laboratories, like the residences, dated from the early twenties. Five large, tin-roofed, whitewashed buildings looked down over paddocks of thick grass sloping gently to the lake shore.

My laboratory was large, lofty and, like our house, had a green concrete floor, except that this one was perilously smooth and highly polished. Three tall windows allowed the light reflected off the lake to illumine the wide bench running beneath them.

Clustered about the main buildings were the stores, stables, experimental animal houses, autopsy room, incinerator and a large square water tank, 30 feet in the air. This tank, an insurance against the failure of the town supply, provided some amusement when the town supply did fail. It was found that it had never been connected to the mains, and had stood empty for over 20 years!

A hundred yards down the hill below the laboratories was the Library, a centre for tea breaks as well as reading and research. Below this again, was the Nutritional Chemistry laboratory, and halfway round the promontory a series of buildings housed the Veterinary Assistants Training School. Right at the bottom of the hill on the flat, somewhat swampy lakeside, was the Livestock Improvement Farm.

Several of the senior research staff joined us for morning tea in the Library. Dick, a tall gangling Irishman, was trying to perfect artificial insemination in the local Nganda and Zebu cattle. Bob, a naturalized Pole, fair-haired and strongly accented, headed the Nutritional Chemistry unit which was analysing the thousands of samples from the field experiments of Ken, the fast-talking, bespectacled pasture specialist. Nigel, slight and dark, who could well have been in the sixth form, was trying to produce a vaccine against Nairobi sheep disease, a dangerous viral infection. Tom, Sherlock Holmes-like, the longest serving of all the staff and the ultimate reference on all station matters, was sorting out the peculiar life history of the local liverfluke of cattle, and Ted, chainsmoking at one end of the long library table, was the chief laboratory technician, whose technical expertise was essential to all laboratory investigations.

Entebbe was obviously a far more sophisticated proposition than the one I had left in Jamaica. The equipment I had fought for so desperately at Hope was taken for granted here, and the dozen or so senior research staff were backed by 30 junior technicians, plus a substantial budget.

As a fish, I was still much the same size, but the pond was now a lot bigger.

The first and most pressing problem that Mary and I faced was the language. The local lingo was Luganda, a complicated tongue spoken by only a few Europeans. Swahili, the language of neighbouring

Kenya was, for all practical purposes, the *lingua franca* which could take one in comfort all over East Africa, but I never mastered more than the most elementary phrases. Mary on the other hand, being Mary, was much more persistent, and over the following years, despite multiple pregnancies, passed her elementary, lower and intermediate Swahili with flying colours. Her constantly recurring gravid state became a joke with her examiners. Indeed, it was her fourth pregnancy which prevented her taking the final higher exam which, undoubtedly, she would have passed with equal aplomb.

Swahili words and phrases soon formed part of our everyday vocabulary. *Jambo. Habari gani?*, we greeted our friends, black or white, who would reply *Misuri sana. Kwaheri* we said as we parted. When the kids had a sore, we put *muti* on their *yaya*. If it hurt it was *kali*. We called for more *kahawa* or *siagi*, when the coffee or butter was finished; but quickly, *pesi-pesi*.

Greetings in Swahili always followed the same pattern – 'How are you?' 'Fine.' 'Your family?' 'Fine.' 'Business?' 'Fine.' Then, after a pause, the respondent would introduce a large BUT and follow it with a string of disasters and complaints. It was rude to tell of these before assuring the enquirer that everything was perfect.

If one's car wasn't ready when the garage said it would be, or the PWD hadn't replaced the window pane which they had promised would be done a week ago, the invariable answer would be *bado kidogo* – wait a little. A good name for Uganda, we thought, would be 'The Land of *Bado Kidogo*'. But that, of course, was before we had experienced South America.

There was no doubt that we missed Jamaica. We tried to imagine that Lake Victoria was the Caribbean, that sharks had turned into crocodiles and the danger of *bilharzia* infection in the shallow waters along the lake's edge was no worse than the discomfort of sea-eggs and jellyfish. Sheaves of the *Weekly Gleaner*, two months out of date, arrived from Kingston at irregular intervals. We read Morris Cargill's pithy articles with delight, laughed at Leandro's cartoons, and conjured up the feel of Blue Mountain air, the smell of the sea breeze, the excitement of spear-fishing on the cays, the taste of Bombay mangoes and the camaraderie and politics of our beloved island.

It was easy enough to be nostalgic. The local Buganda, while intelligent and good-looking, seemed over-surly, humourless and lacking the ebullience of the Jamaican. We couldn't blame them. Years of terror and oppression by successive *Kabakas*, or Kings, followed by decades of stiff-upper-lipped, unemotional, British colonial un-civil servants, had kept spontaneity to a minimum. In addition, there was the barrier of language.

273

The large Indian community dominated commerce, from dry goods and groceries to the sale and repair of cars. Kampala, 22 miles away, a mixture of imposing public buildings, peeling Indian *dukas* or stores, elegant houses and tin-roofed shanties, was the commercial centre. Occasionally we would come across an African shop assistant, but I do not remember ever dealing with an African-owned store. It was the Singhs and the Kirefus who took most of our spending money. My parents had had many highly educated and well-read Indian friends during their 25 years in Uganda, but by 1957, these had mostly returned to their home country. Our contact with the Indian community was, unfortunately, entirely across the counter.

Entebbe, the seat of government (in fact *entebbe* in Luganda meant 'seat'), was rather like a military encampment with civil servants instead of soldiers. Inevitably, there was a strong 'pecking order'. One had one's boss, or one's subordinates, constantly at hand. Even at the Sports Club, the social centre of the European community, seniority had to be observed. Play, it seemed, was simply an extension of work for the purpose of exercise, and the social behaviour of the wives played an important role in the advancement of their men.

I don't want to imply that the stiff upper lips were any less friendly, amusing or creative than their West Indian counterparts. They were not, but the stage was different and the public-school atmosphere was all pervading. The Governor was the Headmaster, the Ministers were the Housemasters and the senior officials the prefects. The rest of us had to toe the line. If we didn't, the Colonial Office (our parents) would be notified and we would be removed. Dress helped accentuate this illusion. In some colonies (Uganda least of all, thank God) there was a prescribed uniform for the Colonial Officer, usually a khaki shirt or bush jacket, khaki shorts and long khaki socks. Medical staff had the same, but in white.

A 'non-conformist' friend in Tanganyika (Tanzania), incited the wrath of the establishment by wearing ankle-length socks. He was quoted the regulations by his Director, which stipulated knee-length hose. Tony bowed to these injunctions and duly purchased the correct articles. But since nowhere in the regulations were garters mentioned, his long socks remained, like their short predecessors, around his ankles. I avoided this 'Boy Scout' type of attire by wearing a bush jacket and slacks. I remembered only too well the agonies of *veld* sores in Northern Rhodesia from wearing shorts, and nobody was going to make me wear prep-school stockings!

My colleagues, I imagine, found me a bit uncouth. I preferred rum to whisky, my accent was a mixture of Rhodesian and Jamaican, definitely no longer Cambridge or public school, and my attitude to the

coloured community after ten years in Jamaica was much more tolerant and less militaristic than theirs. But in the end we were all
daubed with the same official khaki paint, and I felt more like a
member of an occupying army – a paternal one, admittedly – but
nevertheless, one that was autocratic and silently resented.

In Jamaica, we had considered ourselves Jamaicans; although too
early to be sure, it seemed most unlikely that we would ever imagine
ourselves as Ugandans.

RESEARCH OPPORTUNITIES

'Time you got to know some of the country,' Denys suggested. 'We'll
start with Ankole.'

'Great,' I agreed.

As soon as he had left the office, I unearthed my map and found
Ankole, a large kingdom in the south-west adjoining the Belgian
Congo and including part of the Queen Elizabeth National Park. It
looked exciting.

To go anywhere from Entebbe, which was on the end of a peninsula, one had to pass through Kampala, which was at its base. Here
we branched west, passing the huge new Mulago hospital and the
well laid-out campus of Makerere College, part of East Africa's first
attempt at a University.

The road was macadamized for only 80 miles, thereafter the surface
was thick dust which clogged the eyes and nostrils alternately with
red and grey soils, and made it virtually impossible to pass another
vehicle. I had decided to break in my new Borgward Isabella station
wagon on this trip. I had bought it both because of its lines and
because it was the only station wagon I could afford. It did me
proud.

I had forgotten how enormous the distances could be in Africa. 50
miles in Jamaica was an expedition, but here, journeys were measured
in hundreds. We drove through patches of tall impenetrable forest
and over endless stretches of yellowing savannahs studded with 20-
foot anthills sprouting dark green euphorbias. In places, eight-foot
walls of elephant grass collected the sun's rays like a solar heater.
This was the country that Dad had raved about and where he had
spent his happiest hours hunting lion. He could have it, I thought.
Give me a reef any day.

At Mbarara, the capital of the Kingdom of Ankole, I was introduced to some of the District Veterinary Officers and their problems.
High on the list was tsetse fly and the cattle disease it carried, trypa-

nosomiasis or *nagana*. The Game and Tsetse Department was cutting out selected areas of bush where the fly bred, and slaughtering certain species of game to stop the fly's food supply, while the Veterinary Dept was trying out the newer drugs to treat the disease in cattle. The combined effort was, however, only partly effective. Clearing bush was both difficult and erratic, shooting game upset the groups of conservationists which were beginning to spring up, and the only drugs available were short-acting so that the animals had to be injected every two to three months, a time-consuming and expensive measure. Moreover, some drugs gave severe reactions.

'Obviously, we need a drug that can be given every six months and has no reaction,' I commented to Denys afterwards.

'Correct, but we've no-one to work on it at the moment and EATRO, the East African Trypanosomiasis Research Organization, at Tororo, are still tied up with fundamental studies on producing a vaccine.'

Another urgent problem, I was told, was tuberculosis in the local Ankole cattle. Ankole, or Sanga, cattle, differed from the common Zebu-type cattle of East and Central Africa. They were larger, more rangy, dark red in colour and had no hump like the Zebu. But their most outstanding characteristic was the enormous size of their horns, which could reach five feet in length and weigh 40 pounds apiece. Also, apparently, unlike the Zebu, they were highly susceptible to tuberculosis. The last tuberculin test on the Ankole herd at the Mbarara Stock Farm, where they were being selected for higher milk yields, had shown an infection rate of 60 per cent. That had been two years ago, and the incidence could easily have risen since then. I decided that this disease would be top priority. There was just one small point. How on earth was I going to handle cattle with such enormous horns? The merest nod from such a beast would most likely take my head off.

We skirted the dark mysterious, almost impenetrable forest of Maramagambo, home of chimpanzees, gorillas and the giant forest hog, and headed north along the eastern border of the Ruwenzori Mountains, known as the 'Mountains of the Moon', whose peaks reached to nearly 17,000 feet. We decided not to visit the Queen Elizabeth Park, that would be an excuse for another safari. In any case, game were abundant on the road. At one point, we found the road barred by an old bull elephant grazing the verge, his huge grey posterior half-blocking the highway. We pulled up to wait while he finished his breakfast, undisturbed. As we waited, other elephants wandered out from the trees on both sides of the road and we were soon encircled by a herd of hefty 'heffalumps'. This was Africa, all right.

I don't know if Denys was scared; he certainly didn't show it. I was, but luckily I could hide my jitters by taking photographs. After a while, the old boy eased a bit further onto the bank and we decided to make a run for it. Denys, taking a turn behind the wheel, gave the Isabella a racing start. As we passed, Jumbo turned, swung his trunk and waved his tusks at us, whether as a friendly gesture or telling us to go to hell, we didn't stop to ask. I clicked the shutter as we drew level, but all that appeared on the film was one eye surrounded by an expanse of dark grey skin. He had been a lot closer than I thought. It proved an excellent photo to show friends, who had no idea that it had been taken from a car. We came across two lions and three cubs, drying off after the overnight storm. We coasted slowly alongside, windows tightly shut. They hardly noticed us. They had probably seen many cars before and decided that they were harmless and uneatable. It was rather humiliating.

* * *

'I've arranged for you to spend a week at EAVRO in Kenya,' Denys told me soon after we had returned. 'Find out all you can about their current research, especially into East Coast fever, and see how we can fit in.'

The East African Veterinary Research Organization, EAVRO, at Muguga in the Kikuyu hills, 25 miles from Nairobi, carried out the more sophisticated research on diseases common to all three of the East African territories – Kenya, Tanganyika and Uganda; research which the individual countries did not have the resources to accomplish alone.

East Coast fever, ECF, caused by a blood parasite, *Theileria parva*, and transmitted by the bite of the cattle ear tick, *Rhipicephalus appendiculatus*, was not a problem in the local African cattle, since they had grown up with it and had inherited an immunity over generations of exposure to the disease. This in-built resistance in local calves was boosted each time they were bitten by an infective tick – like booster injections of vaccine. However, cattle brought in from areas free from ECF, or cattle imported from Europe, where the disease did not exist, had no such immunity and usually died within a couple of months.

So why would anyone be so stupid as to import such susceptible cattle? The answer, as always, was one of economics. The increase in population and the higher living standards meant increased demand for meat and milk. But African cattle were slow growers and low producers, the quickest way to improve them was to cross them with the faster-growing, higher-producing, European breeds. Bulls

277

imported for such purposes were, of course, highly susceptible to ECF and had to be rigorously protected against ticks. The offspring of these matings, too, in spite of their mothers being immune, were still susceptible to ECF due to the exotic blood of their fathers, but their greater production (and profits) meant that their owners could now afford to protect them in tick-proof stables, feed them cut grass and concentrates instead of exposing them to ticks while grazing, and spray or dip them regularly with tickicides.

Dipping, if carried out at weekly intervals, could, in time, make a farm completely free from ECF, but this was not always advisable. An infected tick brought in on hay from another area, or on a person's clothes, or on a wild animal, could suddenly cause a devastating outbreak. Furthermore, an ECF-free farm meant that the highly susceptible progeny could only be sent to other ECF-free farms, and so were of no use for general distribution. The answer seemed to be a vaccine, but although EAVRO and the nearby Wellcome Foundation laboratories were hot in pursuit of this goal, neither, in 1957, were even close.

I set off on the ten-hour, 400-mile drive to Muguga at five in the morning. Most Uganda highways were well graded and macadamized – thanks to Uganda's Italian prisoners of war who, it was said, had refused to repair the already existing apologies for roads but eagerly agreed to construct new ones! Once across the border into Kenya, however, the picture changed and I had to battle with the red dust and corrugations of badly made dirt highways.

I arrived late that afternoon, winding up through coffee plantations and forests around Muguga, with the sun low behind the tall bluegums surrounding the research centre and the air deliciously scented and decidedly nippy. After the heat and humidity of Entebbe (neither as bad as Jamaica), the cool, eucalyptus-laden air was a stimulant to action and thought. I snuggled beneath the blankets in one of the cottages allocated to visitors and listened to the wind in the trees. It was like a Swiss resort, and it was hard to believe that less than five years before, this area had been the bloody battleground of the Mau Mau.

Steve, who headed the research on East Coast fever at EAVRO, and Dave, his number two, knew more about the disease than anyone else in the world. As we walked out to the experimental paddocks, Dave explained their attempts to immunize calves.

'We place a controlled number of ECF-infected ticks onto young calves. At the same time we give the calves a low level of antibiotic in their feed, to ensure that they only have a minor reaction to the disease, but have some immunity, which is boosted by each infected tick they pick up.'

'Seems a bit of a hit-or-miss operation,' I commented. (It is always a wise policy to belittle other people's research; especially when you have nothing to contribute yourself!)

'Not any longer,' Dave assured me. 'We know how many ticks to put on and the most effective dose of aureomycin to control the reaction. Sure, now and again one lets us down, but we're still in the early stages.'

The calves undergoing immunization wore small calico bags over their ears into which the ECF-infected ticks had been placed. After three days these bags were removed to see if the ticks had attached and were feeding. When I began immunizing calves at Entebbe, I substituted mosquito netting bags for the calico ones because the higher heat and humidity on the lake shore made the ears sweat under the calico and prevented the ticks from attaching. Mosquito netting also allowed me to see when the ticks attached and how well they were feeding without having to remove the earbag.

I examined scores of smears under the microscope, taken from the blood and lymph-nodes of infected animals in all stages of the disease, until I could spot single parasites or their clusters – the so-called 'Koch's blue bodies' – in the white blood cells, with complete confidence.

I returned to Entebbe full of ideas for the production of a vaccine. The fact that the combined efforts of medical and veterinary research, worldwide, had not yet succeeded in producing a vaccine against malaria or any other protozoal disease such as ECF, was the last thing to discourage me. I was still full of my usual enthusiasm and naive optimism!

Deviating on my return to Uganda, I visited my parents at Nanyuki, 160 miles north of Nairobi, where the snow-tipped Mount Kenya made a spectacular backdrop to the little upland town. Dad and Mum promised to visit us the following month in Entebbe, when they could inspect their son's wife and their first grandchild.

RECOLLECTIONS OF A ROCKING HORSE

Our family's connection with Uganda had started with my uncle – Henry Hamilton Hunter.

Uncle Harry had been a Dublin lawyer of considerable ability. Short, with closely cut, greying hair and slightly stained toothbrush moustache, he had arrived in Uganda in the 1890s. Just why he chose

279

Uganda, I've no idea, but he had soon set up a law practice in Entebbe and had evidently done quite well, although I am amazed that there were enough clients to keep him alive in those days. Amongst his other achievements, he was said to have owned the first motorcycle and the first automobile in the country. But then Harry had always been a bit of a bush mechanic, and had owned a steam-driven car in Ireland which had blown him over a hedge when he and his brother, in their eagerness to reach a race meeting, had tied down the safety valve to produce a greater head of steam. He was also the first passenger, in 1931, to make the journey on the Imperial Airways Flying Boat from Entebbe to London.

One day, in the early years of the century, a certain Michael Moses and his partner, Ishmael, came to his office. They had been charged with ivory poaching. Harry Hunter defended them and they were acquitted. Moses, impressed by Hunter's skill, suggested that they set up a company together for the legal buying and selling of ivory, and for the export of other products such as cotton and coffee. It was duly called the Hunter Moses Syndicate, or more commonly HM Syndicate.

Michael Moses was a colourful character. As a young man he had been in the Administrative Service where, at the age of 18 and with the sole aid of 14 Sikhs, he had been largely responsible for putting down the Ankole rebellion. It was only on the petty excuse that he was not a British Subject that the race-conscious Colonial Administration found itself unable to award him a decoration.

He must have found it extremely frustrating in those days of ingrained prejudice towards non-Anglo-Saxons. In business he was an equal, but socially he was an outcast. As soon as he had sufficient funds he built the Imperial Hotel, where he could entertain in a way denied him by the social clubs. He was stocky, swarthy, with cataracts and thick lenses, but my childhood impression of him – a flamboyant, corpulent, rajah-like Oriental uncle who could always be relied upon for a five pound note (vastly superior to all my other five-shilling relatives), remains dominant.

As soon as HM Syndicate was established, Harry wrote to Dad, offering him the managership. Dad, who had given up his medical studies in Dublin to join the British Forces in their squabble with the Boers, had landed in South Africa to find the Armistice about to be signed. It would have been a waste of opportunity to return to Ireland and the studies he never really enjoyed, so he had travelled north and joined, successively, Baden-Powell's forces and then the Pretoria Mounted Police, in which he was serving when Harry's offer arrived.

Dad had always been good at sports, and while in Pretoria played rugger for the Orange River Colony (now the Orange Free State) in the Currie Cup of 1908, and for the Transvaal in the Triangular Tournament of 1909, as well as rugger, soccer and hockey for the Pretoria Harlequins. Much as he enjoyed life in South Africa, Dad dropped everything at the prospect of managing HM Syndicate. Harry's offer was probably influenced by the fact that he was about to marry Dad's sister, Bé, and wished to keep the business in the family. Hardly had Dad settled into Kampala, however, before he was on his way again, this time to join the Dublin Fusiliers and show Kaiser Bill what the Empire was made of. In France, Dad stopped a sniper's bullet with his knee during a particularly brave act, was awarded the MC and invalided out. He limped for the rest of his life. Before returning to Kampala, he married a Quaker lass from Lancashire, Isolene ('Squiz') Walmesley. Mother had been at The Mount school with Bé, who had introduced Mum to her brother during the school holidays. It took him nearly 20 years to pop the question. Evidently, indecision in affairs of the heart ran in the family; I was 37 before I had made up my mind, and my brother 40.

Always known as 'The Captain', Dad played a significant role in Uganda sport, as well as in the Buganda Seed Cotton Buying Association. In World War Two, he served in the King's African Rifles, mainly at the recruitment Depot at Tororo, before retiring to Nanyuki in Kenya, where a few years later the Mau Mau gave him and mother some rough moments. In 1972, at the age of 91, he drove himself to the Nanyuki hospital, asked if he could rest there a few days, and passed away a week later. Mother had predeceased him by eight years. He had had a good innings, in fact he had played his last game of cricket only two years before, at the age of 89.

Dad was one of the very few people who, in every sense, merited the title 'gentleman'.

Michael Moses died in Baghdad in the sixties, his memoirs, which he almost certainly wrote, still unpublished and, I believe, now lost. Harry Hunter died in Kampala, in 1944, a senior member of Legco, with his ambition of a knighthood still unfulfilled. He had completed the course with distinction, but had nudged a few officials off the track on the way.

I found an Indian family living in our old house in Kampala, where I had spent my first years. It looked small and squalid and the garden dusty and unkempt, the *mbate* roof (corrugated iron sheets) rusting

281

Gun Hill, Kampala

and the mosquito gauze on the verandah full of holes. Could this be the huge mansion and grounds I remembered roaming around with my five-year old elder brother, hunting imaginary lions with our flimsy bows and arrows?

Another landmark of my infancy, Gun Hill, was now almost submerged in the rising tide of houses. Here I had lain on my back beside the remnants of the old cannon that gave the hill its name, and stared up into the blue sky, wondering how far away it was and what was above it. It had been an adventure, in those halcyon days, to stroll hand in hand with Ucana, our houseboy, to this hillock only half a mile away but still well outside the township. Now, Gun Hill was almost in the centre of the city.

All this family history suddenly burst on me one afternoon. Denys and I were passing through Kampala on the way to a meeting at Head Office. Outside an Indian secondhand dealer, I spied something that stirred up long-forgotten emotions.

'Stop,' I yelled. Denys pulled into the curb.

'What's the matter?' he asked peevishly.

'Got to see a man about a horse. Won't be a sec.'

'Well, hurry. We're late already.' He obviously thought I was crazy.

I pointed to the large rocking horse on the pavement outside the secondhand dealers. Oh yes, the Indian assured me, the horse had indeed belonged to Mr Moses. He had bought it at the auction of Moses' house and furniture, a few weeks before.

I asked him what he wanted for it. He looked at me for a moment, estimating my desire.

'Six hundred shillings. Very cheap.'

I stroked it, nostalgia mounting rapidly. I had ridden this very animal at the age of three, nearly 35 years before. Michael Moses had had it made for my cousin Dennis, Harry and Bé's son, as a

282

birthday present. Riding it was one of our greatest treats. But six hundred shillings! I was already well overdrawn.

'I'll let you know,' I called, as I jumped into the already moving car.

A few days later, I returned to see if I could barter him down, but he had already sold it. I cursed myself for dallying. It was a magnificent horse, my kids would have loved it, but much more – it was an heirloom, a link with the family of the old days. An object sanctified by time and memories.

'TB OR NOT TB'

'For God's sake, how many more do we have to kill?'

'Dunno,' I replied. 'Quite a lot, I'm afraid.'

George, the manager of Mbarara Stock Farm, was not happy. From the results of the tuberculin test it looked as if we would have to slaughter nearly two-thirds of his precious Ankole herd.

'Are you sure that the test is reliable?' he asked desperately.

'It certainly is in other breeds of cattle. The only way we can find out if it is in Ankole cattle, is by slaughtering some of those that tested positive or suspicious, and looking for lesions of TB in them. As you can see, all those we've killed so far have shown lesions.'

I looked down at the carcase spread open on the ground. It was the sixth we had autopsied. All had shown lesions of tuberculosis. Another 50 or 60 'reactors' had been collected together in a separate kraal, branded with a 'T' and awaited autopsy.

'Dammit,' he moaned, 'if we go on like this, it'll be half the herd.'

'Could be, but it's the only way. If we leave even one "suspicious" animal in the herd, it may be tubercular and infect others. If you

283

want to clean up the herd, you must be ruthless. It's better to be safe than sorry.'

This procedure worked well. In three years, tuberculosis had dropped to below 5 per cent. Later, we found that in some herds the test was not quite so cut and dried. For instance, in the Entebbe Stock Farm herd which grazed the lakeside pastures below the Research Station, the skin reactions were rare and were small and hard. Since we found no tubercular lesions in two reactors we slaughtered. I decided to use avian tuberculin on the next test, just in case these reactions were being caused by the poultry or other so-called saprophytic or atypical variants of the tubercle bacillus. Several animals gave the same small hard swellings to both the bovine and the avian tuberculins although the reaction to the avian was slightly puffy in one. We autopsied the puffy one. It was as we had expected.

'Nothing. Absolutely clear. We'd better go over it again,' I said.

Once more David, my technician, and I examined each organ and lymph node. Apart from liver fluke infestation, the only abnormality I could find in this old cow was a slight inflammation of one popliteal gland, a small lymph node behind the stifle joint. The function of lymph nodes is to filter out offending organisms and dead cells from the lymph. Perhaps, I thought, there was an infection somewhere in the leg which was causing the inflammation of the popliteal gland.

I began to dissect out the limb from the knee downwards. As I cut through the skin over the shin-bone, I noticed a number of small yellow nodules, some in the skin itself, others in the subcutaneous tissue. All contained a gritty pus.

'Demodex,' I murmured, 'but we'll take a few specimens, just in case.'

Demodex was one of the mange mites sometimes found in cattle in Uganda. These microscopic beasties made their homes by burrowing into the skin and causing various degrees of irritation.

A few days later, David handed me the slides he had prepared from the skin nodules.

'I think you'll find these interesting,' he remarked.

I slid a stained smear of the pus under the highest power of my microscope, and moved the mechanical stage back and forth. A couple of slender, pink rods came into view.

'Acid-fasts,' I exclaimed, excitedly. 'I'll be damned.' Acid-fasts were the group that included the tubercle and leprosy bacilli as well as other variants.

'They are in the sections of skin, too. Looks like a typical TB lesion.' David was trying to hide his excitement.

'Skin TB,' I murmured unbelievingly. 'Never seen it before. That explains the small hard reactions to the test.'

Skin tuberculosis, although known for many years and reported from several countries in Europe, was still a bit of a mystery. The delicate pink rods looked exactly the same as the tubercle bacillus except that (like the identical leprosy bacillus) they could not be grown on artificial media in the laboratory.

Following this discovery, we searched carefully for skin nodules in all cattle giving small, firm reactions and found several more cases. But the only importance of skin TB, as far as we knew, was to confuse the interpretation of the tuberculin test. I tried many variations of the testing technique to try and eliminate 'false positives', but none improved on the standard procedure.

One thing I did notice was that all our cases of skin TB came from herds which grazed swampy or damp areas, such as the banks of rivers and around the lake. I would like to have followed this up and searched for 'atypical acid-fasts' in water birds, frogs and other semi-aquatic life, but more urgent investigations prevented me. As far as I know, skin tuberculosis is still an open field for study.

Some years later, tuberculosis was to be the motive for another of my major investigations, but this time in a wild animal.

EXPATRIATES AT PLAY

Life in Entebbe was well-ordered, quiet, predictable, and governed by unwritten rules of official decorum, as befitted an outpost of Her Majesty's Civil Service.

Work at the Research Centre was unhurried and rarely ruffled by personal antagonisms. Unlike Jamaica, there was a lack of exposure to the public. There were no upstart politicians to molest us and virtually no influential farmers or farming institutions to needle us. After work we played sports, Scottish danced, gave parties – mostly spaghetti with cheap, red South African wine – gardened, nursed sick children, carpentered, and patronized functions at the club. The nearest cinema was in Kampala, 22 miles away, and the only stage productions were those put on by enthusiastic amateurs.

'Home' was referred to frequently. Airmail editions of the London *Times* provided slop-cloths for cups of Earl Grey on office desks, and there was a preference for the *Weekly Guardian* over the more blatant *Newsweek* or *Time*. The umbilical cord to 'old boy' Britain held firm.

The pride of the war years still lingered, and our first duty was to uphold Britain's hard-won prestige and our Anglo-Saxon heritage. Slipshod methods and shady dealings could not be tolerated. Things had to be done well and at once – none of this *bado kidogo* business, that was strictly for the locals.

Opportunities to enter into the life of the local populace were, unfortunately, limited. Discrimination, although strongly refuted, was undoubtedly there, and whether racial or social in origin, the end point was the same. We met few Buganda who were on our educational or social level, and one had second thoughts about becoming too friendly with the Asians. It seems arrogant and snobbish to admit this, but that was how we found it in the fifties. Those with the same interests were, like ourselves, birds of passage in a foreign land. So we stuck together in small isolated groups, made our own entertainments and ignored the plebs. Officially, fraternization with the 'indigenous inhabitants', as the Colonial Office now described the African, was a 'good thing' (if you could find locals who were willing to be fraternized with in a meaningful sense), but in practice, too much chummery was suspect. In our six years in Entebbe, we only found one African couple in whose company we could relax.

However friendly the relations were between us and the local populace on an individual level, *en masse* we were still an amiable army of occupation.

Social activities were dominated by sport. Team games began at four-thirty and had almost the status of a military parade. Government offices closed at four, meetings being cut short to free a batsman. Shops, if not able to close till later, released their athletes in good time to participate. Formerly, Colonial Civil Servants had been selected as much, if not more, on their prowess with bat and ball as on their academic achievements. This tradition, once held to be an infallible prescription for a successful Colonial Official, had not been entirely discarded.

The centre for European sports in Entebbe was the low, square, tin-roofed Entebbe Club, with its wide mosquito-gauzed verandahs and undisturbed, complacent air of well-being. It lay slumped on the gentle green slope halfway between the Lake Victoria Hotel and the lake itself, surrounded by an expanse of well-mown lawns, stately trees, golf greens, playing fields and tennis courts. There could hardly have been a more picturesque setting for exercise.

Until Independence in 1962, and our last year in Entebbe, club membership was purely European. No-one, white, black or Indian, seemed particularly concerned about it. The Kampala Club, of which my father had once been president, was the same, but the Sports Club, of which Dad had been a founder member, had been multiracial for many years.

A 'club' without a clubhouse was the group of sportsmen known as the Uganda Kobs. The Kobs had for many years spearheaded racial integration in sport by inviting selected players of all colours to join their teams. The colours of the Kobs were brown, black and white, with the white between the black and brown – 'To keep a restraining presence between the African and Indian,' my father once told me!

Mary and I played tennis in the late afternoon sun while the children, under the watchful eye of their *ayah*, romped on the lawns. Later, we drank Simba beer on the club's verandah, while we listened to the latest scandal – never in short supply in such a closed community. It was usually the Amateur Dramatic Society and the Church Choir which provided the tastier morsels of social misdemeanours. Choir practice, especially, seemed to provide the setting for the most delightful sins.

Entebbe was beautiful, peaceful, but dull, so any deviation from what was considered the norm was immediately grabbed, embroidered and made a social currency. Several of our friends swopped partners or left under an immoral cloud which would hardly have been remarked upon elsewhere, and there was no better way to bring a merry dinner party to an icy halt than to refer, inadvertently, to some insalubrious liaison, realizing too late that it had involved one of those present.

Although I preferred tennis, which I could play with Mary, I was finally dragged into a far more demanding sport – rugger. Stuart, the lanky manager of the Research Centre's Stock Farm, was captain of the Entebbe XV while his assistant, John, played full-back. I must have been bragging one day at tea break in the Library, or recounting my former exploits on the rugger field, as I suddenly found myself agreeing to attend a club practice the following afternoon, and two days later, still sore from the unusual exercise, Stuart told me that I was playing in the Saturday match.

'Dammit, man. Saturday's my birthday; I'll be forty-three.'

'Don't worry,' Stuart encouraged me. 'Jack is forty-nine, and he's playing.'

I duly turned out as eighth man in the scrum for the first match of the season. I've no idea who our opponents were, but I remember the game was limited to 25 minutes each way, which seemed far too long. However, being eighth man, I could lumber along after the rest of the scrum and flop on top of the second row after they had packed down, limiting my shoving to the minimum and only tackling those of the opposition who I couldn't avoid.

I just made the final whistle and staggered off the field completely clobbered, but happy that I had lasted the distance. At the club's evening dance, I replaced the gallons of fluid I had lost that afternoon. After all, surviving a game of rugger at the age of 43, after a break of 20 years, deserved a celebration.

'You're playing full-back on Saturday, Pat,' Stuart informed me at Monday's tea break. 'John's on leave.'

I put in some solid training and felt a lot better than on the first outing, even though I let through the deciding try a few minutes before the end. Thereafter I played regularly at eighth man or full-back, and was even included in a trial to select a team to meet the British Lions, who were returning from their South African tour. Mary overheard a selector commenting favourably on my play but, luckily, someone told him I was in my dotage. Luckily, because the home team were beaten by some 50 points to 5! Had I been selected, the Lions might have scored a hundred!

By the end of the season I had become the oldest playing member, Jack having broken his collar bone in a match against Eldoret, whose team was composed mainly of lusty young 'Dutch' farmers, who had emigrated from South Africa.

An expedition of six students from the Veterinary Faculty of Bristol University, enlivened our existence for a couple of months. Two played rugger for Entebbe with great credit, the police plane flying them in from Karamoja or Ankole, or from wherever they were working, for our Saturday matches.

LAKE FLIES AND FURNITURE

Nightfall on the Equator (which, we told friends back home, ran through our garden and was useful on which to hang out the washing) hardly varied, arriving punctually within a few minutes of six, year in, year out. Darkness fell almost immediately the sun had disappeared.

Apart from its abruptness, nightfall was also noisy. Cicadas would pull out all the treble stops and every other nocturnal creature, hidden from the sun throughout the day, would come to life and sing to its mate. Strict anti-mosquito patrols by the health authorities, the regular mowing of the long grass and a nightly spray with a flit gun inside the mosquito-gauzed house, prevented any real annoyance. A far greater pest were those moth-like insects which I had mistaken for mosquitoes on our first day – lake flies. They didn't bite, or carry malaria, but they were responsible for more bad tempers than any other *dudu*, including the 'putsi' or 'mango' fly, whose eggs burrowed into the skin and developed into horrendous maggots.

Lake flies were slightly larger than mosquitoes and were blown across the lake in clouds from their breeding grounds on the far shore. Sometimes, these swarms were so thick that low-flying propeller aircraft had to give them a wide berth. One pilot who steered his Dragon Rapide into a horde was obliged to fly on instruments until he could clear a peephole in his encrusted windscreen.

In daytime, when the dun-coloured clouds were seen approaching over the lake, washing was taken in and windows closed. The flies would arrive like a thick fog and the air would soon be dancing with them. They would clog the gauze screens, fill the garage, kitchen and every sheltered corner, settle on the washing, get up your nose and into your ears or down your neck, anywhere that could cause discomfort. Butter or any other sticky object would be covered with them. If you opened a drawer, there would be a layer of dead flies covering your garments. Evening entertainment was made miserable, even postponed.

Unlike mosquitoes, they found no difficulty in penetrating the mosquito gauze. Even worse than their physical presence was their fishy odour and the dark brown stain they left when you swatted them. Spraying was effective if you swept them up immediately, otherwise the stench of fish drove you out of the house.

Hedges, shrubs and trees would be full of them for days after an invasion, and long smoky wands would wave above the vegetation as if it was on fire. Mary was convinced that lake flies were the origin of the 'burning bush' in the Bible. It could well be so. They would congregate beneath the jacaranda and yew trees on our front lawn, dancing in the rays of sunlight like moths gone berserk.

At least it was possible to cope with them in the daytime, but at night it was a losing battle. Any source of light was immediately smothered in millions of chitinous bodies. After many attempts to outwit them (a fly versus a human – for God's sake!), we found a fairly effective method of defence. Like moths, lake flies were highly phototactic, so we simply placed an ordinary table lamp at the end of an extension lead on the lawn in front of the house. Then we turned out all unessential lights inside.

If a large swarm had come in, we found that the bulb of our lawn lamp would be submerged in less than an hour. So we raised the lamp on bricks. This was usually sufficient, but always there would be a huge pile of rotting, stinking flies to remove in the morning, and beneath the pile the grass would be burnt. Our final solution was to place the lamp in a wheelbarrow. This could be wheeled away at intervals, if necessary, and the lawn left unscarred.

Lake flies had one infallible, extra-sensory perception; they knew exactly when our next dinner party was to be held, and always arrived the afternoon before, so as not to miss it.

When we left Uganda we sighed with relief in the knowledge that the lake flies would stay behind. Not all of them did. When we opened our boxes, the sickly smell of stale fish wafted up to meet us and a debris of lake fly corpses lay scattered throughout our trunks.

Victoria was a stunning lake. The view from our house across the wide lawn between the pale purple jacarandas to the glassy lake surface, would hold us motionless long after our early morning 'cuppa' had turned cold.

Not always was it glassy. From my lab window I watched squalls racing across its surface, often accompanied by waterspouts which would demolish the canoes of unwary fishermen. During the rainy months, storms would arrive in the early hours, heralded by distant lightning and thunder, the full fury crashing around our house as if it were the only target.

Two *mvule* trees, each a hundred feet tall, towered above our tin roof anchoring themselves about fifteen feet from our bedroom windows. I wasn't frightened of them falling on us, but I was terrified that they would attract a bolt of the lightning that crackled all around. I would lie quaking at each flash, expecting the next to score a hit. It never did, so perhaps the trees were more efficient as lightning preventers than as lightning attractors.

* * *

Mary complained that she could no longer cope with the very basic PWD furniture allocated us. Although my salary was considerably higher than in Jamaica, our increasing family seemed to keep us permanently in the red. We couldn't afford to buy furniture, but the Centre's handyman, Sindurji, had made a name for himself as a carpenter. Sindurji was small, turbaned and business-like.

'Certainly, I make furniture, very good, very cheap. Please give me drawing.'

We designed a wardrobe for Mary, a dressing table cum wardrobe for me, a desk and a bookcase.

'How long and how much?' I asked my turbaned friend.

'One month – no more, and three thousand shillings.'

That was about a hundred and fifty pounds. My salary, after deductions and car payments, was less than sixty a month. I had no reserves.

'I'll have to make it myself,' I told Mary. I took her silence for acquiescence.

It was a big step. I had never make anything more complicated

290

than a bird table, and the only tools I had were those in the car. But I wasn't to be put off. Before we were married, Mary had half made a bookshelf for her flat and her saw and screwdriver were somewhere about the place. Dad, on a visit from Kenya, contributed a hammer and an old hand-drill. I bought planks of wood – a soft variety called 'podo', the equivalent of pine – and set to. A few days later I downed my four tools: I needed a workbench. Again I had to make it. I doubt if a more solid bench has ever been constructed. It consisted of six inch by two inch planks supported on six inch by six inch legs, fastened together with enormous screws and bolts. It was a master-piece!

I added an electric drill and saw attachment, tape measure, special screwdrivers, a plane and setsquare, and began to use dowelling to join the planks together. I also made plastic wood from sawdust and glue with which I covered up my many mistakes.

My wardrobe cum dressing table I made of plywood on a frame of 'podo' with three drawers at the top and two at the bottom, sepa-rated by a space for hanging shirts and trousers. It wasn't Chippen-dale, certainly, but just as serviceable. So was the wardrobe I made for Mary.

The desk was more difficult. It took three months to complete. It had a secret drawer and drinks cupboard and, since it was made from *mvule*, the African teak, it weighed a ton. But it was beautiful – anyway to me. It fitted snugly into an alcove off the sittingroom. Immediately, Mary hid it behind a curtain – to give me greater privacy, she said – but I sometimes wondered.

My *pièce de resistance* was a *mvule* bookcase with sliding glass doors. I still have it, full of coffee table books, a little bent and scratched from its travels and the glass doors long since gone, but still an enhancement to our hall and ideal repository for the tele-phone.

It was pleasant after work in those calm, uncluttered days, to trundle whichever child was of pram-ridden age round to the garage cum workshop – where I could keep one eye on it while I constructed my masterpieces. Panda, our newly acquired Alsatian bitch would lie beside the pram as if already aware of her guardian role and Bob, the nutritional chemist, would look over the hedge and regale me with stockmarket news; but since I had no funds, his efforts were largely wasted. Thirty years later he still does whenever we meet, which is often as he lives close by. Neither of us is yet rich!

THE COWS THAT CRIED

Norman, our short, perky, often strident, Australian Deputy Director, was on the phone from Head Office.

'Got a telegram from Jinja, Pat. I'll read it out. "Butterflies are attacking cattle in Bugabula and they are crying. Please help. Signed Kalikwani."'

'Shall I take them handkerchiefs or eyedrops, or what?' I retorted.

'Decide that after you have seen them. Kalikwani is a good man. It must mean something.'

I wired Kalikwani, the African Veterinary Officer for the Busoga province, and set off early the next morning, delighted at a spell in the bush. The highway east from Kampala to Jinja was excellent, and in less than an hour and a half I was passing over the Owen Falls bridge, where the White Nile leaves Lake Victoria, in sight of the giant hydro-electric plant and only a few miles from the sprawling, mainly Indian town of Jinja. There would be celebrations here the following year on the hundredth anniversary of Speke's discovery of the source of the Nile.

Kalikwani was waiting in his office.

'We have to go north to reach the Bugabula district. I'm afraid at this time of the year the road after Kamuli is not very good.'

He was right. As far as Kamuli, 40 miles north of Jinja, the surface was macadamized, but when we branched off north-east to Bugaya, the tarmac gave way to mud, gullies and potholes. Tall *Combretum* forest was underlaid with lush, six-foot high elephant grass and later with equally high spear-grass. After 15 miles or so, we began to slide gradually downhill, the country opening up into grassy plains and areas of swamp.

'Lake Kyoga is quite near, so all this part is very wet,' Kalikwani explained. 'Perhaps that's why we have so many butterflies. They come in the evening, thousands of them and sit on the faces of the *ngombe*, covering their eyes. Then the cows cry and go blind.'

It seemed strange, but I would soon see for myself.

At Bugaya, several herds had been brought near the road for inspection. The local chief, Kabasondwa, an intelligent chap who spoke a certain amount of English (one tended to link intelligence to a facility to speak English), and I walked amongst the animals. They were certainly crying. Tears had scored lines down their faces and in some, the cornea of the eye was white. In others, one or both eyeballs had ruptured, leaving large ulcers and making the animal blind. The conjunctiva was highly inflamed. The technical name for the condition was kerato-conjunctivitis. No butterflies were present, only the

292

usual swarms of the common fly, *Musca domestica.*

Grey, watery eyes were a common sight in most African herds. Eyeballs became scratched by long grass or thorns, or an impatient herdboy might throw a stone at the animal's head or flick it in the eye with a misdirected whiplash, but never had I seen so many cattle with damaged eyes.

'What have you treated them with?' I asked Kalikwani.

'I've tried to wash their eyes in salt and water, I had nothing else.' In the circumstances, it was the best thing he could have done.

'I'll come back as soon as I can with antibiotic eye ointment,' I promised.

We caught some of the affected animals. Their eyelids were ringed with small sucking lice, and from some eyes I extracted long, thin, white eye worms, common in cattle and buck all over central Africa and generally regarded as harmless.

We went on another ten miles to inspect Chief Kabasondwa's personal herd at Buyende. My ever-faithful Isabella station wagon only just made it. The animals at Buyende were in much the same state as those at Bugaya. Sixty-two of Kabasondwa's 110 cattle were affected.

'OK. Let me stay the night so that I can see what these butterflies look like,' I suggested.

I had told Mary that I might have to do this and had brought a safari kit – camp bed, mosquito net, table, lamp, water bottle, fly spray, DDT powder and a supply of beer and reading matter. The chief offered me his visitors' quarters, a two-roomed brick building with an outside loo. One of the dangers in accepting hospitality from local functionaries in the bush was the probability of playing host to a variety of hungry bugs, but both these rooms were stark empty, the concrete walls and floors scrubbed clean. Kalikwani, as a close friend of the chief's, was accommodated in the latter's own thatched hut.

'We must go down to the kraal at five this evening,' Kalikwani told me. 'That's when the butterflies come. But first, the chief invites you to eat with him.'

I dusted my bedroom with DDT, just in case, put up my camp bed and had a snooze. At four o'clock, Kalikwani appeared and took me to the chief's hut. On the plastic-topped metal table were several steaming pots. I noticed that I was the only one who had cutlery. A bent fork, a badly stained spoon and a knife with a chipped bone handle were laid neatly beside my place on a piece of newspaper. Such implements, evidently were a rarity in the bush, even in a chief's house.

The meal consisted of a meat stew, some spinach-like vegetable and a pot of steaming *matoke*, or mashed plantain, the staple food of the Buganda, which could easily have been mistaken for mashed potatoes. It was the first time I had tasted *matoke* since I was a child in Kampala, and the flavour brought back memories of those long ago days as nothing else could. One tasted *matoke* more with the back of one's throat than with the buccal taste buds, a sort of stodgy, woody, starchy flavour. Not a dish for every day, but delicious on occasion.

Those without cutlery dipped their fingers into the pots and transferred lumps of *matoke* and pieces of stew onto their plates and later into their mouths. They were extremely nimble and neat at it.

Afterwards, we walked down to Kabasondwa's kraal in the fading light, where about 100 cattle were standing patiently in a muddy stake enclosure. At first I could see no butterflies, but within minutes the air became alive with hundreds of small, white moths, dipping and fluttering around the heads of the cattle. Many settled on the cows' faces, making at once for the eyes, where they extruded a long, thread-like proboscis and explored the eyeball in search of fluid. It was a most extraordinary sight. This would really be something to investigate.

Three days later, I returned to Kabasondwa's kraal with David, the pathology technician, and Leslie, the technician from the microbiology section. I had also brought hundreds of tubes of antibiotic eye ointment to treat the affected animals. Each one that showed tears or damaged eyes was caught and the *muti* squeezed under the eyelids. It wasn't easy, and I hoped that no more than two applications would do the trick. Before we put the ointment in, Leslie took eyewashings to see if he could isolate the organism causing the keratitis, if there was one.

That evening, as on my previous visit, the unbelievable scene was repeated. Myriads of moths danced in the beam of our torches. David dodged in and out of the herd, and soon had Kodachromes and a very close-up cine film of the moths and their darting probosces. Within an hour, however, we noticed that their numbers had thinned out considerably. Although they were nocturnal, it seemed that their feeding activities were restricted to a relatively short period after dusk.

We paid more visits to Bugabula and Chief Kabasondwa to check the progress of the treatments, and eventually succeeded in isolating a very small, very delicate bacillus from the eye washings by inoculating them direct into the culture media at the kraal, instead of waiting to do this in the laboratory. The bacillus was so delicate that it would only survive a very short time away from its host, unless it was put into a special culture broth immediately. Later we succeeded in transmitting the condition by rubbing some of the culture onto the conjunctiva of a calf, which 'cried' for a week or so and then recovered.

The moth, we discovered, delighted in the name of *Arcyophora longivalvis*, a species which was known to feed on the tears of cattle and buck in other parts of Africa. Under the microscope, the proboscis was terrifying. The whole whip-like length was covered with a mass of sharp spikes. It was these, presumably, which irritated the eye and stimulated the flow of tears on which the moth fed. The tiny bacillus responsible for the inflammation (*Haemophilus bovis*) was probably always present in the eyes of cattle, but assumed virulence only when the cornea or conjunctiva were damaged by the scarifying action of the moths' probosces. A close relative of this bacillus which is associated with whooping cough, also appears to be present in healthy children's throats, only causing the disease when some other factor intervenes to stir it up.

We found records of this eye condition, infectious kerato-conjunctivitis, associated with moths in the Sudan and in South Africa, but none of the reported outbreaks was as severe as the Busoga one.

The infection subsided after a few weeks, and although isolated cases continued to occur, we never saw another outbreak. We estimated that 15 per cent of the cattle in some herds lost their eyesight temporarily, and many of these were left with some permanent eye damage.

Was it the sudden hatch of large numbers of moths that had caused the flare-up? Probably. The impact of thousands of moths, together with their barbed wire probosces, would be sufficient to damage the surface and upset the physiology of enough eyes to provide the bacillus, which was already there, with an even more congenial substrata on which to multiply.

Kalikwani's telegram, which had seemed so bizarre, had been absolutely accurate, except that it had been moths, not butterflies, which were attacking the cows. There was no question, however, that they had made the cows cry!

OPERATION BUFFALO

'How about a couple of weeks' holiday in the QE Park?' Denys asked me as he breezed into the morning tea break.

'Holiday in the Queen Elizabeth Park? Sure. What's the catch?'

'Buffalo dying. Head Office just rang. The Park Warden wants us to investigate.'

'They die every year about this time,' commented Tom, the parasitologist. 'The end of the dry season is pretty rough for them. There's not enough grazing to go round. The Park is overstocked.'

'Maybe it's anthrax,' suggested Nigel, who had once diagnosed this fatal disease in hippo in the Kazinga channel that ran through the Park between Lake George and Lake Edward.

'No,' Denys said. 'They're not sudden deaths. They just get thin and die. Probably parasites or malnutrition, or both. Can you set up an investigation, Pat? The sooner the better.'

I was delighted. The Queen Elizabeth National Park was one of the largest wildlife reserves in Uganda, lying to the west of the country on the borders of the Belgian Congo. It was famous for its elephants, lions, hippo and other game, including large herds of Cape buffalo. I had been waiting for just such an opportunity.

Since the deaths were more likely to be due to worms and malnutrition than anything else, Tom, the parasitologist, and Bob, the nutritionist, helped plan the campaign. We knew that any kind of nutritional investigation would be a lengthy and complicated affair, so we decided to first eliminate parasites or possibly an infectious disease.

Mary was expecting our second child the following month, so I was reluctant to set off on a long safari to such a remote spot just then, and Tom had immediate commitments with the Veterinary Assistants Training School, of which he was acting head.

'Let me go down for a few days,' I suggested to Tom. 'Maybe autopsy a couple and see what's what. Then if it looks like a parasitic problem, we can swop and you can have a turn.'

A few days later, with the sun's rays sliding over the polished surface of Lake Victoria, I set off in the Research Centre's Land Rover, laden with everything I could think of that might help to investigate dying buffalo.

It was grand to get out of the lab and into the wild, even for a few days. Peering down a microscope and fiddling about with petri dishes could be exciting at times, but needed leavening with frequent trips to the field. Besides, the solving of disease problems in the field was, to me, the most stimulating and enjoyable aspect of veterinary work. As we bumped along the main road to Mbarara, I burst into raucous renderings of songs from *My Fair Lady* and other musicals of the time, to the great astonishment and embarrassment of my African driver.

Turning northwards from Mbarara, the capital of the Kingdom of

Ankole, and already caked in dust, we passed, once again, the almost impenetrable Maramagambo forest, crossed the Kazinga channel and, shortly before dusk pulled into the QE National Park. Frank, the warden, had one of the guest cottages ready and said he would pick me up at dawn. After a bath, a couple of beers and a meal in the tourist restaurant, I flopped into bed, totally exhausted after the hot, jarring, 250-mile journey.

I awoke, or more accurately, was awakened, long before dawn by a heavy shuffling and a snapping of branches. I peeped out of the small window of the rondavel. It was moonlight. Huge, dark shapes like mobile boulders moved amongst the trees. Elephants! I watched fascinated, as they lumbered across the lawns, breaking off small branches, upsetting a large metal object – presumably a rubbish bin, and nudging each other playfully.

Before I had time to shave, Frank pulled up in a short-wheelbase, open Land Rover, with two game guards in the back.

'You can shave and eat later,' he called. 'Better we start before it gets too hot.'

We transferred the post-mortem instruments and other equipment to his vehicle and drove off, the sun breaking the horizon in a flaming orb. Almost at once I could feel its warmth on my face, but the air was still nippy and I was glad of my sweater.

The residences and offices of the Queen Elizabeth Park looked down over Lake Edward from the high ground of the Mweya peninsula. We followed one of the many dirt tracks that wound down through long dry grass, clumps of bushes and thorny trees, to the low-lying flats. Here, anthills and thickets interrupted the carpet of coarse brown grass, and every few hundred yards we passed large pools of muddy water from the surface of which peeped curious eyes.

'Hippo wallows,' Frank said. 'There are probably twelve thousand hippo in the Park. One of these days we'll have to start culling them. They eat too much vegetation, and the other animals are suffering.'

It wasn't long before we spotted a herd of buffalo grazing on an open savannah. Frank turned the Land Rover towards them.

'If we chase them for a bit, the sick ones will probably fall behind and we can autopsy one,' he suggested.

The herd watched with mild curiosity as we bumped towards them over tufted hillocks of coarse grass. We were within a hundred yards when they suddenly turned and cantered off across the open plain towards a low belt of trees. Before they reached it, two animals began to fall behind. We slowed down. They stopped and faced us, too weak to continue. Frank dropped one with a single shot; the

297

other stumbled a few yards further before Frank dropped it as well.

We cut them open. There were numerous worms in the stomach, mainly the small, red-striped *Haemonchus*, which had been so common in calves in Jamaica and also in the buffalo on the Chozi flats in Northern Rhodesia. There were also several different kinds of worms in the intestines, which we took for identification, and numerous ticks on the skin but apart from some waxy, tumour-like growths in the lungs of one, there seemed to be little wrong with them. I collected specimens for bacteriological and pathological investigation, and we set off to find another herd, leaving the game guards to skin and cut up the meat.

After bouncing and jolting for another half-mile, the engine began to cough, and within another hundred yards had died altogether.

'Damn,' Frank cursed. 'That's the second time it's done this. It's the carburettor, I think.' After 15 minutes of tinkering, the engine started once more.

'We'd better head back home,' Frank said. 'We might stick again.'

'Don't worry,' I assured him. 'I'll have a look at the specimens in the lab and, depending on what we find, we can arrange for further investigation.'

The recalcitrant carburettor nearly caused a tragedy later that day. Under the impression that he had fixed it, Frank set off with Tubby, the Deputy Director of Veterinary Services, who had turned up that afternoon from Head Office to photograph elephant. As they were returning, Frank noticed a young female lion limping through the grass. They watched it disappear into a thicket.

'Better check it out,' said Frank. 'If it's wounded I'll finish it off, otherwise it may attack someone.'

The animal had seemed too lame to run, so their hearts nearly stopped when, at fifty yards or so, a tawny shape bounded out of the bushes straight towards them. Mrs Leo may have had a thorn in her paw, but there was nothing wrong with her mate.

Frank swung the vehicle round and stepped on the accelerator, yelling to Tubby to grab the rifle from the back. Shock number two – no rifle. It must have been left behind. Meanwhile the irate lion was gaining rapidly on the cabless vehicle, which was misfiring and barely keeping ahead of the pounding paws.

'We only just got away,' Tubby told us that evening. 'I could feel those damn claws in my back. I felt so naked. If only I'd had my shirt on, it wouldn't have been so bad!'

A lot of good his shirt would have done him!

Back at Entebbe, we cut thin sections of the lung growths and stained them to show up their structure and the presence of any bacteria including the tubercle bacillus, which I thought just might be a possibility. We also placed small portions of the buttery lesions into special culture media which would allow the slow-growing TB bacillus, if it was present, to develop without being smothered by other, faster-growing organisms.

The results were disappointing. We found no bacteria in the sections we examined under the microscope, and nothing grew up in the cultures. What was striking, however, was the great number of large tissue cells, known as 'giant cells', throughout the lesions. These cells frequently occurred around tuberculous lesions in cattle and were also encountered in a rare cancerous condition called a 'giant cell tumour'.

We were nonplussed. There was no other evidence of TB apart from these cells, nor were the growths like those in tuberculous cattle, which always showed pockets of creamy pus or a cheese-like substance surrounded by a hard crust. These buffalo lesions were like lumps of soap – no pus and no crust.

We debated the diagnosis for the next two weeks. It was far more likely to be tuberculosis than the rare giant cell tumour, but why couldn't we isolate the causative bacillus, or at least see it in the sections? And why did the lesions differ so markedly from those in cattle? Eventually, I sent the slides to a colleague in London, suggesting that we might have turned up a rare case of giant cell tumour, and asking his opinion.

As soon as Lys, our second child, had safely arrived (at home, in the spare bedroom, as Mary had promised, aided by Maisie, a former maternity nurse and wife of the local policeman), Ted, the senior laboratory technician, Denys and I again set off to the Park. We shot eleven more buffalo. Nine of these were obviously sick, but only in eight could we find lesions. There was now little doubt about the diagnosis. These lesions were much more like the typical tuberculous lesions in cattle, although several were of the same waxy consistency which we had seen in the first buffalo we had shot.

We were more successful in the lab, too. Ted isolated the bovine strain of TB as well as a variety of other TB-like acid-fast organisms which we sent to the Tuberculosis Reference Centre at Cardiff, for final typing. Their opinion was that although they fitted no known type, they were probably harmless, but I wondered whether they were not the cause of the strange waxy growths.

Because of the high incidence of TB in the long-horned Ankole cattle, many of which encroached on the Park when grazing became scarce, it was not surprising that buffalo had picked up the disease. What could be done about it was another matter. Tuberculin testing of large, aggressive wild animals was not practicable. Even if they could have been darted with tranquillizers (then still in the experimental stage), the effort would have been enormous and costly. Neither could we prevent native herds from straying into the Park, which was vast and unfenced. The only thing was to try and keep the buffalo away from the perimeters of the Park and to shoot all apparently sick animals without delay. I would like to have recommended that all cattle straying into the Park should be shot on sight, but this would have created political problems far grater than tuberculosis.

While our investigation was proceeding, the Medical Dept asked us to examine sputum samples from several hundred Africans in Ankole with TB. Ted isolated the cattle strain of the bacillus in 28 per cent of these. I know of no other country where the cattle type of tubercle bacillus caused so many cases of TB in humans.

We had hardly finished our laboratory studies when the results of the sections we had sent to London arrived. My consultant was polite, but thought little of our expertise in pathology.

'No, this is *not* a giant-cell tumour,' he wrote. I could almost hear his snort of contempt. 'But perhaps you should look for further evidence of tuberculosis.'

I was delighted to tell him that we already had, and could now confirm his opinion.

TRIAL BY HOLIDAYS

Our family was growing fast, but our decision to have no more children before we faced home leave was shattered when, exactly 15 months after Lys, Maisie helped Kerry, our son, into the grey light of another dawn, once again in our spare room. Three youngsters within 30 months was perhaps pushing it a little, and I would return from the office to find Mary quietly sewing or studying Swahili inside the playpen, with a carrycot beside her, protected from two rampaging toddlers outside.

Home leaves were important interludes in colonial life. Our first and, as it turned out, our only home leave during six years in Uganda was very much of a curate's egg. Parts of it were indeed excellent. The start, however, was not.

It was a miserable voyage. The cabin was small and dirty and the crew unhelpful. One morning, desperate for an hour to ourselves, we put Shannon and Lys in the 'playroom', a facility designed, so said the propaganda, for this very purpose. Kerry, still in a carrycot, we left in the cabin. Half an hour later, two tearful babes found their way to the sports deck. No-one in the playroom had missed them, the girl in charge being totally preoccupied in writing letters, occasionally intervening in one of the more vociferous hair-pulling encounters that frequently occurred. The 'playroom' did fulfil one useful function. After that single experience, the merest whisper of the word was enough to discourage most misdemeanours!

To add to the general wretchedness aboard the *Braemar Castle*, which the passengers had now re-christened the *Belsen Castle*, a severe outbreak of food poisoning struck, and hardly had we survived that than a vicious epidemic of 'flu took over.

Thankfully, the nightmare voyage which we had dreamed of as the first glorious unwinding stage of our holiday, finally came to an end. We stumbled down the gangway, ready to kiss the muddy soil of Southampton docks, to discover that, owing to the rain, no luggage would be offloaded till the morrow. 'And if it rains again tomorrow – and tomorrow – and tomorrow?' we asked ourselves. Reluctantly, we consigned our absent luggage to the mercies of British Transport Services, who promised to deliver it to Penzance, the nearest town to the 'partially converted mill' we had rented on the strength of a glowingly romantic advertisement in the *Times* personal column.

We picked up our hired car, packed in our peaky, pallid and protesting *Belsen* survivors and set off through the rain to find our Cornish holiday home. The rain, turning to a chilly drizzle, followed us all the way to the front door of what the local postman insisted was our destination.

It was obvious that a lot more conversion had still to be done on the erstwhile watermill and butter factory. Ancient and very worn flagstones formed the floor of the huge ceilingless entrance hall-cum-kitchen, the roof of which was lost in shadowy cobwebs far above. One running tap and a diminutive geyser over a single sink explained the 'running hot and cold' in the advert, and up a worn rail-less stone staircase with a right-angled bend where the steps narrowed to nothing, hovered a rough mezzanine or gallery. Here, improvised curtains partitioned off the various cubicles designated for sleeping quarters. Here too, we finally found the 'loo' – a can of chemicals – in an alcove behind another ragged drape. There was also a room with a bath, for which we would later haul up hot water from the kitchen sink.

Stunned, we at last discovered, on one side of the hall, a truly converted part of the mill, a pleasantly furnished lounge lined with

301

books, and with a large fireplace ready laid. It was May and still cold for visiting Equatorians, so we immediately set fire to the inviting bundle and congregated round, ready to hold out our icy hands. Alas, the only response to our attempt at pyrotechnics, was to fill the room with smoke. Later, we found the chimney solid with rooks' nests.

Mary and I, still displaying the odd flush of youth and conditioned by our recent experience on the high seas, looked upon all this as trying but nevertheless interesting. But for Mary's parents, Hugh and D, well into their seventies, who had flown across from Canada and who joined us a few days later, it must have been a nightmare. To add still further to our discomfort, our luggage seemed to have been lost. A letter, telegram and phone call finally procured a response, to wit, that since there was no depot for British Transport Services at Penzance, our goods had been sent to Perranporth, some 35 miles to the north. Mary's dad and I set off to retrieve them. All we found was the pram. There was no sign of the trunk with most of the children's warmer clothes. I told the Transport Services' official what I thought of his Company, and glumly headed for home.

Then befell one of those extraordinary incidents for which I have no explanation whatsoever. As we were passing the railway station at the little town of Hayle, I had the odd feeling that the trunk would be there. Hugh was rudely sceptical, but I insisted on turning round and drawing up outside the station office.

'I'm looking for a trunk which has gone missing,' I told the one and only official on the platform.

'And what would be the name on this trunk?' he asked me, rather aggressively, I thought.

'Guilbride,' and I spelt it out for him.

'Aha, so you're Mr bloody Guilbride. Well it's about bloody time, i'n it? It's been 'ere for nearly two weeks. Why don' you get off your arse an' collect your things 'stead of leavin' 'em lying all over the bloody countryside?'

I was a little taken aback by such outspokenness from an official, even a Cornish one, but I explained what had happened and how I was just returning from Perranporth on a wild goose chase. He softened up a little.

'Trouble is we don't 'andle goods, but this lorry chap dropped it 'ere one morning an' asked me to keep it as a favour. Said you'd be along in the afternoon to collect it. Bloody people. Anyone 'oo does business with that lot needs 'is 'ead examined.'

I entirely agreed with him.

Hugh could only gape as I trundled the trunk out to the car.

'Go on. You knew it was there all the time,' he accused me.

'Wish I had,' I replied, with feeling.

After a month in Cornwall we crossed over to Ireland, full of misgivings as to how our next refuge, which we had also rented unseen, would turn out. But the Gods, after their initial sport, had now relented. At the River House, near Rathdrum in Co Wicklow, with Ann and Desmond, its wacky, Irish owners, we felt our holiday had finally begun.

We spent a month lazing in the heather or paddling in the river or roaming the moors collecting *frochan* for blueberry pie, and visiting my family's ancestral home, the Mill House, in Bunclody (formerly Newtownbarry), Co Wexford.

When our lease of the River House ran out, we rented a 'castle' a few miles away, near Glendaloch, and continued our carefree life. But one omission we still had to correct was the christening of Lys and Kerry, and what better place, we felt, than the little church almost within the grounds of Laragh 'Castle'. Ann, the dynamic 40-year-old owner of the River House, was soon conscripted as a godmother for Kerry, and Mary's cousin flew over from her practice in Glasgow to godmother Lys.

Mary, suddenly remembering, while driving to the church, that all females' heads should be covered, whipped up a neat little bonnet for our two-and-a-half-year-old daughter to wear. Lys was delighted until the vicar tried to remove it to anoint her head with Holy Water. What did this unknown uncle in the black dress and embroidered tablecloth think he was doing? As we were to witness many times in the future, her face started to turn red and then gave way to the deep purple of total outrage as she squirmed, punched and yelled her way through the service, which concluded with the hastiest and least sincere blessing in the history of the Church!

Shortly after the christening, Shannon and Lys went missing. We found them in the church, which they now considered part of their holiday home, building mud castles in front of the altar. Hastily we set about clearing up the mess, but the vicar caught us at it.

'Ach,' he laughed, as we sheepishly mumbled apologies, 'oi've no doubt that the Lord was deloighted.'

The present owner of Laragh castle was related to the redoubtable Maude Gonne MacBride, who had been closely involved with the early Irish rebels. In addition, his wife was the daughter of Hitler's former Minister of Culture. The large, old fashioned library was filled with Irish history and also contained the handwritten diaries of Hitler's ex-minister. Mary's dad, Hugh, who spoke German fluently, kept us entranced reading from the writer's experiences of war-time Germany, and the trials and tribulations of Hitler's empire, as seen by one of the inner circle. We were told that this gentleman had emigrated to the USA and now held a high position in the government of that country!

The Britannia that flew us back to Entebbe (first class in those days) was also carrying the Kabaka, the King of the Buganda. Shannon and his Highness soon became well acquainted. She considered the aisle her own territory, making the unfortunate potentate step over her spread-eagled form and pick his way through her toys every time he wished to use the 'loo'!

He might have been surprised to learn that the great aunt of this prostrate infant, was one of his several Godmothers! Aunt Bé (Dad's sister and Harry Hunter's wife) had accepted this honour at the Kabaka's christening soon after she had arrived in Uganda in the early twenties. I don't think either of them took much notice of the link!

* * *

Once a year we visited my parents in Kenya. Leaving Entebbe at four in the morning, we could just cover the 500 miles to Nanyuki before nightfall. As often as not, Mary would be pregnant, a condition which seemed to coincide, unerringly, with both her Swahili exams and these trips. As the years went by, our Borgward station wagon became more and more cramped. On our first visit there was only Shannon in her carry-cot. Subsequent visits saw the additional blonde heads of Lys, Kerry and Lindley, bouncing on the mattress which I had placed in the back for Mary to stretch out on.

Between four and five o'clock in the afternoon, we would drive through the gates of Nanyuki's residential hotel, the Sportsman's Arms, with its thatched rondavels separated by bright, well-tended flower beds, the home of my parents since the Mau Mau had driven them from their own cottage. In front of the hotel, over the dark green sea of primeval forest, snow-capped Mount Kenya glittered in the late afternoon sun. It was marvellous after the long, hot journey to step out into the cool, bracing air and the smell of blue gum smoke from the evening fires.

The small house, two miles outside the township, to which Dad and Mum had first retired from Uganda after World War Two, and where they had remained throughout the worst of the Mau Mau fighting, was isolated and surrounded by thick, tall forest. I admired their pluck; Dad, at the age of 75, had no longer been a combatant but had helped to staff the anti-Mau Mau command centre each evening. Mum, armed with Dad's old, cumbersome, World War One Verey Light pistol, which she could hardly lift, let alone aim and fire, would wait alone in the cottage for his return, often in the small hours. She was a very brave lady.

Once, they returned from a brief holiday to find that their cottage had been used for Mau Mau initiation ceremonies; pieces of sacrificial animals and other messy evidence were strewn over the sitting-room floor. Another time they spent an hour, spread-eagled on the floor in front of the cut-stone fireplace – the only solid part of the cottage while police and Mau Mau bullets ripped through the wooden cottage walls. It was more than enough for septuagenarians; they sold their 'chocolate box' and moved into a rondavel at the Sportsman's Arms Hotel.

Kenya, like Uganda, was heading for Independence, but it was still an expatriate's country with a regime dented only slightly by the Mau Mau and the general trend towards a more liberal Empire. There was increasing talk of 'going home if this lot get in', but it was a land still firmly in the hands of the *bwanas*.

Tourism was on the upswing; expensive safari clubs, owned by consortiums of prominent Americans, like the Mawingo, an impressive, former hotel complex, floating in the forest beneath Mount Kenya; or the Secret Valley, another Treetops, owned by Shan, the Indian proprietor of the Sportsman's Arms, were becoming known to the international tourist agencies.

Probably, as my father constantly urged, I could have switched to the more prestigious Kenya service, but I had other ideas. I wasn't going to stay in Africa for ever, the Caribbean still tugged, and I kept hoping for a posting in that area once again. In the meantime, I preferred the less conspicuous, more friendly life of Entebbe.

Although Mau Mau activities were, by then, history, I still felt anxious when travelling with the family over those lonely, rough roads. I wasn't permitted to carry my rifle, so instead, I placed a speargun under the seat. I hoped I would never have to use it – the mess would be awful. Even armed with this terrifying weapon, my stomach would contract whenever the engine coughed or showed signs of malfunction, or when we had a puncture with only long stretches of desolate, forest-bound road, fore and aft. Help in the middle of the nowhere was difficult to find, and could easily be offered by the wrong people. So it was with considerable trepidation that I listened to the peculiar noises which had started in the Isabella's engine one Sunday afternoon as we were returning from Nanyuki.

We were no longer in Mau Mau country, to be sure, in fact we were well into Uganda, approaching the little town of Iganga, between the border and Jinja. The reason that I was so disturbed was that I had been told some rather gruesome tales of folk that had broken down in that area, and I had been warned never, but never, to stop there.

The last incident I knew of had, at least, a happy ending. A representative of a drug firm had had the misfortune to overturn his Volkswagen Beetle near Iganga. When he came to, concussed but uninjured, he discovered that his samples, personal papers and luggage, as well as many removable parts of the car, had been stolen. He flagged down a passing motorist, who took him to the police station at Iganga. Here, at least, was something the town could be proud of. Thieves they had in plenty but, possibly because of this, they had also been allocated a most efficient and dedicated African police officer. He organized an immediate search and, before nightfall, every single item stolen from my friend had been recovered. The police also towed his car to an Indian Garage and found a lift for him to Kampala.

If the worst came to the worst, I decided, I would make tracks for the police station. I hoped their hero would still be there.

The engine noises continued. I changed gear and stepped on the accelerator. 'Putt – putt', pause, 'putter – putter'. We ambled through the town, a mile-long ribbon of tin roofed *dukas* and dusty residences, my fingers crossed, praying hard. But neither my superstitious attempts to thwart evil, nor my prayers, were of any use. On the hill leading out of Iganga towards Kampala, my trusty Borgward gave up altogether.

'What do we do now,' I groaned. Then, more hopefully, 'perhaps it's just a petrol block.'

I opened the bonnet, disconnected the petrol pipe and blew. I could hear air bubbling into the tank. No block. I examined the carburettor and plugs; they seemed OK, but the engine still wouldn't start. I was at the end of my expertise. Several inquisitive locals had gathered round, their shiny black faces thrusting in through the windows, sizing up the *musungu* lady and her three blond *watotos*. It was already half past four and would be dark in just over an hour. I couldn't leave Mary and the kids to look for help; the only hope was that a relatively empty car might pass and give them a lift, while I tried to discover what was wrong. As all this was passing through my mind, a battered 'pick-up' pulled in behind me, with two Indians in the cab and several kids behind.

'We saw you go past,' said the elder Indian, 'and I said to my son, "He's in trouble and if he breaks down, he'll be in bigger trouble,"

306

so I thought I'd follow you and see.' I was staggered. There must be some trick, or was he looking for a reward.

He insisted on towing me back to his house, where he welcomed us into a gaudily decorated lounge and introduced us to his wife and several more children. Tapers of *agarbatti* incense were burning in brass holders under ornate portraits, presumably of Indian gods and goddesses.

My benefactor (I am ashamed to say I have forgotten his name) sent his son to fetch a mechanic.

'Today Sunday; nutting open. But Jethabai, he my friend,' he explained.

While the son was gone, we were offered all sorts of things to eat and drink, of which the kids took full advantage.

Jethabai arrived and opened the bonnet. I pressed the started to demonstrate the problem. The engine caught immediately. We tried again and again. Each time it started perfectly.

'Must been dirt, sir. Gone now.' Jethabai seemed as pleased as I. We thanked the family for their generous help and hospitality. They were embarrassed.

'Nutting, nutting. Come and see us next time you pass.'

The sun was setting as we waved goodbye, accompanied by their cheery farewells and some lovely little cakes which the good lady of the house had presented to the children.

Iganga; a place to be avoided? We could hardly have picked a better spot for a breakdown!

But the saga wasn't over. At nine that night, ten miles from Entebbe, the spluttering began again. This time it was final. Being Sunday night there was almost no traffic, but an hour later a passing motorist promised to ring Denys at the Research Centre. We waited. At eleven-thirty, a truck passed and the Indian driver offered to take Mary and the kids home. He had come from Kabale on the Congo border and had been on the road for 18 hours. His young son had very bad toothache and he was bringing him to the dentist at Entebbe.

After they had left, I wound up the windows, locked the doors and tried to sleep. Several curious faces peeped in at me during the rest of that moonlit night, but they were all friendly.

At nine o'clock the next morning, as the car was beginning to become uncomfortably hot, the Land Rover from the Centre arrived. My delight at its arrival soon turned to apprehension. It appeared that the driver must have imbibed too much *waragi* at the week-end. He was unsteady and his movements uncoordinated. I was even more worried when he showed me his tow rope, so short that it only

307

allowed three feet between the two vehicles. My anxiety, however, soon turned to terror when he set off at 40 miles an hour, deaf to my honking and yells. I was very proud of myself for arriving back at the Centre in one piece.

The driver, poor fellow, wasn't drunk. It turned out that he was suffering from some nervous disorder, probably advanced syphilis. A few days later he pulled up at a petrol station near Mbarara in a highly nervous condition and filled in a requisition for 50 cents' worth of petrol. The Greek owner, alarmed at his behaviour, felt he had better intervene. He confiscated the keys and rang the Research Centre. The driver was hospitalized and never returned to us.

COPPER PLATED SHEEP

Eric, the Regional Veterinary Officer reported a peculiar condition in the sheep at Mbarara Stock Farm. I promised to meet him there the next day.

'They have bright golden livers,' he explained as I got out of the landrover, 'and there are haemorrhages all through the tissues.' He ran a hand over his short red hair, tilted his head on one side like a humorous imp, and added, 'Really quite pretty.'

We walked over to the sheep pens with George, the Stock Farm Manager.

'One died yesterday, which I opened, and another a couple of hours ago, which I've left for you,' Eric told me. 'They've lost about fifteen in the last month. Only the 'Dorper' flock (crosses between East African Blackheads and Dorset Horn) seem to be affected, the local breeds are fine.'

As soon as I slit the abdominal wall, I could see the liver lying on top of the other organs like a golden shield. As I delved further, I came across haemorrhages in the other organs and muscles and the spleen looked as if it was stuffed with blackberry jam.

'Acute haemolytic jaundice. Dammit, that should tell us something. Usually suggests a severe infection like leptospirosis, or an acute attack of a red cell destroying protozoa, or perhaps a virus. We'd better wash well, it may be infectious to humans.'

I took blood smears from the ear vein and collected pieces of the liver and other organs as well as some dark orange urine and intestinal contents. We spent a week at Entebbe examining the specimens and trying to isolate a causal organism, without success. Further cases occurred and we examined them with equal thoroughness, but

308

again without any conclusion. In order not to overlook any lead, we sent samples to the Govt Chemist for analysis, although I still suspected that it was an infectious disease.

The Chemist's report, ten days later, surprised me. The livers had up to two hundred times the normal level of copper in them. Obviously, they were cases of copper poisoning.

We set about looking for the source – the paddock soil, the grasses the flock grazed, the whitewash which they had been licking on the pen walls, the mineral lick, the dip they were washed with to prevent tick-borne heartwater, and the medicine they were dosed with to treat worms. Both the mineral lick and the anthelminthic contained low levels of copper, but there was no obvious correlation between their use and the onset of deaths. Maybe, we thought, some copper containing product had been dumped in the corner of a pasture, or the sheep had accumulated copper in their livers over a period until a certain threshold was reached, or some other factor intervened, which brought about this sudden haemolytic crisis.

Molybdenum was well known to be bound up with copper absorption in sheep, a deficiency of one mineral leading to an excess of the other, but we found no deficiencies of molybdenum in any of the soil or grass samples.

We concluded that the mineral lick and the occasional dosing for worms with a compound containing copper, triggered by some unknown factor, had led to a haemolytic crisis in a breed of sheep that were particularly susceptible.

'It might prove an efficient way of mining copper on low yielding soils,' Eric quipped.

NAKED WARRIORS

Winston Churchill, impressed no doubt by the well-watered, fertile country, the thick dark forests, the crops of bananas, coffee and cotton, and the lush, six-foot elephant grass that fringed the road-sides, described Uganda as a pearl at the source of the Nile, or words to that effect.

His metaphor was accurate if used to describe the south and west of the country, but there were many less blessed areas, with scanty rainfall and poor, sandy soils. Karamoja, for instance. This desolate, scrub-covered province, the size of Wales, was thrust up against the Kenya border in the north-eastern corner of Uganda, like a despised relation. The inhabitants, collectively known as Karamajong, were a hundred years behind the rest of their compatriots. Classified ethnologically as Nilo-Hamitic, with Ethiopian-like features, they lived with, by and for, their cattle, goats and sheep.

Like the tribes across the border, the Karasuk and Turkana, the Karamajong were warriors as well as herders. Tall, wiry, aloof, their faces stern, their bodies covered with battle and tribal scars, as well as those indicating the number of victims they had slaughtered, they stalked through the provincial centre, Moroto, armed with one or more spears, a dark cotton cloak flowing out behind from a loose fastening at the neck – but not another stitch! The women, a little more discreet, wore a dirty piece of goatskin around their waist. Neither sex seemed in the least embarrassed by the fully clothed Europeans with whom they jostled on Moroto's only street.

Starkers the men may have been, but they displayed a dignity not seen in other tribes. They didn't walk, they strode with a long loping gait, followed by their loin-clouted women, bearing chattels atop coiffures stiff with cow dung. While the Karamajong considered members of any other African tribe to be enemies, they were always friendly 'gentlemen' towards Europeans.

Their diet was mainly milk, mixed with blood which they drew off at intervals by shooting a small arrow into the jugular veins of their cattle. As a result, kwashiorkor, the protein deficiency syndrome which took such a heavy toll of children in other parts of Africa, was unknown in Karamoja. As far as crops were concerned, sorghum was the only one that could be even half-relied upon.

Football and other Western sports had hardly touched Karamoja. A much more exciting and profitable activity was to go cattle raiding across the Kenya border. A date would be set, the target defined and parties from several villages assembled. On the appointed night, they would head east through a terrain thickly covered with thorn trees and prickly bushes which would have stopped lesser mortals within a few yards. But thorns were no deterrent to these naked warriors. Off they loped, bare of foot and bare of bottom, at a steady ten miles an hour, their spears and shields the only protection from wild animals and lacerating thorns. I imagined that the latter presented the graver risk. One well positioned three-inch thorn could have played havoc with their social life. If ever a 'box' was indicated in a sport, that sport was undoubtedly cattle raiding in Karamoja – it was far more necessary than cricket!

Taking the Karasuk villages by surprise, they would round up all the cattle they could conveniently take with them and start the 30 or 40 mile trek homewards. 'Gentlemen' they may have seemed towards Europeans, but there was nothing gentlemanly about their raids.

310

Anyone on the opposing 'team' who got in the way was slaughtered, women and children included.

The Administration took a very poor view of these nocturnal excursions, as well they should, but it was difficult to pinpoint the individuals responsible. The most effective discouragement was to impose collective fines of large numbers of cattle – 500, 1,000, 3,000 or more.

It was simple enough to round up these 'fines', but once the cattle were collected, what then? A practical solution would have been the meat markets at Mbale and Tororo, which were always short of supplies, but without transportation it would have meant driving already thin cattle through waterless thornbush which would have achieved nothing but heavy losses; but to slaughter large numbers in that heat, without refrigeration, and expect the meat to be fit for consumption after transporting it 200 miles, even if daily transportation could have been arranged, would have been a costly disaster.

Biltong! Of course! Dry the meat, store it and send it south every fortnight or so. Biltong, or *chaqui*, kept well, needed no refrigeration, was popular and commanded an excellent price. 12 to 20 animals could be slaughtered daily, their meat sun-dried and turned into biltong. The outcome was Namalu, a holding ranch for 'fines' cattle 60 miles south of Moroto, with biltong production facilities.

I spent several weeks at Namalu each year. It was hot, dry and dusty most of the time, or else deep in mud, but it provided a continuous source of animals for studies in parasites, tuberculin tests, grazing experiments, trypanocidal drugs and any other investigation where results depended on examination of animals post mortem.

A spine of rocky hills rose behind the ranch house, and to one side towered the craggy peaks and forested gorges of Mount Kadam. Sometimes, one could make out the mists and clouds covering Mount Elgon, 60 miles to the south, over a shimmering plain of thorny scrub and long grass, interrupted here and there by prehistoric outcrops of massive boulders.

There was little else in Namalu except the prison – and a most unusual prison it was. Although patronized by many dangerous, long-term inmates, security was minimal, since it was the policy of the Government to ensure that all its guests came from tribes outside Karamoja and were therefore regarded by the Karamajong as vermin. An escaped prisoner had little chance of survival, a spear inevitably ending his brief attempt at freedom. Warders were almost superfluous and used more to keep the Karamajong out, than the prisoners in!

One success we had in our experiments at Namalu was the formu-

311

lation of a long-acting injection against trypanosomiasis. As had been explained to me in Mbarara on my first visit to Ankole, the drugs against *ngana*, although good, had to be given too frequently, and the newer, longer-acting ones gave unacceptable local reactions. Mike, who had joined us to try and solve this impasse, was aiming at six-monthly (instead of six-weekly) injections with a minimal reaction. His approach was to mix each of the anti-trypanocidal drugs with various amounts of lanolin, mineral oil and silicone, which acted as slow-release agents. Unfortunately, the thick glutinous mass that resulted could not be injected by normal syringes. The answer hit Mike one day when he was waiting for his car to be serviced. A grease gun! He soon found that this sturdy instrument for lubricating cars could be suitably adapted to force a fistful of grease through the skin of a cow with comparative ease, except that the muscles of the neck, the usual site for these injections, could not cope with such large amounts. However, most tropical breeds, especially the Zebu, had well-developed, pendulous dewlaps – that fold of loose skin hanging down between their forelegs – which was said to act as a radiator. This proved a perfect depot for Mike's tennis ball of grease. He grease-gunned hundreds of head at Namalu, examining the injection sites at autopsy for any untoward reaction, until he was satisfied that both the dose and the formulation were suitable.

'I never thought that we would treat cattle the same way as we treat cars,' I told him.

'What do you mean?'

'Well, we grease and spray cars every three or four months. We already spray cattle against ticks, and now we are going to grease them against tryps as well!'

I looked forward to visiting Namalu either via Moroto, the provincial capital, 60 miles to the north, or by the more direct route, a sandy, overgrown track that skirted Mount Elgon.

Phillip, the young bachelor manager of the Namalu 'fines' ranch, had consistently refused transfer to more civilized surroundings. I could understand his reluctance to leave Namalu. There was something about this lonely, dried-up land, the awesome and mysterious Mount Kadam with its misty gorges and its spear-like crags, that challenged the explorer to scale them. The game-speckled savannah and the cool silence of the star-filled nights were enough to make civilization seem like a dirty word. One could have been forgiven for imagining this to be Hobbit country; even the names – Toror, Parabong, Lubwor, Kadam – had a Hobbit ring to them.

Our visits to Namalu were greatly enlivened by Twiga, a young

312

giraffe abandoned by its mother at birth, which Phillip had rescued from certain death by predators. At nights, Twiga shared the low-ceilinged rest house with us. This was no problem at first, but as he grew (about half an inch a day), his small, furry horns, hardly more than elongated pimples, would poke twin holes in the soft ceiling board each time he raised his head. He delighted in pulling away our pillows in the middle of the night and chewing them. At other times he would actually sit on the camp beds, with predictable and disastrous results. He must have weighed 700 pounds at least.

He was fed a whisky bottle of milk each morning before being shooed out to graze. Eventually a stepladder was needed to hold the bottle sufficiently high. When he was half-grown, about nine feet tall, he was sent to the Animal Refuge, or 'zoo', at Entebbe, where he was a great favourite with everyone until he died, about a year later. We isolated a salmonella, but whether this was the bug that killed him, we couldn't tell.

The Karamajong must have some of the world's top marathon runners. An old warrior once asked me to look at his sick sheep, about 30 miles away. I said I would drive out that afternoon, and offered him a lift. No, he would give me directions, but he would go on foot and see me there. When I arrived, two-and-a-half hours later, there he was, his sheep kraaled and waiting. It was unbelievable.

The Karamajong were also fearless hunters. On one of my visits, a 12-year-old boy brought in a leopard which he had stalked in the long grass and killed with his short, but deadly, spear. His skill and courage were staggering.

It was a pity that the Karamajong tribesmen didn't stick to hunting and herding. Unfortunately, perhaps due to the lack of football and cinemas, or for the want of other excitements, or perhaps simply to fulfil their warlike urge, our herdsmen often joined the cross-border cattle raids, and many didn't come back.

On one occasion, the early hours suddenly erupted in yells and rifle fire. We went outside. A mile below us a battle was raging. Rifle fire, revving vehicles, shouts, then silence. The next morning, only 12 of our 20 herd boys appeared. We asked what the trouble had been. They told us nothing. Later, the District Officer was more informative. It appeared that a detachment of the King's African Rifles, patrolling the border, had run into a raiding party returning from Karasuk. Some of the Karamajong had guns and, very unwisely, used them against the KAR. In the melée we lost eight of our best herdsmen.

313

Of course, the Karasuk were just as eager to raid their opposite numbers in Karamoja. Who kept the score, I've no idea; but one thing was certain – there were no referees.

Most expatriates regarded a visit to Karamoja like Muslims viewed a visit to Mecca: it had to be done at least once. However, presumably because of the primitive and vulnerable life-style of the Karamajong and their attitude towards clothing, the area was restricted and permission to visit had to be obtained. It was the young, unmarried secretaries, I was told, who topped the list of applicants!

OPERATION HIPPO

The Director was on the phone.

'They're going to slaughter six hundred hippo in the Queen Elizabeth Park. I've promised our assistance.'

I wasn't surprised. Our pasture agronomist at Mbarara had spent months in the Park, studying the effect of these barrel-shaped, herbivorous monsters on the vegetation, and had proved that they were gormandizing at the expense of other ungulates, such as buck and buffalo. Frank, the Park Warden, had been advocating hippo culling for years, now he wanted action.

'So, what do you want us to do?' It seemed to me a purely Game Department affair.

'Remember that report by Nigel about hippos dying of anthrax? Well, the Provincial Medical Officer must have read it and had visions of plague and pestilence ravaging the local population, who will be the main consumers of hippo steaks. In his wisdom, he has insisted that each carcase be certified by us as free from anthrax before butchering. Bloody stupid, but that's our orders.'

One could sympathize with the PMO's views, scientifically shaky as they were. Anthrax has a rapid course. Animals are found dead, seldom are they seen to be sick. Diagnosis is made from examination of blood smears taken from the carcase. The likelihood of diagnosing anthrax in a live animal at the time it was shot, especially when there had been no cases for years, was infinitesimal. On the other hand, any illness in the population would certainly be laid at the door of diseased hippos and the Medical Department's neglect in ensuring the wholesomeness of the meat.

But if it put the PMO's mind at ease, fair enough. It would provide me with the perfect excuse for a few weeks' safari in Uganda's most famous National Reserve, and a once in a lifetime opportunity to investigate the innards of this peculiar 'river horse', in depth – so to

314

speak. None of us had really explored a hippo's insides.

Word of the impending carnage soon got around. We weren't the only ones to sharpen our scalpels. Had poor Mrs Hippo been able to see the hordes of drooling scientists who would soon be plucking at her vitals, she would have made a beeline across the border into the Belgian Congo. But no-one thought to tell her, so her life continued undisturbed on the huge expanse of grass, shrubs and wallows of the QE National Park.

Meanwhile, technicians at Makerere University, the Trypanosomiasis Research Organization at Tororo, the Rockefeller Virus Research Institute and the Animal Health Research Centre at Entebbe, and other prestigious bodies, gathered together their apparatus and specimen bottles, their microscopes and slides, packed their landrovers and trucks, and set forth to see what scientific gems the old lady was hiding from them in her voluminous interior.

There was no question of hippo joining the ranks of endangered species. It was estimated that the Park and its surrounds held over 12,000, and the number was rising steadily. Their danger to the ecology was the enormous quantities they had to consume to maintain their two-and-a-half ton bodies. Hippo could easily tuck away 400 pounds of herbage daily.

It was an odd collection of boffins that assembled in front of the Park offices at dawn to hear Frank brief them on the day's procedure. Medical doctors, vets, anatomists, biologists, physiologists, parasitologists – all convinced that their particular study was the most important scientific event that had happened in Uganda in the last decade and should therefore have priority. One group of physiologists from Makerere wanted to be beside the animal when it dropped, to take the skin and body temperatures and sample the sweat glands. A couple of minutes' delay, they said, would invalidate their findings. Another group had to remove the eyes immediately, before they glazed over. The trypanosome hunters from Tororo wanted samples of blood before it coagulated, and the anatomists demanded the first peep into Mrs Hippo's entrails before they were disturbed. But it was the vets who had pride of place. They had to pass the carcase free from anthrax before anyone could touch it – at least in theory!

Bill, a wildlife nutritionist on a sabbatical from the University of California, and Frank, the Warden, would do the shooting. Bill had already been up in his small Leopard Moth the previous evening, assessing the area for the first day's shoot. He and Frank would go ahead, select a wallow and shoot all the hippo in it before the scientists, led by their intrepid vet – me! – were allowed to approach and start rummaging for treasures.

We stood around in the nippy early morning air for about an hour, discussing our various researches and disappearing into the restaurant at intervals for coffee. Finally we heard shots in the distance, there were an awful lot. 'Sounds like a battle,' someone joked, 'the hippos are fighting back'. Shortly afterwards Frank returned and told us to follow him. There must have been a dozen vehicles and close to thirty participants.

I didn't know quite what to expect. I had visions of half a dozen hippo lying neatly on the ground from which I could take my blood smears and examine them at leisure. Instead, I found a mass of semi-naked screaming Africans, some in the wallow, others around it, hauling out hippo carcases with long ropes. A dozen animals were already lying at the wallow's edge and others were floating in the blood-stained water, waiting to be dragged ashore.

It was bedlam, a scene worthy of Hieronymus Bosch. The yells of those tugging, together with the shouts of those in charge – altogether over 60 wildly jubilant, protein-starved villagers, stampeding through the mud – was not, I thought, conducive to a scientific investigation.

I soon realized that the simple procedure of taking a blood smear was going to be a lot more difficult than I had anticipated. A hippo's hide is not like a cow's, through which you can draw blood from a subcutaneous vein with the prick of a needle, or into which you can make a small cut. A power tool would have been more appropriate to penetrate the up to two-inch-thick epidermis. Also, the blood from the bullet wounds, which might have offered a solution, congealed before I could get to it and was mixed with mud. The only recourse seemed to be to hack off an ear. This proved effective, but there were other problems. It required about ten minutes to take the slides from the carcase, stain them and examine them under the microscope, before I could pronounce the animal clear of anthrax. Meanwhile, twenty eager scientific explorers were jostling my table, urging permission to start their excavations.

It was obvious that no-one intended to wait until I had examined each carcase in turn, especially as the panga-wielding teams of excited tribesmen could hardly be restrained from starting to disembowel their victims immediately they were brought ashore. Furthermore, I had no means of identifying each animal (a tin of paint, I realized too late, would have helped), so I decided to take smears from the whole lot at one time and sit down quietly to stain and examine them while the rest of the sleuths made merry with their chosen titbits. It was a million to one that I would find any sign of anthrax, but if I did, I would halt operations at once. Until then, it was free for all. I hurried through the slide examinations as fast as I dared, eager to explore the whole whopping carcase before others tore it apart.

Difficulties of autopsying hippo didn't end with the flaying. It was impossible to move the carcase about as I could a cow or a dog, and the mere size and weight of its organs were discouraging. But help was plentiful; a dozen machetes wielded by meat-hungry hands soon had the ribs removed and all the inner workings displayed for my scrutiny.

The first wallow had yielded 18 hippo, and it was after midday before everyone had claimed their booty. I had felt a cold coming on the day before and had woken with a sore throat which became worse by the hour, with the addition of a fever and a raging thirst. My cold bag contained six soft drinks, which I had anticipated would see me through the day. But now, halfway through the morning, they were finished. I was feeling parched and desperate, and wondering how I would be able to stick it out all through that torrid afternoon, when a small truck laden with crates of soft drinks drew alongside.

Must be a mirage, I thought. I'm delirious.

'Justa keep you goin'.'

A rather plump, swarthy individual in a dirty safari suit, carrying a couple of soft drink bottles in each grimy fist, ambled across to where I was staring down my microscope.

I took out my wallet.

'No, no. No to pay. Thisa free. I see you later. Maybe you wanta more.'

Definitely I was hallucinating. No guardian angel could ever have been half as welcome as this unshaven, paunchy Greek. It turned out that he owned the hotel just outside the Park. Each day that followed, his small truck, laden with crates of elixir, would bump towards us over the horizon.

Not content with his largesse in the field, he offered free drinks each evening to anyone engaged in the operation. As dusk fell the verandah of his one-storey, tin-roofed hotel would fill with sweaty, dusty, exhausted and very thirsty academics, eager to cool off and wash down the day's grime at the expense of this generous fellow.

It was, undoubtedly, a noble gesture, notwithstanding the fact that the franchise for the sale of all hippo meat from the culling had been given him, and that this would come up annually for re-allocation. Some nasty people hinted that his bounty was really an investment. I preferred to think he did it from the goodness of his heart. In any event, he undoubtedly saved my life!

317

Each day was a repeat of the first, except that by the end of the week the number of investigators began to tail off. My cold, however, got worse. I consumed a dozen soft drinks a day and sweated them out as fast as I drank them, but managed to make the friendly Greek's verandah each evening, to recuperate on beer.

At last, my final day arrived. Tom would take over the next morning. It was a day I'll never forget. Everything went wrong. Just as the shooting started, Bill's teenage son was charged by an angry buffalo as he passed a thicket. Luckily, he was only scratched as he jumped into a thorn bush. Bill fired immediately, but only succeeded in wounding the animal in the leg. It disappeared. For the next three hours, everything came to a halt as Bill and Frank went off to track and kill it. To leave an aggressive, wounded buffalo on the loose would have been courting disaster.

Late as it was when they returned, a wallow was selected and shooting began. Frank had estimated that it contained 20 to 25 hippo. He was badly out. Sixty-two were eventually hauled ashore. Once the slaughter had started, it had to continue until every hippo in the wallow was accounted for, otherwise it would have been too dangerous to enter the wallow to haul out those already shot.

I arrived when the shooting was already in full swing. It was a gruesome scene. Although the shooting was expert, an occasional shot would only wound, making the recipient thrash around while the others attacked it, their jaws wide and their huge canine tusks slashing the dying animal. Hippo must be one of God's most stupid creatures. Despite the slaughter of their companions on all sides, the survivors seemed to have no inkling of their danger and continued to stare at us with their large prominent eyes just above the water level and their small ears wiggling to keep off the flies.

My routine was now well established. I set up my table and microscope about 50 yards from the wallow, and as each hippo was pulled onto the bank, my African assistant would hack off an ear and bring me two blood smears. It was a lot easier to work now that there were less boffins left to harass me. But, so I wouldn't feel lonely, a couple of aggressive hippo, which had been grazing away from the wallow when the shooting started, came back to rejoin their friends and insisted on pounding round and round the wallow, surprisingly fast for such huge animals, passing within 30 yards or so of my table at each circuit. Occasionally, they would stop and eye me, and sometimes would defecate in apparent disdain, their stubby tails whizzing round like propellers, spreading excrement far and wide. It reminded me of the saying, then just coming into vogue – 'when the shit hits the fan'. I tried to keep one eye on them and look for anthrax bacilli with the other, ignoring the whining of bullets ricocheting overhead.

Bill passed by and dropped off a rifle.

'You may need it if they come closer. Aim in front of the ear or between the eyes.'

I prayed that I wouldn't have to do either. It would be just my luck to miss and find I had shot some poor unsuspecting African. Luckily, the fact that all was not as it should be in their old wallow finally penetrated their thick skulls. To my great relief, they trotted off to find a new one.

Some of those shot were youngsters or calves, one being no more than a few weeks old, like an enormous pig, more pink than grey. It was heartbreaking to see it follow the carcase of its mother as she was pulled out and then try and defend her on land. There was, sadly, no alternative but to shoot the brave little animal. It would never have been accepted by another group and was probably still suckling. Hippos weigh about 100 pounds at birth, suckle under water and grow fairly rapidly to weigh a ton at three years and over two tons when they reach maturity at eight. Their life span is 30 to 40 years.

When darkness fell, several carcases were still awaiting autopsy. I had to leave them, there was no way to examine them in the dark, nor could we risk butchering them at night, the risk of marauding lions was too great.

As I packed up to go, watching the crimson sky where the sun had ducked over the Ruwenzori Mountains, I tried to estimate the total number of hippos I had autopsied. I made it over 200. I didn't want to see the insides of another for a very long time. I would be only too happy to hand over to Tom on the morrow. The heat, the hordes of biting flies, my cold, which still hung on in my sinuses, the continuous carnage and the long hours in the frazzling sun, made me long for the comforts of Entebbe.

Hippos, outside Disney cartoons, are not friendly, lovable animals; if they were, I think the slaughter would have been unbearable. The ferocity they showed to their wounded fellows was gruesome, and they were responsible for the deaths of many fishermen each year by attacking their canoes, and even savaging unsuspecting pedestrians who got in their way on land. No, they were pretty horrible in many ways, but they were one of the earth's inhabitants and their slaughter, however necessary it may have been from man's point of view, was nonetheless repugnant.

We found nothing as spectacular in the hippos as we had done in the buffalo. There were a few protozoa in the blood smears, including

319

an unidentified trypanosome similar to those that caused sleeping sickness, and a babesia similar to that which caused redwater in cattle. As we expected, there were numerous worms in all parts of the stomachs and intestines, and a few ticks on the softer parts of the skin, but that was about all. Several had severe wounds from fighting and a few had metal objects buried in their hide, souvenirs of attacks by native hunters.

My last involvement with 'Operation Hippo', as we had termed it, was to try and can some hippo steaks, at the request of the Kenya Veterinary Department. We cooked them in our autoclaves and sealed them hermetically in tins we used for sending infectious specimens by post. Later, we were informed that this new culinary delicacy had delighted gourmets in Germany and had great promise as a regular export.

'You know,' said Tom, as we were downing a beer on his verandah, some weeks later, 'we're pretty exclusive, in the veterinary field, you and I.'

'How do you make that out?' I asked.

'Well, do you know any other vets who have autopsied a couple of hundred hippo apiece?'

AN ELUSIVE PARASITE

Since visiting Steve and Dave at EAVRO, the protection of cattle against East Coast fever had become my top priority. Immunizing young animals with infective ticks and dosing them with antibiotics to control the severity of infection, while fairly successful, was cumbersome, fiddly and a little haphazard. What was needed – and with increasing urgency, due to the number of susceptible dairy animals arriving from Europe – was a single shot method of mass protection, in other words, a vaccine.

The usual approach to problems of this kind was to isolate the causative organism, in this case the protozoal parasite *Theileria parva*, grow it in the laboratory in nutrient media, an experimental animal or tissue culture, and treat it in some way to make it less virulent before injecting it back as a vaccine. This was often done by treating the organism with chemicals or heat, or irradiating it, or by serially injecting it from animal to animal of a more resistant species (a process known as 'passaging'), until the organism lost its capacity to produce the disease, but still retained the power to stimulate the body defences and produce an immunity.

Unfortunately, as with the search for a vaccine against malaria in

320

humans, we were scuppered on square one. No-one had been able to grow *Theileria parva* outside the bovine body. This meant that there were no convenient experimental tools available to help us, such as laboratory media or guinea-pigs and mice, or even fertile hens' eggs and tissue culture, which were used to research most other diseases. The only animal species in which *T. parva* would multiply was cattle, and the only way to infect them was the tiresome and lengthy procedure of having to grow the ticks, infect them and then attach them to the animals to be immunized.

Rearing the ticks was relatively simple. The eggs were hatched in glass jars at a controlled temperature and humidity. As a precaution, I banned all insecticide powders and sprays from the whole lab block where I worked; baby ticks were extremely susceptible to such noxious agents. Nevertheless, my complete tick hatch would sometimes be wiped out. It didn't take long to spot the culprit – Mike, in the lab next door.

Part of his research with trypanocidal drugs required the mashing-up of tissue by means of a sonic disintegrator. Although he placed this instrument in a closed cabinet and shut his lab door while it was working, the high-frequency vibrations must have been too much for my delicate tick larvae, which simply turned over and died. Even my mice appeared cowed, probably with a severe migraine. Mike was anything but apologetic.

'I've done you a great service. Why don't you install sonic disintegrators in the cattle sheds? It would be a much easier way of killing ticks than dipping!'

During these studies, I noticed that some animals immunized by infective ticks from one district would still develop ECF if challenged by infective ticks taken from another area. This suggested that there might be more than one immunological strain, which would certainly complicate the production of a vaccine. This was later confirmed.

For one brief moment we thought we had succeeded in growing the organism in the laboratory. We had placed spleen cells from cattle dying with ECF between layers of agar containing special nutrients, but although the miserable little *T. parva* stayed alive for a time, they refused to develop or multiply. The same thing occurred when I injected fertile hens' eggs with infected material. The organism stayed alive for up to a week, but refused to grow or multiply.

Following this, I placed infected ticks on the airsac membrane of fertile eggs, hoping that they might attach and transmit *Theileria* to the egg, as they did in cattle. Some ticks did attach but no *T. parva* transferred. I tried dissecting out the salivary glands of ECF-infected ticks (in which organ *T. parva* passed a stage of its life-

321

cycle), grinding them up and injecting them into susceptible calves. Still no luck. The file containing the protocols of these and many other unsuccessful experiments, I labelled, somewhat facetiously, 'Tricks with Ticks'.

Finally, I decided to try and depress the natural immune system in guinea-pigs, rabbits and mice, to see whether I could undermine their innate defences sufficiently to allow *T. parva* to infect them, and so provide me with a more convenient experimental animal than cattle. To do this I removed the spleens from each mouse, guinea-pig or bunny (a procedure already known to increase the susceptibility of other animal species to infection by blood protozoa), then I injected them with a depressant drug, known to block their natural immunity, the same procedure as is used to prevent rejection of heart transplants. A couple of days afterwards I injected them with infected material from a number of ECF cases. It was no good. No animal showed any inclination to become infected.

Of course, it was very much an individual assault on the disease – myself and a couple of technicians feeling our way as best we could, using equipment we happened to have in the limited time at our disposal. The big guns of the drug firms, however, were waiting in the wings. Megadollars were involved.

In the following years, all sorts of new techniques were developed by these pharmaceutical moguls and their sophisticated equipment, and certain advances were made, but as of this moment, 30 years later, that one-shot protective vaccine, like the 'philosopher's stone', still eludes the modern alchemists!

AN FAO BULL

'You're doing what?' Tom asked incredulously.

'Joining FAO.'

'You mean the Food and Agricultural Organization of the United Nations? That bum set-up in Rome?'

'That's right. Why do you say it's a bum set-up?'

'They don't *do* anything. They just advise. Haven't you heard of the FAO bull?'

'No,' I replied. 'What about it?'

'Well, it seemed that Haile Selassie wanted to upgrade the Royal herd in Addis Ababa, so he asked FAO to send him a top-class bull. The magnificent animal arrived, and for several months was the centre of attraction at the Emperor's Stock Farm. The only problem was that it refused to serve any of the Royal cows. Finally, His

322

Majesty asked FAO to send someone to find out why. An "expert" arrived and Haile Selassie took him out to his farm. The "expert" approached the bull and asked what was wrong. After a short conversation, he came back to the Emperor, looking rather sheepish.

'"So, what's the problem?" demanded His Majesty.

'"Well, your Highness," replied the official, obviously embarrassed, "it seems that the bull considers himself an FAO employee and, as such, is here solely in an advisory capacity."'

There was more than a grain of truth in this tale. FAO's policy was to send 'experts' to advise on the control of specific diseases, on schemes for livestock improvement, on the organization of fishing industries, or on more efficient methods of forestry, and so forth, but they relied on the personnel of the country to actually carry out the expert's advice.

'It's a good story,' I told Tom, 'but I'm not going to pass up the opportunity, "bum set-up" or not!'

My decision to leave the Colonial Service hadn't been a snap one. Everybody knew that Uganda was to gain independence later in the year, and what would happen afterwards was anybody's guess. We had been told that we could stay on if we wished and still be employed as expatriates under the Colonial Office (later the Ministry of Overseas Development), or we could retire with a lump sum compensation, the Golden Handshake, and a reduced pension.

So, when Roger, who had left Tanganyika the year before to head the Wellcome Foundation's Veterinary Research Station in Sussex, wrote that he had turned down an offer of an FAO job in Peru and had suggested my name instead, we were already half-thinking of a move. I had spent 19 years in the Colonial Service and was fairly senior. I could retire on a full pension in another seven. On the other hand, FAO, although it only employed staff on a contractual basis for a specific period only, it was an important agency of the United Nations and paid excellent salaries – in dollars. Once in, there was a good chance of continued employment, with the prospect of an enviable pension at the end. Moreover, there was a certain prestige attached to working for a UN Agency, where the members enjoyed a semi-diplomatic status. Several friends, anticipating the demise of the Colonial Service, had taken up posts in FAO and seemed happy. In due course, I received an invitation to apply for the Peru job.

Mary and I discussed the proposition at length. She was pregnant again, and we feared this might clash with our transfer. But we both wanted to get out of Africa, and a job in South America seemed to be a golden opportunity to return to the New World. It would mean leaving my folk in Kenya, but we should be a lot nearer Mary's family in Vancouver, and we would be close enough to Jamaica to holiday there and see our old friends. It was also an attractive post, that of setting up a country-wide research organization, both at high altitude and in the Amazon jungle. It sounded exciting and just up my street.

A month later, I was told that I had been accepted. With the letter came a bulky envelope full of forms and cyclostyled sheets, all headed 'Living Conditions in Persia' (now Iran). It wouldn't be the last time someone in the FAO Secretariat failed to read their instructions properly. I was delighted to see that the letter was signed by my old friend Peter, who had been in charge of the course of Foot and Mouth disease in Rio, which I had attended the year I was married. He would be my anchor man in FAO.

I was given four months to pack, take some of my accrued leave and present myself in Rome for briefing. Tom would take over as Chief Research Officer.

We had promised ourselves a family holiday on the Kenya coast before we left Africa, so after saying goodbye to my folk in Nanyuki, we flew to Mombasa and took a taxi south through thousands of coconut trees that strung along the Indian Ocean to Jardini beach, where 'Busha' and Nellie, a dear old couple, originally from Jamaica, had established a beach hotel.

It was a month of the most perfect relaxation, with the added excitement of an FAO job in South America to look forward to, and the feeling of financial freedom consequent on my 'lumpers' settlement. A canoe would take the six of us (Lindley had joined us 18 months previously) out to the reefs each morning, where we would collect the most incredible shells and marvel at the red starfish and other colourful sea creatures, so clearly visible 20 feet down in the crystal water, returning at midday to a scrumptious *smorgasbord*. The sun was more brilliant and the sand whiter than anything we had experienced in Jamaica. Soon we were suffering from sunburn and snow-blindness! 'Busha' and Nellie regaled us with stories of old Jamaica as we ate, drank, put on weight and became unbelievably lazy.

We were jolted slightly from our lethargy in the last week of our stay, when Shannon developed a high fever. We borrowed a car from a kind friend and rushed her to the doctor in Mombasa. Cerebral malaria! Within half an hour she was in the air-conditioned children's ward of the local hospital, the only ward that had this facility. I didn't envy the patients in other wards; Mombasa is one of the steamiest places in Africa.

324

The same kind friend lent us her car each day to visit our five-year old. Luckily, we had caught the condition early, and the day before we were scheduled to leave, Shannon was discharged. But by then Kerry, now two-and-a-half, had contracted a severe dose of impetigo. On the way to the airport, we took him to the doctor. There was some delay in the waiting room and we only just made our plane, pick-a-backing the two youngest across the tarmac, one of whom was now covered with bright green patches.

* * *

I had to leave the aeroplane at Rome to undergo my indoctrination at FAO, while Mary went on with the four kids and an eight-month bulge, to spend a week with Roger and Pru in England before flying on to Marjorie and Ken in Jamaica.

Peter and his charming wife insisted that I stayed with them instead of in a hotel. Peter was now head of the section in the Animal Health Division which dealt with all FAO's livestock projects in South America; I couldn't have been happier.

FAO headquarters, Peter told me the next morning, as we walked up from the Metro towards the massive buildings veneered with white marble, was built originally for Mussolini's Foreign Ministry. It was certainly imposing, the size of two city blocks, seven storeys high, overlooking the Roman Baths of Caracalla and Maximilian's Circus where chariot races used to be held.

'How many people work here?' I asked innocently.

'The standard reply to that is "about five per cent". Actually, there are about thirteen hundred at Headquarters and another thousand in the field.' Before I left FAO, these numbers had trebled.

The Animal Health Division seemed to be very much a family, everyone being on first name terms with Keith, the *paterfamilias*, a shrewd, stocky Aussie, bouncing with energy. His sharp eyes studied me from beneath tangled hedges, the makings of a smile constantly hovering above his grizzly chin. He was a born leader, inspiring his staff by hard work, wit and wisdom. One of his many maxims, I remember, was 'If a chap is irreplaceable, sack him, he's not doing his job.'

'So just see that you teach your Peruvian counterpart all you know as quickly as possible, or it's the knacker yard for you, lad.'

Keith had just returned from a round-the-world trip, his third in twelve months. He travelled light; two suits, two shirts and a change of underclothes.

'Everything I wear is nylon or terylene,' he explained. 'I get into the shower at the end of the day fully clothed, wash my jacket, take

325

it off, wash my shirt and trousers, take them off, wash my under-clothes and put on my spares. My washing is dry by the morning and never needs ironing.'

Each evening after work, Keith's office became a club. A bottle of whisky, a siphon and glasses would already be in place on the round coffee table, and for the next hour or so, opinions would be swopped, criticisms aired and experts visiting from the field would explain the problems in Upper Volta, Guatemala, or wherever they happened to be working.

Although the atmosphere in the Division was relaxed and informal, FAO itself was stiff with bureaucracy. There was no such thing as the 'old boy' approach to administrative problems, as had existed in the Colonial Service. Regulations were strictly adhered to and contained in the 'FAO Bible', two massive loose-leaf binders, to which administrators and accountants frequently referred. No deviations or exceptions were permitted.

'We are dealing with fifty-seven countries, their currencies, and four official languages,' Peter explained. 'If we were to vary the rules at a whim, there would be chaos. But the administrators can still be human – on rare occasions!'

I learned more about the job in Peru. I would be Project Manager of a proposed Veterinary Institute for Tropical and High Altitude Research, VITAR for short, which would have its headquarters in the Veterinary Faculty of the University of San Marcos in Lima. It would be my responsibility, together with my Peruvian Co-director, to set it up, run it and get results. I would look after the International staff and funds, and my Peruvian counterpart would deal with the national side.

'Here are the plans for the laboratories they wish to build at high altitude.' Peter dropped some scrolls onto the desk of my temporary office. They were very ornate. Whoever had drawn them was certainly an artist, possibly even an architect, but in no way a scientist. They showed a magnificent entrance hall filled with potted plants, fountains and pools for goldfish, which took up a quarter of the space available. From this swept back two double-storeyed wings at an angle, containing a number of rooms of equal size; these were labelled 'Physiology', 'Pathology', 'Histology', 'Nuclear Chemistry', 'Nutrition', and so on. Obviously, each discipline in the Veterinary Faculty at Lima had been allocated a room at high altitude and was determined to build their own little empire there. No thought had been given to solving altitude problems or pooling resources. There were no preparation rooms, animal rooms, cold storage or general service areas.

After one glance, I rolled the plans up and put them in my brief-case. There would be time enough when I reached Lima to see what the real problems were and design facilities to help solve them.

One of the main problems listed in the Project Document was 'high-altitude disease'. This was completely new to me, so I sought help from the FAO library. Here I found references to high-altitude sickness in humans induced by low oxygen tension, as well as numerous reports from NASA, the Space Agency, dealing with rats in rarefied air. It was all rather confusing.

After a week of conversations, interviews, indoctrinations and instructions as to how I should fill up the numerous FAO forms (twice as many as in the Colonial Service), and eating pizza for the first time, I left for London and a tour of research institutes in the United Kingdom. At one of these, the Poultry Research Station at Houghton, a Dr Beattie was carrying out experiments on hatching eggs under reduced oxygen tension. Incubation of eggs in the rarefied atmosphere of the high Andes was one of the problems the Peruvians had asked us to help solve.

'How long have they given you to set up this research institute in Peru?' he enquired.

'My contract is for four years,' I replied.

'You'll be lucky to get the foundations laid by that time,' he told me. 'My experience of research establishments, even in this country, tells me you'll need twice that time to get it going.'

I thought he was being unnecessarily pessimistic, but I was often to recall his words.

At Glasgow, I met Bill again, now Sir William, and Dean of the Veterinary Faculty, with whom I had spent those anxious hours on the morning of my wedding, visiting peasant farmers in the hills around Brown's Town in Jamaica, and who had had the audacity to whistle 'Lazy Bones' at seven o'clock the next morning, beneath the window of our honeymoon cottage! Bill promised to supply me with consultants from amongst his staff at the Glasgow Faculty.

"Tis a great opportunity ye have, Pat, but dinna be discouraged if things go a wee bit awry. Ai've found that trying to get things done in Latin America is like trying to build sandcastles under water. But now and then ye'll find a genius who can do even that.'

It was a prophetic statement.

PART FOUR

PERU

(1963–1973)

*Part IV is dedicated to the memory of my late friend and collea-
gue, Dr Manuel Moro, DVM, MPH, an outstanding administrator of Veterinary Research in Peru; sometime Dean of the
Veterinary Faculty of San Marcos University, National Director
of VITAR, Deputy Chief of Veterinary Public Health WHO,
Washington and member of many international committees on
animal health. The success of VITAR was due mainly to his dedication, vision and hard work.*

ECUADOR

COLOMBIA

Piura

Iquitos

R. Maranão

Amazon River

Yurimaguas

Tarapoto

R. Ucayali

Cajamarca

BRAZIL

Pucallpa

Yungay
Huaraz
Tingo
Maria
Yanahuanca
R. Pachitea

Oroya
Ticlio

LIMA

Callão
Huancayo

R. Urubamba

Machu Picchu

PACIFIC
OCEAN

Ica

Cuzco

Nazca
Pampas
Galeras
L. Raya
Macusani

BOLIVIA

Puno
L. Titicaca

Arequipa

PERU

0   100   200
KILOMETRES

CHILE

- - - - - - - Roads connecting research stations

Rotting crab. Must be. Nothing else could smell that bad! I followed the other passengers through the chilling midnight mist to the terminal buildings of Lima airport.

Moments before, I had been gripping the arm rests and starring at the dazzling reflection of our landing lights against a white besieging wall of fog, praying that the pilot knew where he was. There were too many mountains in Peru to make the slightest mistake.

As I collected my bags, I felt a hand on my shoulder.

'I'm Axel, FAO Representative.' The receding blonde hair, thin face and high forehead reminded me of Fred Astaire. 'And this is Dr Manuel Moro, Dean of the Veterinary Faculty and your Peruvian counterpart.'

Dr Manuel was taller than Axel, with dark, searching eyes and closely combed black hair. His rosy, rather chubby cheeks and slight paunch suggested that he should watch his weight. In perfect English, he welcomed me to Peru on behalf of the Rector of San Marcos University.

The three of us walked across the parking lot towards Axel's car. The stink of dead crab pervaded everything.

'Whatever is that smell?' I asked.

'Fish meal,' Axel replied. 'This is the hub of the anchovy industry. The *anchoveta* fleet unloads at Callao, a few kilometres from here.'

We drove out of the modern airport into a sandy wasteland covered, as far as I could make out in the headlights, by shacks and hovels thrown together from the pickings of discarded rubbish. Some had roofs of tin, others of matting and some appeared to have no roofs at all. There was not a light amongst them.

'Is this Lima?' I asked appalled.

'This is one of the *barriadas* or slums. Several of the city's rubbish dumps are near–' His words were drowned by my horrified cry. A huge articulated truck thundered across a red light 20 yards in front of us. 'Lesson number one,' Axel smiled, amused at my fright. 'Traffic lights are merely decorative; never take them seriously!'

I was even more frightened next morning as I watched cars roar up and down Avenida Arequipa, a few metres away from the breakfast room of the Hotel Columbus. Did anyone really expect me to drive here? It would be certain death. The only rules seemed to be that the car in front had the right of way without the slightest need to signal. The day was grey, the buildings were grey, the air was cold and clammy and a grey ceiling of cloud hung just above the flat rooftops. The whole aspect was drab and uninviting. Could this be the fabulous

'City of the Kings', which Pizarro and his little band of *conquistadores* had fought so hard to found? Well, as far as I was concerned they had wasted their time.

My thoughts were interrupted by a crescendo of honking. Traffic came to a halt.

'Chocky,' announced the apathetic waiter as he strolled across to the windows.

'Chocky'? I presumed he meant an accident. I pulled out my pocket Spanish dictionary and looked up 'accident'. I was right. '*Accidente, colisión, choque (col)*'. *Choque* was slang for accident. No doubt a much-used word, hereabouts, I reflected.

Manuel drove me out of the city beneath a low, snivelling sky, that pressed down like a dripping blanket, past fields of bedraggled vines and cotton. I envied Mary and the kids, whom I had left with Marjorie and Ken in sunny Jamaica, while I went ahead to find accommodation. 'Welcome to the Veterinary Faculty of San Marcos University,' Manuel said as we turned in through high iron gates behind which were an isolated group of modern flat-roofed buildings.

In front, just visible through the mist, were shanty-covered sandhills which, he told me, led to the foothills of the mighty Andes.

An untidy pile of huge wooden crates half-obscured the front entrance. They had been there a year, he said, because of some administrative mix-up. It seemed a long time to sort out such a small matter; but, I reminded myself, this was South America, *mañana* and all that. They were there for another three years.

Manuel was an important and respected person. Not only was he Dean of the Faculty, Professor of Microbiology and Food Hygiene, but he had also been selected as National Director of the United Nations/FAO-sponsored Veterinary Institute for Tropical and High Altitude Research, VITAR, (IVITA in Spanish) of which I was the International Director.

The friendly smiles and enthusiastic handshakes were encouraging. Handshakes, I soon learned, were obligatory whenever one met or departed. It was an easy habit to acquire but would be embarrassing, no doubt, when one returned to a society which did not understand the need to pump arms at every 'hello' and 'goodbye'.

Everyone was eager to impress on me the difficulties of raising livestock high up in the Andean *sierra*, and in the hot, humid Amazon jungle, or *selva*, but apart from Manuel, I felt that few had experienced these problems at first hand. Then a thought struck me.

'I saw some reference in the VITAR Project Document to the Ministry of Agriculture's Research and Extension Service. Aren't they working in these areas? Surely they must have some answers?'

'The *Servicio de Investigación y Promoción Agropecuaria*? Yes, we've some good friends in SIPA, but the whole Ministry is very disorganized and short of funds. Their research and their service to the livestock farmer is virtually nil. It is this gap that VITAR will have to try and fill. The two most influential universities in Peru, are ours – San Marcos, founded in 1553, the oldest in South America, which has the Veterinary Faculty, and La Molina, which is purely agricultural.'

La Molina had an enviable reputation. I could see why when we visited the campus a few days later. Their facilities were excellent. Many of the teachers had PhDs from American universities, and the University itself had had long-standing financial support from abroad, boosted by a strong USAID mission. Moreover, La Molina drew its students from the more influential and elite Peruvian families, and the *alumni* formed a powerful 'club', active both in politics and in the agricultural field. Whatever we did, Manuel warned, we would first have to appease both La Molina and SIPA.

I was horrified at the attitude of isolationism within the Veterinary Faculty. Each department was shielded from the others not only by the four laboratory walls, but also by a traditional academic jealousy and distrust. This would have been less serious if teaching had been the sole objective, but if VITAR was to investigate and solve the problems hindering livestock production, we would need total inter-departmental co-operation and a team approach. I remembered the proposed plans for the high-altitude labs which Peter had given me in Rome – a separate room for each discipline without thought of co-operative studies. There was no way we could set up a successful research Institute under those conditions. Manuel agreed, but was sceptical.

'It will be very hard,' he sighed. 'People do not like to co-operate in South America.'

'Don't worry,' I told him. 'I hold the ace.'

Each Department head had made out long lists of equipment which he expected VITAR to supply. I told Manuel that unless they co-operated with each other in our research programme, they would get nothing from the half-million dollars FAO had provided for supplies. I was their Father Xmas; if they wanted their toys, they would have to be good lads and toe the line!

The biggest shock was the library. A library is the heartbeat of an academic institution and the librarian as important as the Rector. Manuel was evasive when I asked to see it.

333

'We are having some leetle problems. The librarian only comes one afternoon a week, and we are a leetle behind with our cataloguing. We are trying to hire someone full-time.'

He led me into a dim room furnished with Dexion shelving and filled with the usual bound journals and a few textbooks.

'We haven't bound any journals for several years,' he sighed, swinging open a door to an adjoining room to reveal an enormous heap of unopened periodicals almost as high as the table.

'There are probably five years of journals here,' he murmured sadly.

It looked as if an efficient, up-to-date library would have to be another of VITAR's priorities.

* * *

The following week, Mary and the children arrived from Jamaica. I had had no luck finding a house. Large residences at moderate rates were not easily come by, and the house-proud citizens of Lima were chary of renting to families with small children. To tide us over, we took up residence in a *pensión*, run by a scrimping, retired General and his tight-lipped wife. It wasn't a pleasant time. The kids, accustomed to an abundance of fruit, were shocked to find that their dessert consisted of half a banana while adults received a whole one. Mary remonstrated as only Mary knew how. That was the end of the fruit, and in its place appeared a small jelly.

With Manuel or his charming wife, Amparo, in the driver's seat, we scoured the suburbs of San Isidro and Miraflores for suitable accommodation.

'Let's try Monterrico and Las Casuarinas,' Amparo suggested. 'Homes are bigger and less expensive there. It is rather a long way out of town for most Peruvians, so it is mostly foreigners that live there, and they often go on holidays abroad and need house-sitters. We may be lucky.'

We drove out to the newly established *urbanización*, or suburbs, in the sandhills behind the city where the houses were surrounded by large gardens, the very place for our brood, I thought.

Just as we were contemplating another miserable week in the *pensión*, our house-agent rang with good news.

'The family will be in Europe for six months. Plenty of time to look around for a more permanent home. It's central too, in Miraflores, near the sea.'

It was certainly not the type of house we had envisaged, squashed between other houses in a narrow street with no garden and most of

334

the furniture antique. Huge, gilt-framed pictures of saints and religious scenes by the seventeenth century 'Cuzco School' hung round the walls and up the stairway, and the Louis Quinze furniture in the salon nestled snugly into a deep, wall-to-wall carpet of pure white wool – a paradise for our little horrors with their sticky fingers and grubby, shoeless feet!

We shook our heads. We couldn't risk it. But the lady of the house was adamant. She had taken a liking to us, she said. The fact that they were leaving in two days might have been more truthful. Anyway, what damage could such sweet, well-behaved British children do? If we had been Americans, she would not have considered it. No, we must certainly take it and we could restrict the children to the large upstairs playroom. Buttered-up in this fashion, we agreed, but it was really the cook that decided us. Mariacucha, an ample, white-haired, jovial negress, born a child of slaves 65 years before, spoke no English but she had travelled Europe with her employers who were of Belgian origin, and spoke good French. So with her as interpreter, via French to Spanish, we took over the house in Calle Juan Fanning for six months, placed the downstairs salon out of bounds and hoped for the best.

Surprisingly, all went extremely well – until the day we were to leave. As we proudly showed the returning owner how assiduously we had cared for her beloved salon, she gave a wail and pointed, speechless to the Louis Quinze chaise longue. The 50, or so, upholstered buttons had been carefully removed and placed in small piles on the up-until-now-immaculate white carpet. Their replacement and the cleaning of the deep pile cost us another month's rent!

We had been in the house a month when Melanie decided it was time to put in an appearance. It was a cold, drizzly June evening, typical of the period from May to September when cold mists, known as *neblina* or *garua*, rolled in from the sea to make life miserable. I had been kept late in a meeting at the FAO office, when the door opened and I saw Victor, one of the Faculty chauffeurs whom Manuel had put at my disposal, beckoning me. I slipped out.

'*Señor, su bebé llega. Su Señora va a da a luz. Vamos rápido.*'

I couldn't understand all he said, but the word *bebé* and his sudden appearance obviously made his message urgent. I ran down the stairs after Victor, hoping I would be in time to get Mary to the hospital. Like a true Limeñan, Victor took scant notice of the red lights, he was more bullfighter than chauffeur, and I blessed him for it.

Heaving Mary onto the back seat of the panel-van (the only vehicle Manuel could make available), expecting her to *dar a luz* at any

335

moment, we set off once more, this time more sedately, towards the hospital.

We half-carried her inside, where she kept repeating the phrase Mariacucha had taught her in case of emergency – '*Estoy en labor de parto*'. It didn't seem to impress the moronic receptionist who kept fiddling with forms, asking ridiculous questions about Mary's father and mother and sipping coffee. This was too much for Victor. Leaning over the counter with his face as near his adversary as possible, he yelled,

'*La señora va a dar a luz AHORA. Sabe?*'

Another nurse picked up an intercom, a trolley arrived at high speed, and Mary disappeared. I hung about nervously on a mezzanine waiting area with other sentinels of *accouchement*, all of us enclosed in our own bubbles of anxiety. As I listened, uncomprehending, I wondered if the rapid chatter would ever mean anything to me. Ten minutes later, a nurse told me that Melanie had made her entrance.

The clinic was, we had been assured, modern, with all the latest American techniques and equipment. Mary's opinion was a little different; her account of the ordeal horrific.

'I had my hands and feet tied throughout the whole operation. I thought they might jump on my tummy as well, like the midwives did in the Middle Ages. At least it would have warmed me up. I was freezing and in shock. There was nothing between me and the steel trolley.'

I could well imagine! I was shivering, and I was wearing a sweater and sports coat. Poor Mary had had only a thin shift to shield her from the icy drafts that raced through the corridors. There was no heating anywhere.

'And to top it all, people kept coming in to stare at the size of my feet!'

Mary and Melanie came home three days later, Mary with a severe cold which galloped through the family. It was while lying in bed, recuperating from my dose, that the bedside telephone rang.

'Would that be Doctor Guilbroide?' said a thick Irish accent.

'Indeed, it's himself,' I coughed back waggishly.

'My name is Sean, manager of the Bank of London and South America. I thought ye'd loike to know that ye're ten thousand *soles* overdrarn.' The *sol* was then at about 27 to the dollar. Oh, God, I thought. Just what I need to cheer me up.

'Didn't some money arrive from England?' I asked.

'Not yet, but don't worry. I see ye're a vet and with an Oirish name, as well. Me faither was a vet in the Ould Country. I jest rang to say that we've a bit of a party next week, so if ye've nothing else on, come along and let's have a look at ye.'

So began a long and valued friendship, full of screaming children, to which Sean and Annie contributed almost as many as we did.

Since the banks in Lima seemed to be continually on strike, I asked Sean how people managed if their source of money was cut off for several months.

'Ach,' he laughed. 'We may be on stroike, officially, but we always lave the side-door open in case anyone wants to come in.'

A touch of the 'ould sod', I thought to myself. It looked as if the South American had a lot of the Irish in him!

* * *

We settled into our new home, exposed the kids to education in appropriate British-run schools, made friends and kept our eyes open for future abodes. Once again, we considered the high cost of renting and in the end, rather rashly, decided to use my 'lumpers' (the 'Golden Handshake' to compensate the early termination of my colonial career) to purchase a house of our own.

'You're an idiot,' Axel pronounced. 'You know nothing of South American economy. You could lose your shirt.'

'It's all right for you,' I replied. 'Your kids have flown the nest; there are only two of you. There's seven of us. That means a large house and garden, for which I would have to pay five or six hundred dollars a month. I can't afford it on my salary; I only get eight hundred as it is. And if we go on renting we will probably have to move every couple of years; we'd rather be independent.'

But independence, we were to find, was a costly commodity!

COWS IN THE CLOUDS

I found Doris by accident. Axel mentioned that he had a temporary secretary in the FAO office who would soon be looking for a job.

'She's rather slow and nervous but she speaks good English, and is very pleasant to work with.' I hesitated. I needed someone who was really on the ball.

'Send her along, anyhow,' I told him. 'I'll look her over.'

Short and plump, her dark brown hair controlled in a bun, and her horn-rimmed glasses making her look more serious than she deserved, Doris was neither slow nor nervous – a description we often laughed about later. A young mother, married to a medical student, she was tidy, cheerful, competent and ran the office impeccably. Her English was fluent and, as a bonus to all this, her brother was a lawyer and

337

her father Peru's top racing driver, 'The King of the Curves', ran a garage and repair shop. Both proved their worth in the years that followed.

Apart from supplying the oil that lubricated the official operations, she became our godmother, our oracle, our universal aunt and our ultimate reference. She coddled us, ironing out personal problems with accommodation, transport, schooling, doctors, identity cards and driving licences, and solved the thousand other crises that occurred daily in our lives. I estimated that an FAO expert spent upwards of 30 per cent of his working hours coping with his family problems. But for Doris, it would have been 90 per cent.

The first objective was to design and construct the high-altitude laboratories, the centre of all our research in the Sierra. Until they were completed and staffed, we would have to rely on personnel from the Lima Faculty working in the *sierra* during vacations, an arrangement I knew would never solve the high-altitude problems.

'We already have a site near Huancayo at about three-and-a-half thousand metres altitude,' Manuel told me. 'It is in the centre of a farming district, the Mantaro valley, where there are plenty of live-stock problems.'

'Three-and-a-half thousand metres?' I did a quick calculation, I wasn't yet *au fait* with the metric system. 'Nearly eleven thousand feet! Should be high enough! The sooner I see it the sooner I can finish the designs and we can start building.'

I had already scrapped the 'Country Club' design given me in Rome, and had roughed out a far more practical set of buildings with animal sheds and living quarters, but I still had to see where it would be built.

One grey morning, equipped with a canvas balloon of oxygen, in case of emergencies, Manuel and I boarded an ancient taxi, or *colectivo*, and set off up the winding precipitous road to Huancayo. Barren, sandy hills ('It never rains in Lima') on which thousands of colourless hovels made from woven rush mats, cardboard or other flimsy material, had sprung up, rose on either side. Nothing grew on these dusty, stony slopes save the occasional thirsty casuarina tree or cactus bush.

'These *barriadas* are one of the country's greatest problems,' Manuel said. 'Thousands of peasants come down from the *sierra* looking for work, but there is hardly any, and what's worse there's no housing, so they squat on these parched hills without water or drainage – nothing. Women and children suffer the most. Child mortality is terrible.'

For the first few kilometres whitewashed walls ran close beside the

338

highway, giving the impression of motoring along a wide, roofless corridor. Doors and barred windows every few yards confirmed that behind the façade lay dwellings. By the time we reached Chosica, a small artistically laid-out town some 40 kilometres from Lima and 1,000 metres above sea level, the walls had given way to streets lined with flowering trees and attractive homes surrounded by green lawns.

'They get rain here,' Manuel explained. 'Many of the rich come here to escape the hot summer nights in Lima.'

Our driver, like so many of his compatriots, seemed to be a frustrated Don Quixote, aiming his steed at any person, beast or vehicle that came into view, missing head-on *choques* by the finest of hairbreadths. These 'close encounters of the ultimate kind' at 140kph were made all the more terrifying by the narrowness of the road, frequent sharp curves, enormous precipices a few inches from our wheels, and my unfortunate observation that all four tyres – five, when we had to put on the spare – were bald!

The silencer had also been removed in the belief that the engine would be more efficient at altitude without it, so we had to bellow at the driver above the roar of the exhaust to make him reduce speed. Such requests were met by a pitying smile, several pumps on the brake pedal and a momentary easement of the accelerator. Not for long; a moment later, when he spotted another potential victim, his foot was stamped down and we hurtled once more into the fray.

I swore I would never, but NEVER, travel again in one of these motorized coffins, but when our car broke down some months later and we had to complete the journey in a packed Andean bus, I longed for that old *colectivo* with Don Quixote at the wheel!

After Chosica we began to climb more steeply along the side of the maintains, where grass and trees now covered the rocky slopes. At a transport hotel near San Mateo, a village at 2,000 metres, I was introduced to my first South American public toilet. Even in the higher-class establishments, including the Veterinary Faculty, the custom was to drop the used toilet paper in a box – or if there was none – onto the floor. But there were no polite words to describe the convenience at San Mateo, although the popular phrase 'when the shit hits the fan' came pretty close. Fortunately, there were no fans! When she made the trip some time later, Mary told me that the 'Ladies' was far worse. Thereafter, when passing that way, I sought physical and aesthetic relief amongst the blue gums below the cafe, with a magnificent view of the Rimac river 100 metres beneath me, tumbling down to the sea.

The small wooden roadside crosses, marking the sites of fatal accidents, which I had noticed at intervals since leaving Lima, now became more frequent. We passed the shell of a bus which had failed to make a hairpin bend and had plunged over the precipice, killing everyone on board. Around another corner, a timber truck, hauling enormous logs over the Andes from the jungle, lay upside down. In the scores of journeys up and down that road during the next ten years, I never failed to encounter at least one recent *choque*. My highest score was seven. I began to understand why one of the most frequent headlines in the local paper, *El Comercio*, was '*Camión al Abismo*', reporting yet another truck that failed to stay the course and now lay at the bottom of an abyss.

For a moment, at Rio Blanco, I thought we, too, were going to be headline material. A landslide had narrowed the dirt road to the width of a truck. I looked out of my window straight down to the river, now 200 metres below; there was no road beneath us on my side, that I could see. Manuel was gripping his door handle, but our intrepid driver's only concern was that he shouldn't lose a moment on account of the rough surface. At other times, we roared up canyons between rocky walls too high for me to make out the top, and at one place we saw the railway crossing the gorge above us at two different levels, one line directly above the other. Below, in the swirling torrent of the Rimac, lay the hulk of a derailed locomotive.

Snow began to fall as we approached the jagged peaks of Ticlio in the Anticona pass, where a branch of the Lima–Huancayo railway passed over at 15,806 feet, or 4,843 metres, making it the highest in the world. We had caught glimpses of the line, built a hundred years before, all the way from Lima, as it zigzagged up the steep mountain sides in a series of switchbacks, an engine at each end of the train,

Anticona Pass, Ticlio, 4843 m

340

Accident site, road to Huancayo

alternatively pulling and pushing. Meiggs, the American construction engineer, had died just after the line reached Rio Blanco, two-thirds the way to the summit, and never saw his work completed.

I had not yet felt any effects of altitude, which was as well since our bag of oxygen had exploded in the boot of the car after leaving San Mateo. On future trips we carried oxygen in metal cylinders, and it was a strict rule that no-one, technician, chauffeur, or visitor, went to the sierra without oxygen and masks. Changing a tyre at 16,000 feet could be life-threatening to those unadapted to altitude.

The rough, snow-covered road now dropped sharply and, a few hundred metres lower, brought us to the cold, depressing mining community of Morococha. A solid, drab brick building stood up from the dismal settlement. These, Manuel told me, were the high-altitude research laboratories (now unused) of the San Marcos medical faculty, where Carlos Monge, the most famous of all high-altitude researchers, had worked, and after whom a form of altitude sickness, or *soroche* had been named. Monge popped into my office in Lima, one day, a small friendly old man, long since retired but still very interested in our high-altitude studies.

Below Morococha, the road wound down an almost tree-less, grassy valley, along the centre of which flowed the crystal-clear Mantaro river.

We stopped for '*capitans*' at the Huaymanta restaurant in Oroya, a large mining town. These *capitans* (equal parts of vodka and dry vermouth) became a ritual on trips to Huancayo. We liked to think that they warded off the effect of altitude.

Oroya was famous in medical history, having given its name to an often fatal, louse transmitted anaemia in humans, Oroya fever. In

1885, a young medical student, Daniel Carrion, infected himself with material from the less severe condition, *Verruga peruana*, to prove that the two diseases were related. Carrion died of his experiment, but his sacrifice solved the epidemiology of Oroya fever, or Carrion's disease.

The Huaymanta was no ordinary eating house; pretentious it was not, but probably because of the large numbers of American and other engineers employed on the mines, it offered an almost international cuisine. The rough concrete floor and metal tables with plastic table cloths, the grubby waiters, thick glassware and flimsy aluminium cutlery that could be bent by just looking at it, detracted little from the excellently cooked trout, frogs' legs, snails, T-bone steaks and the wide variety of seafood. No less appreciated were the traditional Peruvian dishes – *Sopa a la Criolla* (sheep's head soup with milk and a hot chilli added); *Papas Huancayina* (potatoes with special hot spices); *Anticuchos* (pieces of cunningly marinated ox heart on bamboo skewers with a special sauce). A Huaymanta menu which I still have lists 35 dishes.

The mine workers lived in lines of bungaloid barracks beside the mine while the foreign personnel and senior Peruvian technicians were accommodated on the other side of the town in a neat, security-fenced estate with golf course, tennis courts and hospital. I reckoned they deserved it; it would take a very high salary and many modern comforts to entice me to work in such cold, bleak surroundings, where the air was often yellow with sulphurous fumes. Tall, black pyramids of slag, connected by an overhead tipping system, lined the route out of the town, but these soon gave way to barren, rolling hills from which years of violent storms had picked the sparse soil and exposed the white, rocky Andean skeleton.

Here and there, silhouetted on the mountainous horizon, I could make out ruins. It was strange to realize that 400 years ago the valley had been inhabited by a people whose agriculture, including ingenious irrigation systems and terraces on which to grow their corn and potatoes, had been far in advance of their modern descendants. Now, international organizations were spending millions of dollars to help turn the clock back through the centuries, to try and achieve the same efficiency as the Incas.

'That road to the left leads to Jauja, once the capital of Peru,' said Manuel as we turned right to follow the Mantaro river along the centre of a wide, cultivated valley. 'But they had to move it to sea level because the altitude interfered with reproduction of the Spanish colonists.' It seemed an unlikely tale. I was sure it would take more than altitude to stop Spaniards procreating. After all, La Paz, the

342

capital of Bolivia, was 1,000 feet higher than Jauja, and it hadn't seemed to make much difference there.

The Mantaro valley, some ten kilometres wide, was well cultivated with potatoes, maize and beans, and had enclosures of grazing cattle and sheep. Avenues of tall Australian blue-gums divided fields, or followed irrigation channels, or appeared in small copses at the edge of villages. In contrast, the smooth rolling hills on each side appeared tree-less except where a green pocket of indigenous bushes colonized the sheltered gullies – like emeralds in the cleavages of massive stone bosoms. Hedgerows were over-run by another exotic importation, the spiky-leafed, yellow-flowered *retama*, or Spanish Broom.

I had a feeling that there was something odd about the villages we passed through. It took me a while to realize what. In Africa or the West Indies, one's car would be continually smothered in feathers as the local *kukus* failed to cross the road in time. Here, no chickens interrupted our progress. I did see a couple of hens in a field but those were the only poultry I saw that day.

'Too high,' Manuel explained, 'too little oxygen for eggs to hatch properly. The common *criollo* birds hatch a few eggs, but their production is very low. The incubation and hatching of better breeds is out. It's something we have to solve.'

The Hotel Turista in the centre of Huancayo, one of a chain of government-sponsored inns, was imposing, clean and comfortable. I was very glad to arrive; my heart was beating twice as fast as usual, to say nothing of a growing headache and the feeling in my legs that I had run the whole way up from Lima.

'Bed,' ordered Manuel. 'It's just a touch of *soroche*. You'll be OK in the morning.'

Lying down made my heart thump more than ever, so I went to sleep sitting up.

My pulse, the next morning, was still over 80, and any attempt to hurry or run upstairs brought searing fireworks, but I felt better and followed Manuel into breakfast.

'Don't you ever suffer from *soroche*?' I asked him.

'Almost never, nowadays. Although I grew up in the jungle, I've worked a lot in the *sierra*. I seem to have become acclimatized.'

The large, bustling, covered market sold everything from guinea-pig and alpaca meat to ponchos, the ubiquitous Indian cape, and *coca* leaves, the source of cocaine. Guinea-pigs were a traditional feast-day dish, and cocaine, sucked from masticated *coca* leaves, was the mainspring which kept the squat, leathery-skinned, bow-legged Andean peasant ticking over, enabling his wiry, half-starved body to shoulder loads I would have thought impossible, even at sea level. A

343

permanent, soggy bolus of *coca* leaves pushed out his cheek as if he were sucking a golf ball, a condition known as *coquera*. It was said that the Inca lords, and later the Spaniards, had encouraged *coca* chewing as a means of increasing the output of their enslaved populace.

Most men wore an elfin balaclava-like bonnet of a bright colour woven, like all their other garments, from llama or alpaca wool. A short, dull-coloured poncho acted as a raincoat, overcoat, and apron. Rough trousers with frayed, muddy ends, reaching only to mid-calf, were fastened round the waist with rope, while cracked, splayed-out feet, bare or in roughly improvised sandals, hastened their hunched bodies along the narrow cobbled streets.

The women, depending from which district they came, wore bowler hats or stetsons, usually of black or white material with a contrasting band. Their skirts were dark but their bodices brightly coloured. They, too, went barefoot, or sometimes their feet would be pushed into rough, wooden clogs.

Both sexes had a web of fine blood vessels criss-crossing the wrinkles of their sun-roasted faces, and the children that followed them had cheeks as purple as California plums, a reminder of the strong ultra-violet radiation in that clear, rarefied air.

Only the hotel, the municipal buildings and a few modern stores were of reinforced concrete, everything else was of dried mud, or Kimberley brick, with sloping roofs of red clay tiles. This was in sharp contrast to Lima, where it never (or hardly ever) rained, and where roofs were flat and covered with absorbent tiles over a layer of earth.

Courtesy calls to local potentates were to form an essential part of our visit. The *alcalde*, or mayor, ('a shrewd politician') we cornered in a bar, where he treated us to piscos (a type of grappa). Another important nabob, the head of the Ministry's Agricultural and Livestock Extension Service, SIPA, sat pompously behind his office desk and seemed to resent our intrusion; but the Rector of the local University, a friendly half-Indian, and the only one who genuinely tried to help us (probably with future benefits in mind), proudly showed us round his seat of learning, a loose association of run-down, scantily furnished, converted residences, scattered over several streets. The few of his staff we met were all recent graduates, working part-time. Laboratories and other academic facilities were almost non-existent.

We met some local farmers, and from what they told us, bad management and undernutrition seemed to be the main causes of low milk production and slow growth, although they were unanimous in

Cow with 'mal de altura'

blaming *mal de altura,* or altitude sickness, for many of their problems.

The site of our proposed High-Altitude Research Station lay beside the main road about 30 kilometres short of Huancayo. Only the dedication stone, laid by the Bishop several months before, marked the spot, 14 hectares of flat, stony, once cultivated land, adjoining SIPA's experimental station. There was no electricity nearby and the nearest water was two kilometres away. I tried to translate my plans for the laboratories into the reality of bricks and mortar. Six months? A year? Two years? Well, at least we had the land. That was enough for optimism.

As we walked across the stony ground, the tinkling of a llama train reached us. Half a kilometre distant, 20 or 30 llamas driven by two children, stalked their way along the side of an irrigation furrow, like cattle in the Swiss Alps, but haughtier.

* * *

'We have a leetle problem.' It was one of Manuel's favourite openings each morning.

The first had been to persuade the University to change its present system of almost continuous lectures interspersed with frequent very short vacations, to a 'semester' system with longer breaks, in which the teaching staff would have time to work on VITAR's proposed field research stations. This he had achieved in a mere four months! It would still be difficult, we' knew, to coax the Faculty staff away from the bright lights and comfy offices in Lima to tackle problems in the bleak *sierra* and steamy *selva.*

345

Then, although Rockefeller had donated $50,000 to construct a high-altitude research station, it was not nearly enough. Manuel haunted the corridors of the House of Representatives each evening, until he had persuaded key politicians to come up with additional funds.

This morning, Manuel was extra grave.

'What's the leetle problem today?' I asked.

'Politics,' he replied.

'Politics? But the General Election is over. Belaunde is President, and you told me he was the best.'

'Yes, but now University politics begin. La Molina and SIPA want to take over all research at high altitude and in the jungle. They want VITAR to be attached to La Molina, not San Marcos. They are very jealous of us. We must be careful.'

I pointed out that the United Nations had already signed an agreement with the Government and San Marcos University to establish a veterinary institute for tropical and high-altitude research. It was binding. SIPA and La Molina had nothing to do with it. Manuel shrugged, as if to convey the fragility of agreements – even those with the UN. I was enraged.

'But we have a secret weapon,' he went on more happily. 'Dr Mauricio. If he is elected Rector of San Marcos in the coming University elections, he can save us. If not – who can tell?'

I had met Dr Mauricio several times, the tall, grey-haired Professor of Animal Reproduction and Genetics, an internationally recognized scientist and, by virtue of his professorship in the Veterinary Faculty, an *ex-officio* member of VITAR.

Manuel went to work amongst his colleagues in the University and, predictably (I was beginning to assume that anything Manuel set his mind on he would achieve), Dr Mauricio became the new Rector. He had the clout, which Manuel still lacked, to ward off the threat from La Molina and SIPA.

There would be a thousand more 'leetle problems' before VITAR was flying, but with Manuel as the chief pilot, I never doubted we would soar above them all.

I began to suspect that Manuel was Bill's genius who could build sandcastles under water.

Trying to accustom myself to South American ways, such as the interpretation of the Peruvian 'yes' for its real worth, and the adjustment to the Latin American clock in place of the European one, were no easy matters.

'Don't forget,' Manuel counselled, 'that there is no such word as "no" in Peru. If you wish to put someone off or to disagree with

346

some action, you say "We'll see – *vamos a ver*", or "we'll talk again – *vamos hablar*" and everyone knows that you mean "no". But you never say it. "Yes" can also have several meanings, including "no".

'And don't be upset if no one turns up for a meeting at an agreed time. *La hora Peruana* differs from *La hora inglesa* by at least an hour.'

I was soon to find out what he meant. The first meeting of departmental heads to discuss the research programme of VITAR was fixed for two o'clock. At five minutes to the hour, I opened the conference room door. It was empty. I returned to my office and checked the day – right; the hour – right; my watch – right. Manuel was nowhere around. He must have had to go somewhere, urgently, I thought, and forgotten to tell me the meeting was cancelled. Ten minutes later, when I checked again, I was even more sure of my diagnosis. He might have told me, I muttered, a bit miffed at his thoughtlessness. Then I remembered his warning about *La hora Peruana*, so to be on the safe side, I tried again after half an hour. Marcus, the Professor of Histology, sat at the long conference table, alone, reading some papers. I joined him. A few minutes later two white-coated gentlemen looked in, exchanged pleasantries, and left.

'They'll be back in ten minutes,' my companion predicted.

'But the meeting was for two o'clock,' I complained.

'Two o'clock, *hora Peruana*,' Marcus laughed and returned to his reading.

We got under way shortly after three. No-one thought it abnormal. Six months later, neither did I!

A HOUSE IN THE SANDHILLS

Mary, poor soul, bore the brunt of our house hunt while Manuel and I beat the bounds of VITAR's proposed empire in the *sierra* and *selva*.

Each time I returned she would recount how enthusiastic (or desperate), arm-pumping, eye-sliding agents had goaded her from flea-infested hovels in the city to magnificent palaces in Barranco, a now unfashionable suburb south of Lima. She had listed a couple of mansions as 'possibles' but neither would fit our financial pocket. We had almost resigned ourselves to renting when we remembered those settlements on the inland sandhills. We scoured the area once more and eventually found a half built bungalow in the *Urbanización* Las Casuarinas.

The house was small and rectangular with the usual flat roof, but the site was impressive – halfway up a sandy hill. Behind, separating it from a rocky outcrop was a terraced orchard and a small copse of blue gums, while in front we had a magnificent view of distant Lima over a sloping lawn and, to the children's delight, a small swimming pool. Green squares in the desert landscape below us showed where soil had been imported and watered regularly to provide gardens.

Apart from a half-finished construction further down the hill, the nearest residence was over 400 metres away. All around were sand dunes and rocky hills, those behind the house rising to several hundred metres. It was just the sort of place we could expand to our liking.

We signed papers, made drawings and looked around for a builder to enlarge it. Perhaps if we could have foreseen the problems of house ownership and building in a country where we hardly spoke the language and where standards were very different from those we were used to, we might have continued renting; but we were naive, confident, and above all excited at the prospect of owning our first home, where we could do what we liked and no-one could tell us to move.

I forget how we found 'the architect'. Someone must have recommended him, although I can think of no-one who disliked us that much. He was thin, sly and very eager – especially for me to hand over the first cheque. He would contract the labour, draw the plans and have them approved, in fact, take complete charge. Since he spoke little English, much of our rare conversations were in sign language. We still had only my rough drawings which he copied onto a dirty piece of brown paper, so I suggested that it might be a good idea to transform these into a proper architect's plan, before we started the actual building

'*No es necesario, señor. Vamos começar inmediatamente y más tarde nos estudiaremos los planos con tranquilidad.*' An immediate start was certainly desirable, but I doubted whether there would be much tranquillity when we came to study the plans.

'All right, if you say so, but what about building permission from the municipality?'

'*Todo está arreglado, señor. No hay problema. Tengo amigos en la municipalidad.*'

Of course, nothing had been arranged and, too late, we discovered that not only were his friends in the municipality imaginary, he was also on their black list!

We moved up from our Juan Fanning house in Miraflores, and a few days later a stocky Andean-Indian banged on the front door.

'*Soy señor Rodriguez, el contratisa. El señor arquitecto me envió.*' He spoke no English, either. Beside him was an equally sturdy individual whom the contractor introduced as his brother, and a lanky, almost Nordic fellow carrying the tools of a mason. Behind them slunk a lad of 12 or 13. So this was the team the architect had chosen to enlarge our dream house! At least they had arrived promptly.

The first priority was the enlargement of the kitchen. Two days of suffocating cement dust and flying plaster chips left us with a badly wounded and unusable kitchen wide open to the patio. A large hole in the floor showed where the drainage from the discarded pantry sink had gone underground. It remained there for another year before we got round to filling it in and tiling it over. Even after this was done, we found ourselves walking round the patch for months, so strong had the habit become of avoiding the gaping hole.

Rodriguez proved himself an able builder, as did his brother and the mason. The boy, however, was dispatched howling down the road a week later after he had been caught exploring the mason's jacket, which he had left hanging on a fruit tree.

It was a trying time. Cement in stacks, bricks by the thousand, mountains of sand, all were dumped outside the front door and carried through the kitchen patio of the extension site. We lived in a fog of cement dust which, in conjunction with the *garúa* or sea mist, permanently etched our windows and the windscreen of our new Ford station wagon.

Our plans were to add two large bedrooms, one with an *en suite* sitting room or *saloncita*, a bathroom, an enormous playroom and a garage with a garden on its roof. As building progressed, we included a mezzanine over a corner of the playroom and a stairway to the roof, in case we wanted to add another storey.

The architect seemed to have every confidence that the scribblings on his piece of dirty brown paper, which he had now given to Rodriguez, would be sufficient to carry out the extension, and it was not until three weeks after building started that he paid his second visit – to ask for more money for supplies, although I was still awaiting his receipts for the first consignments.

Rodriguez and his pals were doing a sterling job so I didn't argue much, but took the opportunity to enquire about the formal plans, and whether the municipality had approved them.

'*Si, si, señor. Todo arreglado.*' He would bring them tomorrow.

But tomorrow never came. In fact, I never saw him again. A few days later Rodriguez complained that they hadn't been paid for two weeks and would have to stop work. Several visits to the 'architect's' home gave no results. He was working in Piura, his wife said, in the north of Peru. No, she didn't know when he would be back. Had he left a copy of the house plans? She didn't know.

I consulted Rodriguez.

'I don't think there are any plans, *señor*.'

'But I have to submit them for municipal approval. Can you draw them for me?'

'*Si, señor*. Next week you have them.'

He was true to his word.

'But these plans are not quite accurate,' I pointed out. 'The new bedroom walls are much closer to the boundary than you've drawn them, and the playroom is in a different place.'

'I know, *señor*, but the municipality won't approve the extension as it is, so I had to draw another set to satisfy their specifications.'

'But they are bound to find out. Don't they make inspections?'

'Probably not, *señor*. Las Casuarinas is too far away. But if they do – we talk.'

It was the usual solution. Regulations were regulations were regulations; but in the end, it was the talking that counted!

I was unhappy about it, especially as there were two ink crosses with a note beside them stipulating the minimum distance between the new buildings and the boundary fence. I was required to sign under both to confirm that I would comply. If I signed, it would be a totally dishonest act since the walls had already been built, but to knock them down, dig new foundations and build them again would cost more than I could afford. Ah, well, perhaps the inspector would never come.

So I signed, and suffered a guilt complex till we left Peru ten years later.

Rodriguez forged ahead, and soon the walls were roof high. Then one evening, strolling round the construction, beer bottle in hand, I sensed that something wasn't quite right. I stopped by a doorway and took a swig from my bottle of Cristal. Yes, there was something odd. It couldn't be! Oh yes it could. The doorway was skew!

There was an old door lying on the lawn. I put down my bottle of beer, picked up the door and placed it against the opening. It reminded me of those ridiculous theorems we had to learn in geometry class. 'Apply triangle ABC to triangle XYZ, so that point A falls on point X, point B falls on point Y', and so on. It was quite clear that if I applied rectangle 'door' to rectangular 'doorway', no points would coincide anywhere.

Next morning I summoned the mason.

'Your doorway is skew,' I told him.

'*Imposible, señor.*'

'On the contrary. Give me your square.'

I fitted the square into the angle on one side. Perfect. The mason spread his hands in a gesture of 'I told you so'. I tried the angle on the other side. It was several centimetres out. His square, home-made from two pieces of wood nailed together, was visibly crooked. I compared it with my draughtsman square. Even the mason was convinced, and explained that his proper square had been stolen some weeks before and he had had to improvise one. It took several days with much chiselling and filling of gaps to correct those drunken doorways and windows.

I had contracted a carpentry firm to instal the window frames, doors and cupboards. I will call it Madera Pronto, although it proved to be the antithesis of promptness. The contract stipulated completion of the work within 21 days of commencement. After a month of chivvying, the work started. A week later it stopped. The frames that had been put in were sub-standard. I complained. They were replaced, but the doors were still missing,

I visited the factory. The works overseer was sympathetic and promised to visit me the coming Sunday and see for himself what was wanted. He didn't turn up. After several letters threatening to cancel the contract and pointing out the 21 day clause, work resumed spasmodically, and a month later was deemed, by them, to be complete.

The company's representative came for his cheque. I indicated the shoddy work and the items I felt should be replaced before I settled up. A more senior official arrived, agreed with me, apologized for all the trouble and assured me that all would be corrected within the next four days. I was mollified, accepted his promise and gave him a cheque for 5,000 soles, half the amount I still owed, signing promissory notes for the rest, which would be paid monthly.

Thereafter, the only activity on the part of Madera Pronto was supplied by an old carpenter, who waited around for two days for the material to arrive and when it didn't, disappeared, never to return. No-one else and nothing else came. When I rang, the person responsible was always somewhere else. I told the bank not to pay out any more to Madera Pronto – promissory notes or not!

Three months later Madera Pronto demanded final payment. I refused until they had completed the work. A few weeks afterwards, a whole year after the affair had started, a small, slimy, well-dressed ferret of a man called at the house to ask if it would be convenient for a director of Madera Pronto to call on me, in the office, at eleven the next day. I told him I would be delighted but suggested we meet at my house, where he could see what my complaints were all about.

351

No, it would be more convenient for him to meet me in my office. I should have guessed why. I was still waiting for him in the office the next morning, when Mary phoned from a friend's house (we still awaited our own instrument) to say that a truck had arrived with a policeman and bailiff. They had already emptied the refrigerator and were now carting off our furniture. I told Doris to ring her lawyer brother while I tore home. As I got out of the car, the weasly little lad who had called the previous evening, pranced up and flashed a demand note in front of my face, shouting that if I didn't pay 10,000 soles, there and then, he would strip the house.

I pointed out that I only owed 5,000 soles, not ten, and that it would be paid the moment the work was finished. But he was adamant, demanding payment in cash, no cheques. Just then Doris arrived; she had spoken with her brother, who said the only thing to do was to pay and sue the company later. Reluctantly, the ferret allowed me to visit a neighbour so I could ring Sean, my bank manager, who gave me an immediate overdraft to cash a cheque at a local branch. Like a cat watching a mouse, my slimy acquaintance accompanied me to see that I drew out the required sum. I felt like a criminal.

I handed over the 10,000, a receipt was signed, the bailiff took note of my protestations concerning the amount owed, the refrigerator was restocked, the furniture replaced and the policeman, who until then had been marching through the house swinging his baton, bowed, shook my hand and assured me that I was a worthy *caballero*. Perhaps the beer which Mary had offered him in my absence had something to do with his change of heart. No such hospitality was extended to the ferret, who now informed me that he was Madera Pronto's lawyer.

I sued Madera Pronto for the return of my extra 5,000 soles plus another 10,000 damages. Doris's brother handled the case. It came up several months later, when I was on overseas leave. We won. The magistrate, so Doris told me, had slaughtered both the firm and the ferret. I wished I had sued for more. Madera Pronto kept 5,000 of the 10,000 I had given their sleazy attorney and which I legitimately owed them, and from the damages, I paid Doris's brother 5,000 soles, and put 5,000 in my pocket.

Justice, I felt had been done.

ALPACALANDIA

Rome wrote that they were sending me an Associate Expert. Never having heard of such a person, I rang Axel in our FAO office.

'It's a recent university graduate who assists an Expert,' he told me. 'They come mainly from Scandinavia and the Low Countries. After a few years, they return to their home country and are employed in its foreign aid programmes, or they may remain in FAO as a full expert.'

Great, I thought. Now there'd be two of us.

Manuel was not so enthusiastic.

'Who's going to pay him? I don't want to waste Project money on trainees.'

He was a little less sceptical when I told him that they were paid by their own governments, and would cost us nothing.

'But why should we train Experts for FAO?'

'Well, he *is* a veterinarian, and I expect he will be a great help. Anyway, how else is he going to get field experience?' I thought it wiser not to add 'in the Third World' – that was a sensitive point with Manuel.

In due course I met a slim blond Swede, with high cheekbones and somewhat hollow cheeks. Even with the naivete of youth, he had a distinct aristocratic bearing and once let slip that he was distantly related to the King of Sweden. But then I believe most Swedes are! His English was excellent.

'Goran?' He pronounced it with a guttural G. 'That's an impossible name. Haven't you another?'

'Ralph.' So Ralph he was called.

Shortly after Ralph's arrival, Manuel told me that we must visit La Raya.

'La Raya; what's that?' I asked.

'It's an Auchenidae station, very high, between Cuzco and Puno. It belongs to Puno University but soon, I hope, we will have it for VITAR. We must visit and talk. La Molina and SIPA also want it, so we must get in first.' I was sure that if Manuel wanted it, it wouldn't be long before it was in our hands.

The most important of the indigenous animals in the Andes, Manuel said, was the group known as the Auchenidae; long-necked, woolly animals, looking like a cross between a deer and a miniature camel, to which family, in fact, they belonged.

Two species of the Auchenidae, the llama and the alpaca, were domesticated; the other two, the vicuña and the guanaco, were still wild. Because of their affinity to high altitude and their value – the llama for transport, the alpaca and vicuña for wool – they were high on our list for research. Guanaco, which mostly lived in Chile and Argentina, were considered pests and hunted for meat or for sport.

Manuel, and his colleague Saul, the Professor of Animal Production, had been working with alpaca at La Raya for years, but only as

353

guests with no control over the longer-term breeding and research programmes. It would have been convenient to use Huancayo for our studies with alpaca, but it was too low and too far from the traditional alpaca farming areas to be of much use. The answer was La Raya.

I was excited, especially as we would spend two days in Cuzco, 'The City of the Sun God', and would be able to visit nearby Machu Picchu, the world-famous 'Lost City of the Incas', one of Peru's main tourist attractions. Machu Picchu, accidentally discovered in 1911 by Hiram Bingham, was one of the fortified towns surrounding Cuzco to which the Incas had retreated in face of the Spanish onslaught.

Manuel, Ralph and I took off just after daybreak aboard Fawcett Airline's DC3, into the thick, blanket of cloud that hung over the coast at this time of the year, and for the next ten minutes found ourselves imprisoned between soft white walls of cotton wool. I was wondering if we would ever emerge, when we suddenly skidded out along the downy surface into bright sunshine. Below, as far as we could see, stretched a white, fluffy blanket, occasionally broken up by dark hills, like hippos basking in a sea of milk.

As the shuddering plane left the coastal fog and struggled to gain height, the Andes rose up like a massive barrier. A dark-haired, petite air hostess walked down the aisle to ensure that everyone knew how to use the oxygen apparatus, a thin rubber tube which dangled in front of each passenger and was placed in the mouth after the first ten minutes of flight. Although the unpressurized DC3s rarely exceeded an altitude of 6,000 metres, one felt distinctly queer if the tube was removed for more than a minute or two.

Spectacular snow-covered peaks passed by below us, some of which Manuel could name, and several tiny emerald lakes, set like jewels between the mountains, flashed back the rising sun.

An hour and half later, we began to descend.

'Surely not into that!' I exclaimed, horrified, as we dived towards the layer of thick cloud which filled the valleys.

'Don't woory,' Manuel laughed, 'the pilots are very experienced. Sometimes the whole flight is in cloud, then they have to fly by their watches. Then I woory.'

I didn't blame him. Descending into a small mountain-fringed valley through thick cloud, after flying blind for an hour and a half, would make me 'woory' too!

A moment later, my nerves somewhat ragged, we fell out of the cloud into the cup-like valley of Cuzco, which we circled before approaching the airport.

Cuzco was only slightly higher than Huancayo, nevertheless I was soon out of breath as we explored the narrow, cobbled lanes, squeezed between walls of massive, cut-stone blocks. Amongst the many churches and shrines we saw, was the House of the Sun Virgins, or Aclla Wasi, now a nunnery, where the prettiest girls had been trained as 'Handmaidens of the Sun'. The immoveable solidity of everything was awe-inspiring.

Cuzco had been the centre of the Inca empire. From it had radiated four 'Royal Roads'. Those to the north and south ran through the Andes like white, cobbled ribbons, reaching to Quito in Ecuador and to Talca in Chile, while another connected the capital to the jungle and a fourth linked up with the coastal system that ran for 2,500 miles through the seaside desert. No other empire in history, not even that of the Romans, had conquered such vast tracts of land and organized life so thoroughly as had the Incas.

We drove up to the huge fortress of Sacsahuaman, perched on a hill overlooking the city. Colossal boulders, some calculated to weigh over 100 tons, had been brought many miles and thousands of feet up from jungle river beds and had been slotted together, in perfect union, without mortar of any sort, to form three lines of zigzagged fortifications. The face of one boulder had 12 visible corners where it fitted perfectly with its neighbours, the edges bevelled slightly, giving the whole an appearance of polished perfection. How it had been possible for the Incas to bring these stones such a distance and to such an altitude is one of the world's wonders. And they didn't even possess the wheel!

How, too, it had been possible for any army to take Sacsahuamán – let alone a small group of Spaniards – was equally astounding. But take it they had, and in that final battle of 1536, which saw the death of Juan, Francisco Pizarro's brother, had ended the great Inca empire of Tahuantinsuyo.

Next morning we boarded a rickety five-coach train, filled with international tourists and pulled by an ancient long-funnelled steam engine, for the 100 kilometre trip to Machu Picchu, the sacred mountain fortress of the Incas. The railway wound down the edge of the Urubamba valley past rows of well-preserved and still used Inca agricultural terraces which extended almost to the top of the steep mountains, where they would catch the sun for longer periods.

We drove up a zigzag track from the siding to the ruins of Machu Picchu, 2,000 feet above, in the back of a truck.

There cannot be many more memorable vistas than the one from this 'Lost City in the Clouds'. All around rose sharp forested peaks, those to the north-east gradually disappearing into banks of cloud as the Andes sank away to the steamy jungles of the Amazon. Two thousand feet below us, the Urubamba river made a horseshoe bend to protect three sides of the stronghold. On the fourth side, a narrow ridge connected Machu Picchu to another mountainous ridge, the Cordillera Vilcabamba.

One can only guess at the amazement of the young explorer, Hiram Bingham, when he first looked down over the acres of cut stone stairways, roofless stone houses, plazas and irrigation canals, half-hidden by centuries of subtropical growth. At one end, a steep, rocky peak, the Huayna Picchu, thrust skywards like the prow of a ship. Here, it was said, the Virgins of the Sun had been kept, safe from molestation. At the other end, in a commanding position above the other buildings, was the Intihuatana, a large stone slab, to which the Incas believed that the sun was anchored, and which acted as a seasonal sundial for the Inca calendar.

The architecture was clean, solid and satisfying. Everywhere the huge blocks of granite hugged each other so tightly that centuries of storms and earthquakes had been unable to shift them a millimetre. The characteristic Inca-style doorways and windows, narrower at the top than the bottom, gave the impression of a stocky Andean peasant standing with feet apart, solid and immovable.

The La Raya Land Rover which called at our hotel early next morning followed the Cuzco–Puno railway along the banks of the Vilcanota, a wide, shallow river, apt to flood the flat valley bottom.

'Liver fluke is a great problem here,' Manuel told us. 'Probably one hundred per cent of the cattle and sheep are infected.'

The cattle fluke, a flat, leaf-like worm, which lives in the bile-ducts of ruminants, requires a particular species of snail in which to complete its life-cycle. Fluke is common in wet, marshy areas throughout the world, causing general ill-health and death. At slaughter, the livers are condemned as they are hard and riddled with thick rubbery bile-ducts, which are liable to disgorge white, slug-like parasites when tackled with knife and fork!

'All these animals are owned by peasants or small farmers,' Manuel went on. 'There is little they can do to help themselves. They can't drain the land, treatment is too expensive, and killing the snails is a major operation. If they take their animals to drier land up the mountains where there are no snails, the grazing is too poor.'

It seemed like an *impasse*. Later, at Huancayo, we discovered that humans, as well as cattle and sheep, became infected with liver fluke. We also discovered a novel way to control the parasite.

La Raya, 'the line', so-called because it formed the watershed separating the source of the Vilcanota, which flowed north to join the

Amazon and the Ayavin, which flowed south into Lake Titicaca, was over 4,000 metres in altitude.

We turned off the main dirt road and bumped along a badly eroded track towards the low, slate-roofed, stone buildings of the Auchenidae Station. Blue gums, which had been plentiful further down the valley near Cuzco, had now almost disappeared, giving way to a scattering of the stunted, indigenous Mountain Ash, the only species that seemed capable of coping with the altitude.

Treeless, snow-capped mountains lined both sides of the valley, their lower slopes sprinkled with the tiny white dots of grazing alpaca.

The sun's rays seared our faces as we alighted, but the air in the shade of the buildings was icy. The Station Manager, himself a veterinarian, sat us down to an immediate lunch of steaks and potatoes. The meat tasted different but delicious.

'Alpaca,' he told us. It was the staple source of animal protein, apart from guinea-pigs, which were wild in this part of the sierra. Occasionally there would be mutton, otherwise breakfast, lunch and supper consisted of alpaca steaks with a slice of dry crumbly cottage cheese and small hard unleavened rolls.

The only alpaca I had seen till then had been a rather mangy specimen in a zoo; Ralph hadn't had even that experience. The herd gathered around us inquisitively as we left the Land Rover. At first I could see little difference between them and the llamas we had seen at Huancayo, until Manuel pointed out that the llama was bigger, had coarser hair and a straighter back, with a tail that curled up from the base instead of down as in the alpaca. The alpaca was a less sturdy animal than the llama, with a longer, finer and more copious fleece.

'Watch out if they get angry,' Manuel warned. 'Alpaca can spit a long way and very accurately, and it really stinks.'

He pointed out the two varieties, the *suri*, with long straight hair and the *huacaya*, which had a shorter curly fleece.

'By the way, we refer to the fleece as "fibre", not "wool",' Manuel explained. 'Wool is only from sheep. There are about three million alpaca in Peru, living mostly at over four thousand metres. It seems that the higher they live the finer the fibre, probably because of the more intense cold and ultra-violet radiation.'

'Are there many alpaca farms?' I asked.

'Yes, but alpacas are raised mainly by their Indian herders, very few of the alpaca owners live on their farms; they prefer the comforts of Arequipa or Lima. The Indian headman runs the farm and sends the annual crop of fibre to Arequipa to be graded and sold. The owner might visit his farm once or twice a year, but as long as the fibre crop is satisfactory and he gets his money, he leaves the day to day chores to his headman.'

'Not very progressive,' I commented.

'No, and there are a lot of problems. The most serious is the very low rate of reproduction, less than half the alpaca females have a *cria*, or baby, each year. This may be due to the males, many of which appear to be infertile, and also because they only seem to mate from December to March. Even when we get a good crop of young, half of them die before they are a year old from enteric diseases or pneumonias.'

'What about diseases of reproduction?' I asked. 'Brucellosis, for instance?'

'We've almost ruled out disease as a cause of infertility. Alpacas *can* contract brucellosis, in fact we had an outbreak a couple of years ago when a herder who had picked up the disease from drinking goats' milk on the coast infected his charges on his return. We have now eliminated all those positive to the blood test. No, we think the problem is behaviourial. It is something we must investigate.'

I noticed dark patches on the hillside near the stockades that housed them at night.

'Latrines,' Manuel said. 'Alpaca defecate in defined areas, rather like pigs. They make these latrines all over the place, but there is always one near their overnight quarters. It probably helps to limit the spread of worms on the range. Alpaca are highly intelligent; watch them in a thunderstorm, they'll lie down with their heads on the ground so lightning won't strike them.'

Probably shit-scared like me, I thought. There was no way I was going to hang about watching them in a lightning storm!

'Let's go and have a look at the vicuña herd. They have the finest fibre of all, but unfortunately they are still semi-wild and highly nervous. That's the problem; hunters have to kill the wild vicuña before shearing them, so that all vicuña products on the market are made from dead animals. Vicuña have become an endangered species. Perhaps we have five thousand left in Peru.'

The La Raya herd consisted of about 30 of these delicate, fawn-like creatures, smaller than alpaca, light brown in colour, with an apron of long white hair on the chest. 'Our idea is to cross them with alpaca,' Manuel continued, 'so that the offspring, the paco-vicuña, will have a finer fibre than the alpaca and a more abundant fleece than the vicuña. They will also be less nervous, so we can shear them. Unless we begin to farm them, commercially, like alpaca, they will die out. One day we will visit Cala-Cala, which is the only farm which has tried to domesticate vicuña.'

We spent two days in La Raya, taking notes of all that would be needed in the laboratories and the field, against the day when we hoped it would be ours.

The following afternoon we flagged down a passing train at the La Raya siding (it was still possible to do that), and continued our journey to Puno, the provincial capital on the shores of Lake Titicaca, where we would tackle Puno University, the present owners of La Raya.

The *Universidad Técnica del Altiplano*, to give it its full name, was new, the buildings impressive, but the infrastructure of teachers and equipment basic in the extreme. Apart from a young pasture specialist just back from studying in Switzerland, all the staff were recent graduates with no field experience whatsoever.

We invited the Rector to dine with us. Wine flowed freely, most of it down the Rector's throat. At the end of the meal, this charming, middle-aged *mestizo* poured his coffee into the saucer, slurped it down, picked up the corner of the table cloth, gave his whole face a good rub over, told us we were excellent fellows and just made it out of the door! It looked as if Manuel was making headway. I didn't doubt that La Raya would soon be ours.

High altitude affects people in different ways: from immediate blinding headaches, nausea and collapse, to delayed indigestion, sleeplessness and diarrhoea. The day we arrived in Puno I began a severe attack of the 'trots'. I thought it was something I had eaten. Manuel prescribed chlorodyne, a concoction of chloroform and morphine, nothing else being available. It certainly helped, but for the next few days I trailed around in a soporific haze, trying to show interest while I popped in and out of toilets or behind bushes. This digestive upset became a regular feature of my particular form of *soroche*, starting after four or five days at high altitude and lasting till I became adapted or returned to sea-level.

By the time we left Puno, I was back to normal, but by then Ralph had succumbed. He had been sympathizing in a half-hearted, amused manner, suggesting I had over-indulged in Cuzco. His come-uppance descended the morning we left Puno. We had been sharing a hotel room, and I noticed that he had spent most of the night visiting the 'loo'.

'Haven't slept a wink,' Ralph groaned as we dressed.

'Here, take a swig of chlorodyne.'

He swallowed about three times the normal dose. When I returned from breakfast, he was still very poorly but made it to the airport without mishap. I waited until Fawcett had called their flight for the last time, before summoning him from the toilet.

A few minutes after being airborne, he disappeared down the aisle at a sprint. The rest of us placed the rubber oxygen tubes in our mouths and settled down for the trip. Five minutes passed. No Ralph. I summoned the hostess, who was patrolling the cabin with a portable oxygen cylinder, and indicated Ralph's empty seat. She flew into action, and a minute later a chalky-faced, shivering Ralph was helped back to his place. Hot water bottles, blankets and an oxygen mask were applied. At first he could only mumble through blue trembling lips, but soon his colour began to return, and as we lost height over the coast, he actually smiled. By the time we reached Lima, we could both laugh at the ambulance drawn up beside the plane, but I knew, and he knew even better, that a few more minutes in the toilet, without oxygen, might have been very serious.

Oxygen, I discovered, was not only a quick remedy for altitude sickness, it had an even more valuable property. Some years later, after a rather too indulgent night in Cuzco with a visiting consultant, I took him, fragile as I was, to inspect the fortress of Sacsahuaman before catching the plane back to Lima. The massive boulders were heaving and rolling in every direction. Still nauseated, I made the plane, but as soon as we were airborne and I had sucked in the first few lungfuls of oxygen, my hangover miraculously disappeared. Could this, I wondered, be the long-sought, instant remedy for hangovers?

AMAZON JUNGLE

Peru, I soon realized, had three distinct territories, each with its own entirely different climate and way of life.

The *costa*, that rainless, sandy strip between the sea and the Andes, was dominated by the *El Niño* and other ocean currents which brought in the chilly mists and fine drizzle from May to October, and warm humid weather from November to April. Most of the coastal population – old Spanish families intermixed with multinational immigrants and a growing influx of Andean Indians – lived in cities where life-styles varied from sophisticated wealth to abject poverty.

The *sierra*, the Andean mountain chain with its snow-capped peaks reaching to nearly 7,000 metres, was predominantly a land of Indian peasants interspersed with mining operations, large *haciendas* of sheep, cattle and alpaca, and small adobe villages or struggling, higgledy-piggledy towns.

The rest of Peru consisted of the sparsely populated *selva*, or

Amazon jungle, half-explored steamy forests and huge rivers, along whose banks lived a number of primitive Indian tribes.

'You OK for Pucallpa next week?' Manuel asked. 'We have to fix the site for our tropical research station. Saul is coming with us.'

Saul, Professor of Animal Production, tall and slender and in his middle thirties, had a slightly hooked nose and faintly slanted eyes, suggesting Inca blood in his veins, which was more than likely since he came from Cuzco.

The DC3 which flew us to the jungle was similar to the one that had taken us to Cuzco. We sucked our oxygen tubes while the pilot dodged snow-capped peaks and wicked-looking crags for the first 60 turbulent minutes, before gliding down over the thickly forested Andean foothills, to level out a few thousand feet above the green carpet of the Amazon jungle. The passengers, more courageous now that the air was less bumpy, began to point out the winding rivers and necklaces of lagoons, remnants of former river courses that criss-crossed the main waterways like strings of silver sausages. 20 minutes later the red-earth streets and jumbled-up houses of Pucallpa came into sight, etched into the dark foliage on the banks of the Ucayali river.

Hot, steamy air engulfed us as we stepped from the plane, and before I had reached the wooden tin-roofed shack which acted as a terminal, 50 metres away over a muddy runway, my shirt was soaked.

The jovial mustachioed *ingeneiro* Ramon (all professionals below the level of a doctor were termed 'Engineers'), an old friend of Manuel's and officer in charge of San Jorge, SIPA's livestock station, drove us the 12 kilometres into Pucallpa, parking in front of the local hotel for a beer and a meal. Since all our belongings were in the open back of the unattended pick-up, I thought it would be as well to take my briefcase inside with me.

'Why do you need your briefcase?' Ramon asked in surprise.

'It has my camera, transistor radio and all my money in it,' I replied.

'*No hay problema*,' he laughed. 'Leave it. There are no police here.'

He wasn't joking. There was a primitive honesty in the jungle, and only the police, so it was said, when brought in from other areas, would rob you.

Pucallpa was, literally, the end of the road. A few short pot-holed tracks, like frayed nerve endings, searched the jungle around the town, but that was all. Apart from the one road that connected Pucallpa to Lima, any onward journeys had to be made by river or by air. To make the journey from Lima to Pucallpa by car, one branched off at Oroya onto a stony dirt road that wound along valley floors, up steep mountainsides with spectacular precipices mere inches from the wheels, crossed frigid Andean plains, and slipped down the tree-canopied foothills, past the dainty tropical colony of Tingo Maria before entering the torrid flat jungle, and flopping, exhausted, at Pucallpa, snoring beside the Ucayali.

The river Ucayali, later to merge with the Napo to form the Amazon, was nearly two kilometres wide, and although ocean-going steamers ended their journey 800 kilometres further downstream, at Iquitos, quite sizeable ships could still reach Pucallpa.

After lunch, Ramon drove us out to SIPA's ranch, San Jorge, 60 kilometres along the road to Lima. Settlers had hacked untidy clearings from the forest on either side of the road, planting bananas and corn in the stumpy ground beside their huts. Here and there, a larger clearing and rough pasture suggested an attempt at livestock raising. Elsewhere, the undisturbed jungle looked impenetrable. Ten kilometres further on was the proposed site for VITAR's jungle station.

'There's a thousand hectares available here,' Manuel told us, 'which I am asking the University to buy. I've told the Rector that La Molina will buy it if we don't. It's a ploy that usually works!'

An overgrown, winding path took us into the jungle. It was incredibly hot and humid, and flies of all descriptions buzzed round our heads. I hoped it would be better when the jungle was cleared. Clearing would be our first problem. It would cost a lot and take a long time, unless we could do it mechanically. I mentioned my fears to Manuel.

'We'll visit Tournavista tomorrow. Maybe they can help. They built their own machines and cleared several thousand hectares.'

Tournavista, I knew, was the brainchild of a missionary-minded heavy industry tycoon from Texas, Le Tourneau, who had established a settlement on the banks of the Pachitea river, a main tributary of the Ucayali, from which he hoped to spread the Gospel and practical forms of education.

By chance, I had come across these godly adventurers some ten years previously, in Jamaica, when an extraordinary vessel, a cross between a ferry and a raft, had put into Kingston harbour. On board were cattle and supplies from the Le Tourneau Company at Galveston, heading for the Peruvian jungle via the Amazon river. The flat-bottomed craft, built with the shallow waters of the Ucayali and Pachitea in mind, had been found to be almost uncontrollable in the open sea, and had had to put into Kingston for modifications. I had been summoned to prescribe to the storm-battered animals on board and see that no quarantine regulations were infringed. The Santa Gertrudis and Brahmans I now saw grazing around me were, undoubtedly, descendants of those I had examined in Jamaica a decade before.

362

The hospitable American missionaries insisted we stay the night. The residences were unusual, but eminently practical, more like sophisticated caravans, propped up by bricks at the ends with a centre axle jutting out each side, so that they could be towed away.

We were taken to see some of their specially constructed tree-crushing machines at work clearing the forest. The parts had all been produced by Le Tourneau in Galveston and assembled at Tournavista. Like mammoth tractors dwarfing the houses, they were capable of clearing ten hectares of tall forest a day, whereas hand-clearing by 20 men with saws and machetes could only achieved a few square yards. The 5,000 hectares of pastures at Tournavista had all been cleared by machines. They were sure they could hire us some when the time came.

The *selva* appeared to be most promising for cattle production, despite the heat and humidity, and despite the poor soil. There was no tsetse fly, no East Coast fever, no rinderpest or malignant catarrh or those other epizootics which decimated the herds in Africa and the Far East. Mineral deficiencies, worms, ticks and the diseases they transmitted, would be the commonest causes of ill-health.

'We should get together with San Jorge and Tournavista,' Saul suggested as we returned to Pucallpa, 'and co-ordinate our research.'

It was the obvious solution. When our station was completed, such a scheme would provide nearly 10,000 hectares for combined livestock production research.

We visited the Summer Institute of Linguistics at Yarinacocha, the centre of an international organization devoted to the translation and distribution of the Bible amongst the more primitive and inaccessible peoples.

The neat, tin-roofed, wooden bungalows, pillowed by flowering shrubs and well-tended lawns which stretched for two kilometres along the banks of a tropical lagoon, could have been mistaken for a Hollywood set. At one end there was an airstrip on which nippy single-engined Cessnas and ponderous, almost obsolete, Catalina flying boats of World War Two had been drawn up.

'Our policy is to fly the missionary with his entire family out to their post, which usually consists of a hut built by the Indians themselves,' the Director told us. 'Afterwards, we visit them weekly – if weather permits – but they can reach us anytime by radio.'

'Your missionaries are brave people,' I commented. 'It must be a hairy experience for the wife and kids, let alone the missionary himself, to be dropped in the middle of nowhere, even if the Indians do appear to be friendly.'

363

'They don't look at it that way,' our guide replied. 'This is their work for God. He looks after them, and so far, thanks to the Good Lord, we have had no real trouble either with the Indians or our planes.'

Nearby, an Indian village straggled along the lagoon's edge. These were Campa Indians, a short, light-skinned, peaceful tribe with straight black hair cut in a fringe just above the eyes. They lived by fishing and hunting and, nowadays, by some cultivation as well. Like all communities beset by floods, wild animals and creepy-crawlies, their wooden huts were raised several feet above the ground on thick poles. The roofs, thatched with rushes and palm fronds, overhung the walls by several feet.

The Campa women wove their own cloth, the colours as bright as their smiles, with skirts and blouses picked out in almost Incaic designs. Strings of bright beads adorned their necks, arms and ankles, but never did I see an ornament in their hair.

Dug-out canoes floated in the green lagoon amongst carpets of water-lilies, or were half-pulled-up onto the turf. Further out, two or three canoes lay stationary on the glassy surface while their occupants waited for a bite.

On the far side of the lagoon, the thick vegetation provided an uninterrupted, dark green curtain, the *cortina verde*, as formidable and impenetrable as any 'iron curtain'.

That night, over bottles of beer, we pondered our impressions and discussed future action. I was confident that Manuel would soon persuade the University authorities to buy the land, and whatever problems we might have with SIPA in other areas, I was sure that there would be none in Pucallpa. Ramon would see to that. How was I to know that politics and personalities would delay our progress for another three years?

One aspect did worry me. Even if we established a station and solved some of the nutritional and disease problems of the area, who was going to benefit from our findings? There were few enough farmers, and most of these were week-enders who had businesses in Pucallpa. Virtually no extension service existed through which the results of research could reach them, and no-one had yet worked out the economics of raising livestock in the *selva*.

'There are over forty million hectares of jungle waiting to be developed,' Saul pointed out. 'I expect ranching will increase rapidly if we can show that it is economic. President Belaunde's great dream is to construct a highway to run along between the jungle and the mountains, from Bolivia to Ecuador, the *carretera marginal*, as he calls it, with branches connecting it to the coast. There is no reason why the jungle shouldn't export meat and agricultural produce in the future.'

'At the moment, of course,' I pointed out, 'it exports oxygen.'

I hoped, fervently, that the development of this lobe of the world's lungs would not follow the example set by Brazil, where millions of hectares of Amazon jungle were being wantonly destroyed, to benefit a few short-term exploiters.

* * *

I sat next to Manuel on the flight back to Lima.

'What made you become a vet?' I asked. His story was a reflection of his character – determination and foresightedness, flavoured with a little luck and the ability to learn from experience. He had grown up a barefooted farmer's son in Iquitos. School work proved easy due to his excellent memory. Outside school hours, he hunted in the jungle or herded his father's cattle. When an animal became sick he had to treat it himself with bush remedies, there were no vets in the jungle. He decided to become one. Passing well in his school exams, he persuaded his parents to let him sit the San Marcos University entrance exam, for which he would have to travel to Lima, the other side of the world for a jungle lad.

With what small resources his parents could muster, they fitted him out for the journey – including a rather *à la mode* trilby hat. It was this hat that secured his future. To reach Lima, he had to take a boat from Iquitos to Pucallpa, where he would catch the bus to the capital. As he was boarding, a gust of wind blew his new and much-prized hat – the first he'd ever worn, into the river. While he and his younger brother made desperate efforts to retrieve it, the boat pulled away without him.

Determined that nothing would stop him from sitting the University entrance, he persuaded the skipper of a Government launch going to Pucallpa to let him sit on the prow, and so arrived, four days later, his suitcase by his side and his rather misshapen trilby jammed firmly on his head, tied down with a piece of string.

The ferry that he had missed never did reach Pucallpa and, for all I know, is still stuck fast in the mud of the Ucayali, where it hit a sandbank. Had his hat not been wafted away by that gust of wind, he would never have arrived in time to catch the weekly bus to Lima, and would have missed the entrance exams for San Marcos, delaying, perhaps for ever, his opportunity to become a vet. As it was, the shy jungle boy found himself in the top 10 per cent of the candidates, qualifying to enter the Veterinary Faculty, where he became one of the most outstanding veterinary scientists and administrators that South America has produced.

'So the fate of VITAR will be determined by a hat,' I taunted.

'Not just one hat,' he replied half-seriously. 'Many hats, I think.'

HIGH UP – BUT HATCHING

I posted Ralph to Huancayo. His job would be to keep an eye on the construction of the laboratories and to start a survey of high-altitude disease, or *mal de altura*, in cattle. His wife and two small children soon joined him from Sweden.

Like humans, cattle varied greatly in response to altitude, both as individuals and breeds. The most marked symptom in cattle was a dropsical swelling of the lower neck and dewlap and of that area between the front legs known to butchers and housewives as the brisket, so it was not surprising that the common name for altitude sickness in cattle was 'brisket disease'. In spite of all the talk about the condition, however, there seemed to be precious few facts.

'Find out how common it is,' I told Ralph, 'and whether it really is as serious a handicap as the farmers say,'

In contrast to the exotic breeds, a large number of which would die within three months when sent to the *sierra* from sea level, *criollo* cattle showed little reaction to high altitude. *Criollo* was the word used to describe the unproductive, peasant-owned breeds of livestock. *Criollo* cattle were the descendants of the Spanish Longhorn, crossed with innumerable breeds over the centuries. Improvement of production in *criollo* cattle in the *sierra* would almost certainly depend on crossing them with the altitude-susceptible exotic breeds, which meant first solving the problem of brisket disease. Farmers rarely keep notes, and the Huancayo farmers were no exception, but on the whole the incidence appeared to be low, since most herds had been at high altitude for generations and had become acclimatized. Even so, some breeds seemed more resistant than others – Brown Swiss, for instance.

'They come from Switzerland and have been adapting to altitude for centuries,' was one farmer's explanation. I pointed out that what was considered 'altitude' in Switzerland was not much more than 'sea-level' in Peru, and how did he explain that Jersey cattle, which came from the Channel Islands only a few feet above sea-level, were also very resistant to *mal de altura*? There was no doubt that breed was important, but it was clear that there were other factors as well. It was to take us several years to discover what.

Meanwhile, the only immediate remedy for the distressing symptoms was to take the patient to a lower altitude. There was some evidence that Vitamin E, by reducing the oxygen requirements of the muscles, would alleviate the condition, but we could never make it work.

Serious as altitude stress could be in cattle, sheep and horses, it was catastrophic in poultry. The low absorbtion of oxygen by the egg at altitude reduced the energy-yielding processes in the embryo to a point where the chick was unable to peck through the shell. We found that less than 30 per cent of the eggs set in incubators in Huancayo would hatch, and of those that did, only a very few chicks grew into healthy adults.

There was nothing, of course, to stop the Andean farmer from buying day-old chicks on the coast and taking them back with him to the *sierra*. Nothing that is, except expense. Probably 20 to 30 per cent would die on the bus journey up, and another 10 per cent would succumb during the process of adaptation to the cold air and low atmospheric pressure, but most of the others, about 50 per cent in total, would adapt and survive if adequately cared for. The Peruvian peasant, however, was as conservative as his counterparts in other countries, and preferred to put his faith in the slow-growing, low-producing *criollo* chicken, a bald-necked bird, similar to those so-called 'peel-necks' of Jamaica and Africa, which would hatch out a few eggs each month, live entirely by scratching around the yard, and never get sick.

Workers in the USA told us that the addition of certain chemicals to the feed, or the introduction of oxygen to the incubators, had given promising results, but neither method seemed to us to be a practical solution. We needed a new approach.

Then we had a piece of really good luck. The Professor of Physiology at Babraham, near Cambridge, whom I had visited on the way to Peru, wrote me about a friend who was looking for a job, and felt we might be interested.

'If there's anything to be done in the field of poultry incubation, Jim's your man. Most ingenious fellow.'

I wrote to Jim who, although not a university graduate, had had 30 years raising poultry and manufacturing incubators.

His solution to our problem was simple.

'If it is a matter of low atmospheric pressure,' he wrote back, 'why not build a compression room at Huancayo and put your incubators in that?'

It was ludicrously simple, but no-one seemed to have thought of it before. The letter contained a detailed plan of what he suggested.

'Come and build it for us,' I suggested, and sent a request to FAO headquarters to recruit him for three months.

His drawings were so easy to follow that we started to build the chamber two months before he arrived. It consisted of a pit about 18 feet square, and 12 feet deep, in which was constructed a reinforced concrete chamber with walls and roof bound together with steel rods. The roof of the chamber was to be of three foot reinforced concrete, and on top of this was to be another four feet of packed earth. Air would be pumped in by a couple of small compressors, and a Heath Robinson apparatus, using pieces of scrap metal as weights, would be placed over the exit pipe to control the internal pressure. Entry to the compression room was through an anteroom with thick steel doors and adjustable nozzles to equalize the pressure. This acted both as a compression and decompression chamber. An intercom connected the pressure chamber to the poultry office in the main lab building, in case of emergencies.

Jim arrived shortly before the pressure chamber was finished. Tall, slim, with bristly, close-cut, greying hair and a neat toothbrush moustache twitching above a permanently positioned briar, he looked the typical immaculate English company director. Impossibly efficient and knowledgeable, always on top of the task at hand, enthusiastic, humorous, stubborn, an inspirer of confidence, a lover of the good life (but only after the job was completed), he came for three months and stayed three years. No expert I ever knew did more to justify his salary or to help those he came to serve.

He was rather disturbed when we told him that the university engineers had recommended only one foot of reinforced concrete on top of the chamber, instead of three, which he had calculated to be necessary.

'When we try it out, Pat,' he advised, 'I suggest you stand well back and protect your vitals!'

There was quite a group present to see the fun. Jim switched on the compressors and stood by the regulator and pressure gauge adding pieces of scrap metal to increase the pressure.

'Only a thousand feet to go,' he called, adding another weight and retreating. A moment later there was an ominous crack.

'Watch it. It's going up! Switch off the mains.' Someone rushed inside the lab building and a moment later the compressors stopped, but not before there were hissing noises and a decided hump over the top of the chamber.

'That was a near one! The ruddy engineers haven't a clue. Next time we'll do it my way.'

Six weeks later, the chamber was rebuilt to Jim's original specifications, and the pressure brought up to that of sea level, without mishap. High-altitude incubation had been born.

Hatching percentages in the chamber proved to be slightly better than those recorded in similar incubators at sea level, and the chicks when hatched had no trouble in adapting to the altitude.

It was a resounding success and a world first for VITAR. So popular did our day-old chicks become that we couldn't keep up with the demand.

But a success is apt to expose more problems than does a failure. Incubation was only the first of many puzzles we had to solve in high-altitude poultry production.

PETS

'We've a dog addressed to you,' the airways official informed me over the phone. 'It's at the airport.'

'Great. I'm on my way.'

'There's six hundred dollars to pay before we can release it.' I must have hesitated a bit too long. 'That's six hundred dollars,' he repeated.

Before leaving Uganda, I had arranged for a friend to send on our Alsatian bitch, Panda, named in memory of her plucky predecessor of Northern Rhodesia days, and already the mother of 22. The day we moved into the house at Las Casuarinas, I cabled him. Now she had arrived and I was faced with a bill for 16,200 soles, at least three times the original estimate for which I had left him a cheque.

After a moment of hard thinking, I noted the number of my next cheque and rang Sean at the bank.

'Would you stop a cheque for me?' I asked.

'Sure. Who to and for how much?' I told him, gave him the cheque number and made tracks for the airport. I gave the airline official the 'stopped' cheque and left with Panda prancing at my heels. The official was onto me the next day.

'What's going on? The bank won't cash your cheque.'

'I know. I stopped it. I'm looking into the whole affair. I had a quote for a hundred and twenty pounds in Uganda, and I left a cheque to cover it. I want to know what's happened to it before forking out any more.'

Of course, I had to pay in the end. My friend in Uganda had done his best, but my cheque was by then out of date, and he had had to send Panda COD. No-one ever explained to my satisfaction why her

369

fare had escalated three-fold in eight months. Having set me back nearly a month's salary, Panda died a few months after arrival, from lymphatic leukaemia, a fairly common complaint in some breeds – especially Alsatians. We felt we had lost one of the family, but I was glad she'd had even a short time with us, long enough for her to know she hadn't been abandoned.

Panda was replaced by Divil, also an Alsatian, named after a play, *The Divil His Due*, in which Mary and I were acting. Nothing, including his name, could hide the fact that he was a nine-month-old drop-out from the police dog unit. He arrived in the company of a colleague who had promised me a half-trained police dog. The half we received was obviously not the trained half! The Jamaican word 'winjy' described him exactly – a large head with ribs and tail attached. And he drooped, not just his head and tail, but everything about him. It was all he could do to drag his scrawny legs over the door mat – until he saw Mau Mau, the cat. With a yelp he was cowering behind the settee.

We looked at him in horror. To refuse my colleague's kind offer was unthinkable. We would have to keep our fingers crossed and hope that he either improved or died.

'*Muy buena raça*, Doctor Patrick,' my colleague kept assuring me. '*El sera un buen guardián.*'

Well, perhaps he was a good breed, but watchdog? He gulped down a plate of food and went to sleep. Poor Divil. Drop-out he may have been, but he was the gentlest of Alsatians. Gradually he gained weight and his head and tail became less noticeable, but he remained an abject coward until the appearance of Shimmer, some months later.

Shimmer, so christened by Shannon when she saw the little dog's eyes shimmering in certain lights, appeared one morning beneath the children's bedroom window, a small, growling virago, patchily covered in long, yellow/brown hair, with a face between that of a Pekinese and a Collie. There were many bare patches and some were raw. Obviously, she had a severe dose of mange. And what else, I wondered?

When I tried to examine her, she bit me – luckily, it was only superficial. She ate the food the kids brought her, but she wouldn't budge from her niche below their bedroom window. In the next two days, she bit – or tried to bite, everyone in the house, although she never drew blood.

I was due to attend a conference in Argentina that week.

'I'll put her down before I leave,' I said. 'She may be incubating rabies, or something.'

370

'Don't you dare,' Mary replied. 'She's just frightened. She'll be OK.'

I returned from Buenos Aires a week later. As I came through the front door, a yapping, furry missile launched itself at me, and it was all I could do to embrace the family and keep my trousers intact. I was an outsider and Shimmer, now the sole self-appointed guardian of the house, had still to give her approval for me to enter. The clinic at the Veterinary Faculty treated her for mange, and within a month she was transformed into a beautiful, cuddly, soft-haired toy, although she lost none of her fire. But it was her effect on Divil that surprised us. Down the road lived two bull-mastiffs, whose distant bellow was enough to send Divil scurrying under the bed. To Shimmer, such baying was an irresistible challenge and she sallied forth in search of these ferocious monsters, leaving Divil to watch timidly from the gate.

The mastiffs must have thought that a rabbit had escaped. Out they came, giving tongue. But they had never encountered aerial attacks on their ears and tail before and, anyway, weren't rabbits supposed to flee, not fight? Within seconds, they had retreated behind their fence and Shimmer was trotting back up the road, head held high and a definite grin on her face.

Divil, suitably impressed, and probably a little ashamed, was soon adding his deep-throated howl to Shimmer's yaps, and it wasn't long before the mastiffs were confined to their billets for good. Shimmer must have appreciated the change in Divil and, being a sound female strategist, would now roll on her back when danger threatened and look to her strong, fierce, Alsatian knight, for protection.

Although an outsider would have immediately dubbed her a mongrel, Shimmer was typical of a long-established Peruvian breed which, from ancient drawings and pottery replicas, was thought to have arrived suddenly on the coast of Peru in pre-Inca days, perhaps from China or Indonesia. But wherever she had originated, she carried with her the characteristics of her race – aggressiveness and bravery, mixed with tremendous loyalty and affection.

She disappeared one summer Sunday. We had heard distant yapping, similar to hers, early that morning, but gave it no more thought. But when we returned from the beach, no Shimmer welcomed us back. Nor was she there for her evening meal. We spent days searching, placed advertisements in the paper and visited the dog pound. Nothing. Tears ran and tempers flared, to no avail.

We never saw her again, but we never forgot her. Poor Divil took it hardest of all.

371

We had found a half-wild tabby kitten in one of the crates when we moved up from the house in Juan Fanning. Mau Mau, as we called her, was with us till we left, ten years later. Her kittens – and their kittens – were born in secluded spots under the eaves and in my junk-filled garage workshop. One day, appalled by the number of feline hangers-on, I did a whisker count. There were 16, of which only 5 could be called 'pets'; the others were half-wild and unnamed. Surreptitiously, I began to put down one or two each week. Barbiturate capsules gobbled down in a chunk of meat wafted them into a deep post-prandial sleep and allowed me to give them a *coup de grâce* with an injection of the same drug. Soon only five remained. No-one seemed to notice, least of all the children.

'Daddy, you bastard!' was Shannon's comment, when I told her, years afterwards. I pointed out that it was better to put down 10 or so then, that wait another few years and put down 30!

Undoubtedly, our most exotic pet was Maruka. On the last day of the term, Shannon appeared carrying a large bird cage. In it was a South American Green parrot of indeterminate sex. We presumed it was a she, although it never laid an egg.

'Isn't it lovely? Miss Ellie asked me to keep it for a week while she's away.' Miss Ellie was Shannon's teacher. 'Her boyfriend gave it to her,' Shannon explained, as if that would justify the whole affair. She couldn't understand why we were so unenthusiastic. We had always regarded Miss Ellie as one of our closest friends. How could she do this to us? But worse was to come.

'Oh, I should hate to take it away after the children have grown so fond of it,' Miss Ellie insisted on her return. 'I shan't miss her.'

Damn right she wouldn't. Her little scheme to get rid of her boyfriend's (now ex boyfriend) unwelcome gift had worked wonderfully!

Since Maruka was now ours, we let her free, half-hoping she would fly away. But Maruka knew a good perch when she saw one. For three years she lived in the blue gums at the bottom of the garden or, on cold misty days, under the eaves of the laundry patio, where she left long dark green streaks of her droppings down the whitewashed walls.

She was a most malevolent and destructive bird. Any flower that dared to bloom was immediately ravaged. Any small, disintegrable toy left unattended was attacked with eagle-like ferocity. Lindley, now four, had been given a beautiful, flaxen-haired doll for her birthday. One morning, her wails and screams brought Mary to the bottom of the garden, where Maruka, perched on a branch just

372

out of reach of the little girl, was busy dissecting her precious 'Rosebud' with fiendish enjoyment. Pieces of clothing, eyes, fingers and hair lay strewn on the grass beneath her. To Lindley, all her dolls were alive, so this was a particularly gruesome murder of a favourite child!

Although a pest for most of the time, Maruka could be extremely sociable – if it was in her interest. She would share the cats' bowl and join us for any *al fresco* meal, plomping down in a whirring of wings next to the salad, or upsetting someone's fruit juice in her efforts to slake her thirst.

Only Lys, our second daughter, had the patience to try and understand her, and the two of them would sit in the fir tree for hours, conversing in parrot language. Lys insisted that Maruka understood every word she said. She was probably right.

Maruka's favourite sport was dive-bombing Divil, who would go berserk, twisting and turning as he snapped at her long tail feathers. Several times he managed to pull out a mouthful, but never quite to sink his teeth into that pesky psittacine's posterior.

Maruka disappeared several times but always turned up again a day or two later. The first time she stayed away more than two days, Lys was devastated. We walked the whole area, calling her name every few yards; but there was no sign of her. Then a small boy told us that a family nearby had her. We rang the bell in the high brick wall that so often surrounds South American gardens. An old servant appeared. No, he knew nothing of any parrot. Could we speak to *el dueno*, the owner? No, he was out. We returned the following day, a Sunday. The owner was surly and offhand, but admitted that a parrot had flown into the garden a few days before. His gardener had taken it home with him. Where did he live? In Surco, some five kilometres away. We hunted him down. He was out. We left a message.

The next day we found the gardener at the surly man's house. He was evasive. Yes, he had taken the parrot home, but it had escaped. Would he bring it tomorrow, if it came back? No, he only worked at this house on Mondays, Wednesdays and Fridays. Where did he work on other days? Nowhere. He was looking for a job to fill the gap.

Mary had sacked our previous gardener the week before. This might be a good opportunity, I thought, to hire a new one and encourage the return of Maruka as well. He agreed that he would work for us on his free days. The next morning, a squawking announced the arrival of the gardener with Maruka on a piece of string, sitting on his shoulder, like Long John Silver. The gardener turned out to be the best we ever had. It was the one good turn Maruka ever did us.

373

The last time Maruka disappeared, a friend further up the hill rang to say he had her. Kerry, our son, then about seven, went with our maid, Luz, to collect her, but on the way home, less than 500 metres from our house, a lorry filled with noisy workmen made her take off again. We never found her, although we suspected strongly that a nearby house, which already had an aviary of parrots, had added her to their collection, a suspicion enhanced by their firm refusal to let us have a look.

After a tearful week, her image began to fade. Frankly, the relief at not having her around to destroy the garden and dirty the walls reduced our enthusiasm for continued search. Only a tearful Lys kept on looking.

Perhaps it is stretching the term 'pet' a little to include four chickens. Anyway, they only lasted a few hours. We were giving a dinner party, and I had asked Jim for some of his culls. Unfortunately they arrived when Mary and I were out. Even more regrettable – they were still alive! Shannon, Lys, Kerry and Lindley had lost no time in welcoming what they considered were new family pets. Mary and I arrived to find their room full of feathers, the beds covered in droppings and our delighted but frustrated young offspring trying to tuck their precious poultry between the sheets!

I bought Bimbo, a minute monkey, known as a *leoncito* because of its lion-like features, off a boy in the streets of Iquitos, and carried him back to Lima in the aeroplane, snuggled inside my shirt. Bimbo spent his days in the tree by the swimming pool and his nights in Melanie's bed. Unfortunately, Melanie, a very solid four-year-old, rolled on him one night. Exit Bimbo.

The last member of our menagerie was temporary and hardly a pet. London Zoo had been trying to obtain a specimen of the high-altitude rodent, the long-tailed, mountain *viscacha*, (*Lagidium peruanum*). The *viscacha* is rather like a hare with a long bushy tail, as if it had been crossed with a squirrel. I agreed to try and find them a pair.

A *viscacha* hunt was arranged by members of the Huancayo Research Station, and after a whole day, aided by 30 *campesinos*, only two were captured, one of which died before reaching Lima.

We kept Cindy, the name the children gave it, in a cage, in the children's room for a couple of weeks before we could get it off to London. Poor little thing. Its mournful, whistling cry would wring our hearts, and more than once I determined to take it back to the *sierra* and free it. But I didn't, and eventually it arrived at Regent's Park Zoo.

I was even sorrier I hadn't set it at liberty when a few months later the Zoo wrote me that it had died, apparently of a massive worm infestation. Or perhaps it was just an unbearable yearning for its family and the cold, clear air of the Andes.

FIRST OF THE FEW

As elsewhere, livestock problems in Peru were due as much to bad management as to disease, but it sometimes was difficult to tell the two apart. Although faculty staff were competent investigators within their own disciplines, they were far too specialized when it came to general field investigations. In Latin America, it seemed, scientific prestige depended more on knowing a lot about a little, than on knowing less about more.

VITAR needed field veterinarians who knew a bit about everything, and who could sift the evidence and call in the appropriate academics when necessary. I wrote Peter, in Rome, explaining our problem. FAO was a haven for ex-colonial specialists, whose careers in the 'Third World' had suddenly been curtailed by the postwar scramble for independence. The 'Developing Nations', who had thrown them out as 'colonial racists', now welcomed them back without loss of face under the UN flag as FAO 'experts'. 'Retreads', some people called them, unkindly, or 'FAO bulls'. Nevertheless, many were highly competent, dedicated scientists with wide practical experience in the tropics, who were only too glad to accept the posts offered by FAO's massive, marbled-fronted headquarters on the Via delle Terme di Caracalla in Rome.

In due course, Bryan, a very experienced field investigator from the British Veterinary Investigation Service and an ideal fellow (on paper) to develop the research at Huancayo and to train Ralph, arrived. I remembered him, vaguely, from veterinary college: a craggy, pipe-smoking, tweedy humorist who, I'm sure, looked perfect striding over the moors or lecturing a farmers' meeting in Cumberland. Unfortunately, he had had little experience in, and even less understanding of, 'Developing Nations'. 'We do it this way in Britain, so that's how we'll do it here', was his attitude.

He was also a most accomplished raconteur and filled our coffee breaks with hilarious stories of his colleagues back home. I laughed as loud as anyone, well aware that, once he returned to Britain, the same colleagues would be rocking with mirth at his stories of us. Not

375

that Bryan would have had to embroider his Peruvian experiences too flagrantly to raise a laugh – especially his first exposure to local conditions. Before sending him to Huancayo, we decided to carry out a simple investigation into the fluctuation of stomach worm populations on coastal pastures, a technique in which he was an authority. He would be able to train two senior students and familiarize himself with local conditions at the same time.

Intestinal worms lay thousands of eggs which pass out onto the pastures in the droppings. Here they hatch into larvae which crawl up blades of grass and are eaten by a passing animal. Once inside their new host, they develop into adult worms and start all over again. The odd worm in the intestines doesn't usually matter but large numbers often cause sickness and death, especially if they are of the blood-sucking variety, and particularly if the animal is young.

Small fields and paddocks can become heavily contaminated with worm larvae, causing outbreaks of severe parasitism. Our proposed experiment would attempt to correlate the number of larvae on the grass with the number of eggs being passed out in the droppings, and with the general health of the grazing animals which, in this case, were to be sheep.

The Director of SIPA's Animal Pathology Institute said he had the very place, a farm of which he was part-owner, in a fertile valley 150 kilometres north of Lima. A bit far away, I thought, but we agreed to visit it and set off the next day with the Director who was acting as guide. He had thoughtfully brought a list giving the number and size of the paddocks, the number of sheep on the farm, their grazing regime, and other details.

The farm manager happened to be away, but we looked around and decided the site would be suitable. Only one thing was missing – the sheep, which the Director told us were grazing an adjoining farm but would return for the start of the experiment.

A week later, with plastic bags for grass samples, bottles for faeces, identification tags for the ears of each animal, and all the other paraphernalia necessary to start the experiment, we again visited the farm, this time without the Director, and for two grilling hours plodded through the pastures under a very hot summer sun, taking grass clippings at predetermined intervals, labelling them and packing them for subsequent examination.

'Fine,' said Bryan at last. 'That's it as far as the grass samples go. Now all we need are samples of faeces from the sheep.'

We turned to the farm manager, who had been absent the previous week.

'Where are the sheep?' I asked.

'Sheep? There are no sheep here,' he replied, a little surprised by the question.

'But we were told that there were a hundred and sixty-five sheep here. I even have a list of their sexes and ages.'

'*Disculpe, señor, pero no hay ovejas aqui.*'

'Look here, my good man.' Bryan's face, although sunburnt, was already turning pale. 'We were told that the sheep grazed the paddocks in rotation – I have a note of the rotation periods.' He thrust a piece of paper under the manager's nose. 'The whole experiment is based on grazing sheep.'

'Sorry, sir, there haven't been any sheep here for years. We had a few cattle, but they were sold last month. Look around; if there were sheep, you would see droppings, wouldn't you?'

'But last week we were told that they were grazing on an adjoining farm.'

'This is the only livestock farm in the valley, *señor*.'

Bryan sank slowly to the ground. I thought he was going to faint, but colour returned to his cheeks and he began to laugh. 'I think a beer would go down well,' was his only comment as we strode back to the car.

The following day I tackled the Director of the Pathology Institute.

'We wasted a whole, grilling day on the farm,' I fumed, 'and at the end of it we were told that there were no sheep.'

He looked a bit sheepish, himself, but face had to be preserved.

'Probably the farm manager didn't know where they were,' he suggested.

'Probably not,' I replied witheringly. 'He said he'd only been there ten years.'

'Never mind; I'll buy some. I'll have them there by next week.'

Whether he did or not, I don't know. We didn't trouble to find out.

Dr Carlos, the Professor of Parasitology, tried to console us. 'There are plenty of sheep farms near Lima; I'll take Dr Bryan around. We'll soon find another place.'

A few days later, Bryan tottered into my office and flopped into the visitor's chair.

'We're progressing,' he giggled hysterically. 'Guess what?'

'Tell me.'

'We've spent three days searching for sheep, and today we finally found one – an old ewe, down by the beach at Villa.'

'Drop the whole idea until you are in Huancayo,' I advised. 'At least we know there are plenty of sheep there.'

Huancayo, unfortunately, did little to restore his confidence. Dr

377

Carlos felt that an investigation into the control of mange, or *sarna*, in alpacas, would be a more important study than worms in sheep. Reluctantly, Bryan promised to start one as soon as accommodation for the alpacas could be provided at the Huancayo research station.

Soon after this had been agreed, Dr Carlos rushed into Bryan's office, all smiles.

'We've bought seventy-five alpacas with *sarna*,' he announced proudly.

'You've already BOUGHT them?' Bryan was aghast.

'Sure; we'll hire a truck and start picking them up tomorrow.'

'And where are you going to keep them?'

'Here at the Research Station.'

'But there are no stalls, no paddocks, no grazing, no water and no-one to look after them. These things take time to arrange. We agreed not to buy any until everything was ready.'

Carlos looked downcast. 'Perhaps a farmer would take them?'

'Seventy-five diseased alpacas?'

One couldn't really blame Bryan for clinging to his conviction that things were often done better in Britain!

* * *

Our small band of FAO 'experts' – Jim, Bryan, Ralph and myself – was soon increased by the arrival of the two Ians, one from New Zealand, the other from Ireland.

Anzac Ian, a pasture specialist in his fifties and a lucky (perhaps that should read 'plucky') survivor of a Japanese prisoner-of-war camp, was stocky, with grey-flecked hair and a neat pepper-and-salt moustache. It was easier to imagine him behind the bar of a hostelry, a cheery 'mine host', than on his knees grubbing amongst legumes and species of grass. His dry humour and fund of stories would have gone down well with his customers, too, but his sojourn as a guest of his Nipponese Majesty had taught him to rely on his own resources, and now his chief desire was to be left alone to carry out his experiments in his own way – and to fish. Not that he was a recluse, or even an introvert, and like many who prefer their own company for most of the time, he could party with the best.

Ian and Stella, dark-haired, willowy and full of fun, rented part of an old farmhouse near the research station, and provided many moments of cheer at the end of the day, which made our visits to Huancayo so much more enjoyable.

Irish Ian, a rugged, thrusting Ulsterman, was just old enough to have served as mate in the Merchant Marine of World War Two. Of unmincing words and high intellect, he helped to organize our investi-

378

gations into infectious diseases, introducing new techniques, up-dating old ones and spreading a general air of efficiency around the Faculty laboratories.

VITAR, I felt, was at last taking shape. All we needed now was to finish the high-altitude station at Huancayo, and on 6 February 1965, 18 months after building had been started, it was finally inaugurated. It didn't matter that the labs were still far from functionable, or that the basic amenities, such as electricity, drinking water and drainage, were still awaited; the ceremonies and long speeches made up for all that.

Over 200 participants helped to swell the strains of the Peruvian national anthem and to tread mud into the wooden floors, so laboriously polished for the occasion. President Belaunde sent his apologies for not attending; while it was customary for him to accept all such invitations, expediency would allow him to appear only at those considered politically worthwhile.

There were plenty of other dignitaries to grace the occasion, dressed in overtight suits and choking collars. These included the Rectors or Vice-Rectors of San Marcos, La Molina and other Universities; the Prefect of the Province; the heads of the United Nations and FAO missions; the Directors of Agricultural Banks and Ministry Agencies, and numerous smaller fry. Under the eye of the Military Commander of the area, and inspired by his very loud, cacophonous band, we watched His Eminence, the Bishop of Huancayo, bless the proceedings. We felt we had left little to chance in the spheres of either human or spiritual contacts!

I had imagined, naively perhaps, that Manuel and I, as chief architects of the whole affair, would somehow be involved in the ceremony; even asked to say a few words. But no, we were, most considerately, left free to guide the visitors to the temporary chemical loos, or to the cylinders of oxygen, if they were feeling faint, and to take photos of the proceedings.

I remember little of the speeches save that they were very long and full of clichés, exaggerations, appeals to patriotism and references to the future welfare of the *campesinos*, or peasants, about whom the majority of speakers knew little and cared less.

The main reason for inaugurating the Station before it was complete was to satisfy the pundits in the United Nations Development Programme, who held the ultimate purse strings of all FAO projects, and who were becoming more and more impatient with our apparent lack of progress. But then it was difficult for them to realize from their well-regulated offices in New York, that the electric

379

generators were not the type we had ordered and had had to be modified at great cost and further delay to produce a three-phase current; and even when this had been done, they would only produce 60 per cent of their sea level capacity at that altitude.

They might, had they read our reports more carefully, have commiserated with us over the water supply, brought from a well two kilometres away, which the engineers had assured us would be plentiful and pure, but was now found to be totally inadequate, contaminated and seasonally muddy, necessitating a completely new well and filtration system.

Undoubtedly, too, it was difficult for them to accept the fact that the plumbing contractor had skipped with the funds, and that it would take many more months to find both a new contractor and the means to pay him. Neither could anyone have foreseen that Bryan, the FAO expert who was to be head of the station, would be unable to adapt to high altitude and had to be transferred back to sea level, or that several of the Peruvian staff, whom we had almost had to bribe to work in the *sierra*, would suddenly leave for better paid and more congenial jobs on the coast.

But the inauguration, if only on paper, so to speak, was sure to keep our masters happy for a while.

THE SCHOOL RUN – AND OTHER FUN

'Manco Capac...Sinchi Roca...Yoque Yupanqui...Maita Capac...Capac Yupanqui...' The kids knew the names of successive Inca chiefs off by heart. No wonder. Spanish subjects which, by law, had to cover 50 per cent of the curriculum, were learned by rote. 'I can't understand arithmetic in Spanish,' Shannon complained. 'It's easy in English, but in Spanish it's stupid.'

In spite of such discrepancies, the children seemed to enjoy their schooling. I can't say that Mary and I did. The 'school run' each morning to drop Kerry at Markham, Shannon and Lys at San Silvestre, and Lindley and Melanie at the Commonwealth Kindergarten (later another three were added), all in different suburbs, and pick them up again in the afternoon, a journey of over 60 terrifying kilometres, was a nerve-racking adventure. Traffic in Lima, never very orderly, was made especially perilous by hundreds of other half-awake mums and dads shuttling their little ones to classes.

Las Casuarinas was growing rapidly; we were now no longer on our own in a sandy waste. Green lawns and trees were taking over the sandhills, reducing the sandstorms which had compelled us to

380

sweep the floor three times a day. The fields of grapes and cotton which once had separated us from the city had disappeared under tarmac and residences, so had the single-track railway which had run alongside the main road below our *urbanización*, carrying punters to the nearby race-track at Monterrico. It had been the children's delight, on race days, to wave to the puffer pulling its three or four dilapidated carriages, and hear it whistle in response.

There was little to do at the weekends in the grey, drizzly winter months from May to October. The kids would squabble round the house, Mary would catch up with sewing and letters, and I would try to mend the washing machine, or the iron, or the stove, or stick together the toys ripped apart during the week. Sometimes, if the *garua*, the heavy Scotch mist which so depressed us for weeks on end, lifted, and the tennis courts, cut into the rocky hillside, were dry enough, my neighbour Enrique (when he wasn't being deported, an occupational hazard for newspaper editors) and I, would play a set or two of singles. At one end of the courts, a brick wall acted as a practice board on one side, while the other side, like every other South American wall, acted as a latrine. Any ball hit over it would roll down the sandy slope until it rested on the semi-decomposed bed of excrement, and had to be discarded from play until properly washed and disinfected.

Occasionally, we would drive up the Huancayo road as far as San Mateo, above the mist belt, where the sun was shining, and picnic beneath the blue gums, or eat *cebiche* (raw fish marinated in lemon juice) and *anticuchos* (pieces of ox heart on bamboo splints) at a wayside restaurant. Or we might visit Cieneguila, 20 kilometres into the sandy foothills, where it was often sunny in winter, and paddle in the river or explore the dusty ruins of the pre-Inca village there.

Once or twice a winter we would scramble up the soft sandhills behind our house to reach a lone tree standing on a bluff just below the summit. Small-leafed, gnarled, no more than 12 feet high, it survived from year to year, its roots sunk deep in the sandy slope. The kids made up stories about it, how buccaneers had planted it over their hidden loot after sacking Lima Cathedral, or how it marked the spot where the commanders of the Chilean and Peruvian armies had shaken hands at the end of their last war. We dug around the roots with our hands, but never found the Lima treasure. Other treasures we did find. Bullets, cartridge cases, the nose caps of shells, all of which were taken home to join Lys' rapidly growing museum, which already boasted a human skull!

When the *garúa* was excessive, the sandhills turned a muddy green from the sudden growth of a succulent, seaweed-like plant, but this greenery would only last a few weeks before the plant returned to its straw-coloured stage. Gay little orange crocuses, the *'abancays'*, popped up through the sand each winter with the mists. The flower was too fragile to survive the journey back to the house, but the bulbs would grow readily in the sand under our hedge.

Evenings were taken up with transporting children to their activities: ballet, sports, swimming, and our own excursions into amateur dramatics, play readings and official cocktail parties. But sometimes in winter when the *garua* swirled in from the sea, veiling the casuarinas and blue gums, and everything was damp and cold, it was nice to sit around a cosy log fire and sip mulled wine.

A favourite outing was the *Parque de las Leyendas*, the 'Park of the Legends', Peru's first attempt to create an open-air zoo. Lima's original zoo, near the centre of the city, had long disappeared beneath hotels and highways, leaving only the disgraceful *jardin zoologico* in the suburb of Barranco to display wild animals to the public. I paid it one visit and found a polar bear roasting in a tin-roofed cage barely higher or longer than itself, with no water or wallow.

I added my protest to the growing public revulsion and was delighted to see the animals – those which were still alive – transferred to the well-laid out *Parque de las Leyendas*, where different areas represented the *sierra* and the *selva*.

Popular with our kids in the *Parque* was the small island with traditional huts of the jungle Indians, and home to scores of uncaged monkeys, and be greeted by 'Willie', a chimpanzee left behind by an American family who had lived near us in Las Casuarinas.

One of the young veterinarians in the Faculty worked there at the weekends and often took Lys to help behind the scenes. She struck up a wary friendship with a rumbustious gorilla, who joyfully dismantled most of her (and, I suspect, her sisters') old dolls and other toys.

Ballet began to play a large part in our social life. The British School of Dancing had a high standard, and three afternoons a week Mary and I would shuttle the girls to their respective classes. Melanie and Lindley from four till five, and Shannon and Lys from five till six, and when Fuffy was old enough, we fitted her in from two till three. I would blow my top at regular intervals, although when the competitions and exhibitions came, I was the first to applaud and record them on cine film. Video was still some years away.

But if I occasionally felt the pressure, it was Mary who bore the full brunt. Renowned for her dressmaking, many mothers would besiege her for advice and assistance as the annual exhibition approached. One year, already eight months pregnant, she agreed to make 18 tutus for other children as well as all the costumes for our own tribe. In addition, she supervised another dozen doting mothers, struggling to beat the deadline.

She worked without pause for three days and nights, watched the kids receive their cups, and then collapsed.

In summer, our excursions were mainly to the beach, the favourite being Santa Maria, 60 kilometres south of Lima. At eight o'clock on a Sunday morning, the little bay would be deserted save for an occasional fitness fanatic, jogging along the edge of the surf, who pretended not to notice the *gringo* family eating their breakfast on the sands.

Enormous translucent rollers pounded in from the Pacific, breaking a hundred metres from the shore, their thousand foamy snouts sniffing landwards until they ran out of thrust and slipped limply back beneath the following sea. Plunging in, the water appeared a light iridescent green, full of fizzy bubbles, just like a gin and tonic – and about the same temperature!

Two hours on the dazzling sand were quite enough. At ten o'clock, the sun now scorching and the beach beginning to throng with city folk, we would pack up, pleased at having had the beach to ourselves during the best part of the day and pitying the families now arriving, laden with umbrellas, food baskets, sports equipment and all the awkward paraphernalia that city folk deem essential for a gregarious day at the seaside.

The sand, now too hot to walk on without shoes, rapidly became covered with bodies on blankets. Long-suffering grannies, those ubiquitous baby-minders, in black long-sleeved blouses and full-length skirts, perched uncomfortably on deck chairs beneath precarious beach umbrellas, dodging the merciless rays while they whisked flies away from sleeping tots.

Back on the highway to Lima, we would encounter an endless stream of cars, bumper to bumper, heading for Santa Maria and the other resorts; over 5,000 on one occasion. Inevitably there were accidents.

'Daddy, a *choque*! Daddy, a *choque*! Stop!'

'No need. There are already five cars stopped.'

'But Daddy ...'

'NO!'

'It may be someone we know, Daddy.'

'It wasn't. I looked.'

No one was going to get me out onto that bubbling tarmac without good reason! Late in the afternoon, when the general exodus from the beaches began, the highway would be punctuated with cars spewing steam from their radiators, cars with flat tyres and no spares, with clutches burned out or simply with empty tanks.

I could never understand what pleasure the majority found in spending the hottest hours of the day crammed together on a burning beach, wiping sand out of their eyes every time someone passed by, or spitting it out with half their sandwiches.

Children became sunburnt and crabby, flies irritated everyone, blaring radios prevented relaxation, the elderly non-swimmers became distressed at the lack of toilets – the sea providing the only available convenience, and too late, one realized that one's skin was on fire.

No. A couple of hours in the warm gentle sun of the early morning, then home for a swim in a freshwater pool, a beer, a leisurely lunch and post-prandial snooze – that was the way to spend a Sunday!

We were roped into amateur dramatics by accident. Three weeks before the opening night of Aristophenes' classic, *Lysistrata*, a row led to the resignation of both the director and his leading lady. The new director, a friend of ours in the British Council, approached Mary in desperation.

'You're just the type; how about it?'

In the short time at her disposal, Mary not only learned the long and demanding part, she gave such a stunning performance that she received a four-minute standing ovation from both the audience and the rest of the cast.

'I couldn't have done it but for that blasted hairdresser,' Mary confided. 'He kept me waiting so long and then made such a mess of my hair that I went onto the stage in an absolute fury' – which was exactly what the first scene demanded.

It was the first of many plays, or musicals, in which she, and some-times I, took part for the British group, 'The Good Companions', or the American 'Little Theatre Workshop'. Mary was an outstanding actress, and we became quite used to seeing a picture of *La Señora Mary de Guilbride* in *El Comercio*, lauding another of her *obras de teatro*.

The Sunday morning after the final performance of *Lysistrata*, I found the laundry patio piled high with dirty clothes. Then I realized, in panic, that the washing machine was again defunct and our maid was sick. There was nothing for it; Mary was exhausted and I couldn't expect much help from our youngsters. I would have to do it myself. Thank God the drier still functioned. I filled the big concrete washtubs with hot water and began. Two hours later, my fingers raw and my temper frayed, I took Mary some coffee.

'Please get up and give me a standing ovation,' I pleaded. 'I've just washed ninety-three nappies, underclothes, school blouses, shirts, dresses, socks and hankies!'

SHOCK WAVES

'I've been invited to the Panamerican Veterinary Congress in Venezuela,' I told Mary. 'Should be a nice break.'

'And what about me?' she retorted, in a voice which clearly established me as a selfish, chauvinistic pig.

'Let's work on it,' I replied hurriedly. 'I'm sure someone will look after the kids for a week.'

The situation became more acute when Marjorie, Mary's veterinarian cousin in Jamaica, wrote that she, too, would attend the conference. Then I had a note from Hank, a close friend in the FAO Regional Office in Santiago de Chile, saying he also would be there.

Try as we might, we couldn't trick a single person into babysitting our five kids, so when the time came I had to leave Mary behind and set off on my own chauvinistic porcine way to Maiquetía, a few miles from Caracas, on the Caribbean coast, where I was greeted by Marjorie and Hank.

Hank had crashed into our lives the previous year.

'This is Hank from the Santiago office,' said a deep Texan drawl over the phone. 'We've not met, but if you get yourself out to the airport, pronto, we can remedy that and I can hand over ten litres of good Chilean wine. My connection leaves in an hour and a half.'

'I'm almost there,' I retorted.

I had heard a lot about Hank, a large, American extrovert and one of the most flamboyant, good-hearted and helpful of the FAO officials. After a spell of veterinary practice in Texas, he had joined FAO; had been captured by Communists in Thailand, shot up by soldiers in Paraguay, and mugged by thugs in Rome. He had organized and fostered small farmer livestock schemes behind the fighting in Vietnam, striding through every assignment with a confident Burl Ives smile and friendly good humour. Politicians, policemen, bandits and the FAO hierarchy – he knew how to handle them all, and many counted him a special friend.

Hank was one of the very few people I've met who really knew how the world worked, how to make friends and keep them and how

385

to make the best of any situation. When his wife lost their fourth child (and their only girl) at birth, due to the negligence of a Santiago gynaecologist, he saw to it that she came home from hospital with an exquisite newly-born, half-Indian, baby girl, complete with papers making her one of the family. Other people struggled for years to adopt a child.

Hank solved our problems, bolstered our morale and brightened our lives for many years. His balding head and large smile would pop in and out of our lives with humour, gusto and panache, until he left FAO to join Minnesota University as their first Professor of International Veterinary Medicine.

The conference was much like any other except that the Macuto-Sheraton Hotel, where it was held, was the ultimate in holiday luxury. Sparkling pools, bars in every corner, gorgeous girls and, if you could take your eyes off them, a magnificent view over the blue Caribbean. We drank and ate in excess. We also attended the odd conference paper. In the evenings, we did the rounds of the numerous little restaurant-bars along the palm-fringed shore.

'What a shame Mary couldn't come,' Marjorie sighed one evening.

'Bloody shame,' I agreed.

'By the way,' said Hank, 'there's another conference, on veterinary education in Latin America at Maracay after this one finishes. It's being sponsored by FAO and I am supposed to cover it for the Regional Office. I don't suppose you could stand in for me, Pat? I've just got to get back.'

'Mary will go berserk if I stay away any longer,' I said.

'Don't worry,' smiled Marjorie. 'I'll go down with Hank to Lima and stay with her for a few days. I'll explain that it was an emergency.' I suspected nothing.

On my second morning at Maracay, I found a telegram in my pigeon-hole.

'MARY ARRIVING MAQUETIA THURSDAY AFTERNOON. HANK'

I should have twigged that something was afoot when Hank had asked me to stand in for him. He and Marjorie had taken over our house!

Mary and I had a marvellous second honeymoon at the Macuto-Sheraton, lazing by the pool, drinking *bomba-cherris* and wandering from bistro to bistro in the evenings. Most of these little bars offered a soup, made from a small local mollusc, called 'Chippy-Chippy'. It was said to have great aphrodisiac as well as fertility potential. We laughed at the idea and ordered more.

Nine months later, Frances Sheraton arrived, evidence that the 'Chippy-Chippy' soup had lived up to its reputation!

It was a toss-up as to whether we should call our new daughter 'Chippy-Chippy' or Sheraton, but we felt the latter was more girlish. She was never called either and is known to this day as 'Fuffy'. Mind you, if she had turned out to be a boy, there would have only been one possible name – Hank!

* * *

On another visit, to attend a meeting of FAO Project Managers, Hank again came loaded down with Chilean wine. There was no parking space left outside the FAO office in the quiet little street, Pablo Bermudez, so we drove round the block and parked beside the garden railings of a stately mansion.

'This will probably be the last meeting we will have in this office,' I told Hank. 'FAO are joining UNDP and several Embassies in a twelve-storey *edificio* on Avenida Arequipa. At least they will have their own parking lot there.'

Multi-storeyed office blocks were also springing up between the 'olde-worlde' residences on Pablo Bermudez, like hollyhocks amongst daisies. One, right next door to the two-storey FAO office, had now reached the tenth floor, with a long-armed crane hovering above it.

'Oh, boy,' I joked, 'if there is an earthquake, that'll flatten FAO.'

'Reckon it would,' replied Hank, 'so don't put your mouth on it.'

About 15 of us crammed into the upstairs conference room. Hank and I occupied the corner behind a heavy table. I know it was heavy because we had to move it to get to our chairs and again later, when the panic started.

I don't remember details of the meeting, but I do remember that we had promised to lunch with Manuel, Saul and Jim, at a fish restaurant, the Todo Fresco.

The meeting ground through the morning, as meetings do. Lunchtime came nearer and nearer. I was about to suggest that we make an excuse and slip out when a sound, like a hundred tanks approaching at high speed, stopped everyone rigid. Then the heavy table started bouncing on the floor like a tap dancer and began to move slowly to one side.

'Earthquake!' everyone yelled at the same time.

Reactions varied. Two or three, who had probably not experienced earthquakes before, panicked and rushed for the door, which they

387

could only open with difficulty. Others, either too terrified to move or uncertain as what best to do, sat still. Hank and I, unable to get out from against the wall, slid under the table to join several colleagues. The bouncing and rolling motion became worse, glass was shattering on the pavement outside and somewhere a woman was screaming.

'Better get out before it gets worse,' I suggested. I had really put my mouth on it this time, and had visions of the construction next door collapsing on us.

As we left, we passed a secretary standing in the front doorway, screaming, until someone, rather unkindly I thought, slapped her face. If screaming relieved her feelings, fair enough. And a doorway was as safe a place as anywhere to scream in.

Outside in the street, glass and tiles were still falling. It looked as if it would have been safer to have stayed inside. Parked cars showed large dents where bits of masonry had bounced off. Underfoot, the ground was rippling, an uncanny sensation, similar to that of standing on the metal plates between two railway coaches.

The noise of falling debris and yells was soon replaced by another more vicious clamour, that of thousands of Limeñans trying to get home to their families. Recklessly driven cars with horns at full blast and engines revving soon packed the streets. Stop signs were ignored, and so would the traffic lights have been had the electricity, either by design or default, not been cut. Thousands of accidents were recorded in the next half-hour.

We stood in the middle of the road, trying to avoid falling shards of glass and dodging any car which decided to take a short cut through the narrow street. The braver amongst us went back to retrieve briefcases; others anxiously sought their dented vehicles. Thank God I had been forced to park mine by the garden railings, far from falling tiles.

As we dispersed, wishing each other well, a shout from above made us look up. On a window ledge near the top of the ten-storey construction, sat a workman, munching a sandwich. Most of the scaffolding had disappeared, but he seemed quite unperturbed as he waved happily to us. His message seemed to be, 'You should have been up here, then you would have found out what an earthquake is all about.' We waved back and shouted encouragement. I imagine it took the crane to bring him down!

A friend in the twelfth floor of the Ministry of Agriculture would have sympathized with our cheery builder. Try as he might, he could only reach his office door by crawling on hands and knees, and when he reached the lifts, he found them all inoperative. In fact many people spent a claustrophobic few hours in them, before they could be released.

At home we were both unlucky and lucky. A garden wall had fallen, breaking a water main which gouged a large hole in the sandy ground, and a large pane of glass on the stairway to the mezzanine cracked, but that was all. The kids had been in school and had been eating their lunch on the playing field. Not one was hurt. Others, elsewhere were less lucky. The more modern buildings were almost all 'earthquake-proof', but the small *adobe*-built shacks and smaller residences crumbled like mud pies. Not a few people were killed and many more injured. It was by far the most severe tremor we experienced during our time in Peru.

If you are frightened of earthquakes, avoid South America and the West Indies. The buildings might be earthquake proof, but you could easily be hit by a demented motorist!

POULTRY FOR THE CAMPESINO

I had given Jim three objectives for the poultry programme. To find a simple way to hatch eggs at high altitude, to find the most suitable breeds of chickens to produce the eggs, and to establish a poultry industry in the *sierra*. The first he had already accomplished, and the compression chamber was now producing some 2,000 chicks a week.

The second would take longer. He had no idea which of the six breeds we were hatching would be the most adaptable to the rarefied atmosphere and freezing conditions of the *sierra*. As a start, we put all the chicks onto range as soon as they were hatched, providing specially designed and heated range shelters for their first few weeks of life. Jim figured that these hardy conditions and restricted feeding would accelerate the selection of those with genes more likely to withstand the rigours of high altitude. After some initial trials, he settled for Light Sussex, Rhode Island Reds and Brown Leghorns.

The third objective – to create a poultry industry in the *sierra* – was much more difficult. Then, one morning, he strode in with a confident smirk, teeth firmly clenched on his pipe.

'I've got it. Should have thought of it ages ago.'

'Got what?'

'How to start a chicken industry up above. It's obvious – *Reforma Agraria*. Why don't we contact Agrarian Reform? They're always belly-aching about rural development and improving the lot of the *campesinos*, but all they do is make surveys and plans. They could start a poultry industry. It could be their big chance. Let's see if they are capable of doing something practical.'

Agrarian Reform was a political priority in South America in the sixties. Redistribution of land from the huge ranches, or *latifundios*, into communal or co-operative farms was in the manifestos of all political parties, and strongly backed by the United Nations. Jim's vision of a large-scale poultry industry in the *sierra*, producing millions of eggs and broilers each year and involving hundreds of villages, would be an ideal opportunity for them to prove their credibility.

Agrarian Reform's Directors were enthusiastic. They would give us all the assistance they could so long as we supervised the operation. We agreed, and a month later, Cachi Cachi was born.

Cachi Cachi was an abandoned (justifiably, I thought) ranch; bleak, windswept, without a tree in sight, isolated between rolling mountain slopes, 100 kilometres from Huancayo and over 1,000 feet higher. It looked pretty hopeless to me as I stood shivering beside the car, appalled at the desolate, lonely landscape.

'Good God, man. You're not thinking of putting chickens here, are you? They'd never survive.'

'This'll be just fine,' Jim replied confidently, trying to light his pipe in the icy wind. 'Just the job. Plenty of space, and a stream with which to irrigate our rangeland. We'll place the electric generator over on that bit of levelled ground next to the old mine working.'

'You're crazy,' I retorted.

Crazy or not, within three months the generator, fencing, housing for staff, 3,000 young chicks and 50 range shelters had been installed. Agrarian Reform had pulled out all the stops. I think they were so delighted to have found something to do other than make surveys, and to have someone who knew what he was doing to guide them, that they put their full resources behind us.

There were problems, of course. The generator packed up just as we received the first batch of day-old chicks from the Huancayo incubators, so we couldn't heat the range shelters and many chicks froze. Feed supplies, organized through the Agrarian Reform office, were often delayed, and the six hectares of special grass we had planted for range feeding failed to grow at that altitude. Nevertheless, six months after our first sight of that uninviting valley, 17,000 chickens were thriving at Cachi Cachi.

We were soon inundated with requests to set up similar operations in other areas. We started with Yanahuanca, a village caught on the plunging slopes of a deep valley, slightly lower than Huancayo and three hours distant from it. It was one of the poorest parts of the

Central *sierra*; the villagers here were starving, and tuberculosis was rife.

With the aid of a grant from UNICEF and funds from the local Government office, poultry houses were built, and within a few months 2,000 birds were in residence, producing eggs and broilers for consumption as well as young birds with which the *campesinos* could establish their own flocks.

Jim could not have done all this without Hans, his Peruvian counterpart. Hans, a recent veterinary graduate, was of German origin. Medium in height with fair hair and blue eyes, hard-working and dedicated, he was the ideal understudy for Jim.

Daniel, another recent graduate, short, thick-set, black-haired and bubbling with energy and good humour, looked after the Huancayo operations and the extension work that went with it. Later he was assisted by three other colleagues and two members of President Kennedy's Peace Corps, both young poultry farmers from California.

Jim was a precise and demanding teacher and fulfilled our Divisional Head's maxim – 'Anyone who's indispensable, should be sacked – he's not doing his job. His duty is to teach his subordinates to take his place.' Jim was trying hard to make himself dispensable and ensure that Hans, Daniel and the others would soon know as much as he did, and in time make themselves dispensable, too.

Puno University suddenly woke up to the fact that they too could enhance their rather low image by becoming pioneers of poultry production in the *altiplano*, that high, barren plateau in the Southern Sierra. Jim and I flew up to see them.

The trip had a sad beginning. Our Fawcett airlines flight shared the departure lounge with that of the opposition airline LANSA, whose air hostesses were attired in miniskirts.

'They look like schoolkids,' Jim commented as one turned and made a face at him; most air hostesses spoke fluent English.

The LANSA flight was called just before ours. Still joking about their costumes, Jim and I watched them file out with the passengers onto the tarmac. Within half an hour, all were dead! An engine failed as they approached the Andes, the pilot tried a forced landing on a mountain slope but hit a rock and somersaulted. But for a decision the UN had taken earlier, that their staff should only use Fawcett, except in emergencies, we might have been with them.

Puno University got off the ground a few months later, with Jim supervising the construction of the compression chamber and training their operatives in Huancayo. Almost before we knew it, poultry production, for the first time ever, had spread through the *sierra*, and it was no longer unusual to collect a few feathers as we drove through Andean villages!

THE KARATE QUEEN

The two hotels in Huancayo were crammed with earnest young sales-men, the car parks jammed with station wagons and trucks loaded with agricultural equipment. The Huancayo Show was about to start.

The universal problem of agricultural research has always been to get the results across to traditionally phlegmatic and suspicious farmers. It was bad enough in Europe amongst an educated and enlightened population, but in the *sierra* where only a few could read or write, disseminating new methods and ideas was uphill work. However, everyone loves a show, and this one would provide a golden opportunity for us to demonstrate the achievements of our first three years of research.

The large *haciendas* brought their prize cattle, sheep and horses to compete for the highest producers or those judged the most beautiful. There were sideshows too, and bars, and the inevitable merry-go-round, creaking and wobbling, but well patronized by shrieking *campesino* children at 5 soles (15 US cents) a ride.

VITAR had been allotted an enclosure 20 metres square. At each corner we had hoisted flags on gum poles. The national flag of Peru, the coat of arms of San Marcos University, the United Nations insignia and a special VITAR flag, designed by the Station staff and sewn together by Ann, Jim's wife.

Within this roped-off area, we had connected cows in various stages of brisket disease to elaborate electronic instruments which recorded their heartbeats, blood pressure and other physiological functions on oscilloscopes. Red-faced *campesinos* in traditional dress or in thick, coarse suits brought out for the occasion, crowded around in wonder, peering down microscopes at worm eggs and bacteria, or gazing at the large placards with photos and cartoons depicting improved methods of feeding, breeding and disease control. But the most popular of our demonstrations, undoubtedly, was the poultry exhibit with its scale model of the compression room and pens of chicks to prove that it worked.

There was another reason for the popularity of this section. In order to ram home the fact that high-quality poultry could be raised in the *sierra*, Jim suggested that we offer free chicken lunches to selected spectators. A hundred tickets would be distributed at random each day, mainly amongst peasant show-goers, entitling them to a free portion of *pollo a la braza* or spit-roasted chicken.

The idea was a worthy one, but while Jim may have got away with it back home at the local show in Gloucestershire, there was no way such a plan would work at Huancayo. Ticketless officials and prosperous-looking members of the establishment continually elbowed their way into the enclosure, claiming precedence by virtue of their station.

'I've brought Senor Alcides de Betanza, Mayor of San Augustin,' or 'Senor Carlos de Mendoza is Chairman of the Central Sierra Agricultural Association, he would like to try your roast chicken,' – for free, of course.

Jim, never one to accommodate those he felt were taking an unfair advantage, was highly incensed at these incursions, but managed to confine himself to snarls from a distance until a high official of the Huancayo Town Council, with whom we had had several skirmishes, pranced in demanding his portion of roast chicken. I thought Jim would explode, and it was obvious that he meant business as he strode across to the pompous councillor and tapped him hard on the shoulder.

Christ, I thought. One punch would sink us all. He had, I remembered, been awarded an immediate MC on D-Day for a particularly brave and aggressive act. A repeat performance in Huancayo would gain no medals. I had visions of him being led away and deported – our poultry programme down the drain – FAO discredited.

'JIM,' I yelled. 'Quick. Crisis at the compression room – the roof's splitting.'

Jim whirled round, his fists still clenched.

'Quick. I'll get the car.' I ran towards our Land Rover parked nearby. Jim jumped in as I started the engine.

As soon as we had cleared the show grounds, I slowed down.

'Come to think of it, a couple of cracks shouldn't harm the compression chamber very much. How about a beer?'

Jim caught on immediately.

'Bastard!' he exclaimed. To this day I don't know whether he meant the councillor or me!

How much we got across to the peasant farmers was hard to tell, but we certainly made an impact on the politicians. The following year Government increased VITAR's operating budget by 400 per cent.

* * *

I usually put up at the stolid Hotel Turista on the Plaza des Armas in the centre of Huancayo until, one day, I noticed a new sign some twenty kilometres short of the town for a *Pensión Chanteclaire*; an attractive name, I thought. A kilometre down a rough side road I found a double-storey doll's house half-hidden by bluegums, sitting beside a meandering stream. A brawny, white-haired Amazon in blue-jeans and cowboy shirt opened the door. Had she a room for the night? I asked in my best Spanish. A smile almost split her

393

sierra-scorched face in half, then she threw back her head and guffawed.

'Hell, you'd better speak in English. Your accent's worse than mine.' I admit that my accent wasn't perfect, but it was a lot better than hers, which had had to overcome a Canadian backwoods' drawl.

Sheilagh had come to Peru many years before as a free-lance journalist. After several other jobs she started a small hotel at Rio Blanco, halfway up the mountain road from Lima to Ticlio, where Limeñans could escape the winter fog for a Sunday lunch or a weekend. At sixty, it had become too much for her so, with an Indian and his small daughter whom she had 'taken in', she built Chanteclaire. There were only three bedrooms, four if she vacated hers and slept on the couch.

There were two drawbacks to Chanteclaire. Just opposite, across the little stream, was a one-man tannery, the operation of which depended entirely on whether or not the tanner was sober. Unfortunately for his neighbours he usually woke from his drunken sleep in the early hours, after which no-one could escape the clatter and clanking of his antiquated machines as they battered the hides in the vats.

The other discouragement was the construction of the dining-room chairs. They were, without doubt, the most excruciatingly uncomfortable bits of furniture ever employed to support hungry trenchermen. Whoever had made them (I strongly suspected it had been Sheilagh and her Indian) had based them on the dimensions of a child's posterior. Not only that, the slightly pointed tops of the four legs protruded at least an inch above the wooden seats. One sat on four sharp poles! Remonstration with Sheilagh was of no avail. She never sat on them. She would perch on her stool behind the counter which divided the cooking area from the tables, and stir her stew in comfort while we ate in agony or brought pillows from the bedroom.

Sheilagh knew everyone and appeared to act as a sort of general ombudsman amongst the locals. On one visit she told me that she had earned herself a new nickname. A brawl had broken out amongst some men in the home of one of her 'women', a sort of women's lib. group, to whom she was teaching reading, arithmetic and – of all things, French! – in order, so she believed, to liberate them from the dominance of their men folk. The terrified woman had come banging on her door late one night, pleading for her to call the police.

'Hell, the police wouldn't do no good, I told her, so I went myself. I grabbed the first man I saw and threw him into the gutter, kicked another in the balls – he sort of curled up – and the others fled.'

Her fame as 'chucker-out' spread fast and she was now known as the Karate Queen! She was often called to act as midwife. One day she told me that the week before she had delivered a child with some gross deformity.

'Sure, I could have saved it to be miserable all its life. So I didn't.'

For all her actions and tough talk, Sheilagh was a most caring lady. Each Saturday, between twenty and thirty children from the nearby villages, ill-clothed and underfed, would congregate at Chante-claire. Sheilagh would give them a short illustrated talk or show them how to make things, organize games and then, to ensure they came again, would hand each a large bowl of sugar-laden porridge.

On another visit I found a young Cornishman, a fitter by trade, who had turned smuggler, then diver, then seaman. He had come for one night in passing, fell under Sheilagh's spell and stayed six months, doing odd jobs, teaching the kids carpentry, coaching them in football and, of all the chilling things, teaching them to swim in a large pool in the Mantaro river, with water temperature below ten degrees.

About this time a well-meaning, or more probably a tax-evading, drug firm in the USA presented VITAR with a ton of veterinary medicinal supplies. Twenty of the crates, we found contained a vitamin mixture for dogs. The veterinary clinic at the Faculty took what they wanted, but the rest remained in our store. Then I remembered Sheilagh's kids. I took up a trial supply. She was delighted.

'Just what they need. I'll put a couple of squirts in each bowl of porridge. Kids is the same as dogs, ain't they?'

It seemed that she was right. There was a remarkable improvement in the vitality and mental capacity of her week-end playmates. No veterinary remedy was ever better employed. All the spare clothes, books and toys that I could scrounge, thereafter, found their way to Sheilagh.

'You could really make Chanteclaire a popular retreat if you bought some decent dining chairs,' I teased her one day.

'Yer backside's too big,' she laughed. 'Yer need more exercise. My kids have top priority here, not yer bum!'

THE FOUR STOOGES

'We should like to come to Peru during our summer vacation, and do something useful,' said the letter from a Cambridge college. Below the signature was added 'Fourth year student, Veterinary Science.'

An expedition of four students was proposed, three from Veterinary Science and a fourth, who would act as interpreter, from the Faculty of Arts.

I was enthusiastic; Manuel decidedly doubtful.

'We have enough problems looking after your Associate Experts, now you want me to nurse your students!'

I pointed out that there would be no drain on either FAO or counterpart funds, and that their welfare would be entirely in my hands, under the overall protection of the British Embassy.

'We had a similar students' expedition in Uganda,' I told him. 'They did a lot of useful work once they were organized.'

Manuel, still complaining, gave me a list of activities with which he thought the students could help. From these, we agreed on the capture of potentially edible jungle animals with a view to domesticating them, a study of the fish in the Pachitea River near Pucallpa, and assistance to the *vicuña* survey at Pampas Galeras Reserve in the southern *sierra*.

I contacted the FAO expert working in the Peruvian Wildlife Service as well as Bill, an American PhD student, in charge of the *vicuña* survey. Both promised their help.

Following several months of 'It's off' – 'It's on' – 'It's off', the quartet arrived by petrol tanker at the northern oil port of Talara and a few days later, ragged, unshaven and very dirty, unloaded themselves from a hired truck outside the Veterinary Faculty. As with all adventurous youngsters, delay was intolerable and they were eager to leave the same day for the *sierra* or *selva*.

'This is South America,' I cautioned, rather pompously. 'It'll take a week, at least, to get through all the formalities, present you to the university authorities and British Embassy officials and brief you sufficiently to ensure your survival.'

The way they looked at each other made it clear that they thought I was in my dotage. I envied them their youth and carefree outlook. It took me back to those first days in Northern Rhodesia

Michael, the twenty-one-year old leader of the group, a slim, almost platinum blond, with locks down to his shoulders, looked a possible sixteen without his glasses; with them, he appeared a confident seventeen and a half. Derek, half smothered in long brown hair and brown beard, was stocky and his face, what you could see of it, full of humour. Randolph ('Randy'), his beard hardly two weeks old, was more mature, more serious, until something jogged his wit, and Andrew, the Arts student and interpreter, a tall bespectacled, fairhaired Scot, seemed a little out of place as he self-consciously clutched his bagpipes and wondered if he really should have become involved with such rabble. Poor Andrew, his lecture-room Spanish was quite unacceptable to the locals, neither could he understand a word they said!

Mary, seven months into her sixth pregnancy, agreed, somewhat hesitantly, to billet the lads for a few days. We crammed our five brats into two rooms, put mattresses on the floor of the third and filled the fridge with beer.

The escapades of 'The Three Stooges' ('*Los Tres Chiflados*' – in Spanish) was running on TV. Within a few hours, Shannon had hung a large notice on the students' door, '*Los Quatro Chiflados*', and as such they were known by one and all.

I don't know who enjoyed who the most. It was a riotous week which left Mary and me totally exhausted and the children completely out of hand. It was the first time I had experienced the trauma of the generation gap!

Manuel, putting aside his apprehensions, welcomed the students with true Peruvian hospitality, including a cocktail party and speeches. There was, however, one 'leetle' problem.

'It's their hair,' he confided.

'Their hair?'

'It's too long. We are not accustomed to such long hair on men, in Peru. Our students are talking – and wondering!'

I knew that hair-styles in Europe were changing, even so I had wondered whether they had grown their hair especially long to prevent sunstroke.

'I'll have a word with them,' I promised. It wasn't taken kindly. They looked at me aghast.

'You're joking! This isn't long. We'd look stupid if we cut it shorter.'

I had to hint that their manhood was in question and that, in any case, we had to conform to our host's requests. The barber, at least, was happy. Soon, of course, Peruvian heads were growing hair as long as those in Europe, the students had simply jumped the gun by a year or two.

* * *

Derek and Andrew volunteered to help Bill with the *vicuña* survey before joining Michael and Randy in the jungle. I sent them up to Pampas Galeras with Martinez, one of VITAR's drivers, hoping that the cold bleak plains at four thousand metres would not prove too much for their sea-level physiology.

'Everything OK?' I asked Martinez on his return.

'*Si, señor. Todo bien.*' But I should have suspected his smirk and the way he looked at his feet while answering.

At the end of the first week, I received a short, but disturbing message from Bill, via the Wildlife radio service – 'Andrew a lot better.' I sent for Martinez.

It seemed that Andrew had suffered severe headaches on the road up to Pampas Galeras and had started vomiting even before Martinez had left. He continued to throw up for several days, only able to totter as far as the outside 'loo', but with commendable guts he refused to go down to a lower altitude. Gradually, he adapted and was able to join in the survey, but I am quite sure he will never forget the cold and nausea of that first ghastly week.

Facilities at Pampas Galeras were rugged. Two small, tin-roofed, brick huts, one for Bill and the students, the other for the rangers, an outside toilet and an open air kitchen. Washing was done in an icy mountain stream, fifty yards away.

While Derek and Andrew battled with the cold and altitude, Mike and Randy set off, by truck, for Pucallpa, eight hundred scary kilometres away, grinding up to a freezing five thousand metres before dropping through the tall, forested slopes of the *selva alta* to the hot, humid Amazon jungle.

The Amazon was a happy hunting ground for exporters of wildlife. Tens of thousands of monkeys, the majority for medical research, hundreds of thousands of birds and tropical fish too numerous to count, as well as bears, jaguars, rodents and reptiles were flown out to the United States each year.

Manuel and other wildlife-lovers were thoroughly frightened. The jungle might be huge, but it was being denuded at a terrible rate. Species which he had seen every day when a boy in Iquitos could no longer be seen within a hundred kilometres of any settlement. The traditional edible fauna which had been sold in the markets, had almost disappeared. Even endangered species, protected by law, were being hunted.

Several dealers had mini-zoos where they assembled their exports and displayed the more spectacular species – anacondas, jaguars, electric eels, and once I saw a huge snow eagle chick, already two feet tall. One dealer had a cage, the size of a sitting room, with twelve thousand small parakeets. The noise was ear-shattering. Corpses sprinkled the floor.

'There were a lot more last week,' the owner said.
I wasn't surprised!

Better inspection at Iquitos and Pucallpa airports might have prevented the more blatant illegalities, but not every inspector could identify every species, neither did every inspector feel it was necessary to do so if it was made worthwhile for him to look the other way.

398

Manuel was convinced that the best way to ensure the future of endangered jungle mammals was, as he advocated with *vicuña*, to domesticate and farm them

The students' first job at Pucallpa, was to make cages for their anticipated captures. This they did in the traditional Indian way with branches and twigs. It was hot work. Day time temperature averaged thirty-two degrees Celsius and rarely dropped below twenty-four at night, with a constant high humidity. After three weeks of nightly expeditions and trapping, all they could show were two *sachacuye* or 'false guinea-pigs'. They would have to move further into the jungle so after Derek and Andrew joined them from Pampas Galeras, they built a camp on the banks of the Pachitea river, three hours' walk from the missionary settlement of Tournavista, and started again.

I went to visit them and found Michael and Andrew who had walked in from their camp waiting for me at Iparia, a forestry station near Tournavista. A Peruvian veterinary student was also with them.

At dawn the next morning, the four of us set off along a forestry track.

'It'll take about three hours,' Michael told us, 'That's if we don't get lost!'

Half an hour later, Michael admitted that he had missed the turn-off. Almost as he spoke a hunter with a gun slung over his shoulder and an assortment of small creatures dangling from his belt (that it was a game reserve, seemed irrelevant), popped out of the bush. He led us half-a-mile back along the track and through the undergrowth to a new path.

Once in the forest proper, I was surprised at how free it was from undergrowth; presumably the dense tree-top cover allowed insufficient light for the growth of ground vegetation. Only an occasional ray of sunlight penetrated the foliage and I had the sensation of walking through a wooded park late in the evening.

We followed the path for about half an hour while it circled small hills and dallied across streams, until suddenly, from one minute to the next, it had disappeared.

Michael was non-plussed.

'Can't understand it. We had no trouble finding our way in from the camp.'

We split into two groups, keeping contact by shouting. Twenty minutes passed and we were still searching when, out of nowhere, appeared our hunter friend again. He'd probably heard us calling each other. Anyhow, he soon put us back on the now almost invisible path.

'Let's slash the bark of each tree we pass,' I suggested, 'then if we get lost on the way back we can follow the slashes.'

We tramped on, gouging trees along the way. The jungle was silent, the raucous parakeets and chattering monkeys of Hollywood jungle scenes were noticeably absent.

Two hours later we came across a clearing and a hut.

'Is this it?' I asked, hopefully.

'No, but we must be nearly half-way.' Michael replied.

'Half-way?' I wailed. 'We've been walking for four hours; I thought you said it was only three to the camp.'

'*Más o menos*,' Michael laughed, airing his newly acquired phrase. 'If you don't get lost.'

We could now see the sky again and noticed a bank of dark clouds gathering in the east.

'We'd better hurry; there's a storm ahead,' I pointed out.

As we were about to leave, Randy and Derek appeared, looking a little forlorn.

'Thought we'd come and meet you. Our hut blew away last night in the storm. Looks as if we're in for another, so we might as well all go back to Iparia.'

The jungle grew darker as the storm approached and without our slashes we would never have kept to the path. As we tried to race the flashes and bangs which seemed intent on catching us, I began to realize that forty-nine was no age at which to career through the bush with a pack of youngsters. My legs were losing their co-ordination, my bush shirt was soaked and I had an unbearable thirst.

A curtain of rain descended as we came in sight of the forestry camp. The others sprinted ahead, but I preferred to take it more slowly, to ensure that I could get myself up the four steps to the canteen which I knew had plenty of beer, and prevent a heart attack before I could sip that life-giving elixir.

The students rebuilt their camp and remained in the jungle for another month before floating down the Pachitea on a home-made raft to where it joined the Ucayali, and so to Pucallpa. At one village where they stopped overnight, Michael was commandeered to referee a football match; after all he *was* from England, the land of Bobby Charlton – even if he'd never played a game of soccer in his life!

Back in Lima, the students wrote up their notes and distributed surplus supplies. I don't think any of their results made the scientific journals, although Randy was sure that he had found a couple of fish hitherto unrecorded. The unused supplies, however, nearly made the local headlines. One of these commodities which a generous sponsor had supplied, was a large box of condoms. The students had never been quite clear whether these had been intended for use by the over-productive Indians, or for their own protection. At any rate there

Students' raft on the Ucayali River.

was no point in taking them back to Britain, and it would be a pity just to throw them away, but who could they give them to in a Catholic country?

The dilemma was solved on the night of their farewell party. A little tipsy from the festivities, they proceeded to blow up the small, expandable rubbers and tie them to the aerials of parked cars in nearby streets. Many a staid and upright Limenan must have wondered at the little balloons that bedecked his shiny limousine the next morning.

Was this a promotional stunt, a political protest, or what?

One of the lads, at least, made something tangible out of the expedition. Flicking through a magazine some years later, I noticed an advertisement for a well-known beverage, the merits of which were enthusiastically endorsed by no less a figure than that intrepid explorer and ichthyologist, one day to hold the first chair of Aquaculture at a British university. He, 'who had braved the thin air of the Andean crags, and stalked the deadly fauna of the Amazon jungle, fighting alligators and *piraña* up the uncharted waters of the Ucayali.' The one and only – Randy!

No mention was made of condoms!

SI, SI, SEÑOR, MANAÑA

'But Las Casuarinas is at least twelve kilometres away,' our Peruvian friends had said, aghast. 'You can't possibly live out in the sticks without a phone. You're crazy!'

'We've already put in an application to the telephone company,' we replied confidently. 'They say it will only take a couple of months, no more.'

We chose to ignore their pitying smiles and for the first few months waited optimistically for the technicians to arrive. Several years later, with our optimism in shreds, we were still waiting.

Telephones epitomized all that was most frustrating in Peru. At first, the Veterinary Faculty could only boast one solitary line to the outside; moreover, the intercom was on the same line. When the intercom was in use, no outside calls could be made or received. It took Manuel in his capacity as Dean, another 18 temper-testing months to obtain two more lines, one for the use of VITAR alone, the other to rewire the intercom independently.

If it took that long to instal official lines to the Faculty, I thought, how much longer was it going to take to stretch a private line to our house? After five years of pleading letters and angry visits to the telephone company, I was told that if I were to buy 20,000 soles worth of company shares, it would be installed immediately. I did. It wasn't! Nine months later, two technicians appeared one morning with a handset and a roll of wire.

'Where do you want it?' they asked. I showed them. The wire was too short.

'We'll be back this afternoon,' they assured me, but it was three months before they appeared again, this time, *gracias a Dios*, with a longer wire. I wrote out a cheque for the installation (another 10,000 soles), gave them each a beer, shook hands like old and trusted friends, and ushered them out.

'Who shall we ring first?' Mary asked excitedly, as we rushed back from the door.

'Try Jim and Ann, they have a phone.'

She lifted the handset. 'There's no dialling tone,' she wailed. I rushed outside, but the van had already disappeared.

'Dammit,' I cursed. 'I thought it was too good to be true. I'll have to go to the company again. Can't even ring them.'

My angry invasion of the company offices, where I demanded to see the engineer in charge, made little impression. Probably, I was just one of a hundred frustrated telephone owners who stormed in daily.

'We still have to connect you to the exchange, *señor*.'

'And when will that be?'

'Soon, *señor*; very soon. I assure you.'

We parted on slightly better terms, but 'soon', I knew, was an elastic word in South America. It could stretch into months – even years. Several more visits, each less cordial than the previous, achieved nothing. Four months passed. We gave up hope. I no longer picked up the phone each day, hoping to hear that long-awaited purr. Then, one day, out of the blue, it rang. We swooped upon it.

'Yes, who's calling?'

'We are testing. You are now connected.'

We had just time to call a friend when the line went dead. It was the last call we made for another two months.

When it did start functioning once more, we found it wise to deal with essentials before the small talk as the phone seemed to tire easily and cut out. It remained in much the same state for the rest of our time in Peru, working for a week, inactive for a few days and unreliable at all times. But by then, we had been in Peru too long to be worried by such small perversities. It was all part of the life in Latin America.

VICUÑA AND KATTIA

'*Reforma Agraria* have taken La Raya away from Puno University,' Manuel informed me with a chuckle. 'We must wait a little longer before *we* take it away from *them*, but we're nearly there. San Marcos has already signed an agreement with Agrarian Reform for VITAR to handle all the research work in auchenidae.'

'Fantastic,' I commented, 'Manuel strikes again!'

'That's not all. The alpaca farmers have given us a house in Macusani to start an extension service.'

'Where's Macusani?' I asked.

'Three hours from La Raya. Very high.'

'And bloody miserable,' I suggested.

'Bloody miserable,' Manuel confirmed. 'But we must visit it soon. We can look at the vicuña ranch at CalaCala on the way. Maybe we will also own CalaCala one day.'

After a stop-over at La Raya, we drove on past Pucará, famous for its clay models of fighting bulls, and turned into some low hills, reaching CalaCala at dusk. The farm house lay on a gentle slope protected by tall blue gums and firs and skirted by a once well-tended garden. Craggy hills formed the skyline behind it and lower down, long winding walls of uncemented rocks formed huge enclosures for the vicuña herd.

Señora Paredes, the owner, welcomed us into the rambling old house that could easily have been mistaken for a Yorkshire vicarage. Over dinner, she told us that her husband had started to domesticate

403

Vicuña

vicuña some 40 years before, collecting as many as he could capture and herding them like sheep.

'No-one cared much about vicuña in those days, except to shoot them for luxury garments.'

When her husband died, she had decided to continue his work, and although she now lived in Lima, she visited CalaCala regularly.

Early the following day, we braved the nippy air to inspect the vicuñas, 200 of which were now eyeing us nervously from their stone-walled pen. Like slender, golden fawns, they came hop-skipping out into the larger paddock where we could photograph them. Even after several generations of semi-captivity and human association, they were still half-wild. One had to approach slowly and quietly or they would flee. Two youngsters, *cria* or *tuis*, as the young of auchenidae are called, were more friendly; they had been reared on a baby's bottle and did not resent gentle handling.

'They'll soon lose their tameness once they join the herd,' Señora Paredes told us. 'It is almost impossible to tame them *en masse.*'

When the paddock gates opened, they were off like a flock of birds, half-leaping, half-flying, to disappear over a rocky ridge a kilometre away.

404

'Our biggest problems are pumas and poachers. We have pretty well scared off the poachers, but pumas can decimate our new-borns.'

Manuel explained our plan for crossing vicuña with alpaca to make a more commercially useful animal that could be sheared for its valuable fibre. 'Vicuña are already in the *Red Book* of endangered species and fully protected, but that's not enough. Unless we can incorporate them into a farming system, they are doomed.'

I could see his point. There was no way in which Peru could stop poaching in the thousands of square kilometres of the high *sierra*. Crossing these wild animals with alpaca to produce a tamer and more valuable *paco-vicuña* seemed the obvious way of utilizing their precious fibre and securing their future.

'Why not do it here?' Senora Paredes asked.

Manuel told her that he hoped CalaCala would, one day, become the National Vicuña Research Centre, and that we would be in charge of the work there.

'I'd be only too happy to see it,' she said, 'but keep *Reforma Agraria* away at all costs, they would kill it.'

It was several years later, after a lot more prodding, that the Government decided to purchase CalaCala for a National Centre, to be administered jointly by the Wildlife Service and San Marcos University, with VITAR responsible for the day to day research.

Meanwhile the vicuña reserve at *Las Pampas de Galeras* was developing rapidly under the supervision of Bill, the American PhD student. No-one knew exactly how many vicuña were in the reserve, but 1,000 seemed a reasonable guess. Within a few years the increase had been so dramatic that thoughts were given to using them for restocking other parts of the *sierra*.

'It's really amazing,' Bill told me proudly, 'the villagers of Pucquio (a village on the edge of the reserve), from once being inveterate poachers, now boast of being guardians of Peru's National Emblem!'

If ever there was a bleak, miserable, muddy (or dusty), impoverished Andean village, it was Macusani. We found it sulking at the end of 60 kilometres of rutted track which left the main road at Santa Rosa, halfway between La Raya and Puno. It seemed to be pushed up against a ceiling of cloud barely the height of a four-storey building.

White specks of alpaca sprinkled the rolling hills like dandruff. There was not a tree in sight. Later, when the low clouds moved away and the sun appeared, I gasped at the beauty of the snow-covered peaks rising majestically behind a long, narrow lake that reflected the clear cerulean sky.

The mud-brick house we had been given for our base was in a

narrow, dirty, half-cobbled street. There was almost no traffic except for the odd llama train. Occasionally, a decrepit, rattling bus, which plied erratically between the Andean villages and Puno, would roar past, exhaustless, polluting the clear air with clouds of black diesel fumes and splashing mud up the once whitewashed walls and onto the windows.

That first night in Macusani I slept with all my clothes on, including my jeep-coat, under six blankets, and only just survived. The thin atmosphere was like a vacuum which sucked the heat from your body. Quick movements to try and get warm were impossible. There was hardly enough oxygen to maintain life even when standing still. Eating didn't help, either. Food, once it was forced down, refused to be digested. In the whole four days of that nightmare visit, Manuel, myself, and the two young veterinarians, one of whom would be stationed there, managed to put away two tins of Vienna sausages, two loaves of bread and a small tin of Nescafé between us.

Most of the farms were of several thousand hectares each, extending up the mountains to the snow-line. The alpaca were magnificent, their coats thick and soft. Parturition was in progress, and small cuddly bundles ran in and out round the rim of the flock, bleating for their mothers.

'Did you know that there's a hotel here? I stayed there once when I was a student. I'll show you.' Grinning gleefully, Manuel drove up a side road to a door over which had been painted 'HOTEL'. 'There's only one room. Everyone sleeps on the mud floor. And if you want a toilet you use the street.' He was enjoying my shock.

For all its stupendous scenery when the sun shone, Macusani was a miserable spot. I left Manuel and his colleague to battle anoxia and refrigeration for a few more days, while I returned to Lima with Martinez in the truck which had brought up some equipment for our new centre. I was never so glad to leave any place.

* * *

'It's a great opportunity for Herman,' Doris explained, as she stood twisting her fingers. 'He is wasted here.'

I knew that Irish Ian had been making enquiries about a job for Doris' recently graduated doctor husband. Now the Ulster Medical Service had offered him a post.

'What's going to happen to VITAR?' I moaned, 'and especially to me? How can I run this project without you?'

'I've a friend who is looking for a job. I'll bring her along tomorrow. Like me, she is slow and nervous!'

406

'If you promise me that she is just as slow and nervous as you, she'll do fine.' I managed a grin.

Kattia was 23, slim, dark and intelligent. Like Doris, she proved to be more than just a secretary and soon became a close friend of each expert and his family. Kattia stayed with the project until after we left Peru and then landed a job as secretary with FAO in Rome, later joining the World Food Programme.

I may have been VITAR's Project Manager, but I was never under any illusion as to who really ran it!

PROF. JACK AND MAL DE ALTURA

VITAR's three-monthly progress report was sent to selected institutes and universities around the world. Apart from helping our international image, it gave us all a deadline for obtaining results, and an incentive to record them.

One day a letter arrived from Australia. Professor Jack had read our quarterly review and wished to visit us. He was working on the adaptation of sheep to drought conditions, and felt that there might be a similarity to altitude adaptation. I couldn't see the connection, but was only too pleased to get fresh ideas.

Proposals sped back and forth between Lima, Rome and Armidale, which led to Professor Jack being contracted for a three-month consultancy to assist our research into brisket disease. He was due to arrive in September.

September came and went. No Jack! Not even an answer to our letters and cables. By January, both FAO and I had written him off. Then a note arrived from a third party. 'Jack apologizes for the delay. He has had toxoplasmosis but hopes to be able to visit you within six months.'

He arrived almost a year after his original contract date, tall, thin, with sucked-in cheeks, coarse black hair starting to grey and, of course, the unmistakeable accent.

'Why didn't you answer our letters?' I asked.

'That damn disease. All I could do when someone spoke to me was to burst into tears. I couldn't talk, I couldn't read and I couldn't write. I was in another world. I don't remember any letters from you. It was ghastly.'

The result of Jack's studies in Australia and Israel had been the discovery that adaptation of sheep to drought conditions depended to some extent on the type of haemoglobin in the blood cells. Individuals with a certain type of haemoglobin adapted well, those with

407

other types didn't. He was eager to try out the same theory in relation to altitude stress in cattle.

Immediately, we set about determining the haemoglobin types in the different breeds of cattle in the *sierra* and on the coast and found, to our surprise, that all Holstein-Friesians – the least adaptable breed – seemed to have type A haemoglobin, while a high proportion of Brown Swiss and *Criollo* cattle – which withstood altitude stress better – had haemoglobin types AB and B.

We were jubilant. It looked like a breakthrough. Now we could screen animals for their haemoglobin types and only permit those with types B and AB to go to the *sierra*. But it wasn't quite that simple. *Criollo* cattle, no matter what their haemoglobin type, appeared to suffer far less from the effects of high altitude than any other breed, and most of the offspring of the Holstein-Friesian herds kept at high altitude for decades were tolerant, even though most possessed haemoglobin type A. Obviously other factors played an important part in the physiology of brisket disease.

The physiologists had a field day investigating other indicators of adaptability; the speed of production of red blood cells, the mechanism of oxygen release in the tissues, the concentration of potassium and sodium and the level of Vitamin E in the blood, and many others. Nothing much of significance emerged, but at least we now knew the risk of sending cattle with type A haemoglobin to high altitude. We also felt confident that we had *mal de altura* by the tail, and had no intention of letting go.

ENEMIES WITHIN

Technical problems were one thing; hostile interference was quite another. A telephone call from the UN Resident Representative's office, one dull drizzly afternoon, requested me to be good enough to call on him at nine the following morning, and to bring Jim with me.

'Whadya know? They're actually taking some notice of us at last.' Jim was jubilant.

He had every reason to be. Huancayo was producing thousands of fertile eggs each week and the compression room was working round the clock, trying to hatch these and the hundreds of others pouring in from Cachi Cachi. The Yanahuanca Poultry Demonstration Unit had extended its influence to local schools, who were now setting up their own flocks, and Jim had presented Agrarian Reform with a four-year plan involving 80 Andean villages which would produce 1,500,000 broilers and 12,000,000 eggs each year.

There were certainly no technical reasons why a poultry industry shouldn't be a success at high altitude. We looked forward to our meeting with the UN boss.

We found him in his tenth-floor office together with the new FAO chief of mission. Coffee was brought and, after the usual familiarities, the subject of the poultry programme was broached. Proudly, we recounted the results at Huancayo.

'And what about Cachi Cachi?' we were asked.

Jim explained the objectives, the results and the proposed expansion under the umbrella of Agrarian Reform. An awkward silence followed his account.

'That's what I'd like to talk to you about,' said the Res Rep. A sour note had suddenly crept in. 'I had a visit yesterday from the head of Agrarian Reform. He's horrified at the extent of their commitment to poultry and terrified at what would happen if anything went wrong. He says you've been pushing the Regional Office too hard and they had no authority to get so involved. As of today, he is withdrawing all support for the scheme and wants Cachi Cachi closed down.'

In the mouth-gaping silence that followed, I could hear a car horn 'parp-parp-ing' somewhere in the street below, mocking us, just as that hyena had mocked me so long ago in Abercorn. This time the message was – 'You can't win. No-one really wants to progress if it means doing something bold and taking a risk. Thought you'd change things? No sir. Conformity is what counts. Go back to square one.'

We argued, gave statistics, elaborated on the benefits to the Andean peasant and the value of the ancillary industries the plan would develop based on the outputs from Cachi Cachi. It was no use. The answer was always the same.

'It's their show. They call the shots. The Director feels his organization has been forced into a commitment they will not be able to fulfil. They don't doubt our expertise, but when they need it they will ask for it. For the moment the Director of Agrarian Reform has given instructions to his staff to terminate their poultry programme at Cachi Cachi, and has asked me to ensure that we do the same.'

'Unbelievable,' growled Jim, as we sat shocked and dispirited in the coffee bar on the ground floor.

'Madness,' I replied. 'What an opportunity they're passing up. All that effort for nothing, and it will be the peasants that will suffer, not the fat cats in *Reforma Agraria*. I think the Res Rep was almost pleased; he never did like our entrepreneurship.'

'Stuff the UN, stuff FAO, stuff Agrarian Reform. We'll just go back to being FAO bulls.' Jim was near to tears.

'We've still got the *selva*,' I comforted.

'That won't help the Andean peasant,' Jim retorted. 'I wonder how many children in the *sierra* have received the death sentence today?'

It was a sobering thought.

The demise of Cachi Cachi was not the last of our poultry problems at high altitude. Before we had time to start on the *selva* poultry programme, another blow befell the chickens at Huancayo. Hans, Jim's Peruvian counterpart, returned from a visit with a long face.

'Too many of the heavy breeds are dying,' he announced.

'What of?' Jim asked.

'Not sure, but their hearts are enlarged and there is a lot of fluid in the abdomen. Looks like brisket disease in chickens.'

Jim took a physiologist and a pathologist from the Faculty to Huancayo. They compared the size and weight of the right and left ventricles of the heart in those birds that died, made endless blood counts on their electronic counters, calculated the haemoglobin concentrations and types (which were not clear-cut as in cattle), studied clotting rates and did thousands of other complicated tests which give these learned gentlemen that superior attitude towards their lesser colleagues.

It didn't take long to confirm Hans' diagnosis. The process was, basically, the same as brisket disease. The condition had already been reported from Bolivia and the United States. The intensively-fed, heavy broiler breeds were affected most, although some cases occurred in the highest producing layers as well. The common, low-producing, 'peel-neck' *criollo* fowl was unaffected.

As always, Jim was optimistic.

'We'll breed it out. Shouldn't be too difficult. We'll start by selecting grandparent stock at about eight weeks old on the basis of their growth and resistance to altitude stress, or any other parameter the physiologists suggest. It'll take a year or two, but we'll do it. Then we'll be able to supply altitude adapted strains of broilers, like we do layers, to poultry farmers throughout the Andes – another first for VITAR!'

Jim's selection programme gave rapid results; within a year the numbers of broilers suffering from *mal de altura* had dropped significantly, and within three years it was down from a peak of 30 per cent to less than 5. The satisfaction of overcoming yet another obstacle almost made us glad it had arisen.

410

IN THE RED

'Pat, can you lend me 50,000 soles?' Manuel was apologetic. 'The University are temporarily out of funds and none of the VITAR staff have been paid for two months.' It was not an uncommon situation in Latin America.

I hesitated. I had no authority to lend FAO money to Manuel or anyone else. Such funds could only be used for imported equipment, scholarships abroad, foreign consultants and the like. All other expenditure, including salaries of local staff, was the concern of the Peruvian Government or, more specifically, of San Marcos University. Furthermore, I was personally accountable for all FAO funds.

On the other hand, families had to live, kids go to school. If the University failed to come up with the wherewithal, our staff would leave and the project fold up. Money, after all, was only worth what it could give you. If FAO funds could save VITAR, I convinced myself, there was no more to be said.

It was the first of several loans that I felt morally compelled to make. Manuel gave me an IOU for each, countersigned by the Rector of San Marcos. The accountants in Rome were anything but happy and kept emphasizing my responsibility if anything should go wrong. I comforted myself that I had the Rector's guarantee – and that was the same as the Government. Of course nothing would go wrong – it better hadn't. The University now owed the FAO account 2,000,000 soles, or $74,000!

But I had ignored that well-established principle – 'If there's anything that can go wrong, it will.'

Manuel was excited. 'Did you hear? The sol has been devalued. There are now forty soles to the dollar instead of twenty-seven.' He smiled thinly. 'Now we only owe you fifty thousand dollars instead of seventy-four thousand.'

'Hey, wait a minute,' I exclaimed, thoroughly alarmed at the possible consequences. 'That wasn't the deal. It may be fine for you, but I still owe FAO in dollars at the old exchange rate.'

Rome was no more amused than I. Several 'We told you so' letters turned up on my desk. Who, they wanted to know, was now going to make up the difference at the new exchange rate? Sure as hell not me, I determined. There had to be a way out.

We discussed the problem for several days until Manuel came up with a possible solution. He pointed out that the University had bought many items of equipment that FAO could equally well have paid for – electric fencing, typewriters, medicines, refrigeration equipment.

411

'I get the point,' I said. 'But even if Rome agreed to discount all such articles, they would still require receipts for each purchase.'

'Impossible, some are four years old and the University accounts are chaotic.'

Eventually Rome agreed, insisting that each purchase be verified by an original receipt. Manuel visited the Accounting Department in the University. He returned looking glum.

'They have a room piled high with bundles of invoices from every Faculty. Some are ten years old. Ours could be anywhere. We haven't a hope.'

But there was no other alternative.

A few days later, Manuel ushered in a stout, balding, middle-aged man with prominent eyes and moustache like a tuft of coarse *sierra* grass.

'This is Dr Delovitch. He's going to search for our receipts.'

Delovitch, it appeared, was a lawyer, hence the 'Dr'. Unfortunately, he had upset the local legal lads to such an extent that they suggested he should find another profession, since he was no longer welcome in theirs. I never discovered what his crime had been, probably a minor misdemeanour that had been turned into a major one for political purposes, and he had been unlucky enough to have been found out.

A defrocked man of the law he may have been, but he proved to be one of the most useful and delightful members of VITAR. His mastery of legal twists, legitimate or otherwise, and his numerous contacts in Government and business circles, helped VITAR over many a rough spot. Within six months he had extricated sufficient invoices from the bundles in the University to reduce the counterpart debt to a tenth of its original level. The legal profession, in my opinion, had lost a cracking good batsman!

A few months after the devaluation of the sol, there was another upheaval. We were staying at the Hotel Turista in Huancayo. It was just getting light when there was an urgent banging on my bedroom door. Manuel was outside in a highly excited state.

'There's been a military coup. President Belaunde is out. Some Army Colonel called Velasco has taken over.'

'What will it mean?' I asked, trying to shake off the last remnants of a dream.

'Don't know. Maybe better, maybe worse. We wait and see. But we must return to Lima at once. There are many people I have to talk to.'

It was a situation, I knew, that Manuel would relish. I could already see him scurrying round the halls of the House of Representatives, buttonholing any *deputado* he thought might be able to help the cause of VITAR in the new set-up.

All was quiet as we left Huancayo, but we kept the car radio on. Bulletins were being issued every 15 minutes, interspersed with martial music. Lima, too, was tranquil, but perhaps the odd tank or armoured car had something to do with it.

In the political furore that followed Belaunde's departure, the United States was firmly established as political enemy number one; mainly, it seemed, because of alleged underpayment of royalties on petrol extracted from the American-operated oil wells in the north of the country. The argument hinged on a treaty of some 30 years standing. The tariffs, which had been listed on page 11 of this treaty, were now deemed inadequate, and Peru was demanding an enormous back-payment. But, surprise, surprise! When challenged, diplomatically, it was found that the original page 11 with its signatures had gone missing. *Pagina once* became a *cause célèbre*. No-one could find it or explain its disappearance.

The treaty was rescinded, foreign oil companies nationalized, American conglomerates hounded out, and all other US-financed programmes terminated, including the US AID agricultural programme, with which we were closely associated.

Velasco's new left-wing Government lost no time in painting their rosy picture of Peru's future, free from US domination. Agrarian Reform, which had been coasting along contentedly for some years, was given a new impetus. Laws governing the amount of land a private person or company could own were promulgated. Most of the large ranches were appropriated and turned into SAISs – *Sociedades Agrícolas de Interés Social* or, more simply, community farms similar to those in Russia.

The original enthusiasm of the Andean *campesinos* faded quickly when they realized that although the land and sheep were now, theoretically, theirs, they were still not at liberty to take a Sunday joint whenever they wished.

Politicians worked themselves into frothing madmen as they condemned the wicked Americans and eulogized the heroic achievements of the Peruvian workers and the golden future with cheap petrol and other goods.

Even football, or should I say 'and, of course, football', was brought into the charade, Velasco appearing at all important matches, to give the new, thrusting fist salute. He didn't last long. Like so many other political opportunists, he soon lost the support of the people and withdrew to his country mansion, where he slowly

413

went downhill with some unspecified complaint, surrounded by Cuban and Russian doctors.

It wasn't long before economics forced Peru to shake hands once more with Uncle Sam. American technicians returned to their jobs in oil, the telephone service and agriculture – including many of our friends in AID. Belaunde also returned again as President, but not until after we had left Peru.

The only reminder of the unfortunate coup is now an annual holiday each 9 November, with the euphemistic title 'The Day of National Dignity'.

VITAR EXTENDED – MARY TOO!

One might have been forgiven for thinking that a military treaty was being ratified, rather than a mere agreement to extend an FAO project.

The small room in the Ministry of Agriculture was crammed with medal-bedecked military gentlemen sporting yards of golden cords and great dollops of scrambled egg. Since General Velasco's coup, all Ministers and their aides had been drawn from the top brass of the Services. Only the Rector of San Marcos, who signed on behalf of the University, the UN and FAO representatives, signing for the International side, and Manuel and I, the two Directors of VITAR (as usual, only as observers) were in civvies. A tray of pisco-sours and *algarobinas* cemented the agreement.

I escaped as soon as I could. Mary was far from well. This, her seventh pregnancy, was the only one that had given her the slightest problem. We had an appointment with the gynaecologist later that afternoon, the last, we hoped, before B-day.

'I think you should have a Caesarian,' he advised after the examination. 'The sooner the better. How about the day after tomorrow?'

On the way to the hospital, we discussed possible names.

'We're running out of girls' names,' I complained, 'so make sure it's a boy, darling.'

The operation was scheduled for eleven. At twelve I was back in the hospital. I met the doctor on the stairs.

'You'd better sit down,' he told me solemnly. I sank slowly onto the top step, my stomach turning somersaults.

'Congratulations,' he bellowed, slapping me on the back. 'You've got twins. Two lovely girls.'

I was so relieved that Mary was all right, I didn't realize the implications for a moment. Then it hit me.

414

Twins? TWINS! Oh, no. He'd never mentioned twins. And both GIRLS! Eight kids – seven girls!

'It's OK,' he assured me. 'They'll be the last. Your wife asked me to fix her once and for all. About time, if you ask me!'

Shevaughne and Corinne, 'Shivy' and 'Coro', weighed a total of seven and three quarter pounds, and spent the next three weeks in an incubator. Shevaughne, the smaller, had great trouble breathing.

It wasn't till a few days later that the doctor explained why he had decided on a Caesarian.

'I didn't want to frighten you, but I thought it might have been a monster.'

A few years later, I could have assured him that his diagnosis wasn't far out. They were both little monsters!

With the signing of Phase II, VITAR now had another four years to pursue its studies, especially our tropical operations in Pucallpa.

A hundred hectares of the 2,000 available near San Jorge had already been cleared with saws and machetes, taking eight months instead of the estimated ten days, had we had sufficient funds to hire the Tournavista tree crushers.

It was to take Manuel another two years to secure the rest of the land and the funds to clear it, and it was only a personal tragedy that made this possible. While in the United States attending a conference, his mother had cut her foot, contracted tetanus and died. Manuel arrived back an hour before the funeral.

Later, checking the progress of the Pucallpa land purchase in the House of Representatives, he found to his dismay that all funds allocated for the purchase of the remainder had been deleted from the budget! In a week of non-stop lobbying and late-night discussions, he finally convinced the relevant politicians that Pucallpa was a matter of priority.

Had his mother not died so tragically, Manuel would not have returned to Peru in time to secure the funds for our station. Another of Manuel's 'hats', I thought.

* * *

We now needed new experts. Anzac Ian, after two frustrating years battling with *sierra* pastures, was about to leave for the more congenial and warmer grazings in Mauritius, Irish Ian had been promoted to manager of a veterinary project in Uruguay, and Bryan had already returned to the British Veterinary Investigation Service. Jim, too, was hoping soon to retire to Switzerland, and we still had to staff our tropical station.

415

Peter, our 'Godfather' in FAO, said he had just the fellow to solve all our tropical pasture problems. I could look him over when I visited Rome the following month on my biennial home leave.

My first meeting with Santi was in a lift. Since neither of us knew who the other was, we offered each other polite 'Good-mornings' and went our separate ways. I remember wondering what the rather lost-looking young coloured fellow was doing in FAO, perhaps an Associate Expert, or looking for a clerical job, or visiting a friend. An Expert? No, not the type. So I was decidedly taken aback when Peter introduced the same slim young man, more like an office boy than an agronomist, as the proposed expert in tropical pastures for Pucallpa.

Half an hour later, sipping *capuchinos* together on the rooftop cafeteria, I changed my mind. His knowledge of pasture management was immense, and I found out that instead of being an 'office boy', Santi was already a senior member of the Queensland Dairy Section of the Australian CSIRO, with the probability of soon becoming the section's director! To widen his tropical experience, he had applied to join FAO. He hoped we would have him.

Santi arrived in Peru clutching a large parcel of curry powder which, to a Sri Lankan, was as essential as spinach was to Popeye. I was soon making excuses to visit Pucallpa just to sample some of Mrs Santi's glorious curry dishes, despite her contention that Mary's curry was the best she had ever tasted outside Sri Lanka.

Without doubt, Santi proved himself to be the most outstanding scientist in the project and had soon upset the findings of several international researchers on jungle pasture management.

To look after the development of the beef herds at Pucallpa, we found an English veterinarian who had been managing a ranching scheme in Uganda. Apart from his wide knowledge of tropical cattle management, Peter had another invaluable attribute – he knew how to handle Santi, a most important skill, we were soon to discover. Quiet, self-effacing, of medium height with gingery hair, given to short, pithy sentences and dry-humoured comments which you wished you'd thought of yourself, Peter reminded me of a rosy-faced country squire.

More difficult to find was an expert to develop the dairying operations at high altitude. Very few people in the world had experience of such conditions. We needed a down-to-earth, practical farmer-cum-scientist who could teach the small dairymen of the Mantaro Valley to produce milk profitably, especially as German Aid had just built a massive milk-processing plant near Huancayo, which was only running at an eighth of its capacity.

Peter in Rome turned up trumps again.

'I've found you a wizard. He's highly recommended in five countries, including Ireland and England, and on top of this he's a New Zealander. What more do you want?'

Ken was tall, rugged, strong of jaw and will, with that determined, clear-eyed look that one associates with the All Blacks rugger squad. His strong New Zealand accent had lost nothing in his work abroad. 'We'll use it to cut the pastures if the forage harvester breaks down,' I told him. 'It'll cut anything.'

But the increasing difficulty of attracting experts willing to face the rigours of the *sierra* and *selva* for three years, with the added problems of finding housing, suitable schools and acceptable medical attention for their families, made us favour another approach – short-term consultants.

There were many advantages to this, especially after our basic programme had been worked out. Many a top specialist was on the staff of a University and was only too happy to advise us on our programmes in the Andes or jungle during his annual vacation, and return each year to check our progress. There were no hassles with family or schools, and we could look forward to continuous, top-level supervision. From the USA, Canada, Australia, Britain, France and Israel they came; in poultry, in pastures, in nutrition, food storage, pigs, rabies and many other fields. Furthermore, some ran University departments, which often offered fellowships for VITAR staff.

There was one field in which we never thought an expert could help – the cocktail party. Cocktail parties were the traditional end to a working day in Latin America. Dishes heaped with *langostinas* (prawns), *camarónes* (shrimps) and *conchitas* (roasted scallops with parmesan), surrounded an elaborate centrepiece of lobsters, crabs and fish modelled in solid ice, while waiters darted about with trays of pisco-sours and *algarobinas* in small frosted glasses.

An occasional cocktail party was enjoyable, but they were far too frequent ('Eight in one night' complained the American Ambassador). The fact that all the ladies sat at one end of the room while the men, who were nearly all officials I saw every day, stood at the other end, made the gatherings insufferably boring.

The only party I remember where sexes mingled freely was the one Mary and I organized to celebrate the first three years of VITAR. It was held in the 'English Pub' attached to the Lima Cricket Club, a very British environment, small and far too crowded to allow any

417

segregation. In place of the central ice sculptures was an arch with miniature flags from all the members of the United Nations.

I am sure it was the most enjoyable cocktail party anyone there had ever attended. It lasted till two in the morning and ended with singing and guitars. It also broke my official entertaining allowance for two years!

So, perhaps the extra-official expertise of foreign consultants *was* needed if only to upgrade the cocktail party. Perhaps not the décor but at least the jollification.

PAICHE, PASTURES AND PINTADAS

The *selva* was an enigma. Contrary to expectations, the topsoil of the steamy Amazon Jungle, unlike the forests of temperate climes, was thin and devoid of humus. Most trees were non-deciduous, so leaf-fall was slight and humus scant. In addition, the few rays of sunlight which penetrated the thick forest canopy were insufficient for a vigorous undergrowth to develop, and the terrifying tropical storms leached out what little topsoil did form, leaving the soil deficient in nearly every element necessary for plant growth. As a further impediment, the soil around Pucallpa contained a high level of aluminium, in itself detrimental to plant growth.

VITAR had three objectives in the jungle. How best to clear the forest; how best to establish pastures on the cleared land; and how best to manage cattle or other animals on these pastures in order to make livestock farming economically viable?

The answer to clearing seemed to be the Tournavista tree-crushing machines. Establishing pastures was more complex. Artificial fertilizers were no solution. Transport from Lima, 800 kilometres away, or by sea from England to Iquitos and then by smaller vessels to Pucallpa, made the cost prohibitive. Luckily, it was possible to introduce nitrogen, severely lacking in the *selva*, by planting legumes which took it from the air and fixed it in the soil by the aid of certain bacteria. Scientists in Australia and southern Africa were developing strains of legumes that flourished in tropical conditions and often on poor soils. We imported a number of these and collected others which grew wild and mixed them with selected tropical grasses, to find which combinations grew best.

'Once we know the best grass-legume mixtures, we must find out their stocking rate and carrying capacity,' Santi explained. 'That is, how many adult cattle can be kept, profitably, on one hectare of pasture, year in year out, without it deteriorating. Farmers have

418

been planting *jaragua* grass (*Hyperrenhia rufa*) for over fifty years. It is a good grass if managed properly, but most of the pastures have been so overgrazed and neglected that they are now almost useless. We must see that this doesn't happen to our grass-legume mixtures.'

By experimentation, Santi found that his best mixture would support just over three cattle per hectare throughout the year, without becoming overgrazed. This was a far higher stocking rate than the old *jaragua* pastures, which hardly supported one animal on three hectares.

Taking into account the costs of land, clearing it of forest, sowing the new pasture mixtures, not forgetting the fertility and growth of the animals, the availability of markets and all the other nuts and bolts of beef production, we concluded that under the best conditions possible, a farmer could not expect more than 8 per cent financial gain on his capital expenditure, a statistic that was hardly likely to encourage beef production in the *selva*. A way had to be found to reduce the cost and increase the production per hectare. The inclusion of dairy cattle in the operation increased profits slightly, but pigs and poultry promised to be much better adjuncts. Pigs could make use of the large amounts of *yuca* or cassava (*Manhioc* species) and other tropical crops, while poultry could scavenge for their supper of insects and seeds. Both these species, because they reproduced and grew so rapidly, would be a valuable source of extra income until the cattle were ready for market.

Another factor encouraged us. One of the commonest trees in the jungle, especially along the river banks, was a slender, large-leafed tree called *Setico* (*Cecropia* species). It was used for paper pulp, but its potential as a livestock fodder, although suspected, had hardly been studied. It grew quickly from seed, did not require fertilizer and flourished in the very acid, aluminium-packed soil. It was highly nutritious and rivalled lucerne in protein content. Cattle would browse it, and after the trunks had been taken for paper pulp, its large rhubarb-like leaves could be turned into silage or dried. Cut branches grew back in six weeks. A final advantage was that it provided shade for animals. We sowed plantations of *Setico* and began feeding it to cattle. As long as the animals could graze grass together with the *Setico*, they rapidly gained weight, but *Setico*, fed alone, was soon rejected.

Yuca also produced excellent results as an energy source and, like *Setico*, wasn't troubled by the acidity and the high aluminium content of the soil. Job's Tears (*Coix lachryma*), was yet another promising fodder. It had been imported from the Far East 20 years before for human consumption, and then forgotten. Its one drawback was the high copper content of the seeds, the most nutritive part.

With these and other feeds in hand, we felt that beef production in the jungle could be a profitable investment, and even if statistics suggested that it wouldn't be all that lucrative, I knew that many people kept livestock as much for love as for money, and would be quite content with minimal profits.

But perhaps we were barking up the wrong tree. Perhaps we could save ourselves a lot of time and money, as they had done in Jamaica, by simply mining the aluminium-rich pasture land for bauxite!!

* * *

Commissions from the family ensured that I would return from Pucallpa or Iquitos, to which ports ships from Liverpool brought regular supplies of European goodies, with an empty wallet. Tinned food, bras of various dimensions, sewing accessories difficult to find in Lima, and always on top of the list of the children's priorities – 'whirly ice-creams'.

'But I can't carry ice-creams. They'll melt within minutes.'

'Take an ice-box, then.'

I would promise to do my best, but found that a large block of Cadbury's chocolate would more than excuse the omission of whirly ice-creams. Perhaps it was all a well-thought-out ploy, failure to bring back the impossible ensuring that I would feel guilty enough to buy them extra-large slabs of English chocolate!

As well as unearthing English delicacies in Iquitos, one could sometimes stumble on a genuine odd English character.

Jim and I were searching the shelves of a hardware store one afternoon, when I received a sharp punch in the ribs. Thinking it was Jim, I swung round ready to retaliate. Behind me, I found a diminutive, grey-haired gnome in khaki shirt and long, baggy khaki shorts.

'Knew you were a *gringo*. Jack's the name. From Yorkshire. Bin 'ere forty-seven years. Made two fortunes an' lost 'em both. They made me Mayor once. I'll be eighty next year.'

Eighty or not, he could still pack a punch. He invited us up to his house.

'Got the best library in the jungle. Take anything you fancy. Shan't need it again.'

We had other commitments, but promised to visit him on our next trip. We never saw him again. The next time we were in Iquitos we learned that he had died. A missed opportunity, if ever there was one. An evening with Jack would have given us more information on the *selva* than all the books in his, or any other library.

One of the jungle dishes I looked forward to most was *paiche* with *chonto*. The *paiche* (*Arapaima gigas*), was probably the largest fresh-water fish in the world. Specimens up to three and a half metres and weighing 400 kilos had been recorded. It was also an anachronism, something that had survived from the jungle's palaeozoic past. Slow-moving and slow-breeding, it preferred the lagoons or deep idling waters of the larger rivers, especially where there was floating vegetation. Unfortunately, like the whale, it had to surface for air every half-hour or so. This made it extremely vulnerable to the guns and harpoons of the lurking hunter. It also took bait.

Sex differentiation had long been a mystery, known only to Mr and Mrs *Paiche* themselves until Dr Marcos, a VITAR histologist, investigated their anatomy. He found that some specimens had a bright red colouring underneath the throat, while in others the pigmentation was golden. By comparing these colour differences with the microscopical structure of what had hitherto been considered a unisexual gonad, he found that those with the red colouring possessed testicular cells and those with the golden throat had ovarian cells. Not that it really mattered to anyone except the *paiche*. Both sexes were equally delicious on the table.

Chonto was the local name for the heart of the palm. It was served in the form of shavings, raw, with mayonnaise or a sauce. I always felt a bit guilty about eating *chonto*, since I knew that my meal had been the death of a whole elegant palm. In order to harvest the heart at the top, it was necessary to cut down the whole tree. I was comforted a little by the thought that they must grow pretty fast, since wherever I went in the jungle, tall, slender palms reached up between the canopy of thicker trees for a sip of tropical sunshine.

* * *

With the ending of Cachi Cachi, we now had more time to plan the poultry programme in the hot, humid *selva*.

Operations started in Iquitos, a city of 100,000 souls on the banks of the Amazon. Although 2,300 miles from the mouth of the Amazon, Iquitos was barely 400 feet above sea level, with temperatures ranging from 22 degrees centigrade at night to 38 in the day – even hotter and more humid than Pucallpa.

421

'We'll carry out our whole production on free range, like we do in Huancayo,' Jim decided. 'We'll select those birds which grow faster and fatter, which means that they are the best foragers for insects and seeds; then we'll breed and select from them. That will ensure hardy stock.'

There were plenty of insects, both crawling and flying, and enough grass and seeds to provide a good diet, but the jungle held many more dangers than the *sierra* for birds on free range. Snakes, large lizards, rodents and egg-eaters like the mongoose abounded, but the greatest danger of all were internal parasites such as worms and coccidia (a microscopic protozoa which attacked the intestine wall), all of which thrived in hot humid conditions.

Setbacks there were aplenty. The generator would overheat, putting the water-pump, incubators, and cold room out of action. Coccidiosis and other diseases took their toll, but the growing number of poultry farmers and the enormous demand for day-old chicks, eggs and broilers, encouraged us.

* * *

We were flying high – then BANG! A propeller came off.

I knew that Jim wouldn't be with us for always, but I never imagined that he would refuse our offer to extend his contract.

We pleaded, begged, appealed to his more altruistic feelings. It was no use. He had done all he could, he said, to solve the problems of high-altitude poultry production and had laid the foundations for similar operations in the jungle. He was 53 and had decided to retire in Switzerland.

It was a terrible blow. Everything he had done had been a success, even Cachi Cachi, if only the crustacean-brained administrators had kept their claws out of the pot.

Rome offered us a replacement. We were not sympathetic. No-one could take Jim's place. Much better to let Hans, Jim's Peruvian understudy, take over. Jim had trained him well and we were certain he could cope, especially if Jim could pay us a visit, now and then. We didn't want someone else rocking the boat.

Rome insisted. They had, they said, an Israeli whose speciality was rural poultry development and extension. He would be ideal to carry Jim's work to the peasants in the Andes and the jungle. One thing about him pleased me. Like Jim, he had no university degree. In my experience, academic poultry experts were a thoroughly useless lot in a 'grass roots' situation. This man had spent his life with poultry in a kibbutz before becoming editor of a poultry extension magazine. We capitulated and told Rome to send him along.

Somewhere in Ben's *curriculum vitae*, I noticed that he had grown up in Bulgaria and only later moved to Israel.

'All we need is a Vulgar Bulgar,' I joked, as we waited his arrival at the airport. 'He's sure to balls-up everything.'

It took half the time it takes to hatch an egg for Ben to convince us that he had not come to balls-up anything. Short, stocky, with dark, curly hair ringing a bald patch on his crown, and black bushy tufts over dark, humorous eyes, he soon commanded the same respect from colleagues and *campesinos* that Jim had enjoyed.

Moreover, he spoke a form of Hispanic Yiddish which, if not entirely understood by the Peruvians, at least helped him to understand them. The small Jewish community in Bulgaria, so it seemed, had originated in Spain and had kept up their Spanish *patois* over the generations. His French, the native language of Solange, his Parisian wife, was fluent, and I could find no fault with his English. He also spoke German, some Russian and, of course, Hebrew.

Ben lost no time in expanding the work Jim had begun. Further demonstration units were set up, courses for farmers and extension personnel given regularly and several field manuals produced.

'Hope you like *pintadas*?' he said to me one day.

'Guinea-fowl? They're OK, I think. Why?'

'We have seven hundred day-old guinea-chicks arriving in Iquitos from France next week.'

As far as I was concerned, guinea-fowl were wild birds which made a lot of noise but always kept just out of range of my gun and which, try as I might I could never run down in the car! But they were tasty eating, all right. Great strides, Ben told us, had been made in Europe in domesticating them and improving their production.

One in five of the guinea-chicks we imported succumbed to the four-day air trip to Iquitos, but the survivors adapted well and hundreds were soon being distributed up and down the Ucayali, either as day-olds or as eggs to be hatched by the villagers themselves under surrogate mums.

Fertile eggs sent to Huancayo for incubation hatched well, and the chicks showed no signs of altitude stress. It was clear that guinea-fowl were equal to and might even prove superior to chickens in the *sierra* and *selva*.

Pintadas had other advantages over the chicken. They were expert scavengers and excellent watchdogs. When disturbed, the noise they made would awaken the most *chicha*-sozzled *campesino*!

SYPHILIS AND SALMONELLA

There was a young fellow of Puno,
Who said, 'About shagging I do know.
A woman is fine, a boy is divine,
But a llama is *numero uno*'

(Anon)

'We've been given fifteen thousand dollars to investigate syphilis in alpacas,' Manuel told me one morning.

'Syphilis? In alpacas? But alpacas don't get syphilis.'

'How do you know?'

'Well, no-one has ever recorded it – scientifically.'

'Exactly, but there have been plenty of rumours ever since Pizarro and his *conquistadores*. The US Public Health Service have asked us to clear up the matter once and for all.' He smiled. 'Probably worried about their tourists.'

It was a common allegation that Pizarro's men had brought syphilis back with them from the New World, and also that frustrated Inca gallants would sometimes use alpacas or llamas as tranquillizers, giving rise, no doubt, to the ditty at the head of this chapter.

'Let's get this clear from the start,' I told Manuel firmly. 'I'm not volunteering for any practical transmission experiments!'

We blood-tested numerous alpaca and llama, but all were negative to syphilis. Others were injected with human syphilitic chancre material but showed no symptoms, although two showed antibodies to syphilis in their blood, which was not surprising.

'What now?' I asked.

'We'll tell Washington that it is safe to screw alpacas and llamas,' Manuel chortled. 'It will probably boost the tourist trade. Americans are a queer lot!'

* * *

One of Peru's chief exports was fishmeal. At certain times of the year, the seas off the west coast of South America teemed with the little sardine-like anchovy which were harvested, ground into fishmeal, and exported for inclusion in animal feedstuffs and fertilizers.

Holland in particular bought large amounts of fishmeal each year, until a laboratory in The Hague isolated a dangerous species of the enteric bacterium, Salmonella, in fishmeal from Peru and had suspended further imports.

Salmonella are an ubiquitous group of micro-organisms, living chiefly in the intestinal tract of man and animals, some are relatively

424

harmless, others, like *Salmonella typhi*, the cause of typhoid fever, and those responsible for food poisoning, can be very dangerous.

Manuel looked serious. 'This is top priority. The Ministry of Health have asked us to investigate it urgently so Peru can start exporting again. I suggest we go to Callao this afternoon and start where the fishing fleet off-loads the *anchoveta*.'

We found the shore-line packed with small, tug-like boats disgorging their twinkling cargoes through what looked like massive vacuum-cleaner tubes. These sucked the silvery, sardine-sized fish from the holds and spewed them into conveyer chutes which took them directly into the 'factory'. Millions upon millions upon millions of tiny, glistening bodies poured, endlessly, from the mouth of the tube and were whisked away to the ovens. What price the individual? I thought, as I watched them disappear.

Once cooked and ground up, the anchovy meal was tipped into heaps in the yards surrounding the factory until it could be bagged and stacked in sheds, ready for export. The air reeked of the same dead crab smell that had choked me on my first night in Peru.

We found no trace of Salmonella in the anchovy. In any case, the ovens would certainly have destroyed the organism. So it looked as if contamination occurred after the cooking and grinding processes.

None of the humans we tested were found to be carriers, but samples of rat and seagull droppings contained the same species of Salmonella as that reported from Holland. Cockroaches, too, were found to be heavily contaminated. Whether the rat or the seagull was the original source was purely academic, but the seagull appeared more likely. These birds hovered over the factories and contaminated the yards with their droppings, which would then, presumably, be picked up by rats and cockroaches as they ran over the pyramids of fishmeal. It was likely to be a cycle involving all these animals.

The obvious solution was to store the fishmeal in rat-proof sheds, but this posed another problem. Fishmeal was prone to spontaneous combustion. Within a night, a whole month's supply could go up in flames, taking the factory with it. The cause was the rapid oxidation of the meal, especially if it wasn't quite dry. Anti-oxidants were mixed in with the meal to try and prevent such conflagrations, but these, in turn, were thought to have been the cause of a devastating disease in poultry fed fishmeal, which broke out now and then, called 'Black Vomit'.

Protecting the piles of fishmeal against seagull droppings and destroying rats and cockroaches soon had Peru exporting fishmeal again.

It was Salmonella, too, that led us to investigate a beetle, this time at high altitude. The Medical Services had received a letter from the US Food and Drug Administration, advising that they had incriminated cochineal as the cause of food poisoning. They had isolated a Salmonella from samples of this red food colouring and suggested, since the bulk of their cochineal imports came from Peru, that we should look into it. The DMS again asked us to help.

Cochineal, I discovered, was made from crushing the females of a small 'scale' insect (*Dactylopius coccus*), which lived on certain cacti in the Andes.

Investigation soon determined that it was not the insect that was responsible for infection, but the human collectors. Salmonella, *S. cubana* in this case, was isolated from the hands of many *campesinos* who collected the little red insect off the cactus.

Soap and water, antibiotics and hygiene education helped mitigate the problem, but I fear that cochineal will always be suspect – anyway to me!

A PARASITE'S PARASITE

'I've something to show you, Doctor.' Jorge, the young veterinarian in charge of the parasitological section of the Huancayo laboratories, stopped me in the corridor.

'*Bueno*, Jorge,' I replied. 'Lead on.'

He ushered me into his lab and picked up a petri dish containing some snails.

'*Son muertos*,' he said.

'Yes, I can see they're dead. What killed them?'

He placed a glass slide under the low-power binocular microscope.

'*Mira*,' he invited.

I looked. Several minute worms were cavorting in the drop of saline on the slide.

'What are they?' I asked.

'*Chaetogaster*.'

'Cheetah-what?'

'*Chaetogaster*, a parasite of snails.'

'It kills them?'

'Yes, especially in dry weather. It lives and reproduces inside the snail's shell. I've seen over forty in a single shell.'

Fantastic, I thought. This little worm could be a real winner. If we could use it to kill snails, we could break the life-cycle of the parasite.

426

Liver fluke was probably the most troublesome parasite of cattle and sheep in Peru, if not in the whole world.

Fluke, you may remember, are small, leaf-like parasites which live in the bile ducts of cattle and sheep and need a particular species of snail in which to complete their life-cycle. Deaths from fluke infestation in the Mantaro valley were high, to say nothing of the ill-health they caused or the financial loss from discarded livers at slaughter or, for that matter, their harmful effect on man.

Treatment of infected animals was very expensive, and killing the snail by scattering copper compounds over the ground, although moderately successful, was again expensive, time-consuming and often poisonous to grazing animals. If we could use Jorge's unpronounceable worm to kill the snails and eliminate the parasite they nurtured, it would be a world-shaking event!

'What are we waiting for? Let's try them out in the field,' I exclaimed enthusiastically.

'That's what I wanted to tell you. We already have. We are going to see the results tomorrow.'

The following morning, I accompanied Jorge and his technician to where one of the many streams which tumbled down the mountainsides into the Mantaro valley split into two branches.

'Both these streams used to be full of snails,' Jorge said. 'Four months ago we tipped one thousand *Chaetogaster*-infected snails into one branch and left the other as it was. Let's see how many snails we can find in each branch now.'

We started searching the *Chaetogaster*-treated branch. After half an hour we had collected less than a dozen, but ten minutes in the untreated stream gave us half a bucket!

'I don't believe it,' I cried, slapping Jorge on the back. 'This is a day to remember.'

But although it was obvious that *Chaetogaster* could kill snails, there were still a lot of questions to answer. First, why had not all the snails in the 'treated' branch of the stream been killed? We felt that the most likely answer was because most of the snails we had recovered had been young, washed down from the breeding sites higher up, and had not had time to be heavily parasitized.

Again, since Jorge had collected snails parasitized with *Chaetogaster* in several places in the valley, why was liver fluke still the scourge of Mantaro? The reason was probably the same – constant replenishment from the snail colonies high up in the mountains, in which Jorge had found no *Chaetogaster*, combined with the old story of Mother Nature's biological tolerance. The snail seemed to be the parasite's one and only landlord, so it would hardly be in *Chaeto-*

gaster's interest to destroy its host completely. Where else would it find such desirable board and lodging?

Jorge repeated the experiment, releasing *Chaetogaster*-infested snails into the marshy areas in the mountains where the streams began. The result was just as spectacular, but always some snails survived. It seemed like a success story, but there was a great deal more work to be done, and at that precise moment, Murphy's Law came into operation; Jorge was awarded a scholarship to Puerto Rico and there was no-one to follow up his work. He had not returned by the time I left Peru. I have not seen any further reports on this potential pulverizer of snails in the Mantaro Valley, and to me it remains one of the great 'might have beens' of VITAR's research programme.

Other predators besides *Chaetogaster* breakfasted on snails. Trout considered them a delicacy, so did ducks and geese – and probably lots of other aquatic birds. In fact, with all these predators, it was remarkable that snails were not on the Endangered Species List! But there was little hope of that, they were far too enthusiastic reproducers, and their only deterrent, climatically, seemed to be drought. Heat, cold and altitude, they took in their slither – just so long as they had enough water to slither in.

Liver fluke as a cause of ill-health in man was often ignored. An exception was Cuba, where the disease had been recognized and treated for many years. Jorge made a survey of the schoolchildren in the Mantaro Valley and found the eggs of liver fluke in 60 per cent of their stools. Cattle and sheep in the same area showed a 100 per cent infestation rate.

The usual sources of fluke infestation in humans were lettuce and watercress and infusions of lucerne, a common 'tea'. In children, the high incidence was mainly from playing in the roadside ditches on the way to school, sucking stems of water plants and sometimes drinking the ditch water.

A second veterinary student expedition from England made another survey by means of a skin test, and confirmed the very high incident of liver fluke in the human population of Mantaro. VITAR inaugurated an educational campaign in the Valley schools, with talks and slide shows on how to prevent liver fluke and other internal parasites. It probably helped. Outside Cuba, I think the *campesinos* of the Mantaro Valley suffered as much from liver fluke as any other rural population in the world.

* * *

Each country I had worked in had a drawer full of unusual maladies. In Jamaica, there had been 'tissic', caused by a worm in the throat of cats; 'nightshade poisoning' and 'dogwood disease' in cattle on the north shore, and 'farcy' in mules. In Uganda there had been the moth-borne conjunctivitis that made the cows 'cry', and 'skin tuberculosis', neither of which I had encountered elsewhere. In Peru we had *mal de altura* in cattle and poultry at high altitude and two others I'd not seen before.

'*Cocquera*', named after the condition seen in Andean Indians who chewed cocaine leaves (although there was no evidence that cattle had adopted the habit), occurred on the coastal plain in times of drought when the feed was limited to dried maize stalks and the pods of the algaroba tree. The excess sugar in the pods, the lack of vitamins and grossly imbalanced diet, interfered with rumination, causing a type of wasting in the jaw muscles resulting in a bolus of food being lodged in the cheek and the tongue becoming hard and protruding. The condition was known in Texas as 'tongue out' and was said to be caused by the pods of the mesquite tree, another species of algaroba. The condition could be quickly reversed by feeding the affected animal fresh green fodder.

But the algaroba tree did have some useful properties. The wood burned slowly and gave off considerable heat, most welcome during the cold, drizzly winter months, and an extract from the pods made a delightful, sweet cocktail, the *algarobina*, an excess of which in humans, like the pods in cattle, could produce some pretty paralytic symptoms!

The other condition, *jacapo*, occurred mainly in sheep grazing high-altitude pastures. The first signs were weakness, restlessness and a search for shade. If they didn't die within 48 hours, their heads would swell and any part of the skin where the wool was thin or absent would become inflamed and peel off, typical symptoms of photosensitization, usually caused by plant toxins damaging the liver.

Certain grazing areas were known to be dangerous, and if sheep were removed from them, cases would cease. Although some livestock owners thought it was caused by a mite that lived in the grass, others were convinced it was a fungus. Everything, in our opinion, pointed to a poisonous plant, especially as several plants in other countries, such as ragwort, were known to cause similar symptoms.

Unfortunately, we could find no-one competent to identify the plants and fungi at high altitude, but it was a sobering thought that even if we had been able to identify the weed, the discovery would have meant little to the sheep farmers. Eliminating an obscure plant or moss in the limitless expanse of the Andean grazing area would have set even Hercules back on his heels. It would have made a

429

nice scientific paper, of course, but in practical terms I doubt whether it would have saved a single animal. Farmers already knew most of the danger areas and kept their sheep off them.

Which only emphasizes the fact that a great deal of research time and money can be wasted trying to find solutions that will be of little benefit except to the author of the scientific paper.

SHIVY JUST MAKES IT

I never felt at ease in the *sierra*. Breathlessness, a racing heart and tightness in the chest, as if the Andes were squeezing me. The mild headache if I hurried, and, later, the stomach upset. In addition, the apathetic, fatalistic, withdrawn attitude of the cocaine-befuddled Andean Indians, whose habit of watching their feet while they hissed staccato sentences through barely open lips, as if afraid the cold air might damage their lungs, irritated me. On top of all this was the constant nose-clogging dust and reek of petrol, the latter due to greater vaporization at high altitude.

How different the *selva*! Admittedly, the heat and humidity could be unpleasant, especially in the unventilated, stuffy cubby-holes called bedrooms, of the grossly mis-named Hotel Comfort in Pucallpa. I would drag my mattress into the corridor to try and catch the almost imperceptible night breeze, or hang a soaked sheet across the room, hoping to cool the air by evaporation.

But it was the 'feel' of the jungle that was so cheering – alive, gay, carefree, almost a holiday atmosphere. Unoppressed by the cold and high altitude, friends talked raucously, sang, shouted to each other. Bars blared with music until late, dancing was gregarious, eye to eye, quite unlike the sad solo *huaynos* of the *altiplano*, where the dancer stomped alone to the plaintive notes of the pipes. The jungle, too, had a camaraderie absent in the Andes.

Perhaps it was a subconscious nostalgia for Jamaica, or the sedative effect of the climate, whatever, once I stepped off the plane in Pucallpa or Iquitos, I felt I could breathe out and relax.

There was one occasion, however, when I was only too glad to get out of the jungle and to see Martinez, the project chauffeur, waiting at Lima airport. All I wanted was to get home and be coddled. The week in Pucallpa had been agony. Nothing I took seemed to have the slightest effect on the stomach gripes and frequent sessions in the loo. Never mind, I was home.

430

Mary opened the front door as I staggered out of the station wagon. She looked unhappy.

'Bad news, I'm afraid, darling. Shivy's very sick.'

'Oh no. What's wrong?'

'She has a serious heart condition. Probably needs an operation.'

God in Heaven! I thought. Shevaughne's only five months old and small for her age. Corinne, her twin, was twice her size. Mary gave me more details over a cup of tea.

'She has a patent *ductus arteriosus*, that's why she hasn't grown like Corinne, and why she pants and vomits.'

The *ductus arteriosus*, I knew, was the blood vessel which bypassed the lungs of the unborn child, allowing it to obtain its oxygen from its mother's blood via the umbilical cord. At birth, this vessel should close, thus diverting the blood through the baby's lungs. If it stays open, about a third of the blood that should have gone through the lungs bypasses these organs and is circulated back through the heart. The baby is, therefore, starved of oxygen, the heart pumps twice as fast as it should, and the results can be serious.

'How did you find out?' I asked.

'Divil bit Fuffy in the eye – well, not exactly bit, more of a bruise with a tooth, and since it was Sunday and I couldn't get our doctor, I asked the German doctor down the road to have a look at it. While he was here, I thought I would get a second opinion on Shivy. After he had listened to her chest, he asked me what we were doing about her heart condition!'

'But hell, the paediatrician at the hospital has been checking her regularly. Why didn't he tell us?'

'Pure incompetence, I'm afraid.'

'So now what?'

'We have an appointment with the cardiologist tomorrow afternoon.'

My problems were forgotten. Tummy upsets were one thing, heart problems in a five-month-old baby were something else!

The cardiologist advised drug treatment until Shevaughne was a bit older and stronger, before attempting surgery to close the offending blood vessel. We took her home and watched her carefully. The treatment seemed to be working.

Hardly had we accepted Shivy's condition, when another crisis arose. I came home from office to find Lys writhing on her bed. Mary had taken the others to ballet class, but Lys hadn't felt well enough. I rang the German doctor who had spotted Shivy's condition, and took Lys down to his surgery.

'Acute appendicitis. Take her round to the Clinica Kossack, right away. I'll operate in about an hour.'

431

There were no complications, but we sat up with her all night.

'Happy birthday, darling,' said Mary in the small hours. I had forgotten all about it. I was 50.

Just as Lys hobbled out of the clinic, Shivy took a turn for the worse.

'Get her into the Clinica Virgen del Carmen at once,' the cardiologist instructed. 'I'll ring them now to expect you.'

Every doctor, it seemed, had his pet clinic, this was the fifth we had patronized in our six years in Lima. He explained how to get there, and we set off in thick fog and drizzle. I couldn't find the damn place, and to make matters worse, we hit the evening rush hour and I was running out of petrol. At last, almost sobbing with anxiety and frustration, we found someone who could direct us. Shivy was placed under an oxygen tent immediately, and so started three weeks of uninterrupted vigil.

One small factor raised my spirits, I remember. I had noticed that Shivy's room in the clinic was number six, one of my lucky numbers. I hoped it would be Shivy's, too. It was something to cling to.

The doctors – cardiologist, paediatrician and, later, the surgeon – were above reproach. The nursing staff, however, were abysmal. Had not Mary or I been with her, constantly, Shivy would not have survived.

She had some infection, and her temperature had to be brought down before surgery could be attempted. Antibiotics had been prescribed and, owing to her tiny body and lack of musculature, the paediatrician had agreed to give them by mouth. They didn't seem to be working. The paediatrician was worried.

'Bring me the bottle,' he ordered the nurse. She brought it. 'Where is the measure?' The nurse produced a doll's size teaspoon. It held less than two millilitres. A normal teaspoon holds five. Shivy was being dangerously under-dosed.

I've rarely seen a doctor so angry. But there was little he could do. Trained nurses were at a premium. The clinic had to take whoever they could get.

'From now on, she'll have to have the antibiotics by injection. I'm sorry, but it's critical. We have to get her temperature down as soon as possible.'

The needle used for her first injection was so large and blunt that I went out immediately and bought our own supply. Even so, her tiny thighs, calves and bottom were soon riddled with hypodermic bruises.

Shivy improved – but the nursing didn't. One night, as the nurse tucked her into her oxygen tent, I noticed that the indicator on the cylinder said 'empty'.

432

'*Está vacío*,' I pointed out.

'*No, señor'; está lleno.*'

'The word "empty" means *vacío*,' I explained impatiently. 'The word "full" means *lleno*. The pointer is on "empty"!'

It took some time to convince her and considerably longer to obtain another cylinder, but Shivy had escaped suffocation.

Mary would spend each day with Shivy and I would take over from her after work, sleeping on the bedside settee, until Mary arrived the following morning, having dropped the kids at school.

The morning of Shivy's operation I was, thank goodness, kept very busy with an English journalist whom FAO had sent to write a story about VITAR and other FAO projects. (Later, I took Ghita to Huancayo, a trip which she dramatized, most amusingly, for the Thursday *Telegraph*.) At midday I returned to the clinic. The operation, they told me, had been successful, but Shivy was in intensive care and couldn't be visited till next day.

When I entered Shivy's room the following evening, Mary was standing by her cot, all smiles. Gone was the oxygen tent, gone the peaky little face and frightened eyes. A grinning little elf looked up at us. It was unbelievable – a miracle. The huge incision (then well-bandaged and invisible) which half-encircled her left side didn't seem to trouble her an iota. She was bright, laughing and breathing without a wheeze of any sort. My lucky 'Number six' hadn't let me down.

Shevaughne never looked back, but we do – often, and quake at the thought of what might have happened if I hadn't spotted the empty oxygen cylinder or, for that matter, if Divil hadn't injured Fuffy's eye in the first place. But then, life is a necklace of 'ifs'!

As I write this, Mary is making Shivy's wedding dress. She has an MA(Hons) degree and is a Black Belt karate instructor and a member of the national team the Springboks. She remembers nothing of her operation, 21 years ago. Only her scar remains.

Mary and I have scars, too.

AN ALPACA DREAM

It was snowing. Two days previously, we had been standing under cold showers and downing iced beer in the jungle, now we stood stamping our feet in two inches of snow that covered the La Raya pastures.

This particular visit was to demonstrate the results of the alpaca and vicuña research to Frank, who had succeeded Peter in Rome as the project's new 'Godfather'.

A tour of VITAR's activities was an exercise in climatic adaptability. One day in Lima at sea level; two days in Huancayo at 3,200 metres to see the high-altitude poultry and Ken's small-farmer dairy demonstration unit; back to Lima and on to a few broiling days and sweating nights in Iquitos and Pucallpa, to see the tropical poultry operations and cattle production in the jungle; back again to Lima for one night, and on to La Raya at 4,100 metres, to see the work on auchenidae and sometimes, like today, to trudge through snow.

Don, the FAO expert in reproduction, Professor Saul and César, the VITAR veterinarian at La Raya, all of whom had been trying to unravel some of the alpaca's extraordinary sexual habits, were with us. César was giving us a rundown on developments.

'Traditionally, it was thought that alpaca males would only serve females during the summer rains, from December to March. But now we've found that if we put males with females in June or September, they perform just as well as in January.'

'So why not leave males with the females all the year round?' Frank asked.

'Because, by the end of February, they seem to slow down and lose interest,' César replied. 'But now we know why.'

'Why?' asked Frank.

'Because they become bored with their harem.'

We sniggered, unbelieving.

'It's true,' César went on. 'One male will serve a dozen different females a day, but he'll rarely serve the same one twice. After a few weeks, depending on how many females are at his disposal, he begins to lose interest, but if he is put with an entirely new set of females, his libido comes back on track – until he gets bored with them in turn.'

'Just like humans,' Don commented dryly. 'And you'll also find that some females are never served – they seem to lack the vital ingredient of sex appeal.'

César went on to describe the act of copulation for Frank's benefit. I had seen it on previous visits. It was an odd affair. The female would lie down in front of a male, which would then squat behind and pleasure her for 20 minutes or more. Several other females would squat down behind the copulating pair, awaiting their turn.

'Twenty minutes, at this altitude, and twelve times a day?' Frank laughed. 'No wonder they have to lie down. My legs would feel a bit shaky too!'

This prolonged sexual bliss was a physiological necessity since, like the rabbit and the cat and, presumably, the camel, the female alpaca required the sexual act in order to stimulate ovulation. However, if copulation was interrupted by another male or impatient female, the copulation would terminate and the length of coitus might drop to six or seven minutes, too short for ovulation to occur. Another contributing factor to the low fertility rate.

But male boredom and interrupted ecstasy apart, it was probably nutrition that contributed most to the short mating season. The coarse *ichu* grass (a species of *Festuca*) became fibrous and deficient in energy during the dry freezing months from June to October; but by December, the rains and warmer weather would encourage the grass to try again, and this new, nutritious growth helped to renew sexual desire.

'But we no longer need sexual intercourse to stimulate ovulation,' Saul broke in. 'An injection of the appropriate hormone gives even better results, and this has opened the way for practical artificial insemination.'

'So you're home and dry?' Frank commented.

'Not quite. We still have to get the sperm from the males, which is much more difficult to collect than from bulls or rams, although we do it in the same way – by electro-ejaculation. A special vibrator is inserted into the rectum of the male and the vibrations increased until an ejaculation is produced.'

'So what about the alpaca-vicuña crossing studies?' Frank wanted to know.

'We're using vicuña semen, obtained by electro-ejaculation, on hormone-ovulated female alpacas,' César told him. 'We have to do it this way round as there are so few vicuña males available, but there are lots of alpaca females. But we still have to tranquillize the vicuña before we ejaculate them. We have now produced about fifty paco-vicuñas.'

'We hope to start a programme of ovum transplantation like they use in cattle,' interrupted Don. 'The hormone-stimulated eggs will be washed out of the females and implanted, one or two at a time, into the uterus of several other alpaca or vicuña dams, where they will be fertilized by artificial insemination. These females will then act as incubators for the fertilized ova.'

'Do you ever get twins or triplets?' Frank asked.

'Never,' César replied. 'Although from autopsies of alpaca in the early stages of pregnancy, we know that twin foetuses occur, but one of them always dies before parturition. We don't know why. Low oxygen pressure, perhaps, or low nutrition, or some innate protective mechanism. We don't know.'

After birth, he told us, the struggle for survival began – freezing cold, poor nutrition and decimating diseases. The young, or *tuis*, were usually born in the morning, so that the sun could warm and dry them during their first hours in an unfriendly world. If they were born later in the day, when storms occurred, or if night descended before they were dry, many would die.

Internal and external parasites as well as enteric diseases played havoc with the *tuis*, but probably the greatest danger were the alpaca farmers themselves. Indifferent to progress, uninterested in the welfare of their workers, many were unwilling to leave Lima or Arequipa and face the rigours of the *altiplano*. So long as they received their annual cheque for the shearings, they were content to leave the care and development of their herds to the apathetic Indian herdsmen, who could hardly be expected to show much initiative.

However, the work that VITAR was doing, which showed that meat and fibre production could be doubled by good feeding and management, and the possibility of developing large herds of the more valuable *paco-vicuña*, was beginning to change their attitude and gave real hope for the economy of the cold, barren wastes of the southern *sierra*.

'When I retire,' I told Saul, 'I'm going to take some alpaca and vicuña back to Ireland and farm them. They should do well on the heather and frochan, even if they are only a few feet above sea level.'

'You'll be lucky,' Saul replied. 'There's a law prohibiting the export of any auchenidae except to zoos.'

It was a nice dream, all the same.

RABIES GALORE

'Viejo! Como le va?'

It took me a moment to recognize the short, bubbling, white-haired ball of fire.

'Aurelio!' We embraced in Latin style.

Aurelio had obtained his degree from Edinburgh ten years before me, and we had met when, as head of the Pan-American Sanitary Bureau's office in Mexico City, he had paid frequent visits to Jamaica. Now here he was again, his cheery face and white, bushy moustache bouncing into my office. He had returned to San Marcos to work on rabies, and Manuel had already conscripted him into VITAR.

His escapades in the control of rabies in the Caribbean were legendary. One island veterinarian told me that if the owner refused to let

436

View from Rockmoor looking north towards Cuba.

Port Maria (1948)
where Ian Fleming was married.

Robin's Bay.

Pigeon Island with 'Invader'.

Jamaica Brahmans grazing Guinea grass beneath Guango trees, Caymanas estates.

Pru and Roger with Roger's Mum. Drunkenman's Cay 1951.

'Farcy' Truetta treatment and healing ulcer.

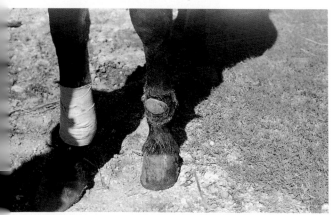

Jack paddling.

'Flat' warts cow from Yallahs 1950.

Lake flies, Entebbe 'Burning bush'.

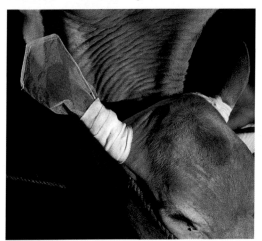

Ear bag with ticks for ECF immunization, Entebbe 1962.

Ankole cow, Mbarara 1962.

Namalu, Karamoja. Hobbit country 1962.

Andes *en route* Pucallpa.

Alpaca mating, La Raya.

Paco-vicuña tuis, La Raya.

Pucallpa. Main street from Hotel Comfort 1968.

Campa Indian girl selling beads, Pucallpa.

Andean girl near Cuzco.

Family, Moorland Hall, Mary Tavy, Devon, on leave. Mary and Shivy, Lindley, Shannon, Kerry, Fuffy, Lys (behind) Mela, Self with Coro, 1970.

Peasant farmers' milk cooperative collection point. Sponsored by Irish Aid. Mozambique 1981.

The Guilbride girls and Gonza, Maputo 1981. *Left to Right* Shannon, Coro, Lindley, Shivy, Mela, Lys, Fuffy and Mary.

Mary with Freak.

them vaccinate his dogs, Aurelio would kick him where it hurt most, and by the time he had recovered, the dogs had all been jabbed!

'What if the owner was a woman?' I had asked.

'Women are never a problem to Aurelio; he can charm any woman into anything.'

There was plenty of rabies in Peru, mainly in dogs and mainly along the coastal strip, but there was also another form of the disease in cattle, occurring principally in the jungle and the foothills, called 'paralytic rabies' or *derriengue*, and carried by vampire bats. Aurelio was soon in the thick of both mad dogs and paralytic cows.

With the expansion of livestock farming in the jungle, reports of paralytic cattle became increasingly frequent. In one area he found that over 150 cattle had died with paralytic symptoms over a period of several months, and all had shown the tell-tale bites of the vampire.

'What's been happening is this,' he explained. 'Colonies of vampires exist in caves and canyons all through the jungle. They've been there for thousands of years, living on the blood of wild animals. And they've always been infected with rabies virus which doesn't cause them much harm. Then along comes man, clearing the jungle to make pastures for his cattle. Sooner or later, the bats find the cattle and readily appreciate the easy source of blood. After a time they establish a colony close to their new source of food, and outbreaks of *derriengue* begin to occur.'

'So how are we going to control it? We can't eradicate all the bats in the jungle.'

'Vaccination. It's the only way. Exterminating bat colonies, housing animals in barns at night, protected by fine mesh wire netting, smearing strychnine paste onto the bite wounds, all help, but vaccination is the only real answer.'

With Japanese mist nets used for catching birds, Aurelio found 12 species of bats not previously recorded in Peru. Although he had been vaccinated against rabies several times in his life and probably possessed a strong immunity, he was, I thought, a little cavalier in extracting the furry, wriggling bodies from the nets each morning without wearing gloves! Inevitably, he was bitten.

'If they *are* infected,' he would quip, 'then they will help to boost my immunity.'

After the bat brains were removed, they were packed in ice and hand-carried to Lima for diagnosis and isolation of the rabies virus. However, one large consignment of 1,000 brains, which was sent by air freight never arrived! To this day, no-one knows what happened to those brains. Perhaps somebody mistook them for one of the jungle's culinary delicacies, and had them fried on toast for breakfast. As long as they were well-cooked, with plenty of pepper and lemon, they probably tasted delicious!

It wasn't only in dogs and jungle cattle that we had problems with rabies.

'Ken wants you on the blower,' Kattia called from the door. I hurried to the radio which connected us to the Huancayo and Pucallpa stations. Ken was the New Zealand expert in milk production at Huancayo.

'Pat. We've a problem. Remember our pet alpaca?' (I certainly did. Ken had brought it from La Raya the previous year. It was part of the family.) 'Well, it has just died of rabies.'

'I don't believe it. Who made the diagnosis?'

'It was behaving peculiarly for a couple of days, then became paralysed and died. The clinical boys at the lab made brain-squash smears and found Negri bodies. They've sent material to the Rabies Institute for confirmation.'

'When did it die?'

'Two days ago; we've just got the results. Now they tell us that a mad dog was seen on the farm last month. The alpaca was probably bitten by it. Problem is that I and the kids all tried to feed it while it was sick, so we've all been pretty well exposed.'

'You must start inoculations at once,' I commanded in my most authoritative voice. 'Come down today? I'll get the vaccine and arrange with our doctor to start the injections tonight.'

There was no alternative to vaccination, however unpleasant. I knew, from both the clinical and psychological aspects, that it was vital for inoculations to begin at once.

Unfortunately, the only vaccine available was one made locally from the brains of suckling mice. It had to be given daily for 12 days. The newer, tissue-culture vaccine, which required only three injections, was not available.

Ken and Helen brought their four youngsters to Lima that afternoon. They had decided to treat the whole excursion as a holiday, with visits to the flicks each day, excess of ice-cream – anything to take the kids' minds off the daily trip to the doctor.

It was a harrowing time for all of them. Injection sites in the skin of their stomachs, shoulders, arms and legs, became so sore they couldn't lie down. They felt ill and ran temperatures. But they stuck it out, almost without a whimper.

'I wish I had a medal I could give the kids,' I told Helen when it was all over.

'So do I,' she replied. 'But they are already heroes back in New Zealand. They've had their names and pictures in the papers.'

'And I bet they are the first kids ever to be vaccinated from contact with a rabid alpaca,' I added.

Rabies niggled us on other occasions. A friend's son was bitten on the way to school. The dog in question was wont to chase up and down behind a garden railing, hurling insults in its own language at the kids who passed by. They, no doubt, returned them with sticks and stones. One day the dog got free and bit the boy. It wasn't a bad bite, a little disinfectant and a Band-aid was all that was necessary.

Unfortunately, the dog died a few days later. This changed the whole picture. The local vet thought it was poisoning, but what the poison was, he couldn't say. He had not considered rabies, and no brain samples had been taken. It was only later that this new, and horrible, possibility, was realized.

Donny rang me. 'What do I do?' he asked anxiously.

'Start vaccinating Ricky immediately,' I advised. 'I know that it is more likely that the dog was just frustrated and angry, but it *did* bite Ricky and it *did* die, so it *might* be rabies. The vet probably said it was poison because he couldn't think of anything else. Don't take a chance. Vaccinate now, otherwise, in a few weeks you'll all be having sleepless nights.'

'Thanks,' he said. 'I will.'

I was a little dismayed, therefore, when I rang up a few days later to see how Ricky was getting along with his jabs.

'Donny's gone to the jungle,' his wife told me, 'with Ricky.'

'Has he taken vaccine with him?'

'No.'

My palm was sticky when I replaced the receiver.

When I next met Donny, a couple of weeks later, I asked him angrily how he could have been so god-damned irresponsible.

'Well,' he replied rather sheepishly, 'the more I thought about it, the more I was convinced that it was not rabies and, since Ricky is so terrified of injections, I thought I'd take him away for a week or two where no-one could contact us.'

'You're a brave man,' I told him. 'And a bloody stupid one.' He also, thank God proved to be a bloody lucky one!

Sometimes, rabies vaccine could prove almost as dangerous as the disease itself.

'Douglas has only had four of his twelve injections,' said a distraught mother, over the phone. 'The doctor says it's imperative to continue with them, but he has a high temperature, a rash and vomits anything he eats. He's really sick.'

'You should get a second opinion,' I advised, 'but first tell me what happened.'

It was another case of a teased dog but, this time, the dog was owned by a woman pedlar, and both had disappeared.

'When did you last see her?' I asked.

'About three days after Douglas was bitten.'

'Was the dog with her then?'

'Yes. It was fine. It was only after we insisted that she take the dog for examination that she disappeared.'

'My advice is that you should stop the vaccinations,' I told her. 'The vaccine is more likely to kill Douglas than the remote possibility that the dog had rabies.'

Since the dog was alive and well three days after biting Douglas, it was a hundred to one that the dog had merely vented its anger on the nearest small boy. But had Douglas shown no reaction to the vaccine, I would have advised her, strongly, to continue.

As it was, I had a few sleepless nights, myself. But that's par for the course with rabies!

HOLOCAUST AT HUARAZ

The Devonshire meadow hummed with insect life. All around, flowers were wilting in the hot June sun. Nearby gurgled a little brook, the headwaters of the river Tavy. If I raised my head, I could just see the ancient stone bridge that crossed it below Wapsworthy, shimmering in the heat. The children, stitchless as always when conditions allowed, were grubbing in the stream for treasures. On another rug Mary was gently snoring.

The soft strains of classical music, oozing contentedly from my transistor radio, came to an end. A news bulletin was announced. No, no, I thought. This wasn't the time or place to hear how self-seeking statesmen were screwing up the world. I reached over to turn it off. As I fumbled for the switch, I heard the word 'Peru'. I turned up the volume.

'Seventy thousand people are reported dead following an avalanche in the Peruvian Andes ... the towns of Yungay and Huaraz...'

Seventy thousand? Impossible. A few hundred perhaps, a thousand at the outside. Seventy thousand? No way! Well, I'd soon know. My leave finished in a few days, the following week I would be back in harness.

Now, two years later, Ben (the new poultry expert) and I were heading for the Callejon de Huayllas, Peru's 'Little Switzerland', where the terrible tragedy had occurred. Not 70,000 had perished, as the first reports had said. The final count was nearer 100,000.

We had turned off the hot coastal tarmac at the village of Pativilca, 200 kilometres north of Lima, and had climbed a winding, dusty road to enter the southern end of the Huayllas valley. The air here was cool and the clouds hung low over us, threatening rain.

Beside the road, the clear, peat-tinged waters of the Santa river, fresh from marshy uplands, flowed over pastel-coloured rocks. A scene from Connemara, I thought. On the northern sky-line, the mighty Huascaran, 22,000 feet at its snowy summit, rose menacingly above the white-crested peaks of the Cordillera Blanca. How many other tragic avalanches, I wondered, had originated on its precipitous slopes?

Within an hour, we reached Huaraz – what was left of it. Outlying parts of the town had been swept away, and with them some 30,000 souls, but the central business area had escaped. It was hard to imagine a dirtier, more crowded and drearier town. Sullen-faced women in characteristic white straw hats with broad black bands and long, mud-splashed skirts, hauled irritable, snotty-nosed kids through the throng, while the menfolk, in their colourful balaclava-like *churus*, cheeks bulging with coca leaves, and the universal sack over their hunched shoulders, ambled between the curbside stalls, which offered everything from food to fripperies.

We were fortunate (a euphemism in this case) to find a room in the Hotel Barcelona, a two-storeyed, once whitewashed, concrete shoebox. With uncarpeted concrete floor, lack of heating, single central unshaded light bulb, iron cots and indescribable end-of-passage toilet, our quarters were unspeakably depressing. The Hotel Turista, which we could have relied upon for basic comforts, had been requisitioned by the authorities co-ordinating the rehabilitation of the area. Medical Missions from Germany, Switzerland, Japan and Britain were still active two years after the tragedy.

We had come to Huaraz at the request of this same Co-ordinating Authority, with detailed plans to establish poultry production units along the lines of Cachi Cachi and Yanahuanca. The high-level meeting at the Hotel Turista to settle the details, however, was not a success. Each of the 20 or so participants had his own ideas of what to do, and all were different. We had been assured that only the final technical details were required before the programme could take off; on the strength of this, Ben had arranged for 10,000 chicks to be made ready at Huancayo to start operations. By midday, however,

441

the only decision agreed upon was that Ben should inspect and advise on the proposed operation sites before further action was taken. Who was actually going to liaise with us, and run the projects on behalf of the Co-ordinating Authority, was still undecided.

'It'll take another six months,' Ben sighed as we headed for lunch at the Restaurante Iris, a converted roadside shack.

By mid-afternoon, our guide had shown us all the proposed sites, only one of which could, at a pinch and considerable cost, be adapted to produce chickens.

'Let's look at Yungay, while we're here,' Ben suggested.

Huaraz, undoubtedly, had suffered a terrible calamity but Yungay, 50 kilometres down the valley, had been obliterated. Here, 60,000 people had disappeared within five minutes. We gazed in awe over the three-kilometre expanse of mud, now hard enough to support roads, which covered the erstwhile town. All that remained was a carpet of flowers, interspersed with small white crosses to mark the spots, 15 metres below, where families had once lived.

The avalanche had been caused, it appeared, by an earthquake which had dislodged part of a glacier on Huascaran, depositing millions of tons of ice and rocks into a small lake. The sudden increase in the volume of the lake, together with another tremor, burst its sides, sending its contents of water, rocks and mud hurtling down the twin valleys to Huaraz and Yungay. Survivors said they heard the rumbling ten minutes before the avalanche hit. Its speed was estimated at over 100 kilometres an hour, with rocks as big as houses bowling along on a cushion of air.

We stood in silence. Words were unnecessary. Here, women had gossiped, men drunk, children played. Now only flowers and crosses remained between enormous boulders, to warn future generations to beware the mighty Huascarán.

The few inhabitants that had been spared included a group of children watching a Sunday afternoon circus on high ground outside the town, and a handful of people already on Cemetery Hill, another high point, amongst whom was a Japanese photographer who filmed the disaster. They were rescued two days later by helicopter.

Renée, one of the VITAR secretaries, had the good fortune to leave Yungay an hour before the tragedy, but her family remained behind – beneath the mud. Some young Peace Corps Volunteers and a New Zealand mountaineering team will also lie there for all eternity.

It was the second time in living memory that Yungay had been devastated, but this time no-one attempted to dig out the victims.

Instead, the area was declared a national park and people were invited to plant flowers, in memory of the dead beneath.

We turned and headed back to Huaraz in silence, leaving this twentieth-century Pompeii to its sleeping souls.

Early next morning, we took the road westwards over the snowless Cordillera Negra to the small town of Casma on the coastal highway. We stopped at the crest of the ridge and watched the sunlight flow into the Huayllas Valley as it had done for aeons past, as it had done on that fateful Sunday two years before, and as it would continue to do for years beyond the future.

The roadside was ablaze with red, yellow and blue flowers, each catching a ray of the sun as it peeped over the mountains. I picked a bouquet of wild heads. They seemed much the same as those amongst which I had lain in the Devonshire meadow when I had first heard of – and disbelieved – the holocaust in the Callejon de Huayllas.

A JUNGLE HEROINE

'Oh, no! Not again! This is their second this year.'

I couldn't believe what my secretary was telling me.

'It's true,' Kattia insisted. 'A hundred students, all dead!'

Four airlines linked the major cities and remoter settlements in the Andes and the jungle, their sometimes vintage planes lurching down between snowy crags or gliding onto muddy, forest-lined runways.

The oldest and most trusted of these was Fawcett. Its record was excellent although some of its planes, like the unpressurized little DC3s, stretched back almost to World War Two days. Nearly as reliable was the army-run airline SATCO, which flew to the remotest corners of the country, often on routes far from economic. SATCO pilots, and the servicing of their rattling machines, were held in high esteem, and had the reputation of flying anywhere in any weather. On one SATCO flight from Tarapoto to Yurimaguas, in the jungle, Jim and I had to sit on bags of coffee beans. The port engine also refused to start, so the pilot raced down the runway on his good engine until there was sufficient wind resistance to turn the lifeless one. He must have done it several times before, I thought, and knew it would work, because if the engine hadn't caught at the last minute, we'd have landed in the Huallaga.

A third airline, Transperuana, dealt mainly with freight. Then there was the fourth airline, LANSA, which had started up recently.

For some reason, I don't remember why, the UN office advised its staff to patronize only Fawcett or SATCO, and only use LANSA in emergencies. Whatever the reason, it proved to be justified.

LANSA's first disaster was that day when Jim and I had flown to Puno by Fawcett and had poked fun at the schoolgirlish LANSA air hostesses, little guessing that they had less than an hour to live. After that crash, LANSA immediately grounded all its Constellations and closed down for several months. But less than a year later it was in operation and now, within months, disaster had struck again.

Fifty American students had arrived on a friendship tour to visit places of historic or archaeological interest. An equal number of Peruvian students had accompanied their American guests as guides to Cuzco and Machu Picchu on one of LANSA's new Electra aircraft. Taking off from Cuzco on the return flight, the plane failed to gain height and ploughed through a wood five kilometres from the runway, killing every student and all but one of the crew.

It was the most disastrous air tragedy that Peru had experienced; fifty young Americans and their forty-nine Peruvian colleagues had perished. Amongst them was the daughter of Lima's popular and dynamic mayor. The sole survivor was a trainee pilot who, because no seats were available, squatted behind the co-pilot and had no seat belt. He was rescued from a tree and recovered.

Evidence at the enquiry revealed that the plane was grossly overloaded for that altitude.

This would be the end of LANSA, everyone thought, and rightly so. Two crashes within one year! But no; some months later, amongst much publicity emphasizing new management, and backed by a well-known American airline, LANSA was once more in the air flying new Japanese Rolls-Royce turbo jets. I even risked a flight on one myself, to Iquitos. It was an extremely comfy and enjoyable trip.

Meanwhile both Fawcett and SATCO had had a disaster. Why Fawcett had hit the hill while taking off from Huanuco, was never adequately explained, but it had, and half a hundred persons, amongst them the First Secretary of the British Embassy and his wife, lost their lives. SATCO's crash could be explained but not excused. It occurred in mountainous country in very bad weather – weather in which only SATCO would have dared to fly.

Then came Christmas Eve, 1971.

The first International Conference on the Preservation of the Vicuna had just finished with a visit to the Vicuna reserve at Pampas de Galleras. Dr Maria Koepcke, a Professor of Zoology in San Marcos, who was working closely with VITAR's programme for wildlife domestication in Pucallpa, had been one of the organizers. The Conference had delayed her return to Pucallpa but the LANSA flight on Christmas Eve, she told me, would get her there in time to join her husband Hans, also a Professor of Zoology, for Christmas in their jungle camp near Pucallpa. Her daughter, Juliana, who had just matriculated from the German school, Humboldt, would accompany her.

The flight appeared to be normal, there were some thunderstorms about but nothing to cause undue alarm – until air control at Pucallpa noted that the plane, which had begun its descent, had disappeared.

Christmas, that year, was a non-event for many Peruvians. Four of the VITAR staff had had relatives aboard and we knew of two other families whose relatives were missing. As with the Caribbean International Airways crash in Jamaica, twenty years before, gloom settled on a large part of the community. The fact that no-one knew for certain what had happened made it worse.

Aircraft from the Air Force, the Linguistics Institute and private sources scoured the jungle, rumours and red herrings abounded, but there was no sign of the plane. The United States sent a specially equipped aircraft to help. Still nothing.

On New Year's Day, Lys and I climbed the sandhills behind our house. As we sat under the lone tree at the top and gazed out over the plain to where Lima shimmered in the heat haze, I told her a secret which, until then, I had kept to myself.

'You could have been on that plane,' I told her.

'How?' she asked, unbelieving.

'Dr Koepcke suggested that she took you across with Juliana for the Christmas holidays. I told her how keen you were on wildlife.'

'Why didn't you let me go, Daddy?'

'I told her you'd go another time. Christmas is for families to spend at home.'

'Lucky you did. I might be wandering about in the jungle with them instead of sitting here.'

'I hope they *are* wandering about the jungle,' I murmured, doubtfully. 'But one thing I know for certain; if either Dr Koepcke or her daughter survive the crash, they'll survive the jungle. They both know it backwards.'

Ten days passed. No hope now, we all said.

Then, on 4 January, came a flash on the six o'clock news. Juliana had reached Tournavista! It's impossible to describe our elation. We danced around hugging each other and ringing friends who might not have heard. I wanted to rush out and yell it to the world. Few things have caused me so much emotion.

'Didn't I tell you,' I kept repeating in a cracked voice! 'I knew they'd make it!'

Juliana was safe, but what had happened to her mum, and the others? There was no news of Maria. We kept our ears glued to the radio.

Soon, the whole story was known. Maria Koepcke had been killed in the crash. Juliana, who had been sitting next to her, asleep, had been knocked unconscious for a time. A few others had survived the actual crash, but the jungle had been too daunting. Only Juliana had had the confidence, skill and pluck, to tackle the miles of hostile forest.

When she had recovered sufficiently to set out for help early that Christmas morning, she did what her father had so often told her. 'If you get lost,' he'd said, 'walk downhill. Soon you will find a stream. Follow it, it will lead you to a bigger one, and then to a river and civilization.'

She did exactly that and, eventually, after ten days of unbelievable hardships, she reached the Pachitea river. There she found a track which led to a hut with a canoe beside it. Two Indian fishermen returning late that afternoon, found a pathetic figure asleep by their craft. When she told them that she was a survivor of the LANSA crash, they lost no time in paddling her down the Pachitea to Tournavista. On the way they fed her the first real food she'd had for ten days, and gouged out the maggots that infested her wounds.

The next day the whole world applauded a courageous young girl who, single-handed and against overwhelming odds, had conquered the Amazon jungle.

Juliana's arrival had given new hope for survivors. From her directions a light plane found the crash site and an amateur parachutist from the Linguistics Institute jumped into the forest canopy. He found no-one alive. The few survivors, some of whom had written pathetic notes in blood, had died of thirst, their wounds, or despair, while waiting for rescue.

Juliana was transferred to the hospital at the Linguistics Institute at Yarinacocha and protected from the scores of international journalists who fought for her story.

The last time I met her, six weeks after the crash, she was walking in the Institute's grounds with her father. No-one would have guessed that this slight, bespectacled girl had just achieved so epic a feat.

After a simple ceremony at Lima airport, the body of Maria Koepcke was flown to Germany for burial.

Eventually, a book, 'Juliana's Story' appeared and a film was made of it. It was called 'Miracles can Happen'.

Miracles certainly – but courage too!

* * *

446

It was not just us. Neighbouring Projects also had their toll of air disasters.

Dougie, the Australian manager of a livestock project in Bolivia, had visited me several times.

'It's your turn, now, Pat.'

'I want to,' I replied, 'and I'm sure Rome will agree. Let me know when it's convenient.'

Although his project operated in the jungle and all his experts lived in the jungle town of Santa Cruz; Dougie himself made his headquarters in the administrative capital, La Paz, high up in the Andes, close to the seat of Government and their ever-changing agricultural policies.

Shortly after his visit to Peru, he wrote that he would be attending the annual livestock show in Santa Cruz and if I could join him it would be an excellent opportunity to see what they were doing. FAO approved my visit and I booked a flight.

A week before I was to leave, a cable from Rome advised me that the new Director of the Livestock Division had had to rearrange his South American tour and would now visit Peru the same week I intended to be in Bolivia. They also suggested that Dougie came over to Lima to meet the Director.

Unfortunately, Dougie had promised to accompany the Minister of Agriculture to the show and afterwards to visit the Minster's Santa Cruz ranch. He felt it politic to stick to the plan as the future of his project might be endangered if he backed out. Would I explain to the Director?

After attending the show and no doubt praising the Minister's cattle, Dougie took a charter flight back to La Paz. On board were the Bolivian National Soccer Team. Somewhere in the Andes the plane hit a mountain. Everyone was killed.

Dougie's twin teenage daughters stayed a night with us on the way from Australia to join their mother in La Paz. There was little comfort we could give the two distraught girls.

For Mary and me there was at least some slight compensation. Roger, of Jamaica and East African days, who had now joined FAO, replaced Dougie as Project Manager in Bolivia. Once more he and Pru were our neighbours.

What made Dougie's death even more difficult to come to terms with was that the day after the Minister returned to La Paz, he was sacked!

TIME TO MOVE ON

It was time to go. However much we enjoyed life in Peru, we couldn't stay there forever, and the end of Phase II was approaching. FAO officials rarely remained in the same country for more than four or five years, and I had been in Lima for nearly ten. 'Quite sufficient to establish a research institute,' I could hear Rome muttering.

I had mixed feelings about leaving. We had built a house and made many close Peruvian friends. Four of our children had been born in Lima and had dual nationality. We were almost Peruvians ourselves! We now spoke of Lima as 'home'. Indeed, to the children it was.

VITAR had achieved some spectacular results, such as hatching in the *sierra*, the reproduction of alpaca and their crossing with vicuña, milk production at high altitude, where Ken, helped by Erik, a young Bavarian pasture agronomist, was now keeping two and a half cows on one hectare of pasture (instead of the normal three hectares needed for each cow). Santi and Peter had stamped their mark on pasture and cattle production in the jungle, and our visions of united livestock development between VITAR, SIPA and Tournavista had now been made official. Our initial forays into liver fluke control with *Chaetogaster*, and our tropical poultry production were also highly promising.

San Marcos University had recently made me an Honorary Professor, an accolade usually reserved as a 'thank you' for the end of one's service. Perhaps I should take the hint. Moreover, Manuel had just left to take up the post of Deputy Director in Veterinary Public Health for the World Health Organization in Washington. VITAR wouldn't be the same without him. It was the end of an era.

Mary had a different view.

'It's taken us ten years to get things the way we want them. The house is perfect, the kids are doing well at school, ballet and sports. Why give all this up for some God-forsaken spot where we'll have to start all over again, and probably have to send the kids to school in England?'

'Unfortunately, darling, it's not my decision.'

I had planned to wait until the end of the project before taking overseas leave, but Rome insisted I should take it immediately. We would use it to find suitable schools in Britain for our elder children, so that they would have some continuity in education, no matter where we were sent. Shannon was 15, Lys 14 and Kerry, our son, 12; critical ages in their schooling.

After six weeks, we managed to place Shannon and Kerry. Then a letter from Rome informed me that a Project Evaluation Mission was due to arrive in Peru in two weeks, and I should return at once to shepherd them around. Leaving Mary to settle Shannon and Kerry into their new institutions, I returned to Peru with the remaining six, aged 4 to 14.

The FAO mission – all old friends – presented no problems, but two other entirely unexpected factors did. Our maid, on whom I was relying to look after the smaller kids, disappeared the day after we arrived. Maybe the thought of coping with them without Mary was too daunting. And I found John, a high-level scientist whom I had met before in Uganda, waiting for me. He'd come to Peru under the aegis of the Royal Society to study heat regulation in alpacas, and needed help with his programme.

As long as I was in Lima, I could cope. The elder three kids looked after the three tots, while I cooked and – occasionally – cleaned. Kattia, my million-dollar secretary, offered to sleep in the house whenever I was away, and to take the small ones to kindergarten. Dinah, one of our earliest Peruvian friends, collected the babes each midday and entertained them till the older children arrived back from school. Even John, the Royal Society boffin, acted as babysitter a couple of times.

'I can now report to the Royal Society that my visit wasn't entirely wasted,' he told me.

Then succour arrived from an entirely unexpected quarter. While in Pucallpa with the evaluation mission, I mentioned to Peter and his wife that Mary was still in England, and I had no maid. Without a word to me, Hefina flew to Lima the following day and took charge of *chez* Guilbride until the FAO Mission left.

The verdict of the Mission was predictable; VITAR would continue to receive UN assistance in certain specialized fields, but there was no longer a need for a project manager.

I was out.

* * *

Selling up after ten years, apart from losing our only home, terrified us. We found it difficult to be polite, to smile gracefully at ridiculous offers, to ignore comments on the paintwork, drains, metal window frames, the smallness of the kitchen and all the other ploys with which house-buyers try to shame the owner into reducing the price. And even after it was sold, there would still be the equally difficult problem of getting the money out of Peru in hard currency. We decided to ask 2,000,000 soles, about $50,000, and see what happened.

449

A gentleman of Chinese origin seemed keen but vague as to payment. An Englishman appeared to be interested, praised everything effusively, said how thrilled he was to have seen it and offered me $15,000 – less than a third of my price! He left without the drink I usually offered prospective buyers.

We had some better offers, but it was obvious that we were asking too much. Devaluation and a number of other financial restrictions had left the Peruvians with little loose change. Perhaps 1,500,000 soles would be more realistic.

The British Embassy, I was told, were expanding and would need houses. I conducted their man round our domain, pointing out the lovely views, the quiet district, the orchard (which never gave us so much as a single *chirimoya*), the lovely blue gums we had planted (which would soon block out the lovely views), the large playroom, so useful for receptions (if the children's artistry was first painted over), the kitchen (well, that could always be enlarged), the small swimming pool (no, there was no filter, but that could easily be installed) – a small pool was so much more manageable than a large one, didn't he think? He didn't. Misguidedly, I felt, the Embassy were not convinced that our beautiful home would help solve their housing problem.

We were still sparring with house-hunters when FAO suggested I take over their livestock production project in Recife in North-East Brazil.

I consulted the United Nations' list of projects. Only two others had been located in Recife, both WHO projects to control mosquitoes. That, in itself, seemed a bit ominous. The FAO livestock project had been running two years and had already disposed of two project managers; the last, an American, had been sacked a few months before. It was a real Cinderella of a project, my spies in FAO told me, but with my experience in Peru, Rome thought I could make it work. I wondered who, at headquarters, had it in for me!

'What's Recife like?' I asked a passing official with knowledge of Brazil's North-East.

'It's a challenge,' he replied, which I knew was just another way of saying it was bloody awful.

'And what's all this I hear about mosquitoes?'

'Don't worry,' he assured me. 'They're so big you can shoot them with a catapult. And there's no malaria.'

A decision to accept or not was made no easier by a letter from Manuel, in Washington, suggesting I should apply for a new post in WHO which entailed the supervision of veterinary public health projects in Latin America. We would be working closely together.

Pedro, his boss (also a Peruvian), would be passing through Lima the following week; why didn't I discuss it with him?

Nothing could have been more attractive. Any job connected with zoonoses, those diseases of animals transmissible to man, which would also allow me to visit friends in Jamaica and Peru, as well as keep in touch with VITAR, seemed too good to be true. The family would also reap the benefits of Washington life – I wasn't too clear what these would be but, for God's sake, they'd be a hell of a lot better than mosquito-ridden Recife.

Pedro confirmed the vacancy, but there were snags. The dollar crisis had frozen all new posts in the UN network. He'd let me know as soon as the post was released.

In the meantime, I gleaned as much information as I could about Brazil.

'Marvellous place, man. Wish I was going back. Knocks spots off Peru,' said one. 'It hums. Peru's a morgue compared to Brazil,' said another. 'Don't go near the place,' said a third, a French lady journalist. 'It's a police state. Are you taking your family? Be careful, three of my friends disappeared, one of them a teenager. I'll never go back. They're a bunch of Nazis.'

Like me, Mary was all for Washington. Then another cable from Rome advised me that if I didn't accept the Recife post by return, they would have to retire me as they had nothing else to offer. I rang Pedro. He still didn't know when the Washington job would be released, perhaps two or three months – if at all. And, of course, there was no guarantee that I would be selected. I couldn't wait; I had a family to support. Anyway, FAO was the devil I knew.

So I accepted, with the mental proviso that if the Washington job materialized in time and I was appointed, I would back out of Recife. It was now the end of November. My transfer date to Recife had been set for the end of February. I would have to hurry.

Several more prospective buyers were given the Grand Tour of our estate, but most remained unimpressed, even at the lower price. However, one appeared particularly interested. He couldn't quite meet the full amount in cash, but proposed a deal which would also help with my biggest hurdle, how to transfer my money out in dollars.

Konrad suggested that he pay $6,000 (about 240,000 soles) into my New York bank, the rest (which would be declared as the official sale price) would be paid in soles in Peru. This would also reduce the 6 per cent capital gains tax, or *alcabala*, payable on the whole amount. He also agreed to let Mary stay on in the house until the following April so the kids could complete their school term, while I found a house and settled into Recife. All in all, it suited us very well.

I took the contract of sale to Kattia's father, an experienced commercial lawyer, to look over.

'I see that Mr Konrad is to pay you three hundred thousand soles immediately, and another four hundred thousand as soon as he can arrange a loan from the *Banco Hipotecario*, the Mortgage Bank.'

'That's right. He says it should only take a couple of weeks. He has friends in the bank.'

Alcides quizzed me over his gold-rimmed glasses. 'I presume all your house documents are in order. The *Banco Hipotecario* goes over them with a very fine comb. Friends or no friends, it can take a long time, even if everything is straightforward.'

'They should be all right; they were done by Dr Carlos.' I mentioned a well-known lawyer.

'Well, we shall see.' They were prophetic words.

The first payment of 300,000 soles was to be made, and the transfer documents signed by Konrad and myself at a notary's office in the heart of Lima's oldest district. The building was Colonial Spanish, two storeys of carved wood with a magnificent, ornate, shuttered verandah, overhanging a narrow lane. Inside was pure Dickens, a film set for *Scrooge*. Heavy, scarred desks and benches were laden with ancient, calf-bound volumes. The musty air, undisturbed by several white-haired, arthritic clerks, smelled of old vellum. To one side of the dark general office, a wooden staircase, hardly more than a ladder and rail, led up to a mezzanine floor. At the back of this landing, in a cubby-hole, hemmed in by statues and objects usually found in junk shops, we discovered a bespectacled gnome who confirmed that he was, indeed, the *notario*.

He may have appeared to be on his last legs, but I soon found that he was not as decrepit as he looked.

'It says here that the price of the house is seventy-five thousand soles. Why, then, Mr Konrad, are you paying three hundred thousand soles as the first instalment?'

I grabbed the contract. Sure enough, Konrad's secretary had left out a zero from the price. You've earned your fee, gnome, I thought.

Alcides' doubts regarding the Mortgage Bank's delay were well-founded. As the time came for me to depart, they still hadn't made a decision. I saw that I would have to leave the final details of the sale until I returned from Recife to pick up the family, in two months time.

452

It was sad saying goodbye to so many friends and colleagues – now over 100 in VITAR alone. The Institute was, I knew, probably the most effective veterinary research centre in South America, due, almost entirely, to the drive, vision and organizing ability of Manuel. To have worked in VITAR, I told the farewell gathering, was in itself, a recommendation.

I made swift farewell visits to the research stations. At Huancayo they had a *pachamanca*. A shallow pit was lined with large round stones and a wood fire lit in it. When the stones were sizzling hot, the twigs and surplus ashes were replaced with portions of sheep and aromatic leaves. Then the pit was closed and left for a few hours until the contents were well cooked. At Pucallpa we consumed large amounts of *cebiche* and beer, and at La Raya we feasted on alpaca steaks.

The day of my intended departure saw me up before dawn. Last-minute talks with the FAO and UN officials on VITAR and (equally important) ways and means of converting my soles to dollars, which they had promised to arrange; discussions with Konrad on where and when to deposit the money he owed me; queuing for hours at the *Banco de la Nación*, the only source of foreign currency, which I needed for my trip; and in making final arrangements with Mary for the two months I would be away, kept me busy till late evening. At ten that night, I jumped into our pool before dressing for the airport.

We had worked out a telegraphic code by which I could describe Recife, its amenities, housing, schooling, shops and climate, in case telephoning proved too difficult. We went over it as I dressed.

'Better get going,' Mary urged, 'we could have a puncture. You never know what might happen.' Indeed you don't. But it wasn't a puncture!

I closed my suitcase, picked up my *Laissez Passer* and travellers' cheques from my dressing table.

'Seen my ticket, dear? It's not here.'

We searched everywhere.

I rang the airport in desperation. They would try and arrange something; I should go out anyway. A small group of friends were there to see me off. At one o'clock in the morning, this was true friendship, and all the more embarrassing when the airline told me there was nothing they could do. I couldn't fly without a ticket.

The group broke up in silence. What can you say to someone who has wasted half the night to bid you farewell, only to be told that they might as well have stayed in bed because you had been stupid enough to lose your ticket!

Only Augusto, the Professor of Physiology, and his wife were sufficiently dedicated, or foolhardy, to see me off a second time. I was glad there were no others. I was still feeling humiliated by the first attempt.

As I was booking in, a woman touched me on the shoulder.

'I think this is yours, *señor*,' she said, handing me a wallet. 'I saw a man throw it in the rubbish. He looked suspicious, so I took it out. It had your photo inside.'

I opened it. Everything was there; my ID card, driving licence (with its photo), travellers cheques – but no money. Then I remembered that I had put my dollars and Brazilian cruzeiros into my inside pocket. Nothing was missing. I thanked her profusely.

'Let me get the hell out of here, darling,' I muttered. 'God knows what'll happen next!'

'I hope it's not a warning to keep clear of Brazil,' she replied.

But whatever 'challenges' Brazil had in store, we were confident we could meet them. Ten years in Peru had rid us of our soft Anglo-Saxon skins and attuned our gullible outlook to Latin American ways. We'd cope, no matter what!

PART FIVE

BRAZIL

(1973–1975)

São Luiz

Fortaleza

MARANHÃO

CEARÁ

Campo Maior

Iracema

RIO GRANDE
DO NORTE

Teresina

PARAÍBA

PIAUÍ

Serra
Talharda

Arcoverde

Surubim

PERNAMBUCO

Recife

Petrolina

Juazeiro

ALAGOAS

SERGIPE

Senhor
do Bonfim

Aracaju

R. São Francisco

BAHIA

Salvador

ATLANTIC
OCEAN

MINAS
GERAIS

- - - - State Boundaries
▬ ▬ ▬ Highways

100   0   100 200 300 400

KILOMETRES

NORTH-EAST BRAZIL

RECIFE – VENICE OF THE NEW WORLD

It was chaos. Rampaging students, flying back to Brazil for the 1973 *Carnaval*, had already begun their revels. Seductive girls of all shades bounced on the seats or on the laps of equally handsome lads. I and the other dozen or so card-carrying old fogies were automatically sucked into the celebrations. To have been a mere observer would have been impossible. Thank God, I thought, that Boeing made such sturdy planes!

The Braniff stewardesses struggled to maintain some kind of order but they, too, were Brazilian and scarcely older than their jubilant passengers. The Captain appeared, trying desperately to keep a stern face, but that only increased the cheers that followed him back to the cockpit. There was no drinking – there was no need. Everyone was high on the anticipation of home and *Carnaval*.

Rio twinkled towards us in the dusk, and a couple of hours after landing I caught the Cruzeiro flight to Recife, the capital of Pernambuco on the Atlantic ocean, 2,000 kilometres to the north and a mere eight degrees south of the Equator. Rio had been steamy enough. Recife, I imagined, would be unbearable. Well, perhaps I wouldn't be staying that long – if the Washington job with WHO became available.

'Glad you finally made it.' Harry, a hefty, florid, grey-splashed Australian, on the edge of retirement, greeted me with a smack on the shoulders. 'This is Pancho, our Administrative Officer,' he added, as a dark-haired fellow with a sharp but smiling face stepped forward to shake my hand. He came from Paraguay, he told me, but I would never have guessed that he was anything other than American. Later, he impressed me equally with his fluent French and impeccable Portuguese.

Harry and Gwen, his petite, vivacious wife, had an apartment on the fifth floor of a high-rise facing the sea, in the suburb of Boa Viagem. They insisted I stay with them.

'You'll need this.' Harry flung a piece of brightly coloured material at me as soon as I had put down my hand luggage. 'Sarongs are the only comfortable evening wear in Recife. It's just too hot and humid for shirts and trousers.'

We sat in front of the open lounge windows, naked except for our coloured wraps, trying to catch the last of the dying sea breeze. Sweat poured from me in spite of the cold beers which Gwen brought at regular intervals.

Between gulps, Harry gave me a run-down on the Project. It was

457

worse than I had feared. The last Project Manager had been sacked – no easy accomplishment in a large bureaucratic organization like FAO – leaving Harry, the specialist in sheep and goats, to hold the fort. It hadn't been easy, he admitted. Apart from the normal frustrations of climate and trying to devise a programme, there seemed to be constant bickering between the Federal and Provincial Authorities as to which of these two organizations the project should be attached. I could see that tact would be as important as any professional skills I might have. Already I felt homesick for VITAR!

As the breeze died down, I was introduced to Recife's dreaded speciality – mosquitoes. Even in this fifth-floor seafront apartment, they were ferocious. The heat was bad enough – now this. For the first of many times, I wondered how I would be able to cope.

Sometime, well after midnight, I staggered to the guest room and oblivion.

A bang on the head brought me back to reality.

'You're my friend,' squeaked a small, bronzed and totally naked boy by my bedside.

'I won't be for long,' I retorted, 'if you keep banging me on the head.'

Charlies was a late-comer to the family, six years old and solid as Ayer's Rock. I looked at my watch; five. But the sun was now well over the horizon and the air already sticky. Again, I wondered how long I would stand it?

We breakfasted at six in front of wide, sliding windows overlooking the busy thoroughfare which separated us from the beach. The yellow strand was filling with joggers and other body fanatics. Before we had finished our paw-paw, family groups with Sunday lunch hampers, and clusters of teenagers with footballs, had taken over much of the available sand.

The sea was like a highly polished slate floor, devoid of movement save at the very edge, where an occasional hiccup – more a twitch than a lap – showed that somewhere in the depths, life still lingered. As far as the eye could see, the glassy sheet of the ocean was dotted with small, white, triangular sails.

'*Jangadas*, Gwen told me. 'They are a sort of balsa-wood raft. Fishermen go miles out to sea in them. They can't sink, but they can upset. Then the fisherman hangs on till he drifts inshore or is picked up – or is eaten by sharks. The *jangada* is the symbol of the North-East. You'll see models in all the tourist shops.'

Charlie, now announced in a shrill, confident voice, that 'Me and my friend are going to swim,' and hauled me down to the highway that separated the wall of high-rise apartments from the ocean. Cross-

Jangada

ing was scary. Every motorist had his accelerator flat on the floor
and his hand hard on the horn. There were no traffic lights or cross-
ings to be seen in either direction, and six lanes of madly-driven cars
to navigate. No wonder Brazil had so many top racing motorists, I
thought. Every road was a race track! Luckily – at least for us – an
accident further up the road blocked one side and slowed the other.
We weaved across.

It was the same coming back. It was too risky to sprint through
a gap, so we could only wait on the now burning pavement for a
possible lull. I looked up at the apartment building. There was Harry
at the window, puffing nervously on a cigarette. Probably, he'd been
watching us the whole time. I didn't blame him.

* * *

Next morning, Harry drove me out to the Project offices at the
Federal Research Station, 22 miles behind the town, the air conditioner in his new Mercedes turned full on.

'Taking it back with me to Australia next year when I retire.
Worth a bloody fortune there.'

On the way we picked up another of the Project staff, a tall, gum-
chewing, high-heeled Texan, who had arrived the previous week. Don
was an FAO specialist in range management who would be advising
on the best way to develop the dry grasslands of the North-East for

livestock production. An almost unintelligible Texan drawl filtered through a crack in his stone-like jaw, but once I had adapted my ears to his assibilations, I learned a great deal about how to keep animals on a few tufts of burnt scrub.

The fact that he brought an aroma of vodka into the car with him didn't worry me particularly. In that heat, fluid intake in any form, whether it contained alcohol or not, was essential to survival – even at eight in the morning!

'Welcome to IPEANE,' Harry grunted (he pronounced it 'Ippy-Arny') as a uniformed guard checked us at the gates of a large estate. 'In other words, the Federal Institute for Agricultural and Livestock Research in the North-East.' We passed along tree-lined avenues where red-brick buildings were separated by spacious, well-kept lawns. But these, evidently, were not for us, for we came to a stop outside a tin-roofed shed.

'We'll be moving into new offices soon,' Harry assured me apologetically. I hoped that 'soon' had a more optimistic connotation in Brazil than in Peru. No-one could possibly work in the small, stifling rooms into which we now filed.

Pancho greeted us, and in deference to my exalted status, aimed the only available fan at my desk. It certainly felt better and had the added advantage of blowing away all the bumf that had been stacked there to await my attention.

'Our new offices will be air-conditioned,' Harry added quickly.

As he spoke, a dark-skinned man in his early forties, wearing a brightly flowered shirt, entered.

'Meet André. André, this is Pat, the new Project Manager.'

André put out a hand. 'Thank God someone's replacing you at last, Harry. Welcome to Hell, Pat.'

André, the cattle production specialist, was a slightly built negro from Surinam. Below his intelligent, smiling face was a straggly, Trotsky-like beard. He'd been in Recife a month and already had a good knowledge of Portuguese and of the livestock situation in the North-East. He was beginning to explain this to me when an attractive, grey-haired lady brought in some small cups of coffee.

'This is Erika, our Secretary – and Boss,' André broke off to introduce me. 'If you think you're going to run this project, Pat, think again.'

'I understand that the North-East is a desert,' I prompted.

'Most of it, yes. It's a potential disaster area the size of France, Spain and Italy together. Hundreds of thousands of its inhabitants emigrate to the industrial centres in the south each year. Child mortality is a scandal, and thousands go blind each year from lack of Vitamin A, so the Government is now adding it to all sugar that's sold. The North-East is the "outback" of Brazil, it's her biggest rural slum. Actually, there are three distinct climatic zones. The coastal area, or *mata*, has plenty of rain and is nearly all forest, sugar cane and pastures. The *agreste* zone, further inland, still has enough rain in good years for crops and livestock, and then there's the desert area of the interior, the *sertão*, or *caatinga*, where it may rain every three or four years.'

'What about subterranean water? Can't you sink boreholes?' I asked.

'Most are salty as hell, and very deep. They have rather a novel test to gauge whether the water is fit for livestock. They drop a frog into it; if the frog survives for a certain time, they reckon the water is OK. If it dies, the water is too salty.'

'Aren't there any rivers?'

'They make full use of those that are big enough but, apart from the San Francisco, there are few that they can exploit.'

It seemed a little optimistic, not to say boastful, that a handful of foreigners, however well-qualified, could make any impact whatsoever on the livestock situation of this vast desert region in the short time at our disposal.

'Looks like we're going to have to do some hard thinking,' I commented.

'You can say that again,' Harry agreed, lighting another cigarette in the chain he had started when he got out of bed. 'But before we go any further, I had better introduce you to Paulo. He's the nearest thing to a counterpart that we've got. Damn nice lad, but going blind. I expect he'll take you to see Dr Soss, our dear, disrespected head of IPEANE, who hides himself in an ivory tower and thinks up ways of frustrating us.'

We found the stocky, cheerful Dr Paulo enveloped in a white laboratory coat three sizes too large. His chubby cheeks creased into a wide smile as he examined me through thick, metal-rimmed spectacles.

'*Todo legal?*' he asked Harry, still smiling broadly.

'That's the Brazilian way of saying "Is everything OK?"' Harry explained. 'Sometimes he greets me with "*Fogo, não é?*" which means "Things are bloody awful, aren't they?"'

Paulo listened to all this with increasing merriment.

'Those are the polite sayings,' he spluttered. 'We have some more – er, juicy ones, which we use when Dr Soss rejects our programmes.' He bent double and slapped a knee, laughter shaking his whole body.

He showed us round the laboratories of which he was in charge.

461

They were poorly equipped and, as far as I could see, doing little research of any use. A feeling which he evidently shared.

'You see, we are waiting for our new laboratories, then we'll be able to solve all our problems.' He placed a hand over his mouth and guffawed. He didn't believe it either!

It was a situation all too common in South America. When the new labs were built, there would be other problems to prevent progress. It was as if nobody really wanted to begin, or were too frightened, or couldn't figure out the next step.

'The Director is awaiting us,' Paulo announced, screwing up his eyes to examine his wristwatch from a distance of four inches. 'Let's go.'

The main office was a red-brick building like an old British railway station, full of useless niches and decorative arches between impossibly small windows. In fact, the windows in the Director's air-conditioned office on the upper floor were curtained off, the lighting totally artificial. A slim man with rather a small head, made even smaller by his white crewcut, rose from behind an enormous desk.

Dr Soss spoke only Portuguese, in itself an admission of failure for a scientific administrator of his rank. I had difficulty following his *nordestino* accent, quite unlike that of Rio.

'Do you smoke?' I asked, offering him my cigarette case.

'*Sim; mas só "se me dão",*' he replied smiling.

'Never heard of that brand,' I replied.

'*"Só se me dão",*' explained Paulo as Dr Soss helped himself, '"only if they are given me" – that is, other people's cigarettes. It's a common brand in Brazil!'

We laughed, it broke the ice a little, but it was not an encouraging meeting. I was eager to discuss IPEANE's research programme for the barren North-East and to suggest how the FAO team could help. Dr Soss's reply staggered me. There *was* no policy – either local or national, apart from the vague slogan, thrown out on all official occasions and which, evidently, needed no further clarification, to wit, 'improvement of livestock production' and that equally vague chestnut, which I had been hearing in every country I had worked in, 'self-sufficiency in protein.'

I had been told that there were 21 research stations in the North-East under IPEANE control. Dr Soss seemed embarrassed when I repeated this. Apparently, he was only considering one for our use – Surubim – and only part of it at that. He could give me no idea of priorities or the specific problems to be solved. That, he said, would be the job of the FAO team to define.

Good, I thought. At least we'll be able to start from scratch

462

instead of trying to revamp semi-moribund and impractical investigations.

'We'd better have a look at Surubim right away,' I suggested when we were outside.

'I've already arranged a trip for tomorrow,' Harry replied. 'Actually, there are several far better stations than Surubim; Arcoverde and Serra Talhada, for instance.'

'Why didn't Dr Soss mention them, then?' I asked.

'Because they belong to the Pernambuco State Agricultural Research Service, IPA. IPEANE doesn't talk to IPA, and vice-versa.'

'We must see them anyway,' I said. 'We're an international team, and our responsibility is to advise the government of the country as to what is best. If they don't like it, tough titty!'

That afternoon, an IPEANE driver took us into the city. Recife, founded more than 400 years before, now had over 1,000,000 inhabitants. It was a chaotic mixture of old and new. Ancient churches and forts, quaint narrow streets and shaded squares, colonial mansions, massive cuboid office blocks and high-rise apartments, through all of which the Capibaribe river wound like a giant, smelly intestine.

'They call it the Venice of the New World,' Harry said.

'I bet Venice never gets half as hot as this,' I replied.

An Imp must have overheard, for at that moment the car stalled in a narrow one-way street. The battery, the driver admitted, was *um poco fraco*, a bit weak, and what with idling in the traffic and using the air conditioner continually, it had finally run flat.

A cacophony of hooting – a thing never encountered in Lima – erupted. Brazilian drivers were not renowned for patience; in fact, rumour had it that the shortest interval known to man was that between the changing of a traffic light from red to green and the horn of the car behind!

So Harry, puffing hard, Pancho, immaculately dressed as always, and I, already soaked in sweat, had to push that damned saloon a searing 50 metres before it started. It was terrifyingly hot and with the air conditioner now inoperable, I felt considerably more than *um poco fraco*. Harry, older and less fit, was puce.

The Surubim research station lay 100 kilometres to the north-west of Recife, just over the arbitrary division that separated the lush, coastal strip, the *mata*, from the semi-dry *agreste*. The station soil was sandy and impoverished from years of cotton growing. Nearby, over the low, rolling, scrub-covered hills, I could make out the small town of Surubim.

'There used to be cattle here,' one of my station staff told us, 'but that was long before my time.'

The station director grudged us a brief interview and offered a meagre 40 hectares for our cattle and sheep experiments, but made it clear that Surubim was a cotton station, and cotton was, and always would be, the top priority. It was not an auspicious beginning. It was evident that he and Dr Soss were not on speaking terms.

I wondered whether it would be the poor soil or the unfriendly Director which would prove the more insuperable. Well, perhaps Arcoverde or Serra Talhada, IPA's stations, would be the answer. Surubim's one and only advantage was that it was close to Recife.

Paulo the Peacemaker, as we had now come to call our counterpart, had already rung his friends in IPA to smooth the way, so when, a few days later, Harry, Don, Andre and I arrived at the Arcoverde Experimental Station, 300 kilometres to the west along a ruler-straight, polished highway, Peter, the Station Manager, welcomed us warmly.

From the moment we drove up the long, rutted approach road, I began to feel optimistic. The station was well-laid-out and well-kept. There was hilly land for sheep, rolling pastures for cattle, with plentiful water and, most important, housing for researchers.

Above all, this was a livestock station, there was no cotton or other crops, and Peter was a cattleman. Short, rugged, with fair, close-cropped hair, he looked more of a teenager than someone in charge of a large station. His parents, he told us, had emigrated from Germany at the end of the war. Seeing that not a single scientific journal ever found its way to his desk, he was surprisingly up-to-date, but most encouraging of all, Don discovered that Peter had been one of his PhD students at Texas A & M. For the first time, I felt we might achieve something – if IPA would agree to our using Arcoverde, and if IPEANE would let us accept their offer.

Serra Talhada, another 240 kilometres further west, was a different story. One could sympathize with the authorities for siting the station on the best land available and beside a lake, but it bore no relation to the *caatinga* that surrounded it, with its smattering of goats and one emaciated cow to every 60 hectares of thorn trees, cacti and parched soil. Experimental results from the station would be meaningless in the *caatinga*, where the few cattlemen, the *caatingeiros*, and the horses they rode, had to wear special leather aprons to protect them from the vicious spikes of that inhospitable terrain, just like Karamoja in North-East Uganda. However, Harry asked that one small thorn tree-covered hill be reserved for his goat production experiments; it would be the only part of the station we could use.

Arcoverde would provide for our pasture and range-management experiments and for the breeding stock, the progeny of which could be fattened elsewhere, such as in the *mata*, where sugar-cane tops and lush pastures were plentiful. Then I had a brainwave.

'How much land is there at IPEANE?' I asked Paulo the next morning as we looked down from his lab window over the scrub which rolled away inland. Here and there I could see small patches of cultivation, but most was covered in tall grass and bush. I had never seen such an untidy research station.

'Land?' Paulo laughed. 'Lots.'

'And those buildings down there that look like cowsheds?'

'They *are* cowsheds. And all filled with furniture.' He doubled up in mirth.

'Furniture?'

'That's right. There are pig pens as well, also full of furniture. I'll take you down.'

I collected André. 'You're wasting your time,' he advised. 'I've already been refused permission to use them. Every one of them is filled to the ceiling with beds, tables, desks and household equipment. Don't ask me why. They say they are being stored for various officials. It would have been ideal for us.'

'And all this land; what are they using it for?'

'Good question. The cultivated patches are private gardens. Evidently there is a law which entitles a government employee, after a certain period of service, to purchase a plot of land on the station where he works. It's mad, but there it is. A large part of IPEANE is now owned by the employees.'

Dr Soss was embarrassed when I asked him why we couldn't use such ideal facilities.

'I can do nothing. It is all decided at the Federal Headquarters in Brasilia.'

It was one of the many puzzles I was to find in Brazil to which there was no rational explanation.

RESEARCH REMAINS REMOTE

I had to visit Rome. There were many loose ends to tie up regarding my transfer, and I needed to discuss the future staffing of the project. I would so much have preferred the Washington job, working with Manuel and Pedro – if it had materialized, but at 53 I didn't have too many options.

For the first time in my life I felt afraid of the future, worried lest

465

the family would be unable to cope with living conditions in Recife, but equally fearful that if the Washington job did materialize, the family, after 16 years in slap-happy Third world countries, would be unable to adapt to the tempo of life in a big American city. Above all, I was scared of being too old and incompetent to hold down a new job, whether in Washington or else-where. Looking back, I can find no real basis for these fears, but I suppose that everyone goes through periods of doubts as they grow older.

On balance, I felt it might be better to stick with FAO in Recife than risk a completely new field at my age. There was no doubt that the Pernambuco beaches were wonderful, the beer first-class and the natives, except when behind the wheel, extremely friendly. But the heat, the humidity, the traffic, and Brazil's escalating cost of living were daunting. The effort of getting out of bed made one sweat. Inflation – officially 25 per cent – was probably double that, and as for traffic, my probability of survival plummeted every time I entered a car or tried to cross a road.

The language, too. Portuguese, I decided, was an impossible tongue. Many words were similar to Spanish, but you needed a potato in your mouth or ill-fitting false teeth to pronounce them properly. The clear-cut syllables I had been used to in Spanish were replaced by a series of 'shh's' and a nasal 'aowng' that was quite horrid. The basic words and phrases which had become a reflex were also different. Gone was the familiar *gracias*. I now had to say *obrigado* when I thanked someone. Monday was no longer *lunes*, it was *segunda feira*, second day. Tuesday was *terça-feira* and so on, although Saturday and Sunday were still the old familiar *sabado* and *domingo*.

The North-East dialect didn't help, either.

'Why do you call a street *"hua"* when it is written *"rua"*?' I complained.

'That's just the *nordestino* accent,' Erika told me. 'All Rs at the beginning of a word are pronounced as an H.'

'Just like the Scots pronunciation of "whore",' Harry chuckled. 'I've never met a city with so many!'

As soon as I arrived in Rome, I rang Pedro in Washington, who confirmed that all new posts in WHO were still frozen, and likely to remain so. In a way it was a great relief. I knew Mary would be disappointed but I was beginning to feel a little guilty at my duplicity, and although Rome knew nothing of my Washington option, they had made it quite clear that they were depending on me to rescue the Recife project.

I loved Rome, the tranquillity of the sculptured fountains, the burnt siennas and soft ochres of the crumbling plaster along the narrow streets, and the bright flowers tumbling from window boxes. The dignity of its ancient monuments, unperturbed by the riotous traffic, gave a feeling of timelessness, of walking with long-forgotten gods who still watched over the city, aloof but protective. Rome, once the centre of another great empire, had been a good choice I thought, for the headquarters of an international philanthropic organization such as FAO.

A couple of incidents on the way back made me feel that Brazil, after all, was the right place. As I sat in Rio airport waiting for my flight to Brasilia, where I was to meet the UN and FAO Representatives, I rechecked my bags. Where was the one with all the presents I was taking back for the family? I must have left it on the pavement. I ran outside. Nothing. Hell, someone must have swiped it. Bloody Brazilians! A moment later the flight was called. I collected my things.

'*Senhor*.'

I looked up. A short, unshaven individual stood in front of me, his sweaty shirt half-open to show a hairy pot-belly. In one hand he held an umbrella, in the other my missing bag.

'After I dropped you, I went for a *cafecinho, Senhor*. Then I saw this bag between the seats, and this umbrella. So I hurried back to see if I could find you.'

'The bag is mine, but not the umbrella. You can keep that with my compliments. A million thanks.'

I handed him a 20-cruzeiro note, about three dollars. He was obviously surprised, bowed and thanked me effusively as we shook hands. When he had gone I looked in the bag. Of course, nothing was missing. Where else in the world, I wondered, could I have found so honest a cab driver? Certainly not London, or Paris, or Rome. Chungking, perhaps? I felt uplifted.

The other incident occurred that evening in the Hotel Palacio in Brasilia. A family of four entered the restaurant and took the table next to mine. I couldn't keep my eyes off them. The man was a dark-haired, broad-shouldered, bronze giant. The woman, tall, slender and of darker skin than her husband, had navy-blue eyes that made me gasp. The children, a boy about 12 and a girl a couple of years younger, were two of the most striking youngsters I had ever seen. Both were the colour of copper with the figures of young athletes; the boy with dark brown hair and grey-blue eyes, the girl with long auburn tresses and eyes like black olives beneath golden eyebrows. Their manners were impeccable. How different, I thought, to the

467

pasty-faced, over-weight, whining kids one usually encountered in Latin America.

That evening, I wrote Mary. 'If these incidents are true of Brazil in general, then to Hell with Washington. Brazil is for us!'

* * *

Back in Recife, I was just in time for the First Regional Conference on Agricultural and Livestock Research. I was delighted; we would meet the people from the various north-eastern States, hear their problems and design programmes to help them. I found, too, that we had moved into new offices, six air-conditioned rooms in a new block. IPEANE was at least trying!

The FAO Representative in Brasilia had told me that a US AID team from the University of Wisconsin was working with IPEANE. This was news to me. I tackled Harry.

'Why didn't you tell me that there was an AID team here?' I griped.

'I was hoping to introduce you this week. They are growing rice and some other crops. Let's take a coffee off them.'

We found three of the group with their feet up, drinking their elevenses. They looked the usual young, clean, bright PhDs which I had come to associate with American AID personnel. Americans always looked so scrubbed.

'How long have you been here?' I asked them.

'Six months, six terrible months,' they replied. 'No-one will take a decision. The high-ups are too apathetic and the juniors too scared. The possibilities are enormous, but no-one will move.' His dismal opinion of IPEANE coincided with that of everyone else I had spoken to. I was soon to join their ranks.

The Conference, the first of its kind in the North-East, was no different from any other. Enthusiastic speeches and totally unrealistic predictions were made, papers presented and working parties set up. The FAO team outlined what we thought should be done from our still scanty knowledge of the area, which was to obtain basic data, define the most important problems, design experiments to solve them, and press Government to set up an extension service to carry the results to the farmers. There were few disagreements. What was disconcerting, however, was the evident suspicion with which the delegates treated IPEANE. It was obvious that our counterpart organization was thoroughly distrusted. Despite this, we were optimistic. Although researchers in the other states were reluctant to co-operate with IPEANE, they were only too eager to work with us

468

as an FAO project. We promised to visit them and discuss their programmes, starting with the States of Ceara and Piaui, which lay to the north-west.

A week later, we touched down at Fortaleza on the Atlantic coast. The town had seen its fair share of fighting over the last four centuries and had once been held by the Dutch, but now, with 1,000,000 inhabitants, a university and other amenities, it was the capital and principal tourist resort of the State of Ceara.

The stifling hot city centre was as congested and noisy as Recife, but the hustle and bustle faded away before the palm-lined streets had reached the sandhill suburbs which stretched along the Atlantic shoreline.

We drove to Iracema, the principal research station, 200 kilometres to the south. Like nearly every other so-called research station we would visit in the North-East, the facilities were minimal, the younger staff discouraged and inexperienced, and the senior researchers wallowing in ignorance and apathy.

Teresina, the capital of Piauí state, was a most attractive city, quiet and clean, with flower-filled *praças* and tree-lined streets. But the local livestock experimental station at Campo Maior was on its last legs, its residences and animal houses in acute disrepair, the cattle as languid as the staff, and the sheep – or were they goats? – parasite-ridden and woebegone.

The country here was unusual, consisting of flat *pampas* dotted with tall palm trees. These palms had, until recently, provided a thriving industry, their resin being used in the production of the old 78 gramophone records. This was now no longer an industry, but some resin was still collected for other industrial processes. There was certainly no lack of water, in fact, the problem was the opposite. Since the water-table was only a few feet below the laterite soil, heavy rain would immediately turn the area into a series of lakes.

In the following months, we visited a dozen other stations. One we found abandoned, devoid of staff, animals or crops. On another, which we happened to visit on a Saturday morning, the agronomist in charge refused to show us around. Saturday was a holiday, he insisted, and he had better things to do!

Desperate for suitable sites, we explored the far west of Pernambuco State, past Serra Talhada and Panamarim in the centre of the *caatinga*, to Petrolina on the banks of the Sao Francisco river, 800 kilometres from Recife. It, too, proved useless. Some trials with soya beans and a few hectares of irrigated lucerne along the river's banks were all we found. The lucerne was being dried, pelleted and exported to Japan as poultry feed. The Nips must pay a lot for their broilers and eggs, I thought.

We spent a week in Bahia state, to the south. Much of the area was fertile, and at least two experimental stations had adequate infrastructure, but the long journey from Recife, half by plane and half by car, made them impractical.

After the high hopes which the conference had raised, we all began to feel a bit let down. Even if we did find a suitable place to develop our investigations, the end would be the same. Without an extension service and easily available credit schemes, and hampered by the lack of statistics and the incompetent, bureaucratic administration which pervaded all departments, we could only be fighting a losing battle.

All the reports by national and foreign advisors which I could find told the same sad story. No area needed improvement more urgently. Only 40 cows out of every 100 produced a calf in any one year, compared to an expected 85 in developed countries, and half these calves died before they were a year old. Animals that survived six years of North-East droughts and disease would reach a carcase weight of 165 kilos, compared to the 250 kilos expected in a two-year-old carcase in the USA.

But the really discouraging aspect was the attitude of IPEANE itself. No-one seemed to want to solve the problems if it meant making decisions or spending money. No-one had done anything like that for years, so why start now?

It occurred to me that I should tell Rome that the project was a non-starter and should be scrapped. But what if they agreed, and did scrap it? I was due to return to Peru the following week, to finalize the sale of our house and escort the family back to Recife. With the Washington job off the list, I had no other alternatives. Anyway, I found it easier to convince myself that it was my duty to see it through, not quit. FAO was depending on me. If I had known what was to come, I might not have been so altruistic.

* * *

Mary had suggested that if we didn't go to Washington, we should buy a house in Recife. After all the problems we had had with our house in Peru, I was dead against the idea. Anyway, the *Banco Hipotecario* in Lima was still holding up the mortgage payment. Until this was solved, we wouldn't have a penny for any new real-estate ventures.

Moreover, the first week's search had convinced me that purchase was out of the question. A real-estate lady friend of Harry's took me round a succession of half-finished constructions and weather-battered skeletons, selling for upwards of $50,000. Those that were habitable at all had some expensive problem to resolve, or were in what was known as the 'flood risk zone'. There was no option, we would have to rent. All I had to do was to find the right house.

The highway which ran the length of the Boa Viagem seafront continued southwards to peter out in the straggling beachside settlements of Candeias and Piedade. They were attractive areas, reminiscent of the north coast of Jamaica. A house there would suit us fine.

One Sunday morning, Harry dropped me at the farthest point in Piedade and I started to walk the six or seven kilometres back towards Boa Viagem, asking at each of the more attractive houses I passed whether they were for rent, or if the owner knew of any that were.

The early-morning sun, which had seemed so balmy when Harry had dropped me off at six-thirty, was soon a roaring furnace. I had scorned Harry's offer of a hat and refused his suggestion to pick me up two hours later. No, I would walk the whole way back and look at every possible house on the way. I must have been crazy.

Few owners seemed to resent my impertinent suggestion that they might like to rent me their home. One or two considered it, but their idea of rental was a little above my estimate. Sometimes an expectant householder, having heard that a *gringo* was looking for a house to rent, would run after me and haul me back to inspect an unoccupied hovel in his back garden, overgrown with tropical vegetation and quite unfit for the lowliest of bachelors, let alone a family in our exalted position.

Although unsuccessful, it was an interesting morning. I saw some lovely homes, met several delightful people, drank the water of numerous 'jelly coconuts' which I bought from palm-fronded push-carts along the way, just as in Jamaica. At midday, aching, sore of foot, soaked in sweat and sunburnt, I staggered through the door of Harry's apartment. Fortunately, he had seen me from his window hobbling along the sidewalk, and was able to hand me a beer as I flopped into an easy chair. Not even 'my friend Charlie' could get me out of the house that afternoon.

'Did you find anything?' Gwen asked.

'Not yet, but that's the area where I want to live.'

'I'll ring the real-estate lady,' Harry said. 'She may know of some place to rent in Candeias.'

Sure enough, the next evening the good lady took me down to almost the same spot where Harry had dropped me off the previous morning, and showed me a dream of a bungalow mansion. It was not one of those that I had stopped to enquire about, it had looked

471

far too magnificent for my pocket. It belonged to a wealthy hotelier's wife, who used it for a beach house during the summer months. (My God, if this was winter, I thought, what was summer going to be like?) It was modern, spacious, had four bedrooms, a large internal patio and a separate, two-bedroomed flat at the back. All the flooring was of exotic tiles. Large exterior patios made it ideal for entertaining, and a rather stylized garden led down to a sandy beach, protected by a reef 50 yards out at sea. Nothing could have been more ideal to soften the shock of leaving our home in Lima and helping us adapt to the heat of Recife.

'If you can afford six hundred dollars a month, you can have it till December,' said the estate agent.

Six hundred dollars a month! That was a hell of a lot, but I knew that it was less than it was worth. I also knew that I couldn't refuse.

'The owner, Dona Mimi, is a friend of mine. She wanted eight hundred a month, but said that she would accept six if I could find the right person. I think I have.'

A few days later, I flew back to Peru to complete the sale of our house and fetch the family.

PERUVIAN POSTSCRIPT

'Konrad is in Germany, on business,' Mary told me on arrival at Lima airport. 'Nothing has been paid into our account, and there is some problem with the *Banco Hipotecario*.'

I had hoped that by now the Mortgage Bank would have granted Konrad's request for a loan and that he would have paid the $6,000 into my New York account, as he had promised. I also expected to hear that the UN Office had found a way to convert my excess soles into hard currency. The UN Res Rep told me that he was still exploring ways of getting my money out; several a little unorthodox, but nothing illegal. First, however, he thought I should approach Foreign Affairs again, this time in person. They had refused to consider my previous written request to transfer funds. He furnished me with a letter in which he argued that, after ten years of service to the country, it was only fair that I should be allowed to convert my savings to dollars, including money from the sale of my house.

I had visited Foreign Affairs once before, soon after arriving in Peru, when Axel had introduced me to Protocol. It was housed in one of the most decorative buildings in old Lima, the half-Spanish, half-Moorish, eighteenth-century Torre Tagle Palace. To enter Torre Tagle was to retrace Peru's history. Massive, brass-studded doors

opened onto a cobbled patio bordered by tiled walkways and overlooked by ornately carved wooden balconies. The reception rooms
were spacious and filled with memorabilia from the days of the
Spanish Governors. Huge, gilt-framed paintings of martyrs and religious scenes by the 'Cuzco school' hung from the walls, interspersed
here and there by ancient portraits and a tattered flag.

I handed the letter from the UN Res Rep to an attendant and was
asked to wait. After half an hour, a pompous little man in a dark
pinstripe suit bustled in and shook hands without lifting his eyes
from the floor. My letter was in his hand.

'*Siento, señor; es imposible.* We cannot authorize foreign exchange
on the sale of property. In any case, it was illegal for you to purchase
a house in the first place. No member of a diplomatic mission may
buy property without permission from this office. It is very rarely
given, and I can find no such authorization in your case.'

He put the letter back into the envelope, thrust it at me, gave one
pump to my hand – still without looking me in the eyes and scuttled
back to his lair.

I was thunderstruck. Illegal? It was news to me. No-one had ever
hinted that I would be breaking the law if I bought a house. This
was serious. It looked as if I would be left with all my worldly capital
in a completely useless and rapidly devaluating currency – Peruvian
soles.

I walked out of the Torre Tagle Palace too shocked to admire the
exquisite courtyard. I was really up the creek – paddleless at that.

Konrad who had now returned from Europe, phoned to say that
the *Banco Hipotecario* had discovered two serious errors in the house
documents.

The first was that the land on which our house was built had never
been transferred, legally, to the previous owner. This had to be done
before anything else could move. I rang the man from whom I had
bought the house.

'This is going to be difficult. Señor Esteves who sold me the plot is
dead.'

Eventually, we found the dead man's lawyer who, by great good
fortune, still held his former client's power of attorney. Thereafter, it
was simply a matter of shuttling between lawyers and *notarios*,
scattering 500 sole notes like confetti, until all was tidy.

The second problem was much more complicated. Rodriguez, the
builder, who had taken over when the 'architect' had left, had created
a fictitious construction company together with a friend, in order to
comply with municipal regulations. To make it, seemingly, more
authentic, he had included the name of a genuine architect whose

473

power of attorney Rodriguez said he possessed. The *Banco*, taking nothing for granted, had checked. No such firm was registered, no power of attorney existed. The documents for the extension of our house were invalid! Square one.

Konrad was becoming a bit edgy. I didn't blame him. I was too.

'Take them back to the lawyer who did your conveyancing,' he advised. 'Both he and the *notario* who signed these documents are responsible. They could be fined heavily. As for Rodriguez, he'll be lucky to stay out of jail.'

Poor Rodriguez. I had always had a soft spot for the stocky Andean contractor who had come to my rescue after the 'architect' had disappeared. I was quite sure that whatever he had done had been purely for our benefit.

My lawyer, Carlos, didn't even frown or, for that matter, apologize, when I told him the problem. 'Ah, yes. We just need a little note of clarification,' he assured me, and wrote out half a page of jargon which, as far as I could understand it, clarified nothing.

'Take this to Señor...' the *notario* who had legalized the original document for Rodriguez. 'He must sign it.'

'Fine,' I said, greatly relieved. But it wasn't fine. the *notario* in question had been arrested the day before and was languishing in jail awaiting trial on charges of smuggling in duty-free cars. Back to Carlos.

'You've got to fix this, one way or another,' I insisted. 'I return to Brazil in ten days – for good.'

'Leave the documents with me,' he instructed. 'Perhaps I can talk to someone.' I laid them on his desk. 'It will probably cost you something,' he added. It did. 'Twenty thousand soles, to be exact!

Konrad had now unearthed a distant cousin on the fourth floor of the *Banco Hipotecario*, who read the revised documents and assured us that if we would call the next day, he would see that they were duly processed and the cheque ready. We lunched at the Aeroclub, to celebrate.

Next day we were met by a rather less confident cousin. The signatures of Rodriguez and his associate were needed to annul the fraudulent document. After that, he assured us, it would be plain sailing.

Finding Rodriguez wasn't that easy. I hadn't seen him for eight years. I looked through the invoices which he had given me for various purchases he had made and which, like the squirrel I am, I had stored – in case. One was the address of a cafe which he had told me his brother owned. It was a dirty hole in a far from salubrious suburb but, miraculously, there was our hungry house-builder, slurping up a plate of *sopa a la criolla*.

474

He was visibly shaken that we had exposed his fictitious company and agreed to sign the documents immediately. Then he took us to his associate, who turned out to be a sickly clerk in the Ministry of Health. Konrad explained the situation in short, angry sentences. There was a pause.

'I want ten thousand to sign it.'

'You can go to jail for fraud,' Konrad bellowed. 'Sign.'

'I'll need time to think...'

'Sign,' roared Konrad again. I thought he would hit the wretched clerk.

'Offer him five hundred soles,' Rodriguez whispered.

Ten minutes later we drove away, Konrad furious and I 500 soles the poorer, but it looked as if we had jumped the last hurdle.

Of course I was wrong.

For what reason I now forget, if I ever understood, a further *impasse* occurred at the Mortgage Bank. The only solution seemed to depend on finding someone at the highest level in the bank, to certify that all the modifications to the documents were now acceptable. Konrad and I lunched at the Tambo, a sprawling restaurant-cum-take-away, on Avenida Arequipa, trying to figure out how to overcome this latest set-back. The Tambo had been the first eating establishment I had patronized on my arrival in Peru ten years before. What a lot had happened since then, I thought. Three hours later, we were still there, now with a group of friends whom Konrad had summoned to his aid. From time to time, one would rush over to the telephone on the wall, only to return with a gloomy face as another hope exploded. I became more and more desperate, only half-understanding the rapid, colloquial jingo, feeling like a pawn already removed from the board and no longer able to follow the course of play. Eventually, one of Konrad's friends returned from the phone with good news. He had reached a friend who was related to a senior lawyer in the *Banco*. The friend must have been a close relative, for the lawyer was with us before we had finished our next coffee.

The situation was explained in a few minutes, a deal was worked out, backs were slapped, there was much laughter and handshaking, and he was off again. It could not have been more simple. But that is the way things are done in South America.

The next day we called again at the Mortgage Bank.

'It just needs the Director's signature,' Konrad's cousin told us, all smiles.

'Great. We'll wait,' I said.

'Unfortunately, it is the Director's birthday, today. He will sign tomorrow.'

I was about to say something caustic when I remembered that very few officials, especially senior ones, worked on the day of their *cumpleaños*. It was an unwritten law that birthdays were personal holidays.

We visited the Bank three more times before I returned to Brazil. The story was always the same, 'Tomorrow he will sign.'

Dealing with bureaucrats in Peru was like playing Snakes and Ladders. You were never sure whether the next official would stamp everything and send you up a ladder, or produce another snag and send you down a snake to start again. One thing was certain, there were far more snakes than ladders!

Apart from the *Banco Hipotecario*, I was fully occupied with the sale of our household effects. The proceeds of these, I was informed, could be converted into foreign exchange without any problem, as long as I provided receipts for all items over 5,000 soles.

I took the list of the items sold together with receipts for those articles over 5,000 soles to the *Banco de la Nación*, which dealt with all foreign exchange transactions.

'This is in order,' said the official, 'but you must give us receipts for all items worth more than one thousand soles.'

'I was told less than two weeks ago that receipts were only needed for items over five thousand.'

'It's been changed.'

There were some 30 items for which I now had to obtain receipts. I had no idea who had bought them. There was only one way out. I made out the receipts and had my friends sign them.

Although I now had permission to exchange the proceeds from soles to dollars, there was still another morsel of frustration to be digested. The figures in the certified cheque from my bank, which I presented for conversion, didn't agree with the amount in writing. Another day ironing this out and another morning queuing, at last gave me some foreign currency.

There was one more bombshell to come, this time from Mary herself.

'Luz has agreed to come to Recife with us,' she told me one evening. 'Isn't that super?'

I looked at her dumbfounded.

'You mean you want to take a Peruvian maid to Brazil? She won't know anyone, she won't understand the language, she won't know her way around – and what happens if she's sick? She's always complaining of back-ache or stomach-ache as it is. We'll be comple-

476

tely responsible for her medical bills. You're really asking for trouble.'

It was not easy to shift Mary when her mind was made up. Anyway, I argued from a disadvantage since most of her mad schemes had turned out to be not so crazy – and she knew it!

I had always insisted that Luz, a buxom, swarthy, affable and intelligent girl in her mid-twenties, with a generous portion of Andean blood, was a slob, but she had a knack of rallying round in a crisis, and since our life was one long necklace of crises, Mary found her almost indispensable.

The first step was to obtain her a passport. For this she required a birth certificate, necessitating a trip to an almost inaccessible municipality in the *sierra*, also a health certificate and a certificate of good behaviour from the police. Then, of course, she needed a visa, which stipulated almost as many pre-conditions as had her passport. All this took time, during which I continued to harass the *Banco Hipotecario*, trying to persuade them to approve Konrad's mortgage.

I maintained pressure on the UN office as well. Their promises of extricating my funds, which had flowed so freely, now seemed to have dried up. It wasn't their fault. They did try. One departing expert had agreed to hold back his salary for his last two months and use my soles instead. It was a help, but I was a little mortified, when I received his dollar cheque, to see that he had calculated the exchange at black-market rates, which gave him 40 per cent more than the official rate, and me 40 per cent less!

Before I left Peru, I gave my power of attorney to Ben, the poultry expert, in case there were any more documents to sign, and so that he could receive the money from the Bank once the mortgage was approved and deposit it in my account. I could think of no-one better to look after my affairs and keep an eye on Konrad, than this stocky, balding, bushy-browed, tenacious Israeli.

How I was to get all this money out of Peru once it was in my account, I had, as yet, no earthly idea!

EMBRAPA EMERGES

Despite my protestations, Luz was with us as we floated down through dawn-pink clouds over Rio.

Shannon and Kerry were still at school in England; Lys had remained in Lima to finish her school year and, hopefully, to hurdle for Peru in the forthcoming South American Games. Lindley, Melanie, Frances and the twins were sprawled half-asleep over two

477

rows of seats. Mary, utterly exhausted, was snoring gently just behind me. It was impossible for me to sleep, I was sharing my seat with two cylindrical containers of crockery!

I had told Mary simply that I had rented a beach cottage – which was true, up to a point. Her reaction to the seaside villa in Candeias was worth every cent of its outrageous rent. After all I had written and said about Recife, the heat, the squalor and the mosquitoes, she couldn't believe the elegance, the beauty of the sea and the fresh balmy breeze. It was like a dream.

The children were ecstatic. Such a house on the sea could only mean they were on holiday, and it was with the greatest difficulty that I made them realize that the school term had already started and one day on the beach was all that would be allowed for them to recuperate from the journey. They perked up when I told them that the American school in which I had entered them finished classes at one, so each afternoon could be spent on the reef. Life, for them, was a dream.

There was nothing idyllic about life at IPEANE. I had my first sniff of crisis as I walked into the office. Don was stomping around in his high-heeled Texan boots, having just returned from Surubim where, after a great deal of persuasion, we had been allowed to start a programme of pasture research. Now, it appeared, all work had stopped because the station director had received no written instructions from IPEANE. It was of course, another flimsy excuse and another way of telling us we were not wanted there.

'Surubim is a dead loss,' Don ranted. 'They're only interested in cotton, and Dr Soss won't even talk to the director, or vice-versa. There's no way we can work there.'

'So where do you suggest we go?'

'Arcoverde. It's the only place.'

'But until IPA and IPEANE come to an agreement, we can't move. IPA, I'm sure, would agree; it's IPEANE who are dragging their feet.'

The problem was not simply one of experimental sites; it was much more complex. The FAO terms of agreement, the so-called Project Document, stipulated certain responsibilities on the part of both FAO and Brazil. A Project was always considered to be a bilateral, co-operative effort between the national and international teams, requiring certain infra-structure and inputs on both sides. In Peru, the national inputs had been well taken care of by Manuel's dedication and hard work. Unfortunately, I did not have a

Manuel in Brazil – in fact, I didn't have anyone. Paulo helped where he could, but he had no responsibility for the Project, and Dr Soss, the IPEANE gauleiter, was more interested in the weather bulletins than us. Not only did I not have a national co-director to help smooth out our problems with IPEANE, none of my FAO experts had counterparts whom they could train to assist them in the field.

Nearly as serious as the lack of local counterparts, was the lack of local funds. It was all very well for me to import equipment, vehicles, drugs and other unavailable items, but without an operating budget to supply fuel, pay for repairs, labour, building materials and the like, the project couldn't move.

Then a miracle occurred – or so we thought at the time.

'Ah, Dr Patrick.' Dr Soss smirked at me from behind his large desk. Everyone was called by his Christian name in Brazil. 'You must read this.' He pushed a letter across.

It was from the Ministry in Brasilia. In brief, it stated that the Federal Agricultural Research Service was to be disbanded. In future, all agricultural and livestock research would be placed in the hands of a semi-autonomous, agricultural research enterprise, the *Empressa Brasileira de Pesquisas Agrícolas*, abbreviated to EMBRAPA. The Federal Agricultural Research Service, of which IPEANE was the north-eastern branch, would disappear.

I was overjoyed. Agricultural and livestock research would now have its own special agency uncluttered by government bureaucracy.

'Terrific,' I exclaimed, handing back the letter. 'We shall really be able to forge ahead now.'

Dr Soss regarded me with a one-sided smile and accepted a cigarette. '*Oxalá*. We shall see. I will send you a copy for your files. Yes, we shall see.'

'We're in the clear,' I told the experts jubilantly. 'There's a new organization for agricultural and livestock research called EMBRAPA. We're about to take off. Fasten your lap straps. IPEANE can stuff it!'

Our euphoria didn't last long. Within days, another directive told us that until EMBRAPA took over, all field work should be held in abeyance.

'We can't stop work at Surubim,' I protested. 'We'll lose a year if we miss the rains.'

'Sorry,' Dr Soss simpered. 'My budget has been cancelled. There's nothing I can do. EMBRAPA is preparing a list of IPEANE staff. Some will be kept on in EMBRAPA, some will be transferred and others will be sacked. We call it the *lista preta*, the black list.' He

479

chuckled. 'We're all on it. Everything will now be centralized in Brasilia under separate National Programmes for rice, wheat, cattle, sheep and so on.'

Depression set in once more.

A week later, Dr Soss and I were summoned to a meeting of EMBRAPA's brass hats in Brasilia. I noticed that none of the former Ministry research staff, some of whom had been most sympathetic to our project, attended. In particular, I missed Dr Mereilles, the former Director of Livestock Research, a very wise and knowledgeable agronomist, whose advise and criticism we held in high regard.

During a break, I called on him. His office was bare, he was moving out. He warned me not to be too optimistic about the future under EMBRAPA.

'The directors are all administrators who love administrating. They know nothing about research. They'll recruit good men and then drown them in bureaucracy.' He must have been clairvoyant.

The immediate message from the meeting was that all research had to stop at once and a new list of experiments drawn up on special, multi-page forms for approval. All equipment costing more than 1,500 cruzeiros (then about $150) could only be ordered by means of a lengthy process through Brasilia. Smaller purchases would be permitted from a common central fund, but would still need justification on complicated forms. The bureaucratic cherry, however, was that field labour could now only be hired under a written contract. Temporary employment of local field workers would no longer be possible. Furthermore, each group of labourers would have to appoint a manager, whom EMBRAPA would pay by cheque, and who would be responsible for paying the rest of the gang. It was totally ludicrous.

'What the hell is he supposed to do with a cheque?' I demanded angrily. 'He has probably never seen one and will almost certainly be unable to read what's on it. The nearest bank could be a hundred kilometres away and he would have to open an account to cash it. It's doubtful whether one in ten *caboclos* can sign their names.'

Equally idiotic was the stipulation that all such labouring contracts must first be put out for tender. Everything EMBRAPA did seemed to ooze bureaucracy, even a routine trip to Surubim by an EMBRAPA vehicle would now take ten days to arrange. It was unbelievable. Our faith in EMBRAPA dropped to below zero.

The most serious consequence of the EMBRAPA edict for us was that we would have to halt preparations for our grazing experiments and fattening trials at Surubim, but unless the land was cleared, ploughed and sown before the rains, we would lose a whole year.

480

Don spent most days roaming round my office, gesticulating, hurling threats at everyone from EMBRAPA to myself, and stamping his Texan heels into the new parquet flooring.

'If we haven't tractors, fertilizer and seed within ten days, I'm off,' he growled. 'We can put up the fences and buy the cattle later, but if we miss the rains, that's it!'

'Look,' I said, 'I know it is counterpart's responsibility, but if they can't pay, I'm willing to stick my neck out and advance what we need from our FAO imprest account. I did it in Peru, and I don't mind doing it here. That's what Project Managers are for. It's either that or we pack it in.'

Dr Soss made it quite clear that he could never reimburse me and warned that EMBRAPA would do everything it could to stop all experiments until they had been approved by Brasilia.

'But if you want to go ahead, it's up to you.'

'It's that or we clear out,' I replied.

'I'll help you all I can,' he assured me. It was the first friendly or encouraging thing he had ever said to me.

I drained my imprest account, and work started once more at Surubim.

SURUBIM FOR STARTERS

We decided to station Eijnar, our first Associate Expert, at Surubim, to help Don and André with the pastures and feeding experiments. The station director welcomed Eijnar politely, but regretted that no house was available. I mentioned two or three that I had seen.

'No water,' smiled the pompous little man.

We selected one and had the plumbing fixed. The roof needed repairing. We repaired it. The electricity was more difficult. I confronted Dr Soss. He spread his hands, but promised he would see what could be done. I knew that he would be only too glad to get the better of the station director. A week later, Eijnar moved in.

Production of pastures and fodder had our highest priority. Without good inexpensive feeding, there could be no improvement in livestock.

It wasn't simply a matter of growing grass and forage crops during the few rainy months. Animals had to graze or be given fodder all the year round, so methods of conserving both natural and cultivated forages, particularly in the *agreste* and the *sertão* for use during the dry months, were just as important.

One method of doing this was to turn the cut grass or crops into hay or silage (a sort of fermented grass cake with a peculiar sour smell which cows evidently liked). Silage was made by compacting chopped forage in concrete towers or bins, or in trenches, and adding molasses to stimulate fermentation. Digging ditches was usually easier and cheaper than constructing towers – but at Surubim we found the topsoil to be less than two feet deep, beneath which was solid laterite. It took several weeks to blast and hack out a trench silo, which under normal conditions would have been completed in half a day using a bulldozer.

While silage was fine for milk production or for fattening steers, it was far too expensive for feeding the slow-growing, low-producing, beef-type cattle which populated most of the *agreste* and *sertão*. For these cattle, André came up with a better solution.

'We'll use the *agreste* and the *sertão* as breeding areas and send the progeny to the high rainfall *mata* zone, where they can be fattened on cultivated fodder, silage or unwanted crops such as sugar-cane tops and corn cobs. By doing this we will reduce the overgrazing in drought areas and make use of surplus sugar-cane and other by-products which are going to waste in the *mata*. Everybody will benefit.'

For such a 'stratified' system of production, we needed a large area of rangeland in the *sertão* on which to run the breeding herds. Without asking EMBRAPA, we approached IPA, outlining our ideas and asking whether we could use Arcoverde as our cattle production centre in the *sertão*. IPA were delighted, promising to supply the land and all labour for clearing and fencing if we could supply the capital inputs of wire, fence poles, water pumps and pipes.

It was as if we had scaled a rock face and had caught a glimpse of a promised land. We shook hands, and tried not to appear too joyful as we piled into our car.

Dr Soss was less jubilant. 'You'll be on your own. EMBRAPA are unlikely to sign any agrement until they've sorted themselves out, which could be another year.'

'Dammit, we've been waiting for them to sort themselves out for at least nine months,' I told him. 'The project only lasts another two years.'

'*Fogo, não é?*,' was all he could reply.

With Eijnar supervising the field work and my long-suffering imprest account footing most of the bills, we began to progress.

First we had to rebuild a small but vital bridge which joined the land we had been allocated to the rest of the station. I was quite sure that the station director had given us this particular area so that we

482

would build a bridge for him – gratis. As soon as it was completed, we started to clear the land and prepare it for planting pasture and maize. Things were going almost too nicely!

'The tractor's gone!' Don stormed into my office.

'Gone?'

'Gone. Taken away. Removed. The contractor said that he had only been paid for fifty hours, and that's finished. We've still half the land to clear and plough. And the rains will be here any day.'

It had taken me weeks to convince the station Director to hire the tractor, and for him to obtain funds from EMBRAPA to pay for it. Now these had run out. There was nothing he could do, he said. Ten days later, the tractor was back at Surubim – courtesy of the FAO imprest account, which was now looking very sick.

Then another problem arose. We needed cement to finish the stalls where our feeding trials would be carried out.

'You must buy at least five hundred bags of cement,' Dr Soss told me when I asked him to help.

'But we only need fifty.'

'Sorry. It will have to be five hundred or none. If I buy only fifty bags, it comes out of a small items budget and means that I can't buy any more small amounts of anything, for anybody, for another thirty days. If I buy five hundred bags, it will go through the budget controlled by Brasilia. It will take longer, but I can ask for another five hundred bags tomorrow if I want to.'

EMBRAPA's new purchasing methods made no sense to me or anyone else.

'OK. I'll take five hundred bags and sell you back four hundred and fifty. Then you'll have all the stocks you need,' I suggested brightly.

'No way. Once they've been bought for your project, they're yours. But I'll store them for you, and if I need some, I'll just take them.'

I agreed. As long as we got our 50 bags, I couldn't care who took the rest. They were EMBRAPA funds, not mine. Mine were exhausted. It was about time EMBRAPA spent a little on us.

But problems continued. Our tractor broke down. The contractor hadn't another he could give us, so we would have to wait till it was repaired. Where good workshops and service existed, this would have meant the loss of a day or two at the outside, but in North-East Brazil, in the bush, things were very different. For an agonizing two weeks, in which we watched the rain fall steadily, we waited the return of our precious machine.

When, at last, we were ready to plant, the rain had stopped and the

483

ground was already dusty again. Pangola grass (*Digitaria decumbens*), which we had intended to use, had to be planted from runners, not seeds. A coastal farm had promised us planting material. We hired a truck to fetch it.

'Sorry, sir,' the farmer apologized, 'you said you'd be here a month ago. I've already sold most of it.'

We took what was left. The day after planting, in which we all helped the eight contracted labourers (paid by the last of my FAO imprest), the rain came down in torrents.

'It will all be washed away,' André groaned. But, in fact, the storm saved it. We recorded about 40 millimetres that afternoon, almost unheard of in the *agreste*. Thereafter, not a drop fell for over two weeks.

'It will never survive,' Don predicted. 'It'll dry out.'

But sufficient moisture remained in the soil from that downpour to keep the roots alive. At the next shower, life suddenly awoke in the straw-like tufts we had planted, and within days the whole field was green – as if someone had sewn a dark green patch onto a brown blanket, the only green patch for miles around!

THE WATCHMAN

Home, at least, was relaxed and enjoyable. Lolling on the beach or patio after work, gin and tonics at hand, we would listen to the waves beating on the reef and the wind rustling the coconut fronds. As long as we stayed in the breeze, the mosquitoes lost interest.

Once a month, a huge disc of white gold would creep up out of the ocean, directly in front of us, and throw its eerie light over the whole coastline.

All would be serenity – until the watchman came!

I had objected fairly strongly when Dona Mimi, the owner, had first mentioned Antonio. The last thing we wanted was someone sneaking around the garden in the evenings. But she had insisted that he was necessary and would cost us nothing. She would pay his salary. True, Antonio cost us nothing in actual money, but in peace of mind and nervous exhaustion, he cost us dear!

I had already noticed that there was a type of feudal relationship between master and servant in Brazil. A servant considered himself one of the family, a poor relation perhaps, but still entitled to protection from his master and patron. In fact, he usually addressed his boss as *patrão*. This had been brought home to me a few days after we had moved into our new offices. A settee had been placed in front of my desk, presumably for the convenience of visitors, so I was a little taken aback the next morning to find the office cleaner lounging on it, reading my morning newspaper. He greeted me with a friendly wave and a '*Bom dia, patrão,*' and went back to his study of *O Comercio.*

I was nonplussed. Should I throw him out? Did all Brazilian lackeys share their superiors' amenities? Would I hurt his feelings if I asked him, politely, to leave? I sought out Erika.

'Well, sometimes an office messenger does sit in his boss's office in case he is wanted for anything,' she explained, 'but I wouldn't encourage it. I'll see what I can do. I'll tell him that *gringos* are different.'

When I returned from lunch, there was no cleaner in my office. Nor was there a settee. Both now contributed to the decor in Erika's. The only reason that Antonio, the watchman, didn't make himself comfortable in my lounge, I suspected, was because there was more action outside.

He was supposed to arrive at six, just on dusk. Sometimes he arrived before, but more often not till eight or nine, or later. This was fine with us, the later the better; we didn't want him peering at us through the bushes while we sipped our martinis or entertained friends. Unfortunately, no matter what hour he arrived, he would belabour the metal bars of the front gate with his truncheon, creating a loud, resonant boom, which set off every dog for kilometres around.

I think his idea was to send a warning to any prospective trespasser that 'Antonio the Terrible' was now on the job, and they'd better beware. At six, it didn't matter, there were plenty of other noises around. But at nine or ten, it either terrified our guests or, if we had opted for an early night, woke us up in a cold sweat. We persuaded him eventually to forego this cacophonic ritual, but could never convince him that flashing his torch into the bedrooms and examining the occupants was not amongst his watchman's duties, especially as he had a revolver strapped to his belt and a bottle of *caxasa*, a type of crude rum, stuffed into his shirt pocket.

One night, about two o'clock, the telephone rang. I rushed through to the lounge, expecting it to be one of the kids calling from England.

'*Está o senhor Antonio?*' asked a rather bleary voice.

'*Quem falla?*' 'Is it urgent?'

'*Sim, muito urgente.*'

I paddled outside and called Antonio. After several loud hollers, he appeared from the region of the beach.

'There's someone on the phone for you. He says it's very urgent.

I stood in the passage while Antonio took his call. There was much laughter and loud talk, none of which seemed either serious or urgent. Mary called from the bedroom.

'It's OK,' I answered. 'It's Antonio taking a call. It's urgent.' Mary's list of expletives always amazed me.

After five minutes, I decided that enough was too much and stomped into the lounge. Antonio was sprawled on the couch, an outstretched arm held a cigarette, from which ash was dropping on the floor.

'Finish,' I bellowed. 'Now!'

'*Sim, patrão*. It is a friend who has just arrived from Caruaru. We will talk again tomorrow.'

'Not on my phone, you won't. And I'm not your bloody *patrão*.' I pushed him outside and locked the door.

A few nights late, the problem of Antonio resolved itself. He didn't turn up. Next day, two policemen called. They would like to speak to Antonio; he had shot someone during a bar-room brawl. Unfortunately, the victim had since died. When they had gone, I rang Dona Mimi.

'Yes,' she assured me, 'we know all about it.' She didn't seem particularly concerned.

We found, later, that Antonio had headed straight to her husband, his *patrão*, who had sent him to hide on a friend's farm for a few months, until the affair was forgotten. Presumably some money had changed hands in the right places. The police soon forgot about him. After all, life was cheap in the North-East. What did one more dead *caboclo* matter?

Our own feelings were of relief that we no longer had a watchman to guard us at night. We certainly slept the better for it!

NEW FACES AND A NEW HOME

Erika, now in her sixties, decided to retire. She had smoothed our paths and valiantly championed our struggles, but she felt it was now time to think of herself. We could hardly have had a more sympathetic, pleasant and efficient secretary.

Graciette, her successor, a cheerful, well-fleshed mother of three, was equally calm and competent, and a courageous optimist, to boot. Soon after her arrival she tiptoed into my office and closed the door behind her.

'There's a Dr Everardo to see you,' she whispered. 'Says he's been sent by EMBRAPA to help us. Looks a queer sort of person. I'll get rid of him if you like.'

486

'No, If he comes from EMBRAPA, you'd better send him in.'

What was EMBRAPA up to now?

Graciette's description of my visitor was well justified. A slight young man of medium height, with a thin straggly beard and long black hair falling down over his shoulders, blinked at me through small, round, metal-rimmed spectacles. A dark blue open-necked shirt hung outside his faded jeans, pulled in at the waist by a loosely-tied white, tasselled cord, similar to those worn with dressing gowns. His bare feet were sandalled. If he had rigged himself out for a fancy-dress party as a Bolshevist, he could have done no better. There was one thing in his favour – as far as I could see, he carried no bomb!

'Please sit down, Dr Everardo. Do you speak English?'

He did, perfectly. In a quiet, bashful voice, made almost inaudible from his examination of the floor while he spoke, he told me that EMBRAPA had appointed him to work with our project as my Co-Manager.

Good grief, I thought. He looks as if he has crept out of a commune.

'Have you a letter or anything?' I asked, unbelieving.

'Nothing, but Dr Soss knows about me.'

We chatted about his experience and the aims of the project. He was an agronomist, he told me, with a PhD in plant nutrition from an American university. He had been teaching in a university in southern Brazil, but had returned to Recife for family reasons.

As he shook hands to leave, I had formed the impression that, whatever his appearance, he was certainly no fool. I only hoped he could solve some of our problems with EMBRAPA.

Ten seconds later I was invaded.

'What the hell was that thing? Graciette says it's our new National Director.'

'That's right,' I told them, unflinching. I felt I should stand up for him.

'You're kidding!' Harry guffawed, unbelieving. 'We shoot those on sight in Australia. You're the Project Manager, Pat. For God's sake send him packing.'

'Look,' I said firmly. 'He's been appointed by EMBRAPA, he has an American PhD, and he's certainly intelligent. Let's give him a chance.'

'Just keep him in your office, then. Don't let him loose on us.'

They left, half-amused, half-angry with me for not kicking him out from the first. I think they felt I had let them down.

I didn't know what to think. Surely EMBRAPA could do better

than that? Or was it just another way for them to show their contempt for FAO? Or would he turn out to be a genius? We could only wait and see.

* * *

'We'll have to move soon,' Mary reminded me. 'Dona Mimi wants the beach house back at the end of October. We'd better start looking round. I still think we should try and buy, rents are so astronomical and they go up twenty-five per cent each year.'

'Over my dead body,' I retorted. 'I'm not going through that Peruvian experience again.'

'All right. This time I'll do the buying and selling.'

'OK darling,' I replied, confident that nothing would come of it. 'But you'd better start finding out what's available right away. And try and find a source of finance while you're about it,' I added sarcastically. I still hadn't heard from Ben in Peru.

We started in Piedade, a little further along our beach. There were plenty of houses for sale. One, I remember, was a series of railway carriages joined side by side, another was an enormous two-storey structure, owned by an architect. Mary was rather taken with it but there was at least $20,000 of work to be done before we could have moved in. The architect, a long-haired, wind-blown fellow, was full of pride in his creation. He pointed out how sturdy it was, how easy to manage, how rapidly it would increase in value and how, if we could advance him 100,000 cruzeiros (which he would deduct from the outrageous purchase price), he could complete it in six months. He hinted that we would be unbelievably stupid to reject such a bargain.

I couldn't help feeling sorry for him a few weeks later, when a heavy storm distributed his incomplete masterpiece all over his still undeveloped garden.

We tried other areas as far afield as the inland suburbs of Casa Forte, Panaficadora and Casa Amarella. When I told Graciette where we were looking, she blew up.

'Don't on any account consider a house in Casa Forte or any other place that side of town.'

'Why not? A lot of people seem to live there.'

'You haven't seen our floods, or the real mosquitoes. Stick to the Boa Viagem area, at least it is out of the flood zone and you have a breeze off the sea. And my advice is DON'T BUY!'

I was in total agreement with her last observation, but renting also had its problems. No-one would agree to rent for less than a year, and in addition demanded at least three months of their exorbitant rent in advance. I realized how very lucky we had been with the beach house.

Mary soon abandoned the idea of buying, and eventually we found a house for let in Rua Setubal, one of the sandy, pot-holed roads parallel to, and one block behind, the elegant sea front of Boa Viagem. It was not a particularly good district. The land in front, after rising a few feet from the shore and supporting a palisade of high-rise apartment blocks which cut off the sea breeze, fell away behind our house to a series of stagnant pools, canals and swampy ground that stretched inland for several kilometres. Drainage, we could see, might be a problem. So might be the mosquitoes. But if others lived there, apparently in contentment, so could we.

The house itself was a spacious, tile-floored, tile-roofed bungalow, with a wide verandah enclosed by burglar bars, up which entwined bougainvillaea and other creepers. At the rear was a double garage with three rooms on top. Behind this, where the land fell away to a canal, there was a walled area, 'the garden' – to use the owner's words – filled with heaps of rubbish.

Another factor influenced our decision to take this house. Our American neighbours at the beach house had moved to Rio and had bequeathed us their two horses. The 'garden' area could easily be cleared to accommodate them, and there were plenty of grassy spaces nearby where they could graze.

We had bought the Brazilian version of the Chevrolet station wagon, a cross between a minibus and a panel van, and called a *veraneo*. It was, by any standards, a monstrosity. Bright orange, high off the ground and difficult to steer, but a first-class investment, the salesman had assured me. What car wouldn't have been with inflation at over 25 per cent? It made a sound like a truck, juggled its occupants between the roof and the hard springs of the seat, guzzled petrol and made my back ache, but it never let us down, even in three feet of water.

Half a dozen trips of the *veraneo* moved us from the beach house to Rua Setubal. We had hardly moved in before we realized two major problems. The first was water. The municipal supply only worked at intervals, with a pressure barely sufficient to reach our roof tank. We complained to our landlord.

'It's the same all over Boa Viagem,' he assured us. 'The only thing to do is to put in a well and a tank.' He even offered to pay half the cost – most unusual for a Recife landlord! The well wasn't very deep, less than 20 feet down into the sand. From it we obtained a fair supply of slightly brackish, slightly smelly, peat-coloured water. We soon became used to the colour and odour and, after filtering and boiling, it tasted as good as the municipal supply. Nevertheless, I couldn't help wondering how many septic tanks and surface drains contributed to our subterranean elixir.

The other snag, one which we had certainly anticipated, although not to such a degree, was mosquitoes. Cut off from the sea breeze by the high-rises, we were left to the mercy of the infernal beasties. There had been mosquitoes in the beach house and there were plenty at the office, but these could be kept at bay by swatting or spraying. Not so the Setubal 'mossies'; an AK47 would have been more appropriate! They were huge and had a whine like a steel saw, and they didn't hunt in ones or twos – not even in tens or twenties – but in thousands. The lovely burglar-barred verandah, on which we had contemplated cool, quiet sundowners, was out. Even a fan, playing directly onto us, didn't help. So, as soon as dusk fell, we closed all the doors and windows and retreated to the inner rooms, where an air conditioner in our bedroom helped to cool the adjacent rooms as well.

Air-conditioning, of course, was the logical answer – if you were a millionaire! Turning it on for two hours each evening added another 1,500 cruzeiros (about $150) to our monthly electricity bill, which was already nearly half as much as the rent. No wonder few people could afford to use electrical appliances. A neighbour offered us an enormous brand-new electric range, absolutely free, because they couldn't afford to run it and were unable to sell it. We also turned it down.

No, the only alternatives after dark, were to retire early and get under a mosquito net, or to take the gin bottle, tonics, soft drinks and cold chicken down to the beach, 200 metres away, where we could lie on the soft warm sand and let the sea breeze blow the insidious insects back to their swampy lairs.

To house our newly acquired steeds, Trigger and Star, we laid a concrete slab against the wall that separated the bottom of the garden from the canal, and thatched it with palm fronds. We engaged a lad (several as time went by) as gardener cum horseboy, whose first duty each morning (if he turned up), was to sweep the droppings into the canal through a hole in the garden wall. This worked well until the rains came; then the canal flooded, pushing the water with its rim of droppings and other debris, further and further up the garden and confining the two horses to a small area behind the garage. It was not very pleasant, but did save us the trouble of cleaning the concrete slab each day.

490

EMBRAPA MUDDLES IT UP

Things were looking up. The pangola grass pastures and the sorghum variety trials at Surubim, on which we were to base our grazing and fattening experiments, had done well. Preparations for the more extensive range management, bush control and animal production experiments at Arcoverde were in full swing, and Harry had persuaded Serra Talhada to clear land and build shelters for some sheep and goat experiments. All this had been done by a trusting IPA, without any sign of official approval from EMBRAPA.

Literally, no funds were coming in from the Brazilian side of the project, only my FAO imprest account was keeping the project alive, while we waited for EMBRAPA to clarify its policy.

It was a pleasant surprise, therefore, when Brasilia suddenly instructed us to resubmit an update of our experiments for final approval. We felt that EMBRAPA might actually be on the move. That we had a mere two weeks in which to do this, was no problem, our ideas had changed little since the original plans had been sent them, five months before.

Everardo, however, wasn't impressed.

'They are stalling,' he warned me. 'They don't really want us to initiate studies. They have no idea how to administrate research, or what to do with the results. You might as well go home – but don't say I said so.'

Then, one day, Dr Soss summoned Everardo and myself.

'*Os cabrões na Brasilia tem reijetado seu programa de pesquisas*,' he told us. '*Cabrões*' was not a very respectful word.

'They've rejected our research programme? I don't believe it. Why?'

'They say it's inadequate. You didn't give enough background and references to justify the work, particularly in statistics.'

'For the simple reason that there *are* no references or statistics to quote. They must know that.'

'Well, you have to resubmit them by next week, or they will give us no funds for this year. The...' He finished with a word much worse than *cabrões*.

'Typical bloody bureaucrats,' I exploded, as Everardo and I walked out into the sunlight. 'All they want us to do is to write lengthy, detailed, impractical plans. Never to actually do anything.'

We felt betrayed, worse – we felt that EMBRAPA didn't want us any more than IPEANE had. Probably Everardo was right; the only reason they tolerated FAO at all was for the prestige factor and because we brought in equipment, unavailable locally. But for doing anything constructive – that was out.

EMBRAPA sent an official to demonstrate how to fill in the long,

491

intricate research *formulários*, involving the use of several coloured inks! We resubmitted our programmes, adding a lot of irrelevant justifications and fictitious statistics, and were rewarded by partial approval and a limited, daily budget, but only for Surubim. The funding, in any case was made almost impossible to use due to the lengthy, unintelligible and wholly unworkable forms, which had to be submitted for each expenditure. No funds whatever were forthcoming for the work at Arcoverde or Serra Talhada.

I began to feel sorry for Dr Soss. As the representative of EMBRAPA in Pernambuco State, I harassed him mercilessly until I realized he had no more influence with Brasilia than I, perhaps less. I, at least could appeal to the Chief of the FAO Mission and to the Res Rep of the United Nations.

After several months of frustrated attempts to cope with the new financial regulations and conflicting edicts of EMBRAPA, I felt we had suffered enough. I wrote to both the FAO and UN Representatives in Brasilia, suggesting we terminate the project.

Pride was dented. The UN's immediate and energetic protestations to the EMBRAPA chiefs resulted in my being summoned to a meeting in the capital, at which EMBRAPA approved all our research programmes. I returned a conquering hero. But it made no difference; EMBRAPA omitted to allocate any funds!

One encouraging concession they did make was to allow us to start recruiting counterpart staff to understudy the various FAO experts. In the following two months we selected 15 young veterinarians and agronomists for the work at Surubim, Arcoverde and Serra Talhada, but no sooner were they installed and helping to run the experiments, than EMBRAPA decided to embark on a crash postgraduate training programme for all their young professionals. Within three months, all but two of our young hopefuls had departed overseas. Nor were we able to find others. Nearly every recent graduate was taking advantage of EMBRAPA's scheme for higher qualifications. Undoubtedly, the idea was excellent for the long-term needs of the country, but quite disastrous for a short-term project like ours. We were back to where we had been six months before.

THERE ARE HORSES AT THE BOTTOM OF OUR GARDEN

Being a vet, one might suppose that I should love all animals – and up to a point, I do. But I exclude insects and worms as lovable companions, also crocodiles and snakes, although I've known several people who adored their reptiles.

Within the limits of the more common domestic mammals, I have to admit that the horse and I have never had much of a rapport. This has nothing to do with their performance on the race track – I don't bet. Although I admire their grace and beauty, I've never felt that emotional affinity with them which I feel for, say, dogs.

In fact, I've always considered Ogden Nash's 'One end bites, the other end kicks, and they're uncomfortable in the middle,' as a pretty fair description of most members of the equine species.

After a few months in our Setubal house, I suddenly woke up to the fact that we had four of these monsters in our garden. The original pair of Star and Trigger, bequeathed by our neighbours at the beach house, had been augmented by Copper, 15 hands of vicious chestnut, and Meu Bem, a lively, grey-flecked pony which Lindley had acquired from a departing Swedish school friend.

The real problem with our troop, however, was that they were all males – three of them stallions. Only Star was gelded. It was not surprising, therefore, that the small, palm-roofed shelter which I had built over the concrete slab at the foot of the garden, and in which we housed Star, Trigger and Meu Bem, was continually being kicked to pieces during their nocturnal battles. I must have repaired it, on average, twice a week.

Copper, kept separately under a coconut tree in a small unroofed pen, reserved his malice for the daytime – and for me in particular. It annoyed me intensely that Mary or any one of the kids could handle him with ease, but the moment I came near, up would go his top lip, his head and his forefeet. Occasionally, when no-one else was available, I would steel myself and lead him down the road to whatever piece of grazing I could find. I was doing this early one Sunday, clad only in swimming shorts and wearing flip-flops on my feet when, without warning, Copper buried his teeth in my shoulder. I swung round, hurt and angry, only to be confronted by a pair of hooves a few inches from my face. Luckily, we were next to a lamp post. I managed to wrap his rope around it and tie it securely. Several passers-by stopped to offer good-humoured advice. Ignoring them, I strode home, collared the first child I saw, which happened to be Shivy, and returned to the recalcitrant beast.

There was now a small group waiting to see what I would do with this fiendish animal. I stopped 20 yards away and watched my six-year-old calmly untie the monster and lead him away to his bit of pasture, as tranquil as a slug. It wasn't my shoulder, covered in blood and smarting, that hurt the most – it was my pride.

Everyone around us, it seemed, owned a horse, so that grazing sites, either vacant lots or roadside strips, were in short supply and the competition acute. It was not unusual, when the children returned in the evening to collect their steeds, to find them replaced by other, often aggressive, equines. Too often, my first greeting after returning from the office with visions of a swim and beer topping my list of priorities, would be a wail that Trigger or one of the others was missing. There was nothing to do but pile into the *veraneo* and search up and down the sandy, scrub-edged lanes that crisscrossed the low-lying ground behind Boa Viagem.

Sometimes we were lucky and would find the missing animal within minutes, but sometimes we would search till dark and have to start again at four o'clock the next morning. Now and then our enquiries, or offer of a reward, would prompt someone to bring back the wanderer to us, for which 10 or 20 cruzeiros would change hands. I began to suspect that our wandering equines provided a regular income to some of the less scrupulous citizens of Boa Viagem.

Many of the horses around us, like ours, were stallions. Mary came limping home one day after a terrifying ordeal. She had been riding Copper when a large, white stallion had attacked. There was little she could do with flailing hooves and gnashing teeth filling the airspace around her, but before she could consider any evasive action, Copper dumped her, butt-first, into some bushes, thus leaving him and his adversary free to continue their running battle into the distance.

Which horse won, I've no idea, but later we found Copper, grazing peacefully by the roadside, with no sign of the white stallion.

From the time I spent cleaning or repairing their wretched stable, taking them to feed and searching for them through hot fly-infested swamps, there was no doubt that, to me, the horses were equally as exasperating as the heat and the mosquitoes!

CATS ON THE KEYS

Horses were not the only animals that tried to dominate our lives; cats and dogs were nearly as bad. We had a house full, but only one was, so to speak, legitimate. Puppy had been given to us as a pup and, unable to agree on a better name, the kids had continued to call her Puppy. The other seven or eight strays that adopted us at various times ranged from an obese, short-haired, scarred-nose, mastiff cross, as sloppy as yoghurt, to an alert, brown bitch, Missy, of no predominant breed.

Agile almost to the point of dancing, Missy was tolerant of Puppy, but death to any other canine or beggar that put a nose inside our gate. She was our constant and devoted companion for nearly a year until, returning from an early morning dip, she ran in front of a car on the coastal road. Sadly, we buried her in the sand at the top of the garden.

One particularly friendly stray stationed himself at the garden gate, welcoming us enthusiastically as we came and went, and howling each night when we turned the lights out. The kids had strict instructions not to feed it, but like all the others it was soon inside. Unfortunately it was old and had a persistent mange, so in due course it joined its predecessors in our sandy cemetery.

Not only were strays a threat to our domestic tranquillity, they were a health hazard as well. Apart from hookworm (more about that later) and some other parasites, I had to consider the possibility of rabies, which was prevalent in the North-East. All I could do was to vaccinate any stray we adopted, knowing well that if the dog had already been exposed to the virus from a previous bite, the vaccine would have no effect.

Most of the dogs that queued up in front of our gate in the hopes of a permanent meal ticket, I finally had to put down. But our garden cemetery had only room for so many, so I had to resort to taking the carcases out into the countryside at the dead of night and dumping them in a ditch. Sydney, the British Consul, told me that there was a dog collection service whom we could have rung up, but he warned me that, once collected, the usual practice was to throw them, alive, into the municipal incinerator. Unbelievable, he said, but true.

Rabies was the main danger. The pattern of its spread in Recife was bizarre. One usually associated the disease with slums or *favelos* where dog control and vaccines would be minimal, but a researcher carrying out a survey in Recife found the incidence of rabies far higher in the prosperous suburbs. He soon twigged the reason – the richer districts had more leftovers in their dustbins! Strays stood no chance at all in the slums, where the half-starved human population provided no scraps. The hungry hounds soon learned to high-tail it to the richer suburbs, where dustbins were worth upsetting and their contents worth fighting over. It was an ideal situation for the spread of rabies.

Cats also considered our house as a residential club. Nearly every week we had a new, and more often than not pregnant, pussycat lapping milk in the kitchen. A few we kept but, remembering Peru, I drew the line at five, and made it a rule to put down any pregnant stray before the event. I relented in one case and found that our

495

feline fraternity had doubled overnight. Tears, arguments and promises that homes would be found for each of the kittens, prevented their immediate demise, and led to my meeting a most extraordinary character.

In desperation, I told Dr Paulo about our surplus kitties and asked if he knew anybody who might want one.

'*Fogo, não é?*' he laughed, adding as an afterthought, 'Why don't you give them to Mrs Mac?'

'Mrs Mac? Who's she?'

'Haven't you met Mrs Mac? She's English. She lives somewhere in Afogados.' Afogados was one of the lower-class suburbs.

It was dusk and pouring with rain, but Paulo insisted on taking me to see her. All I could make out in the headlights was the torrenting rain and narrow, dark streets.

'I haven't been here for a long time,' Paulo admitted, 'I hope I can find her place.'

After a couple of wrong addresses, we stopped to ask a woman sheltering under a tree.

'*Senhora Mac? Sim. Ella mora lá.*' She pointed to a door in a high wall a few yards in front of us.

Thumps on the wooden door in the garden wall brought no-one, but started an incredible cacophony of barks, yaps, growls and wails. There was no street lighting, and now that we had switched off the headlights, it was almost pitch dark. I tried the handle, and was surprised to find the door open.

A multitude of curious canines, dimly lit by a single bulb over the front door of a dilapidated, tin-roofed cottage, 20 yards away, hurled themselves at us. They didn't appear particularly aggressive, but they were incredibly muddy. Paulo, who always wore a suit, and I, who had on light-coloured slacks and shirt, were immediately transformed into mud-plastered hobos.

We closed the door quickly, hoping that none of Mrs Mac's entourage had escaped meanwhile, and stumbled and slid towards the house. Even in that dim light, we could make out heaps of droppings, half-melted in the rain, which we would have to navigate. We were not entirely successful!

The front door was ajar. We called. A faint voice, barely audible between the continuous barks, told us to come in and guided us down a dimly lit corridor to a bedroom at the back. The stench was suffocating. Dogs and cats were everywhere. So were their droppings. As we approached the bedroom door, a faint voice called 'In here'.

On a low bed covered with old blankets, lay an emaciated, white-haired lady, half-smothered in cats. A newly born litter occupied the end of the bed, two other litters in cardboard boxes were against the wall, and the bottom drawer of a tallboy had been removed to supply a home for yet another feline family.

'*Boa tarde, Senhora.* Perhaps you remember me, Dr Paulo. I have brought a friend to see you, an Englishman.' He gave his usual chuckle.

The old lady lifted her head and looked at me, then let it flop back onto her grubby pillow. Her cheek bones were sharp and her eyes fiery. She raised a fragile wrist.

'Very glad to meet you,' she whispered. 'Sorry I'm a bit under the weather. Please sit down.'

We looked around. There was only one chair, and that was occupied by a snarling Pekingese. Certainly there was no room on the bed. We said we'd rather stand.

I was shocked to see this obviously cultured old lady in such dismal and demeaning circumstances. The stench, the squalor, the rain beating on the tin roof, her makeshift bed and filthy bedclothes, were overwhelmingly depressing. I asked who was looking after her. She told us that while she had been sick, a neighbour had brought her soup and bread twice a day.

'I'm much better now. I'll be up tomorrow; but it takes time to recover when you're seventy-seven.'

We didn't stay long. There was nothing we could do or say, and certainly I wasn't going to increase her menagerie with my unfortunate kittens. I promised to look in again in a couple of days.

As we had no phone in the house, I went straight round to the British Consul.

'Sydney, I've just met the most unbelievable old lady, a Mrs Mac, and her thousand and one dogs and cats. Do you know her? She says she's British.'

'I certainly do – only too well,' Sydney sighed. 'She comes in for her pension every month – about a hundred pounds from her late husband's company plus a small allotment from a daughter in Rio.'

'Is there nothing we can do for her?' I pleaded. 'She's overrun with cats and dogs. There must be a real health hazard. Can't the authorities step in?'

'Goodness knows, we've tried to help her. We've given her money, but it goes, literally, to the dogs. If we take her food which the animals can eat, they get it, not her. Both her daughter in Rio and her son in Australia would give her more help if they were sure it wouldn't be squandered on those flea-ridden skeletons.'

The following Sunday I went back to see her, taking some vegetables, tinned soups and fruit. Mary added a homemade cake and biscuits. 'From what you say,' she grumbled, 'they'll probably end up inside her pets. But at least we've tried.'

Mrs Mac was up and walking with the aid of a stick, her unkempt, white (well it was probably white when washed) hair hung lifelessly over her torn cotton blouse. The house, I now saw, was of mud brick, roofed with sheets of corrugated iron. The front yard was of bare, red earth and covered with thousands of smelly piles. Under a mango tree, by the wall, a score of dogs lay scratching.

We picked our way round to the back, where a couple of outhouses with open doors and windows were spilling over with all shapes, sizes, colours and sexes of cats and dogs. Fights were continuous, both between and within each species.

The first room we entered had probably been a store, or servant's quarters, or whatever. It was now a cats' hostel. There must have been close to 50 inmates – on the table, on the shelves, on a heap of sacks in the corner, on ... Oh no, it couldn't be! Oh yes, it could. It was!

Horrified, I approached the dark wood instrument. Faeces, spilled food, muddy paw marks, and scattered rubbish couldn't hide the dignified lines of a grand piano! I opened the lid. Grime, mould, years of dirt and dust covered the keys, but didn't quite obliterate the name etched in golden letters beneath the lid – BECHSTEIN! Unbelievable! A masterpiece of musical craftsmanship rotting in a cat-ridden outhouse; scratched, mouldy, warped by the heat and by the rain which blew in through the unpaned window. Even as I gaped, two terrier-types rushed in, jumped onto the lid via the keyboard and routed the half-dozen cats which had been sleeping there.

'I expect I'll take up playing again sometime,' she told me, rather shamefacedly, before I could say anything. 'There's no room for it in the house, you see.'

'But surely you should cover it with something to stop the animals destroying it. It must be worth three or four thousand pounds.'

'Do you think so?' She seemed surprised.

'If you want me to help you sell it, I'd be only too happy,' I urged.

'Thank you. Perhaps I will. We'll see.' But she never did.

'How many pets have you got here?' I asked. I reckoned she must have at least 100 dogs alone.

'About a hundred and seventy dogs and about a hundred cats,' she answered proudly. 'I want you to have a look at one or two; they're sick.'

As far as I could see, this was the understatement of the year, at least half appeared to be on their last legs.

We went into her – well not hers, her pets' – living room. She grabbed an emaciated puppy from under the table and put it on top. Its limbs were grossly deformed.

'What's wrong with it?' she demanded.

I examined it. The legs were like rubber, and could be bent like those of a Barbie doll.

'It's about the best case of advanced rickets I've ever seen,' I told her.

'Can it be cured?'

What could I say? To suggest she gave it cod liver oil and bone meal, plus vitamin injections, was quite impractical. Besides, it was by no means the only one. Several others had bandy legs and swollen joints.

'Look,' I said, adopting a slightly severe but sympathetic tone. 'If you want me to help you with your animals, I will, but we have to be realistic. You haven't the means to look after all of them. Half are diseased, and all of them are hungry. Look at that one with the sores.' I pointed to an old campaigner, probably with bull terrier blood in him, which had slumped under the (I presumed) sideboard.

'Ah yes. He always was a bit of a fighter,' she replied cheerfully.

'The first thing to do,' I went on, 'is to examine them all and put down those that are incurable. This will save a lot of misery and allow more food for those that are left.'

'NO. I won't have a *single* one put down. If you want to help, then treat the sick ones.'

'There are a great many sick. *I* can't afford medicines for them all, and I know *you* can't. Many treatments would have to do be done daily. Who would do it? You couldn't possibly cope.'

'If you can't cure them, there's nothing you can do here.'

I was wondering whether this was a hint for me to go, when she went over to the sideboard and began rumpling through a drawer.

'I wrote to the RSPCA in London, asking them to pay for an animal shelter here,' she pulled out a handful of papers. 'I've got their reply somewhere. Here.' She handed me a dirty sheet. 'When are you going to England next?'

'In about three months.'

'Take it with you and go and see them. They ought to help.'

I glanced at the letter. It was signed by a Mr J. Hall, Chief Secretary, in Jermyn Street.

'But this was written more than ten years ago,' I pointed out. 'Didn't you ever answer it? They wanted more information.'

'Can't remember if I did. Anyway, it doesn't matter now. Go and see them.'

499

I pocketed the letter and, after trying once more to persuade her to weed out the incurable cases, and getting the same fierce refusal, I left, promising to return the following week with any medicine I could lay my hands on.

I never did get to see the RSPCA, but I wrote, referring to her letter. Originally, she had asked for £300 to build an animal refuge, and an annual grant to run it. I pointed out to London that it would now cost three or four times that amount to build the roughest of shelters, and running costs would be proportionately higher. I also doubted her ability to organize any such venture, but emphasized the need for a centre to care for and humanely destroy strays in Recife.

Their answer was as I had expected. There was little they could do without an active local branch of the RSPCA to run such a shelter. Money sent to Mrs Mac would, almost certainly, be squandered on all the wrong things.

I continued to visit Mrs Mac, taking vegetables, fruit and anything that I knew her horde wouldn't eat, but I could not persuade her to reorganize her menagerie.

A year after we had left Recife, Sydney wrote that she had died. 'I've had all the animals destroyed humanely,' he added.

What a pity, I often felt, that such dogged (no pun implied) determination and kind-heartedness, had only added to the suffering of the strays. I often wondered, too, whether it would have been possible to renovate the Bechstein or whether it, like many of the strays, was past treatment. Ironically, the proceeds from its sale might well have gone a long way towards the costs of Mrs Mac's proposed animal shelter.

TOO MANY COOKS

I had collected the names of nearly 30 other agencies, sub-agencies, institutes, Federal or State operated departments, universities (both local and foreign), and *superentendencias* or controlling bodies which, like our own FAO Project, were dipping their philanthropic fingers into the North-East Agricultural and Livestock pie.

Some of these agencies operated from dingy offices, others from grand palaces – depending on who was supplying their funds. Many of the less motivated or less-well subsidized seemed to do little except shuffle papers, write enthusiastic plans and host visiting dignitaries, from whom they hoped to extract further contributions. The three most active and important institutions were SUDENE, a semi-auton-omous organization, which oversaw the whole development of Brazil's North-East, financing a great many projects in industry and

500

rural development; the Bank of North-East Brazil, the BNB; and the Development Agency for the Sao Francisco River Valley – SUVALE.

There was nothing basically wrong with most of the others, except that the vital ingredient necessary to blend them into the developmental pudding, namely co-ordination, had been omitted. As in other parts of Latin America, little thought had been given to co-operation. The result resembled a cam-shaft driven by a score of conflicting pistons firing at random – nothing advanced very far, and many promising beginnings soon broke down. So we were only too pleased when SUDENE asked us for assistance with their cattle programmes, and BRASCAN, a Brazilian Canadian co-operative programme, offered us facilities for pasture and cattle production at their farms near Pesqueira, a delightful, hilly area 200 kilometres to the west of Recife. DNOCS, the irrigation service, whose objective was to alleviate the water problems of the region, also asked us to advise them on pasture production in drought areas.

Several excellent opportunities for co-operative research emerged, but each time a start seemed imminent, the clammy hand of EMBRAPA would descend and, with the flimsiest excuses, draw a red pencil through our proposals.

These constant disappointments and inactivity began to erode our confidence and shorten our tempers. The office became a nightmare.

Don was particularly unhappy at the slow progress of his range-management studies, accusing me of favouring André's Surubim feeding trials at his expense. I tried to point out that, unlike his long-term range management studies, André's fattening experiments could give results in a fairly short time, which would be of immediate help to local farmers.

For a time we were all at loggerheads, scowling at each other and carrying on acrimonious arguments that would last all day.

'You're like a lot of spoilt children,' Graciette told me after a particularly unfriendly day. She wasn't far wrong!

In desperation at the delay and our deteriorating morale, I wrote the Director of EMBRAPA personally, with copies to the UN and FAO Reps, suggesting that since we had no Brazilian staff and no easily accessible budget, we were all wasting our time. It was EMBRAPA's responsibility to supply the facilities, and we could not hang around any longer waiting for them to move. Our experts were fed up and losing their professional motivation, and the farmers of the North-East were desperate for answers to their problems. A week later the FAO Rep rang. 'The UN Res Rep and I are arriving tomorrow night. Please arrange meetings with all those involved.'

Dr Soss, once again the Big Bad Wolf as EMBRAPA's representative in the North-East, was present at most of these outspoken discussions. I felt sorry for him. Like us, he was completely at the mercy of his peers in Brasilia, and kept referring to me for support against their ridiculous regulations.

'We'll have a final meeting with EMBRAPA's directors in Brasilia next week,' the Res Rep said as he left. 'Bring all the ammunition you need. This time we either get action or we get out.'

EMBRAPA could not have been more co-operative. As on the previous occasion when the Res Rep had championed our case, our programme was re-confirmed. 'I'll send up our chief livestock consultant to iron out the details,' the Director of EMBRAPA told me. 'Meanwhile, go ahead with everything. I'll see that Dr Soss receives funds in a few days.'

For the first time in two years, I felt I was justified in writing an optimistic six-monthly report to Rome.

While the future looked brighter for us, the US AID group from the University of Wisconsin, working next door to us, were not so optimistic.

'We're certain we can produce ten tons of rice per hectare using the new CR26 disease and insect-resistant strain,' boasted one of the group, easing his plaster-encased leg (the result of an attempt on the Brazilian night parachute jump record the previous week) onto a chair. 'That's about six times the present yield in the North-East. Christ! It's a breakthrough, but it's no use. The bastards have sabotaged our field work.'

EMBRAPA's unbelievably bureaucratic accounting system had made it virtually impossible to hire labour to plant or harvest the rice, so that the research staff had had to do this themselves, assisted whenever possible by their wives, children, the office staff and any caring friends. Understandably, it was not long before their team decided it was a bit too much, and returned home to Wisconsin. The University of Florida group, working near Brasilia, also ran out of patience and left.

We had been attending as many of the local conferences on livestock production as we could, shyly presenting papers based on the scanty results we had obtained from Surubim and putting forward our strategy for the livestock development of the North-East. Unfortunately, these meetings only emphasized the sorry state of livestock research in the region. Ideas there were in plenty, but knowledge of basic techniques and facilities was almost absent.

To try and fill a few of these technical gaps, we arranged short courses in pastures, nutrition, range management and small ruminant production. Also, to show that we had actually done some work and obtained some results, however meagre, we arranged a Field Day at Surubim to demonstrate the production and conservation of fodder.

Eighty farmers and livestock officials attended. We showed them how to make silage from sorghum, how to conserve pastures as 'standing hay', and explained the grazing experiments on Pangola grass and the fattening trials on silage and sugar cane tops. The two-hour discussion following lunch (paid for from my hospitality budget) could have lasted twice as long, if we'd had the time. It was the first occasion for many years that the farmers in that area had received practical, sympathetic encouragement.

The whole day was an outstanding success. All the past frustrations and dead-ends suddenly seemed worthwhile. We drove back to Recife on cloud nine.

'Let's call at the office and see if there is any mail,' André suggested. André had a mania about mail.

On my desk was a cable from Rome. That put an end to our beautiful day. It requested Harry to report to Rome by the end of the following week, pending retirement.

I was dumbfounded. I was well aware that his time was nearly up, but Rome had agreed to extend him until after the first lambing season at Serra Talhada. What we didn't know was that EMBRAPA had flatly refused to approve his extension. Everyone else had been advised of their decision, except us.

Within half an hour, jubilation had sunk to gloom.

I flew to Brasilia and fought with the high-ups in EMBRAPA. They weren't interested. In any case, they were going to reorganize the whole research service once again, this time into National Research Centres for each species of animal or crop. Yes, they would certainly need an expert in the Centre for Small Ruminants, but not Harry. He had offended too many officials by his forthright Australian approach, which could be a little lacerating when dealing with people he considered stupid or dishonest. There were several such people in EMBRAPA who he considered fitted that description. Finally, as a gesture to FAO, they agreed to extend his contract for one month.

I came away with the feeling that it wasn't only Harry who was on the skids. It began to look very much as if this was the beginning of the end.

BEN INTO BATTLE

While I was struggling with EMBRAPA, Ben, back in Peru, was relentlessly prodding the *Banco Hipotecario* in an effort to obtain the

503

mortgage money. I had great faith in Ben, but I was worried. His contract was nearly at an end, and when he left there would be no-one else I could turn to. He was my last hope.

'*Doctor. Telefone.*'

I had just finished supper, soup and *churasco*, a name which seemed to cover any cooked meat. The scruffy, white-tiled, toilet-like dining room of the Surubim hotel had two other guests in open shirts, and a group of local *caboclos* or peasants, making nearly as much noise eating as they did talking. I decided to forego whatever was for sweet, and had started up the concrete stairway to my room when the receptionist hailed me.

I descended to the antiquated instrument that hung on the wall by the hotel entrance. It was Harry on the other end, yelling through a lot of static. I could just make out 'Cable ... money ... mortgage ... your account Banco de Londres...'

'Yippee, he's done it,' I yelled at no-one in particular. 'Good old Ben!'

I found the bar and sank a very bad, very expensive whisky of unknown brand. I drank it neat and warm. They had no soda, and I didn't trust the water – or the ice.

Harry gave me a copy of the cable when I returned to Recife. It confirmed what I had guessed.

'Glad you could understand the phone message. Thought you'd like to have the news as soon as possible.'

That night, Mary and I, with Harry and Gwen, celebrated in style. I had barely recovered when a letter from Ben, in Rome, on his way back to Israel, described how he had been determined to have one last attempt to bludgeon the funds out of the Mortgage Bank before he left Peru.

He had called at the Bank on his way to the airport. The officials, for some unaccountable reason, were all smiles, and within minutes he had been given a cheque which he had immediately deposited in my account, just making the airport in time for his flight!

'I was just as relieved as I'm sure you will be,' he wrote. 'My honour was at stake. If I, a good Israeli, couldn't have got money out of that lot – I'd have to think of changing my nationality!'

I hoped that Solange, Ben's charming French wife, would appreciate the topaz pendant and earrings which I bought the following day from a clandestine dealer in precious stones. Ben, I know, had I told him, would have appreciated the discount I was given.

GUY'S SPECIAL EPITHET

Overseas holidays, as a family, were a thing of the past. It had been several years since all ten of us, three in nappies, had bundled aboard a jet to terrorize relations in Canada, Britain and Jamaica.

The children were older now and their school terms had to be observed more strictly. Those in England could come to us for their holidays with much less trouble than us going to them and, in any case, the long 'summer' holidays for South American schools were at Christmas and so did not coincide with holiday weather in the northern hemisphere.

There was a further problem. It was impossible for both Mary and I to be away at the same time. Someone had to look after the children still at school – and the horses.

We compromised. Every other summer, I would go to Britain for a month, paying a duty call at Rome on the way, and Mary would despatch a couple of the children to spend their two-week mid-year holiday with me there, before travelling back together. After I had returned, Mary would spend a month with her family in Canada. It worked well.

* * *

Returning from one such trip, I found a new face in the Recife office. For nearly a year, Rome had been promising us an expert in cultivated pastures. They had even told us his name, Guy, a pasture agronomist from Belgium.

He had been 'coming' and 'not coming' for so long that I had forgotten about him. Now, suddenly, here he was – and not a moment too soon. Don had already left, to advise oil-rich Arabs in the Middle East on costly irrigation schemes to provide expensive grazing, leaving André to cope with the range work as well as the cultivated pastures and feeding trials.

I would never have taken Guy for a pasture expert. He was short and, although not actually plump, definitely pink and fleshy. There was none of that hard, lean appearance or that faraway look in sky-blue eyes which one might expect from the daily tramping of wolds and the survey of pasture lands. His eyes were small and flickered through unframed lenses. His high, domed head was almost bald but showed no signs of exposure to solar rays. He looked older than his 35 years. An accountant, or bank manager, you'd say, or a business consultant, or perhaps an associate of his famous compatriot, that fictional sleuth, Hercule Poirot. But a fieldman dealing with the tilling of soil, of sowing and reaping and grovelling amongst grasses? ... Oh, no!

His English was passable, except for a tendency to qualify every noun with the same earthy adjective.

'It vas a shit journey,' he announced at our first meeting. He had been transferred from Mali, which was a 'shit' country, and he had spent a day in Brasilia, which was, indisputably, a 'shit' city.

The Scientific Development Department of the Bank of the North-East had, at our instigation, initiated a widespread programme on private farms to determine the most suitable pasture grasses for the region.

It was agreed that the scheme, PROPASTO, would be run jointly by the Bank of the North-East (BNB) and EMBRAPA, using Guy as EMBRAPA's technical expert. The BNB would supply the grass seed, fertilizers, fence posts and cattle, and be responsible for all the non-technical activities and administration, while the farmers would prepare the land and sow the seed.

Dealing with the BNB was quite different from dealing with the Government. Materials usually arrived on time, people were there when they said they would be, and funds were released with a minimum of red tape. Bureaucracy still existed – Brazil would not have been Brazil without it – but it was reasonable and could be manipulated. The weather, of course, couldn't, and in some states enthusiastic farmers sowed their free seed at the first shower, only to find that no more rain came for another month. But that was the North-East. It looked as if PROPASTO would fold before it started. However, the Bank came up with a further supply of seed, and eventually the rains came.

Guy was in his element. By nature a loner and allergic to office work just as Anzac Ian, the pasture expert in VITAR, had been, he would drop in at Recife about twice a month, check the pasture work at Surubim, recuperate from his 'shit' travelling and report progress. It would have made life a lot easier for me had he been able to write an understandable account of his doings, but his frequent deviations, punctuated by irrelevant anecdotes in a type of pidgin English, amusing as they often were, meant that I had to rewrite his report from start to finish. Quite definitely, they were 'shit' reports. There was one occasion, however, when I had to agree that his pet adjective was entirely appropriate.

Guy's fiancée had joined him. She was a gorgeous, almond-eyed, 19-year-old Balinese. Since his flat was near our house and he couldn't always take her with him on his travels, Lili often came over for a chat. There was never a sweeter girl. Soon she was teaching our

506

kids Malay or Bali or whatever she spoke, and they were helping her with her English which, although poor, at least excluded Guy's, now famous, adjective.

It was Guy's determination to improve Lili's English that led to the unfortunate incident. Arrangements were made for her to attend a language school in England. The local consulate provided her with a special student's visa, and off she went.

The following afternoon Graciette brought me a cable. 'It's for Guy,' she said.

'Must be from Lili in England,' I told her. 'I'll take it round to his flat tonight. He's off to Piaui tomorrow.'

'Yes, it *is* from Lili, but she's in France, not England.'

'France?' I read the cable. Lili had been refused entry to Britain. She was on her way back to Bali.

Guy was demented. I was furious and extremely embarrassed. I had helped him find the course and lent him the sterling to pay for it. And Britain was my country.

I took Guy round to the British Consul's house. He had been away and only just returned. I told him what had happened, Guy reinforcing my complaints wherever possible with his one-word expletive.

'It's entirely our office's fault,' Sydney admitted. 'My deputy should have checked first with Brasilia. Students' visas were cancelled for all Indonesians due to the recent troubles there and the influx of so-called "students" into Britain. We could have easily given her a normal visa.'

A ticket and normal visa were cabled to Lili, now back in Bali, with the compliments of Her Majesty's Government, but once bitten and considerably disillusioned, she preferred to remain in Bali rather than again confront the implacable immigration officials at Heathrow who, she wrote, had left her imprisoned in a cell with a fierce Police matron for 12 hours and made her feel like a terrorist.

Yes, I thoroughly endorsed Guy's opinion that it had been a 'shit' affair.

DEATH SQUADS

Police death squads were common knowledge. It was far less trouble to bump off a few rebellious lawbreakers and throw their bodies down a disused mine shaft than to take them to court, especially as the prisons were crammed way past capacity.

A woman journalist who had worked in Brazil for a year, had

warned me that it was a police state. 'People disappear all the time,' she said.

She was quite right. People *did* disappear, and rumours of torture were generally believed but difficult to prove. Those who returned were too frightened to tell of their sufferings, so it was not until an American pastor, whose children attended the American school with ours, was arrested and a detailed account of his torture appeared in an American weekly, that we knew for sure.

The good Reverend had been careless enough to befriend various liberally minded persons in Pernambuco, well-known to be critical of the government. He had to be taught a lesson. In broad daylight, in front of a downtown restaurant where he and his friends had been eating, he was set upon by a group of young men, blindfolded, bundled into a van and whisked away to the headquarters of the local army garrison.

For 12 hours he remained naked, handcuffed to the bars of his cell. No food or drink or other amenity was offered. Nicely softened up, they started on the electrical treatment. Terminals were attached to his head and genitals. The jolts threw him about the cell. After a few days of intermittent treatment of this nature, his Embassy was allowed to see him. Pressure was brought to bear, he was released and deported. He was one of the luckier ones.

My Co-Manager, Everardo, himself a rebel, had seen many of his friends disappear, some for ever, others to reappear so terrified that they were useless for months, refusing to tell of their ordeal from fear of reprisal.

I was only required to enter a police station on two occasions. The first was following an attempted sexual attack on one of the smaller children by a neighbour's employee. While the alleged offender was being questioned in the local *posto de policia* in the presence of Mary and myself, a tall man in a white suit entered. The culprit immediately began to shake in terror. Some rapid Portuguese was exchanged between the visitor and the interrogator, who both had their eyes fixed on the hapless prisoner. For a moment I thought that the man in white was going to take the accused away, but the poor miscreant was shaking so much, I doubted he would have been able to walk. Eventually the stranger left, and the wretch's shakes diminished. In the end, he was warned and still terrified, staggered out of the door.

'He won't trouble your little girl again,' the official assured us. We were sure of it!

I mentioned the episode to Everardo.

'The man in white was the "doctor". Sometimes they are real

508

doctors. They are the ones who supervise the electric shocks and gauge the state of the victim's resistance. Another method they use is to hold the victim's head underwater till he almost drowns.'

Some months later, a theft of money from a drawer in Pancho's desk occasioned another visit to the police, this time to the headquarters of the *Policia de Investigação* – the CID. Our office boy, Eugenio, the same one who had sat so chummily on my office settee the day we had moved in, was under suspicion. Pancho and I were required to give evidence. We drove through a heavily guarded gate in a high, turreted brick wall covered with rolls of barbed wire. We showed our papers and were asked to wait on the verandah of an office block. Pancho was soon called inside. I remained, regretting the waste of a morning and studying the topography of the surrounding encampment, not, I hoped, that I would ever need it.

Two sides were enclosed by brick bungalows; on a third side, opposite me, were a number of small brick huts with barred windows, obviously cells. In the middle of the grassy yard was a round, concrete water trough and a mound of sand. The trough, I presumed, was used to douse the more stubborn inmates. The use of the mound was soon made apparent when a young policeman wandered across and began unloading his pistol into it. Several of the rounds didn't go off.

A little later, a darkish-skinned youth, clad only in the scantiest of underpants, appeared from behind one of the cells, urged along by a policeman flourishing a revolver. Hardly had they disappeared into one of the office blocks, when the most appalling yells and screams came from inside. I was horrified, but there was nothing I could do. Plainly, the semi-naked lad was being tortured.

'Either electric shocks or having his balls squeezed,' suggested Everardo later when I told him.

I was still feeling rather nervous when a door was flung open at one end of the verandah and a very large, extremely coarse-featured woman, her hair swept back into an untidy bun and a thick leather belt pulled tight round her very ample waist, screamed at me, in Portuguese, 'In here, at once.'

I was staggered. This was not the treatment one expected when asked to give evidence, especially a person with diplomatic status. I rose slowly and took a few hesitant steps towards her. She yelled again and began to march down the verandah to meet me, her fleshy arms swinging determinedly, her breasts thrashing forward like the snouts of bull terriers. I began to feel distinctly uncomfortable. I didn't fancy her manhandling me, neither did I want to hit a woman – even an official Amazon! We were both advancing on a collision

509

course when a small man rushed out through the same door and confronted her, talking rapidly and bowing repeatedly.

The Belsen Bitch had evidently mistaken me for some poor miscreant she had been about to interrogate. With a final, malevolent glance, she turned and retreated into her lair, like a dog whose bone had been suddenly snatched away. The little man hurried up to me full of apologies.

'*Disculpe, senhor. Um error, um error.*'

At that moment, thank God, Pancho emerged.

'What in the hell kept you?' I asked angrily.

'The investigator was an old friend; I met him at the German Shepherd Breeders' Club. Hadn't seen each other for some time. Very good chap.'

'And when do I go in?' I was decidedly irritated.

'You don't have to. They will warn Eugenio, and if anything disappears again, they'll nail him. He was the only one who could have done it.' As we got into the car, I realized that my heart was still beating at twice its normal speed. What would it do if I really had been under suspicion? I thought.

Another incident involving the police was told me by a Danish friend. He was about to marry a Brazilian girl and had to obtain some certificate from the police. While waiting for the official to stamp it, he was shocked to hear female screams coming from somewhere in the building.

'What's happening?' he asked.

'Oh, we're just spanking a couple of prostitutes before we let them go,' the official replied with a chuckle.

No wonder the police were held in awe. No wonder that no-one argued with them. And 'very good chap' as Pancho's detective friend might have been, I was willing to bet that he could administer shocks, duck heads, squeeze testicles and spank prostitutes with the best of them!

KILLER BEES AND CREEPING ERUPTION

The rubbish-strewn area, the so-called garden, which fell away from the back of our house down to the canal, was soon taken in hand by my indefatigable wife.

Mary never did anything by halves – even to bearing children! Her cooking was superb, she had won several prizes for embroidery, and her acting was exceptional. Her rare letters, usually restricted to close friends and relatives, would contain upwards of 25 pages in delightful and highly decorative prose, capering the reader through all the activities, problems, successes and opinions of our chaotic family, in a series of side-splitting anecdotes. But it was her obsession and tenacity which marked her off from the common herd.

So it was no real surprise when the rubbish dump soon began to show signs of order and elegance. Flower beds were dug along the side walls and terraces made in the sandy soil which led up to the house, all covered with loads of earth and manure. The ground in between was cleared of rubbish, fertilized and sown with grass. In a few months we had an attractive garden.

Attractive, perhaps, but not devoid of peril. It was dangerous to loiter beneath the half-dozen coconut trees, which were very tall and apt to shed their fruit when least expected. Luz, strolling in the garden one evening, caught a nut on her wrist. She came running up to the house, moaning that her wrist was broken and would have to be amputated. X-rays showed nothing broken and, after a few days in a sling, with Mary doing the housework, her plump, purple appendage returned to normal. Perhaps it was a blessing; it warned us of the Damoclesian properties of our stately palms, but try as we might, we couldn't knock down the coconuts, they were too high.

In the end, the problem was solved by another drama. I came home to find everyone locked in the house with the windows shut. The reason was obvious. The whole place was besieged by monster African bees that whizzed past like mini-jets, emitting much the same high-pitched buzz. We unearthed our tennis racquets and put in some well-needed if unorthodox practice, swiping bees at will round the verandah and kitchen, neither area having more than burglar bars to prevent the winged terrors from entering and attacking. But there were too many of them and, eventually, streaming with sweat, we had to retire inside to the dining room, close the outside doors and turn on the air conditioner. None of us were stung, but one of the dogs, which was unlucky enough to collect an irate drone under the tail, went off through the front gate yelping like a mad thing. Thank God the horses escaped!

At dusk, the gregarious brutes called it a day and retired, leaving their dead and mutilated for us to sweep up. Next day, when a few of the more valiant again attacked, we discovered the reason. Part of a large nest had fallen from the top of a coconut tree. The inhabitants, divided between memories of their old home at the top of the tree, and the vulnerability of their new home at the bottom, and miffed at our quite unwarranted interference, were confused, angry and aggressive.

José, our garden boy, knew of an old man who could fix them – so he said. We sent for him.

'*Sim, senhor*. There are nests in several of your *palmeiras*.'

'Just get rid of them,' I told him. 'And knock down all the coconuts at the same time.'

'*Sim, senhor*. One hundred cruzeiros each tree.'

That was a bit steep, we thought, but once we had watched him shin up the goalpost trunks, clothed in a thick coat, long thick trousers, gloves, and a hat draped with mosquito net, and bearing a crude torch of cotton waste soaked in kerosene, with which he hoped to incinerate the beasts, we had to admit that his fees were reasonable – some of the trees were 45 feet tall. We had sent the kids to a friend's house for the day and warned our neighbours, but the bees seemed to lose heart with the loss of their homes. They conceded defeat and left.

Bees weren't the only danger lurking in the garden. Mary's enthusiasm for an instant lawn in the small gravelled area in front of our house prompted her to order a truck load of turf. She spent a happy afternoon, clad only in the briefest of bikinis, fitting the cut squares of grass into the area to be transformed. The next evening I found her in considerable distress.

'I'm being eaten,' she wailed. 'It must have been ants in the garden yesterday, but I didn't see any. My fingers are itching, my feet are itching and my bottom's itching. It's unbearable.'

It was another 12 hours before we twigged the cause. Little red weals began to appear between her fingers, on her legs and on her posterior ... 'Creeping Eruption'!

This affliction is caused by the larvae of a dog hookworm, common in Brazil. The female of *Ancylostoma braziliense* lives in the dog's intestine and lays eggs which her obliging host distributes for her in his droppings. The microscopic larvae that emerge from the eggs crawl up blades of grass, biding their time till another canine treads on them or sniffs too closely, when they attach themselves to the preferred part of the dog, burrow through the skin and grow to adult hookworms in their new host's intestine.

If, of course, a nice soft, unprotected human foot, hand or bottom, happens to pick them up, the little larvae wriggle through the delicate skin, delighted at their easy penetration. But they are being fooled. By some process of immunological specificity, the human body defences do not allow the dog parasite to go any further. Piqued at this wholly unjustifiable interference, the larvae cruise around beneath the skin, making themselves as insufferable as possible and leaving thread-like tracks behind them, giving rise to the term 'Creeping Eruption'.

Luckily, there is a very rapid and effective cure, if done correctly. A cream containing a special anthelminthic, or worm killer, is rubbed into the skin over the front end of the track. The parasite dies within hours. Unfortunately, Mary rubbed the ointment in at the wrong end of the thin red weals, and instead of killing the burrowing beasts, it seemed to make them go berserk. In no time at all, her behind resembled a map of Mars!

But even with all these dangers and the added annoyance of mosquitoes as soon as the sun was below the yard-arm, our garden provided an undisturbed, often cool and pleasant haven, and being below street level, the raucous strains from the nearby bar could hardly be heard.

SUPERNATURAL GOINGS ON

The supernatural, in one form or another, dominated the lives of most *Nord-Estinos*, rich or poor. The general name for such voodoo-like practices was *feitiçaria*, not exactly witchcraft, but definitely to do with the occult.

In the North-East it was called *Candomblé*, *Xangô*, or *Catimbó*; further south it was known as *Macumba*. Different regions had different ceremonies and different gods and goddesses. The most important of the *Candomblé* deities, who had been brought across with slaves from Dahomey and Togo, was Iemanjá, goddess of the sea, mother of all other gods and goddesses and closely associated with the Catholic Saint Barbara, protector against storms and lightning.

Iemanjá favoured Saturdays and early February for her feasts, which took place on certain beaches, where white-clothed girls danced and threw gifts into the waves, while singing songs to her glory. Once, it was customary to sacrifice children at these ceremonies, but now sacrifices were restricted to chickens or the occasional white castrated kid goat. Offerings, in the form of flowers, poems or sometimes articles of jewellery, were thrown into the sea. Those that sank or were carried away were considered to have been accepted, but those that were washed up, Iemanjá was said to have rejected.

What exactly a supplicant did with a soggy chicken washed up at his feet, I don't know. Perhaps he left it there in case Iemanjá changed her mind. One thing was certain, any jewellery would certainly sink and be accepted, but the number of beachcombers after

513

a *Candomblé* ceremony suggested that not all the populace believed that Iemanjá would actually spirit her presents away!

One of the 'fathers' of the *Candomblé* cult, *Pai* José, lived nearby. Now and then we would meet him on his way to the beach, white-robed acolytes in tow; but the only so-called *Candomblé* ceremony I witnessed was during a trip to Bahia.

The small *Todos os Santos* hotel (the owner presumably wasn't leaving anything to chance, so he invoked all the Saints) where we stayed advertised a *Candomblé* ceremony in one of the *barrios*, or suburbs, that evening. The cost was 26 cruzeiros (about $3), including transport there and back.

The 'church' was a large room in a private house in a narrow, dirty lane. The district was decidedly slummy. The 60 or so spectators sat on wooden benches, segregated as to sex, men to the left of the centre aisle, women to the right. They were really more of a congregation than onlookers, and probably attended as regularly as others did mass. At the front, there was a vacant space like the dance floor of a restaurant.

First, a group of young men appeared. One of them, a slim, light-coloured fellow with an attractive smile, acted as a sort of compère-cum-usher and gave a short address in an accent we found hard to understand. The other men in the group, all negroes, turned out to be drummers. As they started their beat, a huge negress, evidently the priestess, or whatever she was called, waddled in, a bored expression on her face, and sat down in a large, wooden armchair.

The three drummers soon dominated the proceedings, the noise from the small drums and a tin can, becoming so shattering under the low ceiling, that it was impossible to converse. After some minutes of this softening-up activity, the drums slowed and a dozen girls (two almost white) appeared, all dressed in long flowing whitish gowns, barefooted and with fixed, uninterested expressions. Soon, however, they were bobbing and spinning and stamping to the rhythm of the frenetic drums. Their stamina was remarkable and they outlasted the drummers, who were replaced, one by one, leaving the original three to flop against the wall and drink deeply from a bottle which the compère passed to them.

Shortly afterwards, the priestess began to stir and eventually arose and took a few half-hearted steps, the same bored expression on her face. I thought she would be too fat to dance, but she soon showed that she could do anything her girls could and, for the next 20 minutes, led them in their whirlings and bobbings.

I had had enough of this primitive non-stop disco. The heat was too oppressive, the noise too deafening and the antics of the perfor-

514

mers too repetitive. All I wanted was to sneak out, get a bit of fresh air, sink a pint and let my eardrums stop vibrating.

I was wondering how to do this when one of the girls began to scream. The other dancers took no notice, but when her screams stopped and she began to froth at the mouth and sag at the knees, the priestess and the compère were quickly at her side. Together they helped her back through the stage door.

Several more girls met the same fate until there were only five left. Sensing the imminent culmination of the proceedings, the compère hurried round the congregation with a large tin. From the occasional tinkle, it seemed that very few of the faithful had been motivated sufficiently to contribute to the priestess and her troupe, and any hope of financial gain now depended on the appreciation of myself and the other dozen outsiders.

Candomblé might have been the right name for the exercise, but it had all the appearances of a tourist trap. It was much the same as the Pocomania I had seen in Jamaica, and probably differed little from many revivalist meetings in the Southern States of America. It bore little relation to the true *candomblé* ceremonies on moonlit beaches, where barefooted, white-robed girls threw flowers into the waves and sang songs to Iemanjá, the all-powerful Mother of the Sea.

NOVA JERUSALÉM AND CARNAVAL

The Brazilians' flair for the dramatic came through in every aspect of their culture. Their architecture, which fashioned huge high-rises balancing precariously on spindly legs, their pageantry which knew no bounds either on the stage or in the streets where their *Carnaval* was world-famous, or their religious festivals were unforgettable.

One of these spectacles, less known but just as stunning as her *Carnaval*, took place each Easter in a bleak area of bare hills and stony outcrops. This was the unparalleled presentation of the Passion of Our Lord, at Nova Jerusalém, 100 kilometres inland from Recife.

I had never seen the Passion Play at Oberammergau, but those who had rated the pageant at Nova Jerusalém as its equal, if not its superior, and instead of having to wait for ten years for the next performance, it was produced each year throughout Holy Week, drawing an audience from all over the world.

The seven square kilometres of the old *fazenda* probably constituted the largest open-air theatre in the world. A five-metre-high stone wall with seven gates and seventy towers enclosed twelve

515

distinct sites, on which were enacted the Stages of the Cross. Some 600 actors, all amateurs, took part. On the two occasions that we saw it, the role of Jesus was taken by one of the senior officers in IPA, with whom we had many discussions on livestock matters.

We arrived at dusk and parked with hundreds of other cars and buses outside the high stone walls. The landscape in the failing light was bleak enough, much as the Holy Land must have been 2,000 years ago.

All the guides and attendants were dressed as Roman Legionaries, handling the crowds just as their far-off prototypes might have done, directing them, firmly and efficiently, to the first site within the walls. The play started as darkness descended, and lasted three hours. Centurions with flaming torches steered the several thousand spectators from site to site as the drama unfolded – the Garden at Gethsemane, the Interrogation, the Scourging and the Crucifixion. The atmosphere was chillingly authentic; one could easily imagine what the real thing must have felt like.

When, in the final scene, a white-robed, floodlit Christ rose heavenwards from the tomb behind a rocky hillock, the crowd, many of whom were now carrying their sleeping children, fell to their knees.

It was the most moving theatrical moment I have ever experienced.

Carnaval, of course, was Brazil's best known extravaganza. It was more than a mere *fiesta*, it was a sacrosanct tradition, an annual holiday, a brief rejection of the dreary, slogging existence that most of them led; a safety valve. To prohibit *Carnaval* would be to deny many Brazilians their reason for living. Everyone took part, either as an individual or as a member of a *Sociedade do frevo*, a sort of club whose members participated together each *Carnaval. O Frevo* meant a frenetic type of communal dancing to the military beat of special *frevo* music, ending in musical hysteria.

The participants spent millions and millions of cruzeiros each year on their costumes, which varied from authentic period attire to the most outrageous and gaudy outfits covered with pearls, lined with silk and matched by magnificent headdresses, outfits which had taken months to create and cost more than half the owner's annual salary! There were others who wore nothing more than a jockstrap or bikini and a few splashes of paint, but these were not the serious *Carnavalistas*.

No-one could escape the *Carnaval* spirit, although only the most dedicated were able to last it out, day and night at such a frenzied pace. No work was done and nothing functioned – everyone was too busy dancing in the streets. Thank God no domestic crises arose during our *Carnaval* time in Recife.

We watched the processions in Olinda, a small scrunched-up town a few kilometres up the coast. Olinda, I was told, was given its name by a Portuguese Queen in the early 1500s, who, when looking for a suitable site for her summer residence, cried *'Oh, que linda,'* – 'How beautiful' at her first view of it. Be that as it may, the history books state that Olinda was founded by a Duarte Coelho in 1537, who, incidentally, also introduced sugar cane.

The principal procession took place along the wide coastal road that circled Olinda and from which cobbled streets wriggled up through quaint *praças* to a church on the town's highest hill. We drove up one, looking for a parking space. It was picturesque, reminiscent of a Cornish fishing village, but certainly not an ideal place to view a *Carnaval*. Very soon, we were stuck in a sea of cars and milling crowds. All we could do was to lock up the *veraneo* where it was, in the middle of a small *praça*, and seek out the action on foot.

I hate crowds, especially with six children to shepherd, three of them small. Holding up a succession of clamouring kids for an hour or two, in high humidity, at sea level, less than nine degrees from the Equator, was apt to take its toll when in one's mid-fifties.

We struggled back to our car some hours later, leaving the procession still in progress. We found a mini-*Carnaval* in full swing around our orange *veraneo*, with several guitar-wielding youngsters on its roof. They were polite and exuberant and insisted – to the children's delight – that we shared in their dances and bottles of wine.

As the sun disappeared behind Olinda hill and the heat began to lessen, the crowds thinned and we found our rather inebriated way out of the *praça* and headed for home.

Carnaval was a marvellous experience, especially for the young. Gaiety and bonhomie pervaded everything, and no-one was left out. But for me, the best part of that day was the swim at dusk and the mug of beer that followed it!

FLOODS

Erika had constantly warned us about floods when house-hunting. It was a problem that the *Nordestinos* lived with, especially those in towns at the sea-end of large rivers. The more that bad farming and overgrazing destroyed the vegetation inland, the more rapid became the run-off from storms, the quicker the rise in river levels and the greater the disaster.

'We have floods every five to seven years,' a resident told me, as if he were discussing leap year. 'They can be quite dangerous; it depends where you live.'

It began raining early in the week. By Thursday much of the low-lying ground around Boa Viagem was under water and there were rumours of dams bursting above Recife. One such rumour created a stampede near the city centre which injured several people. The alleged instigator was caught and given three years to ponder his indiscretion.

The kids waded to school through muddy water up to their short skirts. By fortune or forethought, the American School had been built on a low ridge, a few metres higher than the surrounding land, so once inside, classes proceeded normally.

We watched anxiously as the flood water crept up our garden from the canal at the bottom. First the stalls were submerged, then the water inched up the slope to the back of the house, pushing a scum of horse droppings and other rubbish before it. Little space remained for our steeds themselves, except Mary's hard won flower beds. It was just as bad outside the garden. The grazing area was severely restricted by the rising water with consequent fiercer competition for the few remaining grassy hillocks still above surface.

On Friday, there was a general flood warning. Those who had already gone to the office returned home immediately to move out their belongings, or lug them upstairs if they had a second storey. But by now, many people couldn't get away from their houses, even if they'd wanted to.

That night both the rivers Capiribibe and Beberibe, which met in Recife, flooded, washing away cars, animals and people. Over a hundred and fifty of the city's inhabitants perished. Thousands were left homeless, thousands more left without drinking water or other necessities. The drainage system ceased to exist, it was simply washed away. Everything was mud and confusion. Acts of heroism were legion.

By Monday, the waters had subsided and I thought I could probably reach the office. To my surprise, Graciette was already there.

'Pleasant week-end?' I asked, facetiously.

She didn't smile. 'We spent Friday night on the roof; me, the children, a neighbour and her kids, and our maid. My husband was away.'

'Couldn't you get away?' My smirk had disappeared.

'The water was over two metres deep and running very fast. We prayed a lot and we survived. It was very frightening.' She managed a weak smile. 'We're still paddling in the lounge. What happened to you?'

There was nothing I could say. What price our little inconvenience? I wondered how many thousands of other citizens had faced the same desperate situation so calmly and philosophically. If I had had a hat, I would have swept it off and bowed low. I felt immensely proud of her.

I went back with her to her house. Her furniture, fridge, cooker and beds were tossed about and covered in a thick layer of slimy mud. She had had no second storey to help save her goods, and was now living with a sister in a non-flood area.

Later, Mary and I drove round the city. All six pools of the swimming club to which we belonged, were filled with mud. Cars were stranded everywhere and in one place were strung, higgledy-piggledy, along a mesh-wire security fence, which had filtered them out of the rushing waters.

A friend in the American Embassy, we learned, had swum a hundred metres across a swirling torrent to help a colleague whose wife was about to give birth. Mother and child had survived, but he hoped he would never have to repeat it.

Recife was a city of heroes – many of them dead. I blessed those good people who had warned us against flood areas!

A TIME FOR TEARS

The coastal road, which ran along the sea front of Boa Viagem and continued down to the beaches of Piedade and Candeias, was a death trap. How many people were killed on it each week we couldn't tell, but we had witnessed several fatal accidents and had seen the police truck arrive to throw the corpses nonchalantly into the back – and on one occasion a still alive youth.

'He'll be dead before we get back to the station,' they had said unconcerned.

So the road was out of bounds to our three 'smalls'. If they wished to cross it for a swim, then one of the 'bigs', or an adult, had to be with them.

One Sunday morning, I took the three youngest, all under seven, to a party at a friend's house in Piedade. 'We'll bring them home about four, this afternoon,' the host promised.

At five, they still hadn't arrived. I was worried. Maybe they had had an accident. Since neither of us had a telephone, I couldn't check. Half an hour later, I set off for Piedade in the *veraneo*.

'Terribly sorry,' my friend apologized. 'Couldn't get the car to start, so we sent them back by bus. They left about ten minutes ago.'

Without waiting for my friend to explain further, I tore back along the road to Boa Viagem. I was furious. Not only furious – I was petrified. Although the bus drivers, in general, were reliable, and the bus stop was only a block from our house, it was on the *opposite* side of the road, which meant they would have to cross Avenida Boa Viagem at the peak of the Sunday afternoon traffic, when everyone was in a hurry to get home. It would be a race track. I put my foot down harder. I had to reach the bus stop before they did.

As I approached it, I saw a group of people at the roadside. On the ground, something small was covered with a bathing towel. My heart literally bounced. I knew it. How could anyone have been so irresponsible as to have allowed young children to return alone, knowing they would have to cross a highway in weekend traffic?

Partly from the fear of making the discovery, and partly from the faint hope that my fears were unjustified, in spite of an overriding presentiment that one of the twins – probably Shevaughne, the more impulsive of the two – lay beneath that towel, I screeched down our side street and into our gate. 'Fuffy, Shivy, Coro,' I yelled, my voice cracking with fear. 'Come here, NOW.'

No answer. I rushed inside, still yelling their names. Mary appeared.

'Where the hell are the babes?' I screamed, so frightened now that I could no longer control my voice.

'I sent them to the *barraca* to buy sugar and an ice-cream. They shouldn't be long. What's the matter with you?'

'They're back from Piedade?'

'Yes, they came in a few minutes ago.'

'All three of them?'

'Of course. Why? What's wrong?'

I couldn't speak. I'd tell her later. I stumbled out of the house and down to the bottom of the garden, where the horses were. There, I leant against the wall and sobbed with relief.

Somewhere else, I knew, someone else was sobbing. But not from relief.

COPING WITH CALAMITIES

Brazil was such a huge, vibrant country that when catastrophes hit, they hit in seemingly uncontrollable proportions. Floods were a local affliction, epidemics were national.

We had heard about the outbreaks of meningitis in the cities of the South and remarked on it without interest. That's what you'd expect in the teeming *favelas* around Rio and Sao Paulo, we said. But as the disease spread northwards, we regarded the reports with growing concern.

The press, as usual, made the most of it, publishing heart-rending accounts of the high death rate and rapid spread, and increasing public hysteria to such an extent that the Government placed a ban on reporting the number of deaths. Inevitably, rumours started.

'Hundreds are dying daily.' 'Whole families have been wiped out.' 'No-one can travel without a special permit.' 'Hospitals are full.' 'Corpses are being buried in mass graves.' Everyone knew (or said they knew), someone whose child, brother, aunt or maid had succumbed to the disease. We knew that vaccination campaigns were being carried out in the South, but nothing seemed to be happening in Recife.

I cabled FAO for vaccine and enough antibiotics to treat all our staff and their families, should the need arise. Before we received it, a vaccination campaign was announced for the North-East. Everyone of every age was urged to be immunized at one of the numerous vaccination posts to be set up round the city.

The campaign was scheduled to start on a Friday. That morning, the American school took all their pupils to a vaccination centre at a local sports ground. They found the place milling with thousands of other youngsters, but not a vaccinator was to be seen. After some hours, they were taken on to the airport, where several teams of vaccinators were scheduled to operate. Here again, they waited all afternoon without result. The vaccine never arrived.

On the Saturday morning, we decided to try for ourselves. I drove the whole family into the city. Nearly every street corner had a queue of citizens, baring their arms. At the head of each queue, a white-coated vaccinator wielded a vaccination gun connected to a reservoir of vaccine, just like those used by farmers for dosing calves against worms or for vaccinating large herds. An assistant stood about ten paces down the queue, helping the public to roll up their sleeves as they shuffled past.

We must have been about fiftieth in our line, but were abreast the man with the gun in less than five minutes. Any objections raised by smaller fry (in our case this meant Shivy) were immediately smothered in the strong grip of another burly assistant, whose job was to hold arms still and see that the queue kept moving.

No records were kept. It was assumed that anyone receiving the vaccine would 'take' and not present himself again. Nor was there any attempt to sterilize the skin. It wasn't considered necessary, as the gun had no needle but shot the dose out through a nozzle with such force, it penetrated the skin. It was virtually painless.

Now and then, a cruising van would replenish the refrigerated boxes with vaccine. The campaign was well-organized, well-patronized and entirely successful. That weekend, over 12,000,000 people were vaccinated in the North-East towns, and in a few weeks, the epidemic fizzled out.

It seemed that, when put to it, Brazil was well able to match its mammoth plagues and pestilences with heroic control measures!

THE BEGINNING OF THE END

A so-called Tripartite Review was held every two years or whenever the objectives of a Project required revision. It consisted of officials from the Government, the UNDP and FAO. It was, I felt, high time for such a discussion on the future of our project, BRA 71/552.

Flying down to Brasilia for the meeting, I found myself seated beside Dr Mierelles, the former head of the Federal Agricultural Research Service, who had warned me about EMBRAPA two years before. He asked how things were going. I told him.

'Well, I warned you,' he said. 'Not that there was anything you could have done. It will take some years for EMBRAPA to sort itself out. Don't hang about longer than you have to.'

The meeting was short, amicable and, from our point of view, disastrous. EMBRAPA told us that they were still in the midst of reorganization (as they had been for the last two years), and now made it clear that there was no place in the new structure for an FAO project in the North-East.

'The project is finished,' I told André on my return. 'We don't fit in any longer. All dairy cattle research will be done in Minas Gerais, beef cattle research in the Matto Grosso, and small ruminants somewhere else, possibly Bahia. They want Guy to continue working with the PROPASTO project, and they thought they might be able to use you at the dairy cattle centre. The one person they will not need is a Project Manger.'

'So what are you going to do?' André asked.

'Look for another job, I suppose,' I replied cheerfully. I was glad that I would no longer have to try and kick life into a dying project, or continually explore new avenues, knowing that they would almost certainly lead to dead ends. Even if I did feel a failure in being unable to resuscitate the Project, the future, once more, held the excitement of adventure.

Everardo, too, was on his way, about to leave for Rothamstead

Research Station in England, where the British Government had awarded him a Queen's Scholarship. Although contributing little scientifically, except his brilliance in statistics, we would miss his interpretation of Brazilian politics and his insight into EMBRAPA's nefarious policies.

The UN Res Rep had suggested at the Tripartite Review that he could, if they wished, organize a Reformulation Mission to advise the Government as to how FAO could best assist the country. The offer was accepted.

I met the Mission six weeks later and, with André, accompanied them to the proposed sites for the dairy and beef research centres. I had expected to find better facilities for research in the South, but the stations were not much better than those that had depressed me so much in the North-East. It was obvious that at some time a lot of hard work and planning had been put in and beneficial results achieved, but in the last decade management had slipped. Machinery needed repair, vehicles were inoperable, fences, sheds and laboratories were disintegrating.

The older staff were complacent, the younger frustrated. Bureaucracy was rampant. Perhaps, after all, the crash postgraduate training programme for their younger staff was the soundest move they could have made – but for us, of course, it was too late.

Before disbanding, the Mission came to Recife.

'It's a great shame to see you lads go,' commiserated their leader, 'but there's no alternative. I doubt whether EMBRAPA will be able to organize anything worthwhile for at least a year. Have you started job-hunting yet?'

I said I was about to.

'Try the IRI, the International Research Institute in New York. They should have something in your line.' I promised I would.

Excitement of an uncertain future alternated with depression. We had had such high hopes. Our 'experts' had all been excellent and our research programme sound. We could have achieved so much with a little financial and logistical support. I felt bitter that EMBRAPA had led us on with false promises and bits of carrots, when they knew that they had no plan into which we could have fitted. We were just a nuisance to them. Well, I thought, no-one could accuse us of the ultimate sin – that of having given up trying!

I waived the Mission goodbye and returned to the office to hunt through the veterinary journals for job vacancies, and to write letters to friends in high places, as well as to FAO, WHO and the IRI.

One of the friends I contacted was Tony, the Animal Health Adviser to the Overseas Development Administration in London. We

523

had been on a postgraduate Colonial Studentship together at Cambridge, many years before. 'We have a niche in the Yemen and a possible post in New Guinea,' he wrote. 'I wouldn't recommend either.'

'A choice of Arabs or Headhunters,' I told Mary. 'Bit dicey.'

The IRI was more hopeful. 'We have rather a nice job coming up in north Spain,' they told me, 'but there's a freeze on new appointments (the dollar was again misbehaving, just as it had when I left Peru). I'll probably be able to tell you definitely in six or nine months.'

Spain! Oh, boy. Just the thing. Near the UK. Language I knew. Fair climate. Cheap living. But six to nine months! I doubted if I could wait that long. I crossed my fingers.

Another proposal came from Sir William, of honeymoon memories. He had just come back from Uganda, where he had been told that if I wished to apply for the post of Director of Animal Health Research, the Uganda Government would like to hear from me. It was a nice thought, but did I really want to go back to Uganda?

Then a cable arrived from Rome, proposing me for the post of Project Manager in Mozambique. Mozambique? Portuguese East Africa? Who the hell wanted to go there? No way. The only thing I knew about that country was that they seemed to be fighting a perpetual civil war – and the Communists were winning. It would be no place for a family. There must be better jobs elsewhere; I'd sit tight and see what happened about Spain. If that failed, Tony was sure to come up with something; overseas aid was still the in thing in British politics.

Or maybe I should retire early and find a part-time job in the UK to augment my pension. The PDSA or the RSPCA would be good bets, or I could be a sales representative. Or perhaps the National Trust would take me on as a resident incumbent in a castle or stately home; that would be great. I could take up my old hobbies of trout fishing, sketching and photography again. Meanwhile, I kept myself busy writing my final report.

BACK TO AFRICA

I was late into the office. André had already opened the pouch from Rome and was sorting through its contents, mostly a hodge-podge of scarcely legible twelfth copies of letters or minutes of meetings which someone thought might have a vague relation to our project. In 1975, the computer had still to replace carbon paper and photocopies.

524

There was also the usual batch of documents printed in all four of the official languages of the UN, which FAO said was easier to distribute together than sort out into who should have English, French, Italian or Spanish. Later, Arabic and Chinese were added.

We could always rely on at least one missive that would drive someone up the wall, or rudely interrupt our placid routine. A travel or medical claim, for instance, disallowed on a technicality. A copy of some stupid (to us) query from a technical division on an experimental result. An absurd (to us) financial ruling. A reprimand because there was a discrepancy between my last Network Analysis ('Guesswork Paralysis', we called it) chart and the previous one, or a 24-hour notice of an FAO official's arrival when we had planned to be in another state.

I unfolded the Foodagram which André flicked at me. A Foodagram was a message in cable form, but sent by diplomatic pouch, to save on cable charges.

'FOR GUILBRIDE. TRANSFER MOZAMBIQUE
CONFIRMED. REPORT ROME EARLIEST.'

Dammit. This was a bit sudden. I knew I was being considered, but I needed more time. Mind you, 'earliest' was open to very liberal interpretation, especially by an experienced bureaucrat like myself.

I replied, asking for more details, such as the project objectives and where its headquarters would be. I also asked for a copy of the Plan of Operations. This, I reckoned, could delay matters for a considerable time. My letter by pouch would take at least a week to reach our 'Godfather's' desk, and his reply, also by pouch, at least another ten days to reach me. I could then, justifiably, taken another ten days or two weeks to consider all the aspects before giving a definite answer. Maybe the Spain job might be cleared by then, or another opportunity come up. I hoped so. I regarded Mozambique as a last resort.

The reply took nearly three weeks. There were no formal Plans of Operation (Planops), I was told, only a draft Emergency Document, still to be discussed with the Government. It was vital to start the Project as soon as possible. There were no other FAO personnel in Mozambique, in fact, the United Nations office had only been there since Independence from Portugal, a few months previously.

I delayed a reply as long as I could while Mary and I discussed the pros and cons of Mozambique.

'Probably like Uganda but not so hot,' I suggested. 'Mind you, Lourenço Marques is on the coast, could be steamy. Wasn't it the wickedest city south of the Sahara? Should be fun – except it is now Communist.'

'At least the language is the same – Portuguese. What about schools?'

'Let's write to Martyn (whom she had known at university), he's next door in Swaziland, he'll know. There's always South Africa.' And so on.

I also wrote the UN Res Rep in Lourenço Marques, and to the British and American Embassies there. We figured that there was plenty of time for Mary to visit her folk in Vancouver while we were still on the same side of the Atlantic, so off she went, leaving the deep freeze stocked with 'meals'.

It looked as if nothing else was going to turn up so I gave FAO a date six weeks ahead for my transfer, which would allow me to sell the car and furniture, pack and let the children finish their school year. It wouldn't quite extend to the Christmas holidays, but I was confident that I could arrange another delay when the time came.

* * *

I kept up my delaying tactics with Rome by sending them brief queries and suggestions, until a curt Foodagram arrived, hinting that if I was no longer interested in the Mozambique post, I should inform them at once, otherwise my presence in Rome within ten days, *en route* to Mozambique, would be appreciated.

There was no way I could comply. Mary was still in Canada and wouldn't be back for another two weeks. We hadn't started to sell our furniture or pack. But I had a master card still to play.

'Would it not be preferable,' I wrote to the Head of the African section, 'for me to go to Mozambique first, make contacts with Counterpart, see what was really needed, draft the Planops accordingly and come to Rome to discuss the whole matter? I could then return to Recife, pack up and take the family to Lourenço Marques.'

It was logical, and since I could make the whole round trip, including a visit to England, for only $300 more than my single ticket, extremely practical.

No reply came in the next pouch, but the following week a cable arrived.

'FOR GUILBRIDE. ESSENTIAL REPORT ROME BEFORE NOVEMBER FIRST OR APPOINTMENT MOZAMBIQUE CANCELLED.'

I knew I had to do something fast. I didn't want to be without a job. Attack, I've found is always the best method of defence, especially when dealing with bureaucrats. I phoned the head of the African Desk in Rome, whom I didn't know, but had been told was extremely competent.

'Look here,' I said in my most hurt tone, I sent you a long letter explaining why it would be better for me to go to Mozambique to size up the situation before seeing you in Rome, and all I get is an abrupt summons to Headquarters. I suggest, again, that I go to Lourenço Marques as soon as possible, and then call at Rome to discuss the whole matter, on the way back to Recife.'

'I entirely agree,' he answered. 'I've been away and didn't see your letter. I'll arrange your travel authority at once ... See you in about a month.'

The plane seemed reluctant to leave Recife; it refused to gain height, and a couple of minutes later we were on the ground again. Followed an almost Gilbertian performance. The pilot descended and joined a group of airport staff who, after arguing for a while, sent an over-alled mechanic up a ladder to open a hatch beneath one of the engines. While he was doing this, another ran back to the airport buildings to fetch a large manual. This was consulted and portions shouted up to the man on top of the ladder, whose head was inside the works. After several more consultations, arguments and fiddlings, the hatch was slammed shut, backs were slapped and we trundled down the runway. Whatever had been amiss was, apparently, now fixed for this time the plane rose steeply into the cloud-flecked sky, and we made Rio a couple of hours later.

During these goings-on, I had struck up a conversation with a young lad in the seat in front. Mark had been a member of a crew bringing a yacht back to South Africa from the States. At Recife, he had received a message that his father was seriously ill, and so was completing his journey by air. He was a schoolteacher, he told me, and had grown up on a farm on the south coast of Natal. We discussed the situation in South Africa at length.

'Most of the young people are totally against apartheid. Things are changing fast, I reckon it will have disappeared in five or six years.'

I was delighted to hear it, however optimistic his prediction seemed. Racial discrimination had been destroying his country for too long.

He shared my hotel room in Rio, as he had had no time to book, and next day we took the Varig flight to Johannesburg, a matter of five hours in the air but ten hours on the clock.

* * *

The flight gave me plenty of time to mull over the events of our three years in Brazil. Technically, they had been a disaster. The Project had never got off the ground. Our results had been minimal and confined almost entirely to pastures and forage production. We had trained no-one and left nothing behind that could in any way resemble VITAR in Peru. But we had worked out some sound livestock development policies for the North-East which, I knew, would be valuable when EMBRAPA had sorted itself out and could support field research programmes. (Four years later, I heard that EMBRAPA had adopted most of our development proposals, so, perhaps, our labours had not been in vain.)

That we had not achieved more was not our fault. We had really tried, but with EMBRAPA continually revising its policies and structure, and burrowing deeper and deeper into outdated bureaucracy, it had become impossible to plan or execute the simplest research. I was sure that they would sort themselves out in time, it was just unfortunate that our Project had coincided with the worst years of their disorganization. There was no doubt that, had I known what we were in for, I would have insisted on cancelling the entire Project at the beginning.

Guy, André and Eijnar would carry on for some months more, and when they left the Project, BRA 71/552 would sink slowly and thankfully into oblivion.

The family, thank God, seemed to have enjoyed Recife. The kids had never been so happy or done so well in school. they had become expert jockeys – bareback, of course, with noosed ropes as bridles. Hours of sunshine each day had tanned their bodies and bleached their hair. They had made many friends and spoke fluent Portuguese, even if it was with a *nordestino* accent. There was no doubt that they would be sorry to leave. Even Mary, despite the heat and the mosquitoes, had enjoyed the riding, the swimming, and developing the garden, although she was the first to admit that Brazil was a bit of a come-down after Peru.

I hoped that Mozambique, with its Communist government, its civil war and its poverty, wouldn't be an even greater *fracaso*. But I was still young enough to feel a tingle of excitement at the prospect of working in an Eastern Bloc country. Like a spy story, I thought. Far too much like a spy story, I was soon to find out!

PART SIX

MOZAMBIQUE

(1975–1982)

TANZANIA

R. Ruvuma

ZAMBIA

L. NYASSA

MALAWI

Montepuez

Pemba

Lichinga

Nacala

Mozambique Is.

Tete

Nampula

Angoche

Harare

R. Zambezi

Gorongoza

Quelimane

Chimoio

ZIMBABWE

Beira

R. Save

Massangena

Mabote

INDIAN
OCEAN

Vilanculos
Mapinhane

R. Limpopo

Muabsa

Pomene

Inhambane

Resano Garcia

Nelspruit

Chokwe

Mbabane

Xai-Xai

MAPUTO

SWAZILAND Namacha

REP. OF
SOUTH AFRICA

*Elephant
Reserve*

MOZAMBIQUE (1980)

■ ■ ■ ■ Main roads

•••••••••• Side roads

0   50 100 150 200 250 300

KILOMETRES

COMRADES ALL

'*Camarada* Guilbride? I'm Pereira, United Nations' office. Welcome to Mozambique.'

'What's all this *camarada* stuff?' I asked as we went through immigration. I noticed he called everyone *camarada*.

'We're all supposed to be comrades, at least in public. It's a Communist greeting, means nothing.'

'I take it you're not a comrade, then.'

'Only when it suits me. Survivor would be a better name. Anyway, since I work for the UN, I can't take sides.'

Long sullen queues wound across the parking area outside the airport buildings. 'All leaving for Portugal,' Pereira explained. 'TAP has two jumbo-jet flights a day trying to cope with the exodus. More than three-quarters of the Portuguese have already left.'

Lourenço Marques, 'LM' for short, was a pleasant surprise. In my experience, African towns were usually dirty and swarming with humanity. LM appeared clean and empty.

'Where is everybody?' I asked. 'Is there a curfew?'

'No, but it's not healthy to laze around in the Peoples' Republic. Unemployment is sort of illegal. They send loiterers off to re-education camps.'

All I knew about Mozambique and its politics was that the long drawn-out revolutionary struggle had ended a few months before with independence from Portugal, leaving a Marxist resistance movement called FRELIMO (Frente de Liberação de Moçambique) in power. I had written to the United Nations Resident Representative and to both the British and American Embassies, enquiring about living conditions, schools, medical facilities and so on. The British Embassy and the UN Office had replied in stilted diplomatese, giving the voltage of the electricity supply, regretting that there were no longer any private doctors, suggesting we consider schools in Swaziland or South Africa, and describing the social activities of the British Club. It was left to a young official at the US Embassy to hint at the real state of affairs.

'The country is now Marxist and the US Embassy is no longer officially accredited,' he wrote, 'but if and when it is, I will be able to write you again and confirm your worst fears!'

Pereira dropped me at the Polana Hotel, which had served as the centre of both British and German Intelligence in World War Two and from where, in a fit of depression, the young MI6 officer, Malcolm Muggeridge, had tried to drown himself. A line of massive

531

palms, like a guard of honour, separated the impressive white Riviera-type building from the street. On the other side of the hotel, facing the sea, spacious lawns enclosed a rose-shaped swimming pool. Across these could be seen the glassy surface of the bay, and the peninsula of Inhaca shimmering on the horizon. This could be the Mediterranean, I thought. Whatever the politics might be, the scenery was certainly spectacular. Communism couldn't destroy that.

My room faced landwards, the skyline of trees and mansions dominated by a giant concrete lemon squeezer which, since there was a cross on its peak, I assumed to be a church. St Anthony of Polana was one of the few still functioning.

Balinsky, the UN Resident Representative, was an old friend from Peru, who had been dug out of retirement to head the especially delicate mission to Mozambique.

'You'll have to change your conceptions completely,' he warned me. 'This is a Marxist state. Everyone has to conform to FRELIMO directives, but FAO is here at the request of the Government, in your case to improve livestock production and health, so you must say what you think – but do it tactfully. And remember, we are totally outside politics. You are also the first FAO member to be appointed to Mozambique, so until an official Head of Mission arrives, I would be grateful if you would act for him – unpaid, of course.'

As we talked, two men entered his office.

'Let me introduce you to Torre, my Deputy.' The Res Rep indicated the taller, 'and Dr Joaquim, head of the Veterinary Services in the Ministry of Agriculture. Now, if you'll excuse me, I have a meeting with Foreign Affairs – if they feel inclined to keep the appointment.'

Torre, a Norwegian, spoke excellent English with a slight American accent. I discovered later that he also played an excellent game of tennis. Dr Joaquim suggested we go to his office in the Ministry where wall maps showed the Department's activities, and where he could introduce me to some of his staff.

It was a terrifying drive. His foot went down on the accelerator and we screeched away in his aged Peugeot saloon on a road that was all bumps and potholes. I gripped the door handle, pressed my feet hard against the floorboards and resolved never again to travel with this maniac. Apart from the return journey to the hotel, I only did so on one other occasion, screaming down narrow, blind lanes at 140 kph, taking half the roadside vegetation with us.

The Ministry of Agriculture was a four-storey, flat-roofed, concrete box stretching along one edge of the *Praça dos Heróis*, a large circular field from the centre of which radiated paths, like spokes of a wheel. At the hub, some excavations indicated the proposed site for the National Monument and a mausoleum for the Heroes of the Revolution.

Listening to Joaquim explain the livestock policy took me back to Northern Rhodesia and Uganda and those other Directors of Veterinary Services who had gone through the same exercise for the benefit of the new boy, aeons ago. The problems, too, were depressingly similar: lack of nutrition, ticks, worms and the occasional epizootics like foot and mouth. East Coast fever, that scourge of cattle in East Africa, apparently, was rare. Two-thirds of the country was infested by tsetse fly, the carrier of trypanosomiasis or *nagana* – probably the single most serious restriction to animal production in Mozambique.

'Tsetse control is one of the jobs we hope your team will tackle. There's a small field station up here at Muabsa,' he indicated a spot apparently in the midst of endless tsetse-infested bush, halfway between LM and Beira. 'It will be our training and research centre.'

'What staff have you got?' I asked, dreading the reply.

'Most of the Ministry staff were Portuguese. About eighty per cent have already left and more are going every day.' I remembered the long lines at the airport. 'There are only half a dozen Moçambiquans with a university degree in the whole Ministry. They will be the only technical staff we'll have left in a couple more months – apart from the *co-operantes*.'

'*Co-operantes*?'

'Young professional volunteers from the Eastern Bloc and other sympathetic countries. A sort of Communist Peace Corps.'

It was a bleak outlook. Whatever else our work would be, training would have to take top priority.

'We've already received the name of a tsetse control expert from FAO,' Joaquim continued, brightening a little. 'I hope he'll be coming soon.'

'Who is he?' I asked, surprised. FAO had mentioned nothing to me about him.

Dr Joaquim rustled through a file and extracted a letter with the candidate's name. I was horrified. Frank was an excellent microbiologist and disease investigator, but an expert in tsetse fly and trypanosomiasis control, he was not! He had spent most of his FAO years in South America, where there was no tsetse fly, and had never been to Africa!

Good old FAO, I thought. Jobs for the boys, regardless of suitability. Frank would come to Mozambique over my dead body. There were plenty of other jobs in FAO where his talents were needed. Pity, though. He was a delightful lad, easy to work with and enthusiastic, and being both a Spaniard and a bachelor, would have had no trouble with the language or living conditions.

We discussed the need for other experts in milk and beef production, sheep and goats, poultry and, most important of all, pasture management.

'I already have a number of people interested in these posts,' I told Joaquim confidently, although I hadn't yet mentioned anything to André or Guy in Brazil, who I knew would soon be looking for jobs, or to Ben, who had written that he was once again on the market as poultry expert.

'I'll draft out the Project Document for you to approve before I go to Rome. That's really why I came here first; to find out what you needed and see that you get it.'

Joaquim gave me an office with a view over the *Praça dos Heróis*. Concrete beams, both horizontal and vertical, crisscrossed the outside of the building – for what reason, I couldn't imagine, modernity perhaps. Although they interfered with the view, they did serve one purpose, that of perches for pigeons. Two squatted on a beam just outside my window and kept up a continuous gurgling dialogue.

'I've named them after the twins,' I wrote Mary. 'The grey one is Shivy and the white one is Coro.'

They, or their offspring, were still there when I left Mozambique, six years later.

Michael, a young Columbian administrative officer in the UN office, who had been educated in England, was also a new boy with the same top priority – to find a house to rent before his family arrived.

Together we searched the higher class suburbs of Somerschield and Polana, stopping whenever we saw packing cases piled on the pavement and enquiring, tactfully, if anyone was taking over the house. There never was. Could we rent it? Certainly, but payment must be made in foreign currency in Portugal. That, we explained, we couldn't do. They shrugged. They were sorry, they couldn't help us. Mozambique escudos were no use to them.

Many departing owners were, understandably, emotional. They had lost their country, their homes, their cars and their businesses, and were now faced with a precarious existence in Portugal. Tears were frequent as they told us of all the terrible things the FRELIMO soldiers had done and how the Government was preventing them taking their possessions out.

We were literally overwhelmed with houses. Large, larger, huge, old and new. Houses with two bedrooms or six, with pools or without, all with gardens, many with carpets and furniture, and even one with a grand piano. But, alas, many had been abandoned, the doors left open to pilferers and the windows open to the elements. Most removables had vanished except for the wall to wall carpets, often soggy and rotting from rain.

Some residences had even been sabotaged by their owners, out of spite, before they left for the airport. Taps had been opened, toilets and baths broken, lights smashed. But the most heart-rending of all were the pets left to fend for themselves, which still hung about the gardens, wagging their tails in expectancy before realizing that it was not their masters who had returned. In the shower of the servants' quarters of one beautiful home, I came across an almost-dead Alsatian, thin beyond belief and hardly able to wag its tail, let alone get up. I rushed to the nearest store and brought back some bread and a tin of fish – no meat or milk were available. I filled its bowl with water and left it struggling to swallow what I had brought. Next day, it had gone.

Other house-seekers had found corpses of dead pets in upstairs cupboards, probably forgotten in the last-minute confusion. I refused to believe that anyone could have locked them up intentionally. It was hard enough to understand the mentality of abandoning pets at all, until one realized that there was no room for animals on the plane and that veterinary services for putting animals to sleep were nonexistent.

Michael and I were convinced that housing would be no problem, it was simply a matter of making up our minds as to which gorgeous residence we wanted. We short-listed a number, all far more luxurious than anything either of us had ever lived in. Then the fun began. There was no legal way we could take possession.

'The only answer is to rent from persons staying on in the country, who are prepared to accept escudos,' the UN Office advised. 'Foreign Affairs will rule on abandoned houses soon, since those left unoccupied for more than two months will automatically become the property of the State.' 'They'd better hurry,' I said. 'There are at least another fifty house-hunters besides me, and more are coming every day. The hotels won't be able to cope much longer.'

Hotel Polana, certainly, was overflowing, and although comfortable was, I considered, too expensive for my needs.

'Try the Avis,' I was advised. 'Or the Girasol; but the best of all is the Cardoso.'

I found the Girasol run-down, the rooms damp and mildewed and the small pool dark green with algae. The Cardoso had large, well-furnished rooms and a large pool set in a flower-filled garden, with a

535

magnificent view over the lower part of the city, the *baixa*, to Catembe, five kilometres distant across the estuary. It was also a lot less costly than the Polana – but it was full.

The Avis, (pronounced Arveez), the only other alternative, was an ugly six-storey concrete edifice near the Cardoso. A corpulent African with a large smile, almost the first cheerful person I had seen in LM, asked if he could help.

'I want a room for about ten days.'

'Of course, *camarada*. I'll show you one.'

It was on the fourth floor, spacious, with a bathroom twice the size of my Polana bedroom. The cost was less than half. I don't remember the name of my fat friend, who was the head of the committee who ran the hotel, but he was so like photos I remembered of the Russian general Zhukov, of World War Two fame, that I christened him 'Generalissimo Zhuki', which delighted him enormously. I also discovered that he was one day older, than I. Some years later, calling on a colleague at the Avis, I was distressed to learn that 'Generalissimo Zhuki' had been arrested, and no-one knew what had happened to him. It was, I'm afraid, a common enough occurrence in those days.

A NEARBY OASIS

I had written my old friend Martyn, who was running an FAO project in Swaziland, about schools in that country. 'Why not come up and see them?' he suggested over the phone.

'Be careful of road blocks,' Torre warned me. 'Sometimes there is only a petrol drum on the side of the road, but if you don't stop they'll shoot.'

The road to Namaacha, the border post with Swaziland, left LM through the industrial area where drab, once whitewashed walls were now scarred with Marxist slogans. Ten kilometres from the city, we passed through the outskirts of Matola, a colourful dormitory town for LM. The attractive houses, now mostly deserted, had large gardens full of flowers. Just past the army training school at Boane, we took the left fork to Namaacha. None of the road blocks presented a problem once I had identified myself as *Nações Unidas* and therefore *diplomático* – a magic word that was to get me out of many a spot. Lesser mortals could be searched for hours. One bright traveller from Swaziland became a little annoyed when asked for his birth certificate. Quite by chance he had it, but as he handed it over for inspection, he couldn't resist a small jibe.

'I'm so sorry, I forgot to bring my death certificate.'

'*Não tem certificado do morto?*' The soldier frowned. '*Então, tem que esperar.*'

During the hour that he waited, four other motorists joined him. They had also forgotten to bring their death certificates!

Namaacha, at the northern end of the Libombo hills, was an attractive little agricultural town built of stone and brick and roofed with red tile. It had the same relationship to LM as Chosica had had to Lima – a summer weekend retreat from the heat of the city.

I was shocked at the unkempt dirt road on the Swazi side, a severe letdown after the macadamized highway from LM. The reason, I was told, was that Mozambique had derived considerable revenue from South African tourists, whose quickest route was through Namaacha, so it was entirely in Mozambique's interest to ensure as smooth and comfy a journey as possible within their borders. Swaziland, on the other hand, had no desire to pass on such potentially lucrative travellers for the fleshpots of LM to milk, and hoped that the rough state of the road to the border might encourage them to stick to the casinos in Mbabane.

Mbabane could have been anywhere in the Kenyan Highlands. I was glad of my pullover and tweed jacket as I went down to meet Martyn in the Tavern Bar. One of the world's most delightful extroverts, Martyn was just as exuberant and full of life as I remembered him. I was to discover that everything he did, from squash to playing the washboard in the local skiffle group, or directing amateur dramatics at the club, or running his beef production project, he did with enthusiasm and flair. He enrolled me in the Theatre Club, the hub of Mbabane's social life.

'You'll be visiting your kids at school every few weeks, so you might as well enter into the social life here. There'll be damn-all in Mozambique.'

That was certainly true. Old LM, once the 'wickedest city south of the Sahara' was no more. Gone were the gambling dens, casinos and organized prostitutes. Also gone, regretfully, were many of the fish restaurants, the cosy crab and lobster bistros and the exotic night clubs. All that remained of the once pulsating city was a handful of rapidly crumbling cafes and two or three unkempt hotels desperately trying to keep up a semblance of their former traditions of service. Where gay groups of tourists once sat in pools of shade beneath curbside trees, a residue of morose menfolk now commiserated with each other over small cups of coffee, while they awaited their flights to Lisbon.

Education, we knew, would be a problem. There were two schools in Mbabane. St Mark's, originally an Anglican Diocesan school, had once produced scholarly and influential alumni. Then, with the changing balance of church and state it had become a Government school catering for anyone who could pay the moderate fees.

'We have no selection for entrance,' the Scots headmaster told me. 'If they can pay they can come, no matter how low their academic standing, with the result that our roll-call contains twice the number of pupils that actually attend. Some come for only a day or two each week, or for a week or two a term. Even boarders will skip a week or two and not come back till the following term. I have little say in the matter.'

Waterford-Kamhlaba, one of the United World Colleges, was the opposite. Its buildings, often hidden in mist, dribbled down the hillside above Mbabane. Here, the sons and daughters of elite Swazi families competed for entrance with other races from all over southern Africa. It was a modern, highly motivated centre of learning. The entrance exam was stiff and the waiting list long.

'Put your girls into St Mark's for a year,' advised Tony, the Deputy Headmaster. 'They'll have a better chance in our selection exam.'

I spent the weekend exploring the shops and getting to know the FAO personnel in Martyn's project. One happy surprise was to find that the head of the FAO mission was no other than Tubby, of college and Uganda days, and another old friend from Northern Rhodesia, to whom I had introduced his future wife, was manager of a training centre.

The dozen or so luxury hotels around Mbabane hosted hundreds of Transvaalians, Free Staters and other *volk* of all colours, who flocked to Swaziland from South Africa to try their luck on the roulette tables and the one-armed bandits at the Casino, or to seek the favours of a dusky maiden, all too eager to sell her charms for South African rand – a transaction rigorously forbidden back home in the apartheid-ridden Republic.

It was hard to tear myself away from that bubbling bunch and return to the dull, sterile, Socialist community in LM.

THE LEFT-OVERS

The Veterinary Faculty and the National Veterinary Research Institute, INIVE (*Instituto Nacional de Investigação Veterinária*), both housed within the same grounds near the Zoo, had been mentioned

538

in the Emergency Draft of my project as needing assistance. Most of the senior INIVE staff had left, funds for vaccine production and research had dried up, and equipment was obsolete or in disrepair. I undertook to buy them two of the most urgent items from my Project's funds – a new freeze-drier and a large autoclave. It wasn't really my responsibility, but effective disease control needed an efficient lab to back it up.

The Veterinary Faculty had suffered even more. Perhaps never comparable to the best in Europe, or to Onderstepoort in South Africa, it had turned out many competent veterinarians in the 20 or so years of its existence. Lecture rooms were modern, the labs adequate and the library still functional, but lack of staff had brought all teaching temporarily to a standstill. The intake of students had been suspended, and those in their final year had been despatched to the field as District or Provincial Veterinary Officers, or for administrative duties in the Ministry. Hopefully, they would return to finish their degree when things had settled down.

If the rest of the staff were half as impressive as the young acting Dean, I thought, there were certainly grounds for hope. Tilak, a tall, good-looking Portuguese, with a trace of Goan, had a PhD from Edinburgh in Genetics. I got to know him well in the years that followed and, like Manuel in Peru, he stood tall amongst all his colleagues.

It was the same at the Agricultural Faculty. Excellent buildings, good facilities – suspended courses. The Agricultural Research Institute, INIA, with its fantastic herbarium and long history of investigation, was no better. No funds, no staff. It was all very sad.

Trips to the field did little to relieve my depression. Perhaps 80 to 90 per cent of the Portuguese farming community had gone, their farms abandoned and their livestock left to die of starvation or be eaten by the undernourished farm labourers. Several estates had been turned into collective farms with FRELIMO soldiers in charge, but as the workers rarely received wages, it was not surprising that animals disappeared and the production of consumables such as eggs and milk fell far below the targets laid down by the Party.

Field trips presented another hazard. It was not only Dr Joaquim who possessed the speed bug; his staff were infected to the man. Dr Gill was one of the worst, but I soon found that he could not drive fast and talk at the same time, so I carefully prepared a list of questions to throw out before each corner, the answers temporarily arresting his meteoric flight.

'What are the dominant grasses in the area?' His foot would come off the accelerator while he told me.

'Are those black and white cattle a local breed? Are you crossing them?' Again he would slow to what I considered still too fast to round a bend. He must have thought me a little overeager for knowledge.

'Collapse' was probably the best word to describe the agricultural situation. Orange trees weighed down with fruit stood on carpets of their own rotting produce, lacking transport to the packing centres. Contacts had been severed and marketing organizations had been dissolved. Of the extensive milk collection co-operative which had served the 'milk basin' around LM, only the abandoned cooling centres remained – inoperative. Everything, it appeared, was at a standstill, waiting for someone to wind up the spring again.

It was quite clear that the very first priority was to organize the recuperation of as many farms as possible before they deteriorated to a point of no return, and to train personnel to run them. A few days later, I was able to air these thoughts with the Minister in his office on the fourth floor; a man in his middle thirties, with as much Indian as African and European blood. Penetrating eyes darted at me from deep sockets.

'I am most disappointed with FAO,' he began. 'They are too slow. I want help now, not tomorrow.' I'd often felt the same, but I could hardly say so.

'I'm going to Rome next week,' I replied, hoping to head off more of his embarrassing observations, 'with a draft of the project which Dr Joaquim and I have been preparing. I already have candidates for several posts.' (Not quite true, but it sounded encouraging.) 'I hope they'll agree to implement the project immediately.' I handed him a copy.

Before he had time to comment on it, I continued, 'There are a couple of things that need very urgent attention.'

'Tell me.'

'The first is the reclamation of abandoned farms. If this is not done soon, many will be past recovery.'

'And the second?'

'A training centre for field staff. With all the farmers gone, there is nowhere to train practical animal husbandry persons. I saw a large farm at Changalane yesterday, which would be ideal. It has livestock, buildings and crops. We cannot do anything without trained staff. My project would be very willing to help with such training.'

He looked at me for a moment, sharp eyes in a sharp face. 'Send me your suggestions before you go to Rome. Tell FAO that we need their help urgently. Good luck and come back soon.'

540

Ministry hours were 7 a.m. to 1 p.m., including Saturdays. It was the second week in December, and the sun rose early. One morning, deceived by the brightness of the day, I arrived at the office an hour early. On the lawn in front of the building an earnest young man was haranguing a group of Ministry employees. I watched from my window while he paced up and down, throwing out political slogans, which were immediately chanted back by his audience. '*Abaixo con os elites*', '*Abaixo con o capitalismo*', and other slogans containing the 'down with...' message, accompanied by a downward movement of the forearm. The last slogan before the meeting finished, given with a clenched fist Communist salute, was unvarying, like 'God Save the Queen' at the end of a public performance in Britain – '*A luta continua*', the struggle continues.

I was told, later, that this was a *dinamização* meeting, held each morning by a member of the *Grupo Dinamizador*, to instil the Marxist gospel and motivate the workers. Attendance was compulsory, but not all the audience appeared enraptured with the proceedings. Several, hidden from the speaker's view, were reading the newspaper, and one bold gentleman was stretched on the grass, apparently asleep. Perhaps he considered his *luta* already finished!

There was a *Grupo Dinamizador* in every office, factory or block of flats to reinforce the workers or residents with Marxist visions and see that they toed the Party line. To any thinking person, they were a pain, but they did, occasionally, have their uses. Cases of thieving, slackness, absenteeism or deviation from the common goal were handed to the *Grupo* to deal with. One Portuguese official, whose family estate had been expropriated and turned into a *Sociedade*, or co-operative farm, with his 80-year-old father continuing to act as technical supervisor, told me that, bad as things were, if it hadn't been for the *Grupo Dinamizador* forcing some responsibility and efficiency into the workers, it would have been impossible to carry on.

When we were burgled, some months later, the local *Grupo* called on us to see if they could help track down the miscreants. They couldn't, but it was a sporting gesture.

* * *

I still intended to spend Christmas with the family in Brazil, so I cabled Rome to expect me *en route*.

My departure was a lesson in the niggardly distrust which permeates Communism. After completing the immigration formalities, we queued up in front of a curtained cubicle. One by one, we entered.

'*Dinheiro, senhor?*' I showed him my travellers' cheques and the declaration I had made on arrival. He wasn't satisfied. Despite my protestations that I was a United Nations official and should therefore be treated as a diplomat, he made me turn out all my pockets, confiscated my loose change, which included some Brazilian coins and a copper talisman with 'Good Luck' engraved on one side. What use it would be to the New Peoples' Republic, I couldn't imagine – not that they wouldn't need a little luck!

He missed one item. Before leaving the hotel I found a five-pound note which I hadn't declared on arrival. Warned of possible problems at the airport, I folded it as small as I could and pushed it to the bottom of my leather spectacle sheath. Although he took out my glasses and shook the case, the note was too firmly wedged in to fall out. Perhaps he was right to be suspicious!

It took a week in Rome to have the draft Project approved. I wrote to André and Guy, and to Ben, who was in Israel, telling them that I had proposed them for the project in Mozambique.

I left for Brazil excited at the possibilities and confident that the Project would soon be operating. If the Mozambiquan officials remained as sincere and dedicated as they seemed, and there was no more shooting, and we could keep our larder stocked, I was sure we would be happy in LM, Marxism or not. And I couldn't wait to show Mary the scores of beautiful houses at our disposal!

EXPOSURE TO EDUCATION

Three weeks in Recife were enough to sell the car and the heavier furniture, pack the rest of our goods, and find homes for the horses.

The last person I saw as the plane taxied down the runway was Sydney, the British Consul, his face beaming and his arms waving backwards and forwards across his ample stomach in a flamboyant farewell.

I was probably the only one of the family who was glad to leave. Although I loved the people and their carefree attitude – just like the Irish – the frustrations of EMBRAPA, the lack of progress, the mosquitoes and the heat had been a little too much. Mozambique could only be better – I thought.

Mary, I think, was neutral, scared of 'swapping black dog for monkey', but also excited at the change. The kids left no doubt how they felt. The smaller ones were in tears. How could anyone leave such a paradise – the beaches, the horses, the American School which was like a second home? Adults were nuts.

After three days shopping feverishly in Johannesburg *en route*, we touched down at LM.

Michael had managed to book us into the Hotel Cardoso. From the first minute, Fuffy, now eight, and the twins – Shivy and Coro, now seven – took the place over.

When they were not at their aquatic antics in the sparkling 30-metre pool, as much at home on the high dive and springboard as under water, they rampaged around the acres of garden, playing 'hide and seek' or 'touch' with the other international children whose parents, like us, were house-hunting. 'Other international children' that is, with the exception of the East Germans, whose glum-faced parents forbade any sort of fraternization with capitalistic kids. Wistfully, they watched their would-be buddies scream round the terraces, across the flower beds and through the spacious lounges, lost in games of 'cops and robbers'.

We enrolled the three 'smalls' in the International School, once called the English School and subsidized by the Natal Department of Education. This occupied them from eight till one each day, leaving their afternoons free to terrorize the hotel guests.

Lindley, now 14, and Melanie, now 12, we took to St Mark's in Mbabane. Already depressed and a little scared at leaving our girls in what seemed an almost entirely Swazi school, the first sight of the dormitory nearly made us turn round and leave. The eight beds were covered with very old, stained and disintegrating mattresses. I turned over the first one and found a gaping hole in the bedsprings, large enough for a child to fall through. There were holes in the mattresses too, and much evidence of rodent squatters.

'Take any you like,' laughed a strong Irish accent behind us. 'They're all as bad as each other.'

We turned to find a short, rather dumpy lady with fair, unruly hair and a twinkle in her blue eyes, regarding our dismay with some amusement.

'I'm Jean, the Hostel Mother. The kids destroy everything, and we have no money for repairs.'

With hearts sinking still further, we noticed the filthy floors, a broken window pane and the dirty curtains, the lower edges of which were almost black.

'They *will* polish their shoes on the curtains,' Jean sighed. 'The first thing I do each term is to get the girls to wash them and scrub the floors. You'd better choose lockers before the rush starts.'

The only comforting aspect about the whole place was Jean. Her evident sense of humour, her authority, her promise to look after our youngsters, and her assurance that things looked a great deal worse than they really were, helped to ease our aches.

WE WIN A MANSION

If one forgave the monotonous food, the lack of coffee, beer and other alcoholic beverages, living at the Hotel Cardoso was almost luxurious – but an hotel could never replace a home of one's own.

Most of the houses I had drooled over in December were still vacant in February, and many more had joined their ranks. We narrowed our selection to three – a magnificent mansion near the UN office, which belonged to a departing judge whose sister agreed to accept an exorbitant rent in Mozambique escudos; a smaller house in the same street, with a rambling, overgrown garden; and a modern apartment occupying three storeys, but with no garden, in a block of flats near the Polana Hotel. Reluctantly, we decided on the Polana apartment, despite the three flights of stairs to traipse up and down, and lack of garden.

'I'll ring the owner tomorrow,' I told Mary, 'and say we'll take it over at the beginning of next week. We can't hang about in the hotel any longer.'

The following day was 3 February, the 'Day of the Heroes', a national holiday. As on all such anniversaries, it was incumbent on the Head of State to make an impassioned address in the furtherance of Marxism. Apart from officially changing the name of Lourenço Marques to Maputo, the point that hit us like a hammer and sickle from outer space was his proclamation that all property not occupied by the owner was forfeit to the state. In future, only the Government would be allowed to rent houses!

I rang the apartment owner. He was apologetic, but he was moving back into the Polana apartment from his small downtown flat, otherwise it would be confiscated. We were back at square one. We joined the other house-hunters in the hotel in reviling the President for his ridiculous new law.

Meanwhile, the Government agency set up to rent housing was in chaos. No-one knew what the ground rules were, only a few of the houses on their books had been inspected, and they couldn't even guess at a rent. I approached the UN office. They were sorry, their instructions were that each Ministry would be responsible for housing its own foreign staff. I should tackle the section that dealt with *co-operantes* in the Ministry of Agriculture.

'But we're UN personnel, not *co-operantes*,' I insisted.

544

'Sorry, but those are our instructions.'

I tackled Protocol on the fourth floor of our Ministry. They had received no instructions on housing, but agreed that if I found a residence I liked, they would try and get it for me. I gave them my list. Two weeks later, they were still trying. I was desperate. It was now late March, and we'd been in the Cardoso for two months.

'That's nothing,' one of the British Embassy staff told me. 'We were in the Cardoso six months before we were allocated a house. We repaired it and repainted it, and then the day before we were to move in the Government declared the whole zone a military area. But they did find us another within two months!'

I went back to the UN.

'I'll have to consider leaving,' I threatened. 'We have three children in the hotel already, and I expect four more for the school holidays. It's just not possible; it costs too much, and the hotel is always overbooked.'

'I'll talk to Foreign Affairs,' Torre promised.

He rang me a few days later. 'They say it will be at least another three weeks before the housing situation is settled.'

'Which means another three months,' I replied petulantly.

One Sunday, after breakfast, or *mata bicho* (literally 'kill the insect' in your stomach), Mary and I took a stroll along the stately avenue, Duques de Connaught, near the Polana hotel, a wide, tree-shaded esplanade, lined with elegant mansions on one side and a paved arbour on the other, from which idlers could look down over the scrubby woodland to the *Clube Naval* and the sun-swept waters of the bay, four hundred feet below. It was certainly the most pleasant area I had seen, quiet, with cool breezes and stunning views. If we could afford it, I was determined that this was where we would live.

At the Polana end of the Avenue a branch road, popularly known as the *caracol*, or snail, zigzagged steeply down the escarpment to join the coastal road, while the Avenue itself continued as a narrow one-way street, Rua Caldera, running obliquely down the side of the hill below the Polana Hotel. Halfway down on the sea side of this road was an apparently empty house fronted by a low cut-stone wall, a reinforced concrete carport and an attractively panelled front door.

We rang the bell – in case. A lad appeared. We asked if the owner was in (the usual approach). No. When would he be back? Never. He'd gone for good. We asked him who paid his wages. A Dona Elena had let him stay on as guardian. He gave us her number. Excited, we hurried back to the Cardoso and rang her.

Yes, the house was indeed empty, her brother was in America and would not be returning. It was now the property of the Government.

We rushed back to the house, where our new friend Eugenio, cheerful at the thought of a new occupant and a larger pay packet, showed us around. The owner had been a doctor, and by the solid grandeur and exquisite finish of the house, he must have been a pretty successful one. Enormous wooden grill screens and massive wooden doors that clicked shut like those on a safe; a panelled library, with floor-to-ceiling shelves recessed into all four walls, opened into a conservatory full of exotic ferns and flowers; an air-conditioning plant cooled the whole ground floor, with additional units in all four spacious bedrooms. A large parquet-floored lounge and a tiled patio overlooked the bay, and there was a huge flagstoned playroom at garden level with another room containing recessed shelves beside it. The garden, small but delightful, was bordered on one side by a grassy slope dotted with trees and on the other by thick, coastal scrub. Below, the polished surface of the bay stretched away to Inhaca Island and the Indian Ocean beyond. It was the most magnificent house we had ever seen, with an unbeatable view to boot. I wasn't going to let this one slip away if I could help it.

Monday morning I wrote to the UN Res Rep and to Protocol in the Ministry of Agriculture, asking them to obtain it for me. Torre promised to hand my request to Foreign Affairs, personally. I didn't trust the usual lines of communication, and I had little faith in the Ministry.

A couple of weeks passed.

'Pat, please go and seen Senhor Lopez Tembe at the Ministry of Foreign Affairs, tomorrow at nine.' Torre sounded hopeful. 'It's about your house,' he added.

At eight forty-five I was seated in a drab, partitioned-off waiting room on the second floor of Foreign Affairs. At twelve forty-five I was still there. At one o'clock Senhor Lopez, a small, thick-set black man, rushed in, apologized, and asked me to come back at two. I did. At three, I was summoned downstairs, where Lopez and his assistant, *Camarada* Khan, were speaking to a greying, short, tubby individual who, I was told, was the Russian Ambassador.

'Please follow us in your car,' Khan called as he and Lopez jumped into the back seat of a military vehicle and screamed off, followed by the Russian Ambassador in his chauffeur-driven Mercedes. I spent the next hour trying to survive and keep up with Lopez's car, whose army driver ignored all traffic signs, although he did slow down for some right-angled bends.

Evidently, the Russian Ambassador was hard to please. One after another stately home was inspected and rejected. Finally, we met back at Foreign Affairs. What the hell I was supposed to have been doing following that mad cavalcade, I had no idea. It was now almost dusk.

'Let's go. We'll follow you,' Khan said.

Eugenio let us in. Lopez and Khan walked round in silence. They were obviously impressed.

'I'm afraid this house must be kept for an Ambassador or high-ranking FRELIMO official,' said Lopez at last. 'You must find another.'

I wasn't surprised. I suspected it had been too good to be true. Mary was very disappointed. It would have been ideal for our eight brats, to say nothing of the gracious living it would have afforded their parents. I sent a list of half a dozen other houses to Torre for him to give to Lopez, and waited.

Three weeks later, in the middle of May, I returned from the office tired and depressed. I lay on the bed and dozed off. The telephone woke me.

'Khan speaking. You remember the house you showed us in Rua Caldeira? Do you still want it?'

'Of course,' I almost yelled. 'Of course I want it.'

'Well, you can come and collect the keys.'

Tiredness and depression vanished. I shoved my feet into sandals and rushed out, combing my hair on the way. I didn't tell Mary where I was going. At Foreign Affairs, a clerk handed me a bunch of keys and asked me to sign for them.

Our house in Maputo

'Look what I've got,' I chortled, dangling the bunch in front of Mary's popping eyes. 'Keys, house keys; our own beautiful house.'

'I just don't believe it,' she gasped. 'I bet they don't fit.'

'Only one way to find out!' I replied. That night, Melanie, Lindley and I slept, most uncomfortably, on the floor of our new lounge, on borrowed cushions. I wasn't going to risk someone else trying to grab it. As it happened, my fears were not too far off-target. The following morning, a voluptuous lady (nationality unknown) rang the doorbell.

'Oh, you're still here. We thought you had left,' she exclaimed fractiously. 'We were hoping to move in today.'

'Well, you can't,' 14-year-old Lindley, who was home for the holidays, told her fiercely. 'It's our house!' and slammed the door.

Lindley must have made some impression for, although we lived in terror for the next few days, the lady never came back and we were left in undisputed possession of one of the most exquisite houses, on possibly the most beautiful site, in LM.

'President Machel, I could kiss you,' I gloated as I raised my glass that evening. 'Your new laws saved us from a real dump.'

It was not for several months that I found out exactly why we had been so lucky. The Swedish Ambassador asked me how we liked our new house. 'Superb,' I assured him.

'Yes, I know. I had already agreed to take it for the Ambassador's residence, but our Foreign Office said the lounge was five square feet less than the minimum permitted for an Ambassador's reception room.'

'Three cheers for your niggardly, bureaucratic Foreign Office,' I hooted.

The timing of the Rua Caldeira house was almost perfect. Our effects, travelling by a series of slow boats from Recife to Mozambique via New York and South Africa, arrived a couple of days after we had moved in – almost as if the boat had waited till it knew we had a home ready to receive its cargo.

Then another fortuitous event occurred, again with almost perfect timing. We are not great churchgoers, but at Easter we had decided to conform, for the sake of the children at least. The congregation of the small Anglican church consisted mainly of expatriates, Embassy officials and a sprinkling of the erstwhile British business community of LM.

After the service, as we loitered on the lawn, a white-haired lady approached.

'I hear you're a vet. I wonder if you could put down our six cats. We would be so grateful.'

This was a job I hated, but I procured some concentrated barbiturate solution from the Veterinary Research Institute and did the job one morning, with the owner, at her request, holding the pets in her arms. It was a bit tricky, but all, except one, died peacefully in her embrace. A wild one escaped before we could catch it and, for all I know, is still at large.

The lady and her husband, both in their late seventies, were embarrassingly grateful.

'Is there anything you can see in the house that you would like?' she asked tearfully after the deed was done. 'If there is, please take it.'

Obviously, I refused.

'Please, you'll do us a great favour. We are leaving soon for an old folks' home in South Africa. We have no children and all our friends have gone, so we have no-one to give our things to. As soon as we walk out of this house, everything will be taken by the Government, or looted. We would rather it went to someone we know will appreciate it.'

'Why not sell it?' I suggested.

'What for? There's nothing we can buy with escudos, and we can't change them into rand. So, please, take what you want.'

'All right,' I said. 'I'll bring Mary along and if there is anything she wants, we'll buy it from you in rand. I'll send you a cheque to South Africa from my account in Swaziland.'

We left it like that, but she made me accept a set of beautifully bound *National Geographic*s, over 60 volumes, contained in glass-fronted oak cabinets.

'That's for the cats,' she insisted.

A few weeks later, the old couple left Mozambique. We took them to the railway station and helped them through the rather rough and unkindly customs. Several articles, including a treasured toiletry set, were rudely pulled out and refused exit.

'Give them to me,' Mary whispered. Once outside the shed we told her that we'd post them to her from Swaziland.

'We'd better go straight back to their house,' Mary suggested, as we drove out of the station. 'You never know.' How right she was. The house was full. Amongst the jostling mass I noticed several police uniforms and a number of so-called Mozambique friends, who had made some excuse for not saying farewell at the station, turning out drawers and filling their cars with anything removable. Who could blame them? If they hadn't taken the opportunity, someone else would have.

We had already removed the smaller items we had chosen, and as a

549

precaution had labelled the dining room set, the refrigerator and the *National Geographic*s as sold, but it looked as if we'd have to remove them fast. I rang the man with whom I had arranged to collect our stuff the following day. He came at once. It was not a moment too soon. As we left, an army truck drove up and half a dozen soldiers spilled out. Sounds of heated arguments arose from within. Big Brother had come to claim his spoils!

* * *

In the first days of March, President Machel announced that he had closed the border with Rhodesia and, as far as Mozambique was concerned, a state of war now existed between the two countries. Several Rhodesian friends in the hotel were arrested trying to cross the border.

Things looked bleak, but worse was to come. At the end of March, in another political outburst, Machel declared that all social clubs were now abolished. Within minutes, FRELIMO soldiers had cleared the angry members from the bar of the English Club, and had removed 80 cases of whisky, gin and beer, and placed an armed guard on the door.

Gone were the Sunday lunches, the amateur dramatics and the badminton evenings. The excellent library with many rare editions on early Mozambique was closed, and the tennis courts sealed off. The last oasis in that beverage-bare and culture-starved city had disappeared. The foreign community, most of whom belonged to this one remaining centre of entertainment and refreshment, was profoundly disturbed. We began to wonder, seriously, whether life in Mozambique would be worth it.

The English Club was eventually taken over by the Ministry of Information as a Centre for Journalists. When I went there some years afterwards, to discuss a publication on rabbit breeding, I found the tennis courts derelict and pitted with weeds, the library still locked, and the bar selling only *sumo*, that weak, tasteless solution of ersatz orange juice.

One friendly face I did find. That was of Roque, a Goan doctor friend of Cardoso days, who had applied for membership just before the club was closed and whose quizzical smile regarded me from the notice board, still patiently awaiting his application for membership to be approved!

550

THE NORDICS STEP IN

It was hopeless. There was nothing on which I could build the Project.

The earnest discussions and field trips with veterinarians and agronomists, so encouraging in the first weeks, had now given way to hurried unproductive chats with junior technicians and office personnel, while the senior staff slipped off to Portugal – usually without notice. One daybreak, I spent an hour waiting outside the home of a colleague with whom I had arranged to visit a dairy farm before I realized that there was no-one at home. He'd left, secretly, the day before.

Dr Joaquim, the original Director, had been replaced by a youngster not long out of university. Carlos was of Portuguese-German descent, hardworking and intelligent, but so overburdened trying to cope with the changing conditions and the thousand commands from upstairs, with no competent staff to whom he could delegate, that he rarely had time to pass the time of day, let alone discuss future policies with me.

Only two other veterinarians now remained in the department, both Portuguese, one more interested in political education than wildlife, which was his responsibility, and the other, Dr Pinho, pushing retirement.

Dr Pinho's office was opposite mine. He had worked all his professional life in Mozambique and intended to stay on until he was thrown out. Quiet, unassuming and efficient, he was the workhorse of the animal production section, and soon became my main informant and adviser.

The final-year veterinary students – brought in to fill the administrative and field posts left vacant by departing professionals, could do no more than try to maintain the *status quo*, but what the country needed was practical ideas to replace the old theories and technologies and to update production.

Although I knew a certain amount about animal production, my expertise remained microbiology and disease investigation, neither particularly appropriate to Mozambique's immediate problems. I urgently needed experts with modern, international ideas, to lay down plans for the future of the beef and dairy herds.

Ironically, it was the unpredictable American dollar that came to my rescue. The United Nations and its Agencies were once again in the midst of a financial crisis, caused by upheavals in the oil price and the depreciation of the dollar, so that many countries were behind in their contributions to the UN Development Programme,

551

which financed all field operations. New posts were being frozen and cuts made in Projects all over the world – the exceptions being the so-called 'recently liberated territories', of which Mozambique was one.

Martyn's Beef Production Project in Swaziland was less lucky. Members of his staff would not be extended after their present contract ended. They would have to seek jobs elsewhere. My old friend Tubby, the FAO Representative in Mbabane, rang with the news that Ted, Martyn's highly prized Beef Production expert, would be terminating in a couple of months. Could I use him in Mozambique? I jumped into the Peugeot and arrived in Mbabane that evening.

Australian, stocky, forty-ish, with a rather rosy, baby face, high forehead and receding hairline, Ted was just the man we needed, but I knew I would have to do some pretty smart sales talk to persuade him to chance his luck in a grass-roots project in a disembodied Ministry and half-dead country, after the professional and social extravaganza he had been experiencing in Swaziland.

We sat swigging beer late into the night. When we eventually hit the hay, I'd found my Project a top-flight beef production specialist. 'I just can't resist the thought of all those crabs and *piri-piri* lobsters,' Ted admitted as we shook hands on it.

Back in Maputo with Ted's promise, I was wondering what the next step should be and how I could best use his experience, when Torre rang.

'Have you heard about the FAO/NORDIC Mission?'

'No. What is it?'

Torre explained that the Minister, thoroughly frightened at the rapidly deteriorating agricultural scene and the flight of the Portuguese farmers, had asked FAO to send a team to evaluate the situation and make suggestions. His request had overlapped an offer by Sweden, Norway and Finland to help finance agricultural development in Mozambique, so it had been decided to combine both forces.

'They should be here early in June,' Torre continued. 'It will be a busy month.'

Ted joined us on 1 June, leaving his family in Mbabane till he could find a house in Maputo. On 9 June, my 57th birthday, the Mission arrived. The day started badly. Corinne woke with tummy pains, fever and vomiting. I rang Roque, my Goan doctor friend. There were no private doctors.

'Almost certainly appendix,' he prognosed, 'but let's wait till this afternoon.'

It was just such an emergency that had caused us second thoughts about accepting the Mozambique job in the first place.

The Mission's first session with the Minister was at three; both Ted and I were required to attend. Before going in, I rang Mary. Roque had just left.

'Definitely appendix,' she told me. Oh God, I thought, what now? The last thing I wanted was to have her operated on in the overcrowded, underequipped and understaffed old hospital in Maputo. Swaziland was the only alternative, but Mary was not permitted to drive the UN vehicle, and we had not yet been able to buy a car of our own. It looked as if I would have to run out on the Mission and take her myself. Ted saved the day. Coincidentally, his small daughter had had an appendectomy three days earlier and was still in hospital in Mbabane.

'Don't worry,' he said. 'I'll rush Mary and Corinne up as soon as the meeting finishes. 'It'll give me a chance to see Helen and the family.'

'That would be great! I expect the meeting will end before five,' I told him, relieved that the problem had been resolved so quickly.

Five o'clock came; five-thirty, but there was no break in the discussions – and one couldn't just slip out of a meeting with the Minister. Luckily, at half-past six, he was called away and we were given a short break.

'You'd better get cracking, Ted,' I urged. 'the border closes at eight.' I ran down to my office and phoned Mary to get ready. She was already in a panic.

Ted was never a slow driver, but that evening he must have flown, crossing the border with five minutes to spare. A couple of hours later Corinne was relieved of an appendix about to burst.

'Our next priority is our own car,' I told Mary when she phoned to report Coro's progress. 'Look around the dealers in Mbabane.' She did, and 19 years later, our Toyota Hi-Ace still gives us good service.

After a week of talks and visits to research institutes and collective farms, the FAO/NORDIC Mission hit the road – or rather the air – and flew north to examine the list of production sites which the Minister wished to develop with NORDIC funds and FAO expertise. Sylvia, a young Dutch secretary to the Minister, married to Abreu, the Portuguese head of the Farm Mechanization Department, accompanied us to smooth out any administrative problems.

There followed ten days of continuous travelling, in small planes, landrovers, and in canoes. Dairying operations were needed in Beira, Chokwe, Guidiza and elsewhere. Beef production units were planned for Mabalane, Buzi and Chimoio. Sheep and goat development for

553

Gondola, pigs for Inhamusa. Abattoirs were required to deal with the expected increase in slaughter animals, and existing dairy plants required new equipment to process the increased milk supply.

We visited two, perhaps three proposed project sites each day, writing up our recommendations and drafting the project documents in the evening. Nonchalantly, we would dispose of a million dollars in a couple of hours for fencing, for vehicles and tractors, for housing, dams, purchase of stock, medicines, staff and so on. Money soon meant nothing to us, the NORDIC funds seemed limitless.

Poor Mozambique! Wherever we went we encountered abandoned ranches, one with a herd of registered Brahman cattle, which we searched for in dense, overgrown thorn bush, but never found. Only the photos of the prize-winning bulls hanging in the ranch house gave us an indication of their quality.

We saw dairying facilities unused for a year or more, robbed of everything the locals could make use of in their everyday lives; and tractors – hundreds of them, in sheds, in the fields, their tyres flat, the bodywork rusting and half-smothered by weeds and long grass. A few former farmhands still lazed around the huts, but without a boss to organize or pay them, they helped themselves to what was going and waited for better times. It was sad to realize all the thought, love, hard work and sacrifices which had disappeared overnight, with no compensation whatsoever. A paradise lost, if ever there was one!

A small Cessna, with a local pilot, Senhor Guerra, at the controls, flew Sylvia, Hokki – the Finnish representative – and myself from Beira to Chimoio (formerly Vila Pery), a straggling town on the railway from Beira to Salisbury (now Harare) and some 50 kilometres from the Rhodesian border. The approach to the runway was terrifying. It was almost dark, and we appeared to be trying to land on the rising slope of a hillside meadow. The airfield shed and windsock were out of sight and only appeared as we taxied over the top of the hill.

'Take-off is much easier,' smiled Guerra.

'Remind me to avoid it,' I replied.

It was in Chimoio that I met Werner, an East German vet and one of the only two East Germans (the other was also a vet) I encountered who acted like a normal human being. About my age, Werner had been a District Veterinarian when he volunteered for his country's bilateral aid programme and was sent to Mozambique. He was jovial, friendly and open, quite unlike his fellow countrymen whom we had tried to befriend in the Cardoso. His English was good, and he had obviously kept up-to-date in his profession. I invited him for drinks at our Chimoio hotel – an old windmill. He was hesitant but agreed. Shortly before he and his wife were due to arrive, I received a message; 'Dr Werner regrets...'

The following day, while out on one of the ranches that would form part of a new cattle breeding scheme, he nudged me and walked off behind some bushes. I followed. Loosening his flies and glancing over his shoulder at the rest of the group, he whispered, 'Sorry we not come last night. Very dangerous. Supervisor arrive. If I with you – phzzt! Back to Germany at once. We not permitted talk to foreigners alone, only with party political official.'

He told me that he had never been a Communist Party member, and that they had only let him out of East Germany because he was over 55.

'If younger, must have *kinder* to stay behind. We haf none, but we old, so we go.'

I slipped him my telephone number. 'If you come to Maputo, ring me, we can arrange to meet somewhere.'

He was doubtful, but agreed to try. He did, and had a bizarre story to tell.

By the time the FAO/NORDIC Mission left, two weeks later, projects amounting to $13,000,000 had been agreed upon, and a staff of 32 foreign experts, either from the Nordic countries or paid for by them, had been listed for recruitment by FAO. At last, I felt, we had a firm base on which to plan our Project.

A DOG ANSWERS OUR ADVERT

We had hoped to send for our poodle puppy which we had left with friends in Brazil, but house-hunting had taken so long and our kind friends had become so attached to him, that we agreed they should keep him.

'We can look for a pooch here,' Mary argued. 'There must be hundreds of people wanting a home for their pets before they leave. Why not advertise?'

We placed an advertisement in *As Noticias*, the daily paper, for a good family guardian, preferably Alsatian. There were several replies. Melanie and I spent an evening visiting the owners. It was most disheartening. The first dog we saw was chained behind a security fence; no-one could get near it except the owner. We left within minutes. The others were much the same. Not one was a normal family pet. They were all chained and only let out at night in a restricted area. Apart from their unsuitability, every owner asked a payment of from $100 to $500, for his so-called canine companion.

'So much for pet owners,' I said to Melanie as we returned from inspecting the last on our list. 'They can stuff it; I'll pick up a stray, there are plenty of those.'

Back home, I sat reading, waiting for Shannon, on holiday from Edinburgh University, to return from a date. Finally, remembering she had the back door key, I decided to lock up.

As I was shutting the small lych-gate from which steps led down from the street to the floodlit kitchen patio, I noticed a large dog sniffing round the garbage bin, a piece of broken cord trailing from its neck. I descended cautiously. The animal loped over to me with a slight wag of its tail. It was an Alsatian, emaciated with a sore where the cord had cut into its neck. There were several large ticks on it. I held out my wrist. It sniffed at it, growled and backed off.

I went back up the steps and in through the front door to fetch some scraps. The dog gobbled them down and seemed a bit more friendly, so I sat on the bottom step and talked to it, but it was still too suspicious to come near me. After a while I went in, shutting the lych-gate firmly behind me. If it was a stray, I thought, I might be able to befriend it and solve our dogless problem.

An hour late I was woken by a hammering at the front door. 'Dad. Let me in!' It was Shannon back from her date.

'I thought you had a key,' I growled sleepily.

'I do, but there's a wolf in the patio guarding the back door, and it won't let me pass.'

The next morning I went down early to warn Eugenio, when he arrived, to be careful. But he was already there. I looked on in astonishment as he and the dog fondled each other like old friends.

'This was one of the master's dogs. He gave it to the police before he left. His name is Gonza.'

Within 24 hours, Gonza had added Guilbride to his name. He was wonderful with the children, letting them maul him without reproach. After a couple of baths and a few days good feeding, his coat became shiny and his eyes alert. He followed Mary like a shadow, unwilling to let her out of his sight for a moment, even to changing ends with her on the tennis court. The only cowardice he showed was towards thunder. At the first distant rumble he would be under the bed, or under the covers if we happened to be in it!

A week after his arrival, we had a shock. I was reading the adverts in paper when one in a special box setting caught my attention.

556

'Lost. German Shepherd male. Dark with brown markings. Please contact Police Dog Unit. Reward.'

Mary nearly had a fit. Gonza fitted the description exactly, and we knew he had been with the police, but he was now a member of our family. We were terrified that the police might look for him at his previous home. But they never did, and in the meantime we kept Gonza below decks as much as possible. Mary was indignant. 'How do they expect anyone to return him after treating him so badly?'

Gonza sired many offspring in the next six years and, true to his Socialistic environment, was not over fussy whether his wife of the moment was elite or not. Of his more pedigreed descendants, one is in Germany, another in Yugoslavia, and one, Cais, lies at my feet while I write this.

I couldn't understand why the police had wanted Gonza back, let alone offered a reward. He wasn't a particularly good police-type animal and hadn't been cared for. Then a friend suggested the reason. 'Of course they wanted him back. It's obvious.' He laughed. 'Do you know of any other dog that reads the newspaper adverts?'

A SECRETARY AND OTHER EXPERTS

Secretaries – *good* secretaries – were harder to find than Bibles in the Kremlin. The girls in the UN office had been co-operative, but I needed one of my own to handle FAO's somewhat tortuous accounting and purchasing procedures, keep the files up to date, translate and generally organize the office. She would have to be fluent in Portuguese and speak English well. Several young aspirants proved to be nowhere near the level I required. One young lady, whom I thought might make it, I arranged to pick up the following Monday. At seven o'clock I rang the bell of her flat. No answer. I rang again. The door of the opposing flat opened.

'*Ela fugió ontem.*' 'She left for Portugal yesterday,' her neighbour informed me. '*Fugió*' was a rather scornful way of saying that she had fled without notice. I was certainly put out, but it was not quite the shock it would have been a few months before; I was getting used to it.

'There's someone advertising for a part-time secretarial job,' Lucilia, one of the UN secretaries told me over the phone. 'Speaks English fluently.'

'Part-time's no good. I want a full-time girl.'

'Why not try her anyway? I can't go on typing for you for ever.'

Fernanda swept into our office like a stenographical Mary Poppins. After a week of mornings only, she began to stay for the afternoons as well. There was virtually nothing she couldn't do – and do well. She knew everyone of importance, she was well-educated, her English was excellent and her husband, Carlos, was Professor of Cardiology and Dean of the Medical Faculty.

Attempts by other Project Managers, Embassies and even the UN Office to lure her away were all repelled. 'I like it here,' she'd say. 'Nice people, interesting work and, who knows, maybe one day I'll join FAO.' Like Kattia in Peru, one day she did!

Soon after Fernanda had established herself, my other long-awaited FAO 'experts' began to arrive. First to appear was Rudi, an experienced milk production specialist from Germany, together with Herman, a young Dutch associate, to help him. Lloyd, an American poultry production expert, was not far behind. Ben, who had done wonders with our poultry programme in Peru, was rejected by this government as Israelis were now *personae non gratae.*

Then came John who, thanks be to our Project 'Godfather' in Rome, had now replaced their original candidate, my good friend Frank, as expert in tsetse and trypanosomiasis control. We had known each other at college and I had exchanged Christmas cards for a few years with his sister Sheila, who had also been at Edinburgh, but that had been our only contact since then.

John, a slight, good-looking, modest fellow with a hesitant speech, had remained a bachelor and was never happier than in a tent far from the pollution and high-life of the cities. In every respect, an ideal field worker.

'I intend to stay single,' he would laugh, 'it saves a hell of a lot of problems. Sheila can keep the family tree in bloom. She's had four or five kids, if I remember right.'

As soon as we could, John and I paid a visit to the tsetse and trypanosomiasis control field station at Muabsa, 60 kilometres inland from Vilancoulos, halfway between Inhambane and Beira.

Tsetse was a major menace. Why? Let me explain. Cattle owners south of the Sahara had long associated tsetse fly with a wasting disease in their livestock and in humans. They called it *nagana* or 'sleeping sickness'. Later, it was shown that the cause of *nagana* was a microscopic protozoa which lived in the blood and was transmitted by the tsetse when it fed, in the same way that mosquitoes transmitted malaria. Scientifically, the disease was termed trypanosomiasis.

Since trypanosomes were so often found in the blood of wild antelopes, it was concluded that game were the chief reservoir of *nagana*. Fences were therefore erected to keep game away from cattle, and large numbers of wild animals were systematically destroyed. It was also found that disturbing the vegetation and clearing undergrowth made the soil in which the fly deposited her *pupae* unsuitable as a nursery. In addition the resting places on trunks and branches, where the tsetse was accustomed to await a passing 'blood bank', now no longer existed.

None of these methods were completely successful by themselves, but together they had some impact. Then in the early 1940s a drug, 'Antrycide', was developed, which promised to be the answer. At the same time the powerful insecticides, DDT, BHC, Dieldrin and the organophosphates appeared. Older methods were largely abandoned, and control now centred on treatment of individual animals and the spraying of vegetation with insecticides. It looked as if Mrs Tsetse was about to bite the dust. But although each decade produced more efficient drugs and insecticides, and despite ingenious methods of control, such as liberating sterile male tsetse flies (tsetse females only copulate once in their life) to break the fertility cycle, or the use of odours to coax flies into traps and repellents to keep them off livestock, trypanosomiasis continued a major problem.

Nearly the whole of northern Mozambique was infested with tsetse. The river Save, just north of Muabsa, was regarded as the limit of the tsetse's southernwards expansion, and a joint campaign with Rhodesia and South Africa, the *Missão Contra Tripanosomíasis* (MCT), had been established to hold it there and possibly push it back. In the general upheaval of the FRELIMO war, this mission had been disbanded, its staff scattered and its records buried in Ministry archives. Only Muabsa remained.

The main road north, which John and I took, was tarmacked and consistently good, if rather monotonous. Where it ran beside the ocean, we glimpsed exotic scenery and yellow beaches, and the small settlements we passed were gay with purple and red bougainvillaea. The view from the cliffs at Quissico was spectacular, but apart from these interludes and a few flood plains and rivers, the scrub seemed endless.

There were several road blocks. At one, the young FRELIMO soldier studied my *Guia de viagem*, and official letter authorizing us to travel on behalf of the Ministry of Agriculture. He obviously couldn't read as he held it upside down, but wanting to create an impression, he told us to unpack the whole vehicle for inspection.

'*Mais este caro e diplomático*,' I pointed out, severely, in an attempt to forestall any such inconvenience. Diplomatic cars were never searched. He gazed at me for a moment, open-mouthed, as if I had told him it was a Magic Carpet.

'*O caro e automático?*' he exclaimed in wonderment. '*Então passa senhores, passa.*' I suppose he had never heard the word *diplomático* before, but automatic cars he knew were very special, so he waived us on. We found, also, that we had to be careful about using the Portuguese for United Nations, *Nacões Unidas*. It was too like *Estados Unidas*, and the United States was still the big bad wolf as far as Mozambique was concerned.

Being marked on most larger-scale maps of Mozambique, I presumed that Muabsa would, at least, be a village with a store and some houses, but there was only a clearing with a thatched mud-and-wattle building and a few thatched rondavels arranged beside an enormous tree. A disintegrating notice at the entrance to the compound proclaimed that this had once been the centre of the *Missão Contra Tripanosomíasis*. We pulled up under the tree where a short, bespectacled man in khaki shirt and slacks was flagging us down.

Mussagy, the station manager, one of many Goans to settle in Mozambique from the former Portuguese enclave in India, was quiet-spoken and unostentatious. For the last few years he had tried to keep the small group of field and laboratory personnel together and to maintain the basic investigations and control routines, under extremely difficult conditions.

Muabsa was in a bad way. Insecticides for spraying operations were almost exhausted and the spray pumps in need of repair, many being full of bullet holes from the recent hostilities. Food was scarce, and the staff hadn't been paid for months. He was overjoyed that FAO were sending people and equipment to help.

560

The experimental herd, a few hundred nondescript cattle, looked uniformly miserable, their coats dull and the skin tight against their emaciated bodies.

'We've run out of drugs and the records are in a mess,' Mussagy told us sadly. 'We will have to start all over again.'

The forest had been divided into two-kilometre square blocks by cutting *picadas* or avenues through the trees. Methodical spraying of insecticides onto the trunks and leaves within the blocks and along the edges of the *picadas* had considerably reduced the tsetse population in the past, but with the shortage of supplies, the fly was again on the increase.

It was unbelievably hot as we bumped and jerked along the steamy, half-overgrown *picadas*, and our shirts were soon firmly stuck to our slimy bodies. The further north we went, the more flies we encountered. The little brown tormentors buzzed around inside the cab, crawling inside our shirts, wriggling under our hats, creeping up our trouser legs, or simply biting through our clothing.

There were other flies, too, that bit. John caught a horsefly and demonstrated the difference between it and the tsetse. 'When it's at rest, the tsetse folds its wings one over the other, rather like a moth. Also, in the centre of the tsetse's wing the veins form a hatchet-like cell. Only tsetses have this.'

The bodies of several tsetses that we caught were swollen with blood, probably ours.

'There's no human sleeping sickness around here, as far as we know,' Mussagy informed us, 'so you don't have to worry about being bitten.' But sleeping sickness or not, the bites were just as painful!

We saw women with water pots on their heads, or pulling small drums behind them in a wooden harness that allowed the container to roll along.

'Some people come thirty kilometres for water,' Mussagy told us. 'There used to be bore-holes with pumps all over this area, but most are now broken, so people have to travel a very long way.'

'Can't they be repaired?' we asked.

'Yes, but Government doesn't want people living all over the bush, only in politically controllable villages, the *aldeas comunais*, so only the pumps near to Muabsa get repaired.'

It looked to me, however, that the populace would strongly resist leaving their lands for the joys of collective living. They still preferred to carry water to their isolated huts, even if it took two days!

'There's nothing we can do at the moment,' John decided. 'I'll come back up when my Associate Expert arrives; Rome says they

561

have recruited someone already. He should be here within a month. I'll put him in charge of this area.'

'Bit lonely if he has a family,' I said.

'The family can live in Vilancoulos or Inhambane, and he can go home each weekend. There'll be too much to do for him to be lonely. I'd like to create a wide barrier by cutting out all the vegetation for a kilometre on each side of the road, and then get people to settle in it so that we don't have to continually clear the regrowth. That should help prevent the tsetse moving further south.'

'Probably mean putting in a chain of bore-holes,' I predicted. 'It won't be a politically popular move.'

'Either they want us to prevent the tsetse or they don't,' John said firmly. 'We're technicians, not politicians. Another thing, we must start training courses for field staff. Training is going to be our highest priority. The whole north needs people trained in tsetse control.'

I didn't say so, but to me the job looked impossible. But then I hadn't yet met George.

* * *

They were exciting days. Nothing, I realized, was going to be easy, even with the additional experts who were now arriving, but the overall enthusiasm, instead of that ghastly quagmire of despair and red tape I had experienced in Brazil, made each day a joy. Instead of the foreboding with which I had approached the IPEANE office in Recife, I now ran up the Ministry stairs two at a time, swapping cheery *Bom dias* with colleagues and cleaners and looking forward to the day's work.

There was no lack of red tape – unfortunately one of Portugal's major exports to her colonies – but everyone was eager to cut their way through it (not always successfully) and get things moving.

Carlos, the new Director of Veterinary Services, was frantically trying to find staff to fill the posts abandoned by the Portuguese.

'We badly need a parasitologist for the Veterinary Research Institute,' he told me one day. 'Do you know anyone we could contact?'

As it happened, Roger had just written me from Bolivia. The same Roger with his wife Pru, with whom I had worked in Jamaica, who had been Chief Research Officer in Tanganyika when we were in Uganda, and who had replaced Dougie in Bolivia. His project was coming to an end. Was there anything in Mozambique? There certainly was!

'I'm putting your name up for the post of parasitologist,' I wrote.

562

'Fine,' he replied. 'I'm a bit rusty on parasites, but I'll start mugging it up.'

Mary and I were ecstatic until I was informed that a Bulgarian had now been recruited for the job.

'I'm very sorry,' sympathized Carlos. 'No-one consulted me. It was a political decision – Bulgarian Bilateral Aid.'

A few days later Carlos approached me again.

'We need two more posts for the Research Institute, a microbiologist and a Director to help develop the Institute on International lines. Any suggestions?'

'Look no further,' I exclaimed in delight. 'Microbiology is Roger's main expertise, parasitology was only his second string. He's also a first-class research administrator and was Chief Research Officer in Tanzania and Director of the Wellcome Foundation's Field Research Station in England before he joined FAO. He would be ideal for both jobs.'

'You're now a microbiologist as well as the International Director of the Veterinary Research Institute,' I wrote. 'I hope it goes through this time.'

In due course, and without further political interference, Roger and Pru arrived in Mozambique and soon afterwards, two top-level laboratory technicians joined him: Kim from Trinidad, with his German wife, and Fernandez from Kenya, with his Nicaraguan spouse.

Looking back for any possible contribution I might have made to the livestock development in Mozambique, the most significant one, without any doubt, was my proposal of Roger as Director of the VRI. Under his leadership, the Institute soon gained a reputation far ahead of its previous glory. Incidentally, the Bulgarian parasitologist never did turn up; so Roger obligingly wore that gentleman's hat as well as his other two!

* * *

Aid to developing countries, especially those newly 'liberated', like Mozambique, was the 'in thing' in European Overseas Aid Programmes, and in due course I received a note from the British Embassy, passing on an enquiry from London as to what type of British Aid would be most appropriate in the fields of Agriculture and Livestock.

I thought about it for several days and finally wrote back: 'I would strongly recommend that the British Government delay any aid to Mozambique in these fields for the time being. The Nordic countries are bringing in considerable funds for their Mozambique Aid

563

Programme, as are the Germans, French and Dutch, and the Eastern Bloc countries have their own assistance schemes. Mozambique, with its dearth of trained administrators and its lack of experience, is already finding it difficult to cope with all this largesse. I suggest that Britain reconsiders possible aid in six or twelve months' time, when there may be gaps to fill.'

His Excellency was a little cool towards me at the next session of Scottish Country Dancing, which was held at his residence every fortnight. But I wouldn't retract, and on looking back, I'm sure I was right. Well-thought-out aid can be vital to a struggling country, but so often it is given in order to assuage the donor's sense of guilt or for some political or commercial reason, and so seldom because of a genuine philanthropic desire or practical necessity. And all too often, it simply helped to ameliorate the symptoms rather than eradicate the cause.

BUSH INTO BEEF

Beef was a priority. Raising beef cattle in the tropics is not particularly difficult, but in a country whose infrastructure has crumbled away, where large numbers of pedigreed breeding stock have died or been killed for food, and where, even had the livestock authorities known what to do, there is no-one to do it, the task can be truly formidable.

Ted and his young Dutch Associate Expert, Gerard, began to introduce some sense and method into the ailing beef cattle industry. Together with Tilak, who had now left the Veterinary Faculty to join the Animal Production Unit in the Ministry, he made a survey of all former private beef ranches and Government Livestock Centres, and drafted a national policy for beef production. It was simple, straightforward and practical. A few Breeding Centres would be established under Ministry supervision, where high-quality bulls would be produced. These bulls would then be sent to Multiplication Centres, also under Ministry control, which would, in turn, supply high-grade calves to collective and private farms, and surplus steers to commercial fattening units near urban abattoirs.

But there was one small point that worried us. Where were we going to find managers for these breeding and multiplication centres? Ninety-five per cent of the Portuguese farmers had now left, and the number of Mozambiquans capable of managing a ranch could be counted on the fingers of a duck-billed platypus. Still more serious, when we had found suitable candidates to train, who was going to train them? Mobilizing some of the more knowledgeable *co-operantes* who had beef cattle experience, we started training courses for beef ranch managers. Again, Ted's approach was simple and practical.

'Every farmer has to carry out certain operations at certain times of the year – whether he grows crops or breeds cattle or pigs,' he explained. 'What better way to train ranch managers than to draw up a calendar of beef production activities for them as a guide, and see that they know when, and how, to carry out each operation, month by month.'

The 50 'rookie' managers produced in the first two years were, without doubt, the foundation of beef cattle production in Mozambique. But the training of managers was only the start.

'Half the breed goes in at the mouth,' says the old adage, and this half, as far as Mozambique was concerned, would have to be grass and other forage. There was no way the country could afford to feed cattle – beef or dairy – with high energy concentrates as was done in developed countries. Pastures, therefore, would be our next priority.

Sowing pastures on prepared farm land would have been straightforward, but after years of neglect most farm land was covered with scrub, thorn trees and brambles, collectively known as *mikaia*. Before pastures could be re-established, the land had to be cleared. Hand-clearing here was far easier than it had been in the Amazon forests of Peru, and a dozen lads with machetes could probably have cleared a hectare or more in a day, or we could have used weed-killers and burning, but both these methods were slow, and considering the enormous areas with which we had to deal, quite impractical.

Instead, we decided to use a system which Martyn's Project in Swaziland had been developing. This consisted of dragging a heavy chain between two caterpillar tractors. It was simple, efficient, far cheaper than hand labour, and many times as fast. MONAP (Mozambique Nordic Aid Programme) promised funds for the work, and the harbour master at Durban, in South Africa, found us an old anchor chain. We equipped each end of the chain with swivels and to every second link we welded a two-foot crossbar.

When this 13-ton, 25-metre-long 'Ely Chain', to give it its official name, was dragged between the two DC-8s, it scythed and rolled its way through the vegetation, uprooting bushes and small trees but leaving the topsoil intact. Afterwards, the litter of torn-up trees and shredded bushes was collected together and burnt. Three to five hectares could be cleared in this way in an hour.

Over the next 20 months, in spite of breakdowns, floods, shortages of fuel and other set-backs, an average of 17 hectares was cleared daily. Natural pasture grasses sprang up in the cleared areas, and within a few months we could graze four times the number of cattle per hectare than before chaining.

Then came the highest hurdle of all – co-ordination. The whole beef production programme had to be very closely controlled if it was to work at all. We had to be sure that the bulls produced at the Breeding Centres were improving from year to year, that too much in-breeding was prevented, that birth weights, growth rates and fertility were up to expectations, and that there were sufficient bulls produced each year to distribute.

This meant the collection and correlation of a great deal of data from the various centres, including the performance testing of the bulls, a slow process involving the appraisal of their offspring. To do this, Ted suggested we create a Data Processing Centre and record all our information on computers. The mere mention of such a sophisticated procedure, in our circumstances, sent a shudder down my spine. In 1978, computers were still impossibly hi-tech.

Again we approached Martyn, whose Swaziland Beef Project was using a computerized system originally developed by the beef industry in Botswana. We borrowed his computer expert for a few months, and he was able to adapt the system to our requirements. Local personnel were trained, computer time was rented from the South African Railways, who had the only computer in Maputo, and soon, 15,000 animals at the beef cattle improvement stations were on discs.

I wish I could say that it was a success. It could have been, but a computer can only produce results in proportion to the data it receives. Records from the stations, especially those in the north, where personal contact was infrequent and mails uncertain, left many gaps. Even those in the south, in close contact, often found it difficult to produce regular and accurate information.

Perhaps we were overenthusiastic and a bit naive, but deficient and inaccurate as much of the data was, it did at least ensure that the ranch manager and his staff kept a constant eye on their stock.

BUCKETS OF MILK

Milk production, on the other hand, is a far more demanding operation than producing beef. A beef farmer can go away for the weekend and forget about his charges. Not so the poor dairyman, who cannot leave his milk cows unattended for a single afternoon.

The dairy cattle of Mozambique, like their more sturdy beef

cousins, had been abandoned for months, in some cases years. Not that there had been very many of them to start with, but the 12,000-odd milch cows in the 'milk basin' around the then Lourenço Marques, had supplied the city's breakfast tables with some 20,000 litres each morning, a welcome, even if shamefully low, level of production.

'Where do we begin?' I asked Rudi, the West German FAO Dairy Expert. He and his young Dutch Associate had just returned from a tour of the area, and now sat sipping cups of Fernanda's coffee while we discussed our next step in the milk production programme. Rudi, a fine-featured 50-year-old, with dark hair and a toothbrush moustache starting to turn grey, and Herman, a tanned boyish face below a thick brown mop, appeared depressed.

'There's only one place we can begin,' Rudi replied. 'At the beginning, with the cow and the cowman. Cows must be fed properly, milked properly and their calves raised properly. The only way to gauge success is the amount of milk in the pail. The better the management, the fuller the bucket. One other thing; as far as possible their feed must be obtained by grazing pastures, we can't afford to stall feed them on concentrates. Namaacha seems the best place to start. At least there are some good cows and basic dairy facilities there.'

Namaacha, the small town of tile-roofed bungalows on the Swaziland border, was the site of the Ministry's Dairy Research Station, established some 15 years previously on 60 hectares of hilly land. The station was obviously in need of an overhaul, from facilities to management. Records showed that two out of every ten calves turned up their little hooves within a month of birth, and the daily milk yield averaged under five litres per cow, an absurdly low figure when similar animals managed properly could produce twice that amount – and this was the national herd, the pride of the Veterinary Services!

The first concern was fodder. There were only 20 hectares of grazing and fodder-producing land for the 150 cows, heifers and calves. Stony outcrops and steep bush-covered hillsides occupied the rest. The only answer was to grow sorghum and elephant grass on this rough land and make silage.

However good Herman's silage was, and at times it was very good indeed (I know, I ate some!), its nutritive value was too low to fulfil the needs of the high-producing dairy cows by itself, especially with the limited pastures on the station, so although it was against our original intention, we were very glad to find a source of concentrates to bolster their rations.

It took Herman a year to drop the calf mortality from 20 per cent to 7, and to raise the milk yield to eight-and-a-half litres per cow per day. The new calf houses, milking parlour and dormitories for trainees were begun, and the Alfa Laval milking machine, which had lain in the store for perhaps ten years, was finally installed. Unfortunately, we were unable to use it as there was still no electricity – the municipality of Namaacha, who had promised a new transformer to increase the supply and provide us with light and power, were still arguing about it. It didn't really matter. Much of the milk in Mozambique would have to be produced without electricity, so perhaps it would be preferable to first train our lads to milk by hand.

Growing grass is like growing any other crop. The better it is fertilized, harvested and stored, the more profitable it proves. Whether it is grown for dairy cows or beef cattle, the principles are the same. It is the particular requirements of the animals themselves that dictate the type and management of the pasture.

Dairy cows, which have to be milked twice a day, are usually grazed near the milking shed on rich pasture, whereas beef cattle, which are only rounded up now and then for weighing and dosing, can graze much further afield and over larger areas of poorer grass. This difference in requirements creates two categories of grassland science – that dealing with sown, cultivated and often irrigated pastures for dairy cattle, referred to as 'intensive' management, and that concerned with perennial, rainfed natural grasses or rangeland for beef cattle, called 'extensive' management. Pasture agronomists, likewise, usually specialize in one or other of these disciplines.

Grassland management had not been a feature of the Veterinary curriculum in pre-war days. Although we learned to identify a handful of grass species, to most of us pastures were those grassy fields with which the Good Lord had seen fit to carpet Britain. Since those undiscerning days, however, a new type of agriculturist had been spawned – the Pasture Agronomist.

Sam, whose work had revolutionized the beef and dairy industries in Jamaica, had been the first of this new breed of specialist that I encountered. By the time I reached Uganda, there was already a team of pasture scientists and nutritional chemists at the Entebbe Research Station, and in Peru, Brazil and now Mozambique, I had put pasture experts at the very top of my priority list. So I was pleased when Guy, whom I had left working for the PROPASTO project in Brazil, agreed to join us. He arrived early one morning, perky as ever, his balding head covered in perspiration and his small eyes sparkling through pince-nez. He described his flight and everything to do with his trip in exactly the same terms as he had when I met him in

Recife, four years before. 'Shit' was still his favourite adjective.

Guy's Associate Expert, a young French agronomist, arrived two days later. Pierre was tall, thin and highly strung. Every statement he made was prefaced, not by an epithet, like Guy, but by a shrill whistle. His English was poor and his French maddeningly fast. He had told us that he was coming alone. He did, but he omitted to mention his large, aggressive Alsatian.

Wives were no problem. Dogs were. The Cardoso Hotel, where Guy was staying and in which we had booked Pierre, flatly refused to contemplate a guest with a dog. So did a couple of others. I was in despair and, at the risk of divorce, was about to offer him and his pet our playroom at the bottom of the house which opened onto the garden, when someone – may they be blessed forever – suggested the *Campo de Turismo*, a former tourist park close to the sea.

We rushed off in the growing dusk. Yes, there was a cottage free, but there was no mattress or bedclothes. There was a brick barbecue outside, and if he brought a cylinder of gas, he could even have hot water for the shower. Perfect. With great relief I headed home and brought back the things he needed.

A week later, I sent him to Namaacha to help Herman sort out the pastures for the dairy cows. The other inmates of the *Campo* cottages were delighted to see him go; evidently his hound had made a habit of raiding their larders.

Guy was still a loner, but what I hadn't appreciated fully before was that he was too unpredictable to work in a team. Rarely would he turn up at a meeting or meet us in time for a field visit. On one occasion, after being granted two weeks' leave, to be taken in South Africa, he stayed away nearly a month, and I found out later that he had been to Bali to see his girlfriend, to Belgium to see his father, and to Brazil to sell a farm in Piaui which none of us even knew he owned!

The day before he terminated his contract, he presented me with his final report, 50 pages of illegible script, stuffed loosely into a file jacket. 'Look through it, Pat, before you give it to the Minister,' he instructed me confidently.

It took two months to edit. Some of it was in English, some in French, but none of it in sequence. His work at Namaacha was interspersed with incidents elsewhere. Facts were mixed with suppositions and opinions – even jokes. There were no conclusions or recommendations. After eliminating his'favourite adjective and his comments on several Mozambican colleagues, I shortened it to eight pages and locked it in my filing cabinet. Certainly the Minister would never get the chance to read it. His literary skills, I fear, had not improved since Brazil. Like his attempts to record his activities in Recife, his present effort was, without doubt, a 'shit' report.

Pierre's report, hand-written in French – what we could understand of it – was no better. Tilak, whose French was good, and I (still at 'the pen of my aunt' level) struggled with it for a week then, wisely, stuffed it at the back of the filing cabinet along with Guy's.

Within 15 months from the week of their arrival, they had both gone, leaving the way clear for the most flamboyant of all my experts – Henri.

WHO'S NEXT?

Lucilia was in tears. The other secretaries in the UN office were trying to comfort her.

'What's her problem?' I asked.

'Her husband has been arrested,' they replied.

Lui, a jolly, compact little Portuguese in his mid-forties, owned a shoe factory. He had built it from scratch and, in spite of being burned down twice, it was again back in production and exporting to other African countries.

The case was simple. Certain materials for finishing his creations had to be imported from Europe. Hard currency for their purchase had been authorized, but when the goods arrived they were found to be of inferior quality. The ever-suspicious *Grupo Dinamizador* in his factory had concluded that Lui had purposely arranged for cheaper material so that he could bank the difference in Switzerland. Accommodation had therefore been made available for him in the Central Prison, which occupied half a square kilometre in the middle of the residential area.

One Sunday afternoon, Mary and I, full of dread at what we might encounter inside those massive walls, accompanied Lucilia on her weekly visit to her husband. We joined a long queue in the tree-lined avenue Kim Il Sung moving towards a large brass-studded wooden portal in which there was a smaller door for persons to enter. There were barred windows above and to the sides of the door and high brick walls stretching away to the ends of the block. Occasionally a hand would be thrust through the bars and someone would call, but it was too dark to see who was inside.

To our surprise, a very polite and jocular guard took our identity cards and examined the food and magazines we had brought. Then we joined the stream of other visitors shuffling past the offices and toilets, to emerge in a park-like square dotted with trees, beneath which dozens of families were strolling or sitting on benches, picnicking in the shade.

Lui waved from a bench on the far side. Several elderly Portuguese men shook hands with us and kissed Lucilia, but whether they were visitors or inmates was difficult to tell. Lucilia unpacked her bag and offered tea. Mary had brought a cake. A holiday atmosphere pervaded everything. Yelling children chased each other back and forth, while a game of football was in progress at one side. Everyone seemed to be in high spirits. Regent's Park on a Sunday, I thought, except for the blue-uniformed guards who ambled about, AK47s slung over their shoulders, talking and laughing with the visitors and inmates alike, but careful to stop anyone who approached too near to the boundary walls.

Lui had heard nothing about his case.

'Some pipple bin 'ere morna year,' he told us morosely.

Luckily, three or four weeks later, he was released and given a '24-20' – 24 hours to get out and 20 kilos of luggage to take with him. No charges were laid, nevertheless, the Government appropriated his factory – without compensation, of course!

The next of our friends to be a guest at the Government's expense was Mario.

During our five months in the Cardoso hotel, our kids had made friends with a group of local Portuguese lads who, no doubt, had been lured into its portals by tales of beautiful blondes residing there. The Cardoso gang, or *malta Cardoso* as we called them, consisted of Luis and his brother Zeca, sons of a rice miller; George, João, Rui and Fernando (known as *Chino* from his slightly slanting eyes), and Mario.

Luis and Zeca were the most constant of the group, and hardly an evening passed without their participation in a rowdy game of *mano rápida*, so called because of the speed at which the cards had to be played. The elderly and decidedly conservative guests, half-hidden in deep leather armchairs, would look on disapprovingly at the boisterous battle being fought around the table by the window.

After we left the Cardoso, the *malta* gradually broke up. George left for Portugal, from where he wrote disgusted letters describing his first two weeks sleeping in the airport, and the bad conditions and low pay of the job he finally obtained. *Chino* and João followed soon afterwards. Only Luis, Zeca and Mario remained.

Mario was older than the others, all of whom were in their late teens or early twenties. He would greet me with an embarrassed smile

571

in the corridors of the Ministry of Agriculture, where he worked as a draughtsman, pulling nervously at his small black beard. He always avoided my eyes, and seemed too shy to stop and converse. When he was with the gang, he was much the same, rarely entering into the conversation, just sitting and listening.

One evening, Luis brought disturbing news.

'*Mario foi preso ontem.*' 'He's in jail.'

'Whatever for?' we asked, dismayed.

Nobody was quite sure. The story Luis had heard was that one of Mario's acquaintances, a *moleque*, or urchin, had come to his flat and asked for money and clothes. Mario gave him some as he had on other occasions, but this time the *moleque* wouldn't leave, so Mario called the police. When they came, the *moleque* accused Mario of trying to rape him. It ended with the *moleque* going free and Mario in the clink.

As soon as he heard, Luis had gone to Mario's flat. It had been stripped. His hi-fi set, his most cherished possession, had gone, but whether into a police home or sold by the *moleque*, we never found out.

We were very concerned. The next Sunday, Lys, on holiday from school in England, visited the jail with Luis and Zeca. Mario told them that he was still awaiting trial. When they went back the next week he'd gone, sent north to a re-education camp near Gorongoza, but no-one could tell them exactly where or for how long.

All Mario's relations were in Portugal, so Mary and I determined to see what we could do for him. We made an appointment with the Director of the jail. We arrived sharp at two o'clock, but were told he had a meeting and could we come back at five? We did, once more ringing the clapper bell outside the massive wooden gate.

The Director, a tall, well-dressed African, rose from behind his desk, greeted us warmly and asked how he could help us. We told him that we wished to know what crime Mario had been convicted of, where he had been sent and for how long.

'Ah, yes. Mario.' He went to a filing cabinet and took out a sheet. 'He was convicted of immorality with another man.'

'Mario? Homosexuality? Never!'

'I assure you he confessed to it standing where you are now. In such cases we do not hold trials, we send the accused to a re-education camp for a few months.'

'Can we write him or send him something?' Mary asked. We had heard lurid tales of the deprivations at re-education camps.

'I'll give you his address (it was care of the police in Beira), but I should just write, he may not receive other things.'

He thanked us for coming and showed us out to our car, personally. He could not have been more sympathetic or charming, so we were most upset to hear, six months afterwards, that he too had been arrested. We never learned why or heard what happened to him, but we prayed that wherever he was, it was not too uncomfy and that he would soon be released.

We wrote Mario a couple of letters, but never received a reply. Probably he never got them. Then one evening, nine months later, I returned from work to find a young, clean-shaven man sitting on the sofa, sipping tea with Mary.

'Look who's here,' she cried.

Mario certainly had changed. He was fatter but more erect, his beard had gone and he looked me straight in the eyes. His speech was stronger, and altogether he looked twice as confident as he had done a year ago. He seemed embarrassed at our joy of seeing him back, and my Latin embrace was hardly reciprocated.

Somehow we understood that any reference or query about his recent doings would not be welcome. In fact, it was with rather a shock that we realized he was no longer on our side! Big Brother had got to him. He told us that he was giving a musical evening, to which he hoped we would come, and was trying to collect some classical records. Could I lend him some, as his had been stolen. I fetched an armful and he chose two, a Mozart and a Stravinsky. Then, because he mentioned that he had been 28 the day before, we gave him a bottle of whisky, an item impossible to find in any Maputo shop.

He never let us know the date of his *soirée*. That didn't worry me, but the fact that he never returned the two records, did. Our friends reported, too, that Mario could only talk of Marxist theories and hardly recognized his former pals in the street.

I met him a few times in the Ministry before he was transferred elsewhere. He marched rather than slunk and gave me the slightest of nods, as if he was now a little too purified to bestow his socialistic felicitations on a foreign capitalist.

'They certainly changed Mario,' I commented to Mary.

'For better or worse?' she asked.

I had no idea!

* * *

Overreaction from excessively zealous vigilantes or young FRELIMO hotheads, especially towards high-spirited, non-conforming children like ours, was a continual concern, and we took every opportunity to hammer into our dearly beloveds the sensitivity of Communist toes. But no matter how protective we were, pitfalls could not be avoided entirely.

Kerry was the first to fall in. David, a coloured farmer's son from Moamba near the South African border, had brought vegetables in to the Maputo market that morning. After collecting money from the bank and loading up with supplies, he invited Kerry and Peter, the American Ambassador's son, to come back with him to the farm for the weekend. They started off at dusk.

David said he knew a short cut which would save them 30 kilometres; unfortunately, the road was much worse than they had expected. Halfway, they hit a rock, the battery fell out and disintegrated, and they found themselves stuck.

A couple of lads passed on bicycles and offered to fetch help. An hour later, a group of local vigilantes arrived. One had a gun. The three boys were questioned and told they were under arrest. Later they were taken back to Maputo and handed over to the police.

This, one might think, was overdoing it a bit, but it so happened that the Rhodesians had made a well-publicized raid into the northern province of Tete the previous week. Now here were three young men, two white and one coloured, in a truck near the South African border with 50,000 escudos in cash and no documents – none had thought to carry their Identity Cards. And David, who was driving, didn't even have a licence.

Fortunately, Peter persuaded the police to let him ring his father. The Ambassador was not amused but managed to have the three released, *pro tem*. The first indication we had was a banging on the front door at three in the morning. A rather dishevelled Kerry apologized for waking us.

'Truck broke down,' was all we got out of him until the next day when the Ambassador's car came to pick him up. 'Have to report to the police. Won't be long.'

They were lucky. Ambassadorial influence soon straightened things out. Without some such protection, it would have been quite possible for them to have been shipped north to a re-education camp with no-one the wiser.

Shivy also had a near squeak. Now nine and always a tomboy, she was caught riding Zeca's motorcycle at Bilene, a seaside resort north of Maputo where Mary and the kids were spending a weekend. Not only was she under age with no licence, she was exceeding the speed limit and a friend was riding pillion – another offence. They were hauled off to the *Posto de Polícia*, where only the aid of Mary, hastily summoned to wave the diplomatic wand, convinced the outraged police official to let them go.

Mary had a more relaxed encounter. Driving home from a dinner party about midnight, she was stopped by a young, rather over-motivated policeman.

'Whose car is this?' he asked gruffly.

'My husband's,' Mary replied politely.

'Where is your husband?'

'In Nampula.'

'What are you doing out at night?'

'I'm going home from visiting friends.' Mary was becoming a little bored with all these questions.

'Alone?'

This was getting beyond a joke. It was only too evident what the chap in blue was leading up to. Prostitution was one of the more serious sins in a Marxist state. She decided to attack.

'Why aren't *you* home with your wife instead of prowling around alone at night?' The young man was quite taken aback.

'I'm not married,' he replied sadly.

'Not married? A good-looking young fellow like you? What a shame.'

'Well, you see, I have a girl in...' One thing led to another, and soon they were the best of friends. Mary proceeded with her drive unmolested.

It was Kerry who eventually established an effective rapport with the law-keepers. Nearly every evening he would visit his Swedish girl-friend in Sommerschield, half across the town, walking home in the early hours through deserted streets. At first he would have to answer questions and produce his ID card at nearly every corner, but after a week or two the police greeted him by name, asked after his lady-love, his family and, of course, bummed a few cigarettes.

'Takes twice as long to get home these nights,' he complained.

One evening a policeman banged on the door and asked to see my son.

'What's he done?' I asked, a bit apprehensive.

'We want him to come down to the – ' he mentioned the name of a nightclub. 'We are having a problem with the son of a diplomat. We think *Senhor* "Kelly" can help us.' It was the first of several occasions when they enlisted the help of *Senhor* 'Kelly'. His efforts in public relations made life easier for all of us as, for instance, when I was stopped for speeding.

'Isn't this *Senhor* "Kelly's" car?' The officer asked.

'Well, he borrows it sometimes. He's my son.'

There was no longer any question of a fine. *Senhor* 'Kelly's' dad could do no wrong!

Identity Cards provided some amusing moments. The first one I received from the Ministry had the photo of a Russian technician. True, his hair was the same shade as mine, what was left of it, but he was twice my weight and I liked to think that, as far as looks went, I had the edge on him!

We had to show our ID cards each morning as we entered the Ministry of Agriculture. They were inspected and kept by the young AK47-wielding guards at the desk inside. At first these cards were thrown onto a pile, so when it was time to go home it became a feat of detection to ferret out one's card from amongst all the others. It took a month before one of the brighter officials thought of shoe boxes so that the cards could be sorted alphabetically, with a special compartment for foreigners. Once the guards came to recognize us individually, they would place our cards in the *estrangeiros* box without further scrutiny, but new guards, unfamiliar with our faces, would examine the photographs intently before letting us in.

One morning, I arrived to find strange faces behind the desk. I opened my wallet – no ID! My other pockets were equally unhelpful. I was about to return home to fetch it when I remembered that I had a couple of old cards from Peru and Brazil, which I kept for sentimental reasons. I gave the guard my Peruvian diplomatic driving licence, with its coloured photo of myself against the national flag, hoping he wouldn't notice. I wasn't prepared for his reaction. Jumping up, he saluted smartly and put my card in a special box with only two or three cards in it.

The same adulation occurred when I claimed my card at the end of the day, except that the other two guards now jumped up and saluted as well. I glanced at the one remaining card in the box – it looked just like mine. What *was* this: Friends of Peru Day? Then I saw that it was the party card for high-ranking FRELIMO officials. I was never without my Peruvian driving licence thereafter. It really was a trump card – especially as most law enforcers were illiterate.

There was no question but that Maputo was the safest town we had ever lived in. No-one in their senses would have walked through Kingston, or Lima, or Recife alone at night, but neither we nor our kids had any fear of returning on foot from a cinema or party in the small hours. I never heard of anyone being mugged, but I suppose the virtual absence of tourists and the plethora of police may have helped. It was the non-official busybodies and vigilantes that were the most likely to cause trouble.

BOTHERATION AT THE BORDER

Mozambique, like other Marxist states, was an economic as well as a political prison. Darting across the border to the well-stocked shops in Swaziland and South Africa was a privilege denied to ordinary citizens and to foreign *co-operantes* who had no diplomatic licence. In any case, neither Swaziland nor South Africa extended their hospitality to members of Eastern Bloc countries, diplomatic or otherwise.

At first, FAO families had no difficulty in leaving the country whenever the UN office gave permission, but a sudden decision by Government, to make each Ministry responsible for the movements of its own foreign staff, drastically changed the picture. Instead of asking the UN for an exit permit, we now had to make lengthy and detailed requests to Protocol on the fourth floor of the Ministry for each journey. Unfortunately, the diplomatic differentiation between a Cuban *co-operante* and an FAO expert entirely escaped them. *All* foreigners were *co-operantes*, and none was entitled to special favours.

We took our grievance to the UN Res Rep. He was sorry, but this was a Government decision. All he could do was to write to the Minister. Meanwhile, the answer from Protocol was always the same. We worked for the Ministry of Agriculture and must abide by their rules.

'Anyway, you went to Swaziland last month. Sorry. Your request has been refused.'

I wanted to scream that it was no bloody business of theirs how many times I went to Swaziland. Instead, I could only insist that my *Laissez Passer* gave me special privileges.

'Sorry, *camarada*. All *co-operantes* are treated the same.'

'For the hundredth time, I am *not* a *co-operante*; I am a senior official of the United Nations and...'

'Then you should go to Foreign Affairs. Sorry. Next.'

It took several months to convince Foreign Affairs to treat us like other United Nations officials. We were greatly relieved. Not only us. Purchasing goods for non-diplomatic friends, although in contravention of our diplomatic concession, was impossible to refuse. A *co-operante* wanted a bottle of wine or whisky to celebrate his birthday, or the mother of one of the children's friends wanted some toiletries or medicines.

'I'll pay you in escudos,' they'd say, 'I have no rand, and I don't suppose you want Bulgarian levs?'

Ministry officials were not above asking favours.

'My tape-recorder needs repair,' explained the Director of Protocol.

577

'Could you see whether they can fix it in Nelspruit?'

I seldom charged. It gave me that bit more of a lean on them. Not exactly bribery – more of a 'Comrades' agreement!

Their gratitude was usually sincere, but there were exceptions. One obnoxious official asked me to buy him a pair of dark glasses – he had lost his and he wanted a pair urgently. I had a lot of trouble finding his special type, and they set me back 24 rand, a tidy sum in those days.

I found him in his office. 'Here are your glasses. You owe me six hundred escudos,' I told him. He was one person who wasn't going to get them free.

'Oh, I found my old pair so I don't need new ones,' he replied offhandedly. No thanks, no apologies, no suggestion that it was his moral obligation to reimburse me!

We lived for these monthly excursions, rushing across the border as soon as it opened, to make sure of a large breakfast at a Holiday Inn. But even after our upgrading to diplomatic status, the trips were not without tension. Road blocks, where young armed soldiers would sometimes make us unpack the car, even after I had pointed out the United Nations sticker on our windscreen, were always a bit unnerving, and health or customs officials could often throw a hammer and sickle in the works. A yellow fever or cholera vaccination certificate, not required previously, would suddenly be demanded. We never knew whether we would be able to pick up the kids from school that day, as arranged, or have to try again the next. It was extremely frustrating.

Occasionally, for no apparent reason, the formalities were unbelievably lax. One morning, I chased Mary all the way to the border after I had found she had left her passport on her dressing table. There was no sign of her at the border post. She's probably having a coffee with Herman and Ineke before returning to Maputo, I thought, but I'll check the immigration officials, just in case.

'Oh yes, sir. Your wife went through half an hour ago. Yes, it was unfortunate that she forgot her passport, but she had an old one, and we know her well.'

Evidently the Swazis were just as co-operative on the other side. But then, Mary had a way with her. It wouldn't have happened with me!

We made many friends in Mbabane. Dick and Biddy, our dentist and his wife, Bernie and Daphne, who loaded us up with crates of bibles to smuggle across for a Mozambique church, and Martyn and Juanita of the beef production project. They, and Ted's family which had remained in Mbabane while Ted commuted back and forth each fortnight, often played innkeepers to our gang.

Less frequently, we shopped at Nelspruit in South Africa. Many of the shops spoke only Afrikaans and were less than polite if we were in company of dusky diplomats on a similar shopping spree. A check-out girl nearly fainted when Mary embraced the very chic, chocolate Ambassadress of a former French Central African state, whom we bumped into in a supermarket.

Another time we met a black youth who had been at St Mark's with our kids. No sooner had we greeted him than two brawny, pudding-faced, white policemen came up and stood behind us, arms folded, legs astride. It was clear that such inter-racial *tête-à-tête*s were *verbode* in their country and might land our friend in trouble, so we wished him a hasty farewell. Things were like that in the Transvaal in 1978.

After a year or two, the sense of escape and of freedom which we had felt when we had first left Communist soil began to fade. The eagerness and anticipation with which we contemplated a few hours in a normal, free, capitalistic society waned, and we found that we were looking forward to our return to Mozambique, Marxism or not. Mozambique may have had shortages, we may not have liked her politics and been frustrated with a thousand things, but it was quiet and had, anyway for us as UN members, a feeling of security. Sports facilities may have been inadequate, and tennis balls and flood lamps hard to replace, but the people were polite and friendly, and drunks, who seemed to populate Mbabane's streets at the end of the day, were almost unknown in Maputo.

Mozambican officials, too, from the police to the post office, while often illiterate, uncomprehending and stupid, were usually cheerful and often charming. And then there was our lovely house and lots of friends to welcome us. Mozambique was beginning to feel like home.

FAGIN'S FOLLOWERS

Marxism, for all its sharing of amenities, didn't necessarily make a person more honest. In fact, the economic effect of the system often made thieving the only means of survival.

Several times street urchins had scrambled in through our windows. Those we caught we handed over to the police, but they were back on the street a couple of days later. Crime in a Communist state, it seemed, was only of importance if it involved politics.

Lys had taken over the local ballet school while she waited to enter university. She took her responsibilities very seriously. I returned one evening to find her almost hysterical.

'Dad, what have you done with my tape recorder? I'm LATE. Why does everyone take my things and NOT PUT THEM BACK?'

I disclaimed any knowledge of her machine and lent her mine. Later, I found that my briefcase was not in its usual place. It contained my passport and *Laissez Passer*, my diary, address book, draft of a short story and some foreign currency. It was now dark. I took a torch and scoured the wasteland outside our garden wall. I found nothing.

Next morning, as the red gold orb of the sun broke the surface of the glassy sea, I set out to search once more. Road sweepers and garbage collectors were active. I told them that there was a reward for a briefcase and a tape recorder. For two hours I combed the scrub within half a kilometre of the house before leaving for the office, angry and depressed. I had now realized that my precious 'ideas' notebook for the last two years was also in the missing case, as well as a recent batch of photos, cheque books on local and foreign accounts, and two half-finished poems.

Around mid-morning, while trying to make some sense of a circular from Rome, there occurred what I can only describe as a tap on the brain, followed by the words 'abandoned house'. This I took to mean the partially built, four-storey construction almost opposite our house, in which the children often played. Of course, why hadn't I thought of it before?

Within minutes I was home. It was a Saturday morning and the twins, with several school friends, were playing in front of the house on skateboards.

'Come with me,' I said. 'I may need your help. But be quiet.'

We tiptoed into the doorless, windowless shell and up the rough concrete stairs. No-one was on the first floor, but Carlitos, a 12-year-old Colombian lad held a finger to his lips and pointed over his head. We crept up to the second floor. Now I could hear it, children's laughter on the floor above.

We rushed into the room together. Two small boys were rifling through my briefcase. Precious papers were scattered over the floor. The immediate cause of merriment was some photos of Mary and I in fancy dress. We grabbed the young thieves and hauled them downstairs to my car. Carlitos and Shivy, thoroughly enjoying their roles as thief catchers, held them in the back seat while we sped to the nearest police station.

The miscreants insisted that they had found my case in the building, but that they knew who had stolen it and where he lived. The police agreed to pick him up if I could supply the transport. His house was on a rough sandy track at the very end of Costa da Sol. Of course, he wasn't there.

Our three young thieves, now eagerly co-operative, helped us to round up other urchins from mud-hutted slums, and from the abandoned half of the semi-detached house, where Roger and Pru lived.

A few items of small value lay scattered amongst empty tins of imported foods. There was also a map of the Somerschield residential area with 'X's here and there, presumably marking past or future victims.

'I thought there were rather a lot of stray kids around at night,' said Pru. 'That probably accounts for the footsteps running up and down stairs.'

It was a typical Fagin-type operation. We all knew the supposedly blind, dark-spectacled beggar who tapped his way from door to door, accompanied by a small boy as guide. It turned out that it was we who were the 'blind' ones. He used his sharp, shielded eyes to look in through the open door and gauge the value of the contents inside. Sometimes, while being attended to at the front door, one of his youthful gang would slip in through a rear window. The police eventually apprehended him, but never recovered Lys' tape recorder.

The day ended on an amusing note – for us, anyway. Before leaving the *Posto Polícia*, late that afternoon, where five or six errant urchins were lined up in front of the corporal, Shivy nudged me and whispered,

'Daddy, I want my jeans; he's wearing them.' She pointed at a skinny youth.

'How can you prove it?' I asked.

'My name is written inside, and so is Ntewane's.' Ntewane was the youngest son of President Samora Machel, and one of Shivy's greatest buddies.

The policeman ordered the boy to disrobe. Sure enough, both Shivy's and Ntewane's names were inscribed in blue biro inside the waistband. He handed the jeans to Shivy.

'What will happen to these kids?' I asked him.

'Depends on you,' he replied.

I would have liked to have taken them home and given them a meal, but under the circumstances that would have been impossible.

'Let them go,' I said. 'They've been well frightened.'

'Yes,' he agreed. 'We have nowhere to put them anyway.'

He gave them a last glower. 'Out,' he bawled, pointing at the door. The small band fell over themselves as they scrambled through the door – all except one, who was trying to hide his nakedness with outspread fingers.

'Out,' roared the corporal again, and the last we saw of our pant-less friend was a black bottom disappearing into the dusk.

But by far the most spectacular *coup* was carried out entirely by our children.

Mary was in Swaziland, and I had gone out after supper to finalize arrangements for a field trip the next day. Half an hour later, returning home along Avenida Julius Nyerere, I beheld a motley group of kids, led by a vociferous, stick-swinging, bikini-clad, nine-year-old girl – to wit Shivy, accompanied by an AK47-armed policeman, driving three half-naked men before them, one of whom was limping.

'What the hell's going on?' I shouted, drawing in to the curb.

'Daddy! We've caught three burglars,' Shivy screamed in delight. 'We're taking them to the *Posto*.' And the band continued down the road to the office of the law, in high glee and with much noise.

I sped off home. Lindley, now 17, was in a highly nervous state. I hugged her as she blurted out what had happened.

'I looked out of the drawing room window just after you left and saw some men crawling across the lawn on their hands and knees. I rushed out to the front and told the policeman who was guarding the Swiss Embassy, but he said it wasn't his responsibility.'

With no help from the Embassy guard, she called Shivy and Coro, who were doing homework in their room, and the three of them ran into the street and screamed '*Ladrões*, thieves, help.' The area erupted. Just up the road was a large block of flats in which lived many of their teenage friends. Windows opened, encouragements were shouted, motorcycle engines roared, and within seconds a dozen excited youths had rushed to the rescue.

One thief was caught in the garden, another in the bushes outside, and a third, who had sprinted up the road in panic, was flushed out from under a parked car and then run down by one of the youths on his motorbike. Talk about Emil and the Detectives! I felt very proud of our lot!

The miscreants were certainly locked up for a time, but were seen a few weeks later on the street again. Possibly the re-education camps were over-full, or housebreaking was a minor offence unworthy of further moral indoctrination.

We took extra precautions after that, not entirely successful. Six months later we were again relieved of jewellery, tapes and a camera while out to dinner. But that, we figured, was about par for the course.

582

SURVIVAL OF THE FITTEST

'If you want to survive in Mozambique,' everyone told us, 'stay clear of army vehicles and Russian doctors.'

They weren't joking. The main reason for our need to cross the border at any time was medical emergencies. There was nothing basically wrong with the Medical Services in Maputo, except lack of experienced doctors, scarcity of medicines and the fact that all doctors (together with lawyers and undertakers) had been nationalized. The deficiency in medicos was alleviated by the influx of practitioners from other nations, especially Russia and, later, Cuba. But it was wise to avoid them if possible; they were mostly young and inexperienced. Those of some other nationalities, however, were excellent.

One morning Mary scratched her eyeball while pruning the hedge. It was very painful, so I took her to the Ophthalmic clinic. She was given an 'emergency' card with 232 on it and joined an immense queue. Five hours and several queues later, she was attended to. The Portuguese specialist was gentle and efficient and gave her the right dope. Her eye recovered quickly.

My own experience was also highly satisfactory. Collapsing on return from Muabsa and finding my pulse rapid and as irregular as a dog's, I rang my secretary's husband, Carlos, Dean of Medicine and Professor of Cardiology.

Carlos had studied at Groote Schuur hospital in Cape Town, where Chris Barnard had performed the world's first heart transplant. Slim, dark, balding, with an energetic walk and quick movements, he had kept as up to date as circumstances would allow. He took his work with quite unusual dedication. Not only did he teach, conduct clinics and supervise research, pedalling his bicycle to the hospital at all hours and in all weathers but, as Dean, he had to serve on numerous committees and cope with insoluble problems caused by shortages, ignorance and the dogma of a Marxist state. He would criticize both Communist and capitalist medicine with equal vehemence when he thought it necessary, and his comments were always positive, practical and nearly always listened to by the authorities.

Perhaps his most outstanding contribution to Mozambique's health was his pioneering of the 'Essential Drugs Scheme'. This scheme, initiated by the UN General Assembly in 1978, called for Third World countries to limit their importations to the really essential medicines and then only in the form and strength which cost the least. Injections, drops and syrups, except for emergencies and the treatment of young children, were discouraged since these cost up to 30 times more than tablets. So successful was the scheme that

Mozambique was able to import six times the quantity of drugs in 1980, for the same amount they had paid two years before. Considering that each Mozambican's slice of the medical budget was only 50 cents per annum, this was no small consideration.

But back to my troublesome ticker. The day after my collapse, I visited Carlos' clinic for an ECG.

'You have a supraventricular tachycardia, or non-sinus rhythm. Your left ventricle is only beating occasionally, it's the atria of your heart that are pumping the blood round.'

He gave me some pills, but after three weeks my heart was still out of rhythm and I felt tired and depressed.

'We'll try an electro-cardio-reversion on you. Come to the cardiology ward on Tuesday morning. You'll be home by evening with a normal beat.'

The procedure, so beloved by producers of resuscitation scenes on television, sends a very high amp shock through the heart, the jolt being synchronized with a certain stage of the heartbeat. An injection had made me dopey but not dopey enough to ignore the two heavy metal plates which were put on my chest or shrug off the 25-pound sledgehammer which lifted me a foot off the bed.

'All over,' grinned Carlos. The 10 or 12 final-year students who had been watching were also smiling. They had never seen an electrocution before. Beside me the monitor screen showed a perfectly regular beat.

I always had a guilty feeling that many of our unimportant ailments, however uncomfortable, might be taking up the time and facilities of the over-stretched medical facilities which could have been better spent on more serious cases.

Then I had a brainwave. 'Why not,' I suggested in a letter to the UN Res Rep, 'have our own medical staff? We now have over fifty families and we are growing every day. Surely our own doctor or, at the very least, a nurse, who could filter out the headaches from the heart attacks, and so reduce the time-consuming trek to the clinics, is justified?'

After some discussion, the UN agreed to appoint a registered nurse, and added a cherry on top by seconding my proposal of Pru, Roger's Canadian trained wife, to fill the position.

If my most valuable contribution to animal health in Mozambique had been to convince the powers that Roger was their man for the Veterinary Research Institute, without any doubt my most appreciated social contribution to the UN family was my proposal of Pru as their nursing sister.

Solid and unflappable, Pru moved in an aura of quiet confidence.

584

The same effortless efficiency with which she had organized those five-day fishing trips for 20 people to Half Moon Cay in Jamaica, she again produced for us in Maputo. UNICEF made a suite available in their offices, equipment was bought, and Pru was in business. As the wife of a UN official confided to me soon afterwards, 'Pru has only to come through the door and your child is already better.'

Teeth were a separate problem. No private dentists existed, so the only recourse for a throbbing molar if you weren't able to cross the border, was to queue up early, before the sun rose (like one does for Wimbledon), to be sure of being treated that day.

Roger, who could well have sought succour in Swaziland or South Africa, decided to try the local skills instead of his usual fang-fixer in Mbabane.

After an hour of queuing in the street, he reached a white-coated attendant who asked his complaint. Roger tapped a molar. The attendant pointed to another queue leading to a surgery. Here, a dentist examined him, said it had to come out, gave him a note and pointed to a third queue. Half an hour later, he found himself in a chair, his mouth open, waiting for an injection.

As soon as the procaine was in his gum, he was given another note and joined yet another – the extraction queue. A few minutes late he was out in the street, minus his molar.

'How was it?' I asked him the next day.

'Not bad, but I've still got toothache. I'm not sure they took out the right one!'

THE MILKATEERS

Staffing the Project was like playing the children's game of 'General Post'. Ted had left for the Western Pacific, and Don, his Chilean replacement, had arrived, proud of his Scottish name and tam-o'-shanter, neither of which accorded with his Latin tongue.

George, John's Associate in tsetse and trypanosomiasis control, a husky five-foot-ten Sierra Leonese with a double-barrelled English name, a PhD, German wife and small son, had swept in and was now installed at the Muabsa Research and Training Centre.

Guy and his whistling Associate were back in Europe, leaving the Mozambiquan pastures much as they had found them. Two other pasture agronomists had come, Jim, a tall Kenyan range management specialist, too well-built to be termed lanky, with clean-cut features reminiscent of the recruiting adverts for the RAF; and Henri, specializing in cultivated pastures, a hefty, bubbling *bon viveur* giant, French from his bushy brown beard to his tattered flip-flops.

Unlike Guy, Henri was gregarious, especially with the fairer sex, but he had the same tendency to *wanderlust* as his predecessor. Hardly a weekend went by without him contriving some excuse to visit Swaziland or South Africa. I ran into him one day in Swaziland, driving an official project car with the circular blue UN emblem on the doors. He hadn't mentioned his visit, and I hadn't authorized his use of the project vehicle. Silly bastard, I thought, he could have saved me a journey.

'*Ça va*,' I greeted him. 'What are you doing here?'

'Dentist. Terrible toothache.' He rubbed his jaw cheerfully.

'Where's your own car?' Journeys for personal reasons were done in the expert's private car, unless in emergencies.

'Clutch broke. I'll get the spares while I'm here.'

'Fair enough,' I told him. 'Good luck. See you soon.'

'Day after tomorrow, for sure, Pat.'

Five days later, Henri was still missing. I rang the FAO office in Mbabane, in case he was having a rough time with his teeth. Nobody had seen him. I might have known.

At the end of the week, in walked a smiling, sunburnt Henri, full of the joys of fornication and luxurious living.

'Where the hell have you been?' I was decidedly peeved. He'd missed several field trips, and I had been placating people all week with whom he had arranged meetings. A week was a long time to spend at the dentist. Anyway, visits outside the country had to have UN approval. His hadn't.

'Had to go to Durban, Pat. Dentists in Swaziland all fully booked.'

'Good God, man. You took a UN vehicle with UN insignia on it through South Africa? Are you crazy?' This could have led to serious diplomatic complications.

'Sorry, Pat. Had to get my tooth fixed, and you should see the girls on Durban's beaches! Zut!'

But you couldn't be angry with Henri for long, he was far too bubbling a character.

Sometimes, however, his ebullient humour was a little too French.

'Close the windows a moment, I hear a rattle,' he told us one day on a field trip.

Tilak, Rudi and I obediently wound up the car windows and listened. We heard no rattles. Then a ghastly stench assailed us. Henri had farted!

* * *

586

Tilak, now working in the Ministry as an FAO employee under the Mozambique Nordic Aid Programme, MONAP, aided by Henri's wide knowledge of tropical pastures and Rudi's long experience of Third World dairying procedures, attacked the urgent problem of milk production. The former milk collection centres were resuscitated, and additional metal rondavels equipped with kerosene refrigerators were placed in the peasant farming area around Maputo as collecting points. The sides of the rondavels were painted with gay Egyptian-like frescos of cows being milked and farmers bringing the churns to the collection point. Each farmer was issued with one or more five-litre churns.

Irish Overseas Aid financed an art competition for young scholars who dramatically depicted their ideas of milk production. Prizes were awarded and the results exhibited in the foyer of the Ministry.

There was opposition – the most severe, surprisingly, came from the one entity which should have given us the most support, the organization in charge of all milk and dairy production – the State Milk Enterprise.

'It's political,' Tilak told us. 'The Minister doesn't agree with collecting milk from individual peasant farmers. It doesn't conform to the political view of State Farms and Cooperatives. It is too much like private enterprise.'

'Ridiculous,' Rudi countered. 'If there are no incentives, there'll never be any milk. Look at what's happening on the State Farms, calf deaths eighty per cent of births, cows producing less than a fifth of their potential. No-one cares.'

To placate the authorities, the peasants were formed into co-operatives. A co-operative was an accepted Marxist structure, so all future references to peasant milk collection used the word 'co-operative' instead of 'scheme'.

Milk collection grew rapidly, and within a year all accusations of private enterprise and deviation from the Party line had been drowned in the 12,000 litres of milk which were being delivered daily to the processing plant in Matola. Milk collection was now given top priority.

Apart from collecting milk, top priority had also to be given to producing it at low cost. The 'Milkateers', Tilak, Henri and Rudi, realized that this 'Low-cost Milk Production' had to be done on pasture alone, without any supplements other than silage or hay, which only the State Farms had facilities to make. After satisfying human consumption, surplus grains went to monogastric livestock such as pigs and poultry, which could utilize them far more efficiently than ruminants, but were, in turn, poor utilizers of grass.

Water was vital. When there were good rains, pastures flourished,

587

but in the annual dry season only expensive irrigation could keep them growing. Henri and Tilak suggested that if they could extend the life of the pasture grasses into the dry season, it would go a long way towards closing the annual grazing gap. Their solution was to sow a mixture of tropical forage legumes into the existing pasture. Legumes such as *Siratro, Desmodium, Glycine* and *Stylosanthes*, to name a few, all of which we had used with success at Pucallpa in the Amazon jungle. These bushy plants were high in protein and stimulated the growth of the pastures into which they were sown by building up nitrogen in the soil, thus extending the grazing period for six weeks or more into the dry season.

They called this cocktail of legumes LEMIX – a word that soon became synonymous with good pastures. In addition, they planted small copses of browse – palatable shrubs and trees – especially *Leucaena*, on which the animals could nibble when the pasture gave out.

Averaged over the year, these 'reinforced' pastures could support three times as many cows as could grass alone. Judged by the maxim, 'He who can make two cows graze where only one grazed before, is a national hero' (an adaptation of Jonathan Swift's '...two ears of corn and two blades of grass'), both Henri and Tilak qualified as 'Heroes of the People's Republic'!

The pasture work was an outstanding success. So was the milk collection – up to the point when the FAO assistance ceased and the embryonic cooperative came under the direct control of the State Milk Enterprise. Thereafter, with no FAO funds to help out, the refrigeration machinery rapidly ceased to function, transport to the milk plant continually broke down, and seed distribution and technical assistance to the farmers stopped. A severe drought over southern Africa and an epizootic of Foot and Mouth disease also contributed to the difficulties, but these calamities simply emphasized the weakness of any scheme for producing a perishable product like milk, from rain-dependant pastures with no extension service to fall back on.

However, we had shown that it *was* possible for small farmers to produce milk profitably, *if* they were integrated into a comprehensive agricultural infrastructure. Admittedly, a very large 'if'.

AN OUTCAST SHEPHERDESS

Native breeds of sheep and goats can usually live on a few tufts of grass, a handful of leaves or a page or two of newspaper when scavenging the bush in twos and threes, but once they are herded into paddocks or housed, they often succumb to worms, pneumonias and the fatal, tick-transmitted disease, heartwater.

Karl, the FAO Expert in small ruminants, a tall, angular West German with close-cut hair the colour of his steel-rimmed spectacles, was trying to revive what was left of the sheep and goat industry, decimated by the FRELIMO war. FRELIMO guerillas, apparently, found small ruminants easier to catch and cook than cattle. Their RENAMO (*Resistência Nacional de Moçambique* – the Resistance Movement) successors found the same!

A centre for small ruminants was established to develop the national flocks. The foundation animals, collected from livestock stations throughout the country, arrived in terrible condition, some so weak that the mere act of vaccination killed them. Many died within the first weeks of arrival.

But disease was not the only enemy. From the start, a personal animosity developed between Karl and the attractive, dark-skinned lady veterinarian responsible for small ruminants in the Ministry. Whether it was something indiscreet that Karl had said to her, or because he was apt to push his ideas forward without first asking her opinion (she was a vet, he wasn't), the result was a total break-down of communication between the two. Meetings arranged by Karl were ignored, leaving him no option but to take decisions by himself and, of course, the full blast for the calamities that frequently followed.

The arrival of his German Associate Expert, Christiana, didn't help to ease matters, either. With auburn hair swept into a bun from her high forehead, a half-surprised look on her thin face as if she had been told something quite unbelievable, she had already experienced more drama than most 24-year-olds.

Finding herself cut-off in East Germany with half her family in the West, she did what many others had done; she tried to escape. Unluckily, she was caught. Luckily, she avoided being shot and spent a year in an East German jail. An offer of tractors in exchange for political prisoners released her to the West. She applied for a job in FAO, and soon afterwards, by what can only be described as unbelievable insensitivity, FAO posted her – an Eastern renegade – to Marxist Mozambique, a country full of rabid East Germans, Russians and Cubans. As can be imagined, her background did not endear her to the more fanatical Reds in the Ministry, a group which included our lady of the small ruminants, who now had an additional grudge to add to her list against Karl.

We sent Christiana to Cabo Delgado to develop the sheep and goat industry in the far north, where a derelict livestock station at Napa, 150 kilometres inland from Pemba, had been marked for the purpose. Almost immediately, she ran foul of the authorities. Whenever she wished to visit Napa or other places from her base in Pemba, she had to beg a Land Rover from the District Agricultural office. One particular day, the driver was to pick her up at seven. At midday came apologies and a promise that the vehicle would be ready by two. At five-thirty it arrived and they set off.

Halfway to Napa, the driver began to doze and nearly ran off the road. Christiana, obligingly, took over. She was even less lucky. Rounding a sharp corner, she skidded on the gravel surface and landed in the ditch. No-one was hurt, but the Land Rover was badly damaged and official ire was raised to boiling point. It was absolutely forbidden, they told her, to drive a Government vehicle without written permission. She would have to pay for the repairs – over a period of years on her meagre salary.

It was obviously the moment to exercise my skills of deception; I couldn't allow such an innocent, well-intentioned act to have such devastating consequences. We had the vehicle shipped to Maputo where, by sleight of figures and budget fiddles (second nature to Project Managers), and by Fernanda's dexterous accounting, we managed to hide the repair bill both from the Government and from Rome.

Poor Christiana. Her stock was now very low. But she battled on, and one day came the news that she had married a young accountant in the district headquarters. Only a few of the bravest dared to congratulate the couple. How could they applaud a good 'comrade's' marriage to an unrepentant capitalist who had actually escaped from the paternal protection of the East German State?

Karl's work made good progress until the internal opposition became too much and he requested a transfer. Although we lost a good man, there *was* one reason for which I was heartily glad to see the last of him. He may have been a good expert but he was, undoubtedly, the world's worst driver. Those early trips with Dr Joaquim were funeral processions in comparison. Karl drove like a maniac – every road was a one-way street, the way he happened to be going. I was terrified that he would kill himself or others, to say nothing of writing off one of our limited fleet of project vehicles. But apart from terrorizing motorists and pedestrians in both Mozambique and Swaziland, he only managed to destroy the gearbox of his own car.

A SMATTERING OF ARTS. LINDLEY RESCUED

Outside office hours, life was pleasant enough.

'Thank God for the Polana hotel,' we would say ten times a week. All we had to do for an early-morning game of tennis was to skirt the excavations and mounds of building materials that were scattered round the half-finished, three-storey mansion on the other side of the road, and walk up through the hotel's kitchen garden to the Polana's courts. At six in the morning, there was nobody about except João, the gardener, flashing the gaudy wristwatch which Mary had given him for Christmas. After a set or two, we would walk round to the front lawn of the hotel, peel down to our swimming costumes and plunge into the pool. What a way to start the day!

The Polana helped fill the gap left by the closure of the English club. We could entertain there or drop in for a drink or dinner or the 'Sunday afternoon tea' ritual, especially popular with the small group of remaining Portuguese. But other expatriates, German, Dutch, French, Hungarian, also regarded the Polana as their club. Soon the facilities became overextended and the hotel authorities had no option but to close the Polana's amenities to outsiders. Their quota of liquor, and other luxuries, could barely meet the demands of the *bona fide* guests. The Polana became 'out of bounds'.

Although there was an eight-court tennis club below the radio station, four kilometres away, it didn't open in the early morning. The *Clube Naval* below our house, although it didn't have courts, had a large swimming pool, so we forsook the Polana, played at the tennis club on Saturdays and Sundays and swam at the *Clube Naval*.

Wisely, the Government kept the cinemas open and well supplied, and even if many of the films were second-rate French, Italian and Indian productions, they acted as a pleasant safety valve for the daily frustrations of the populace. There was no T.V.

For the first time we had hit a country without an active theatre – professional or amateur. An occasional singer might give a patriotic recital, or there would be an exhibition of tribal dancing, or a politically motivated show, but, to my knowledge, no plays of any sort were ever performed. The nearest we came to Thespian activities was the occasional play reading in a private drawing-room, but without the British Council or any library, scripts were difficult to come by until the Theatre Club in Mbabane agreed to supply us.

Art exhibitions were just as scarce. Few artists had remained in Mozambique, and the only paintings or carvings one saw 'were outside the hotels or in the market, or when a hawker knocked on the door. Most paintings were brightly coloured harlequin designs on

591

wood, and the carvings either masks or grotesque statuettes in strange-smelling woods. When a Centre for Artisans was established, where they could exhibit their creations, it provided the only art gallery in the city and, of course, tripled the prices of the *objêts d'art.*

The doyen of the internationally established artists who had remained in Mozambique, Senhor Malangatana, lived in a sandy backstreet on the outskirts of Maputo. A mezzanine ran along two sides of his high-roofed studio, the walls of which were covered by huge gaily coloured mosaics of tortured faces and tangled bodies. The American lady who took me to see him had commissioned a seascape which the portly, grey-haired *maestro* had nearly completed. I could just recognize a boat amongst all the surrealistic shapes, but it was immensely colourful.

* * *

The children's holiday travel sometimes became a major hassle. The finishing school Lindley attended in Lausanne booked her flight, unknown to us, via Tanzania. Tanzania, everyone knew, was to be avoided at all costs.

We met the connecting plane she should have taken from Johannesburg. No Lindley. Panic. Late that evening the phone rang.

'This is Mrs Stanley in Dar-es-Salaam. I have Lindley with me so don't worry. She'll be on Tuesday's flight to Maputo.'

Lindley's tale was scary. She had arrived in Dar on a Saturday afternoon, to find that the connecting flight to Maputo had been cancelled. Furthermore, immigration would not allow her out of the airport since she had several South African entry stamps in her passport from trips to Nelspruit with us. Any connection at all with South Africa was unforgivable. The next flight to Maputo was on Tuesday.

There were no facilities at the airport, no accommodation, no food and doubtful water. Flies and mosquitoes were abundant. As the afternoon wore on she became more and more desperate, especially as there seemed to be a large number of African loiterers, many apparently drunk who were obviously interested in this lost white girl. Finally, she decided to ignore immigration and sneaking out of the building she hitch-hiked into Dar.

Her first objective was the UN, but the guard said they were shut and refused to call anyone. The British Embassy, likewise, told her to come back on Monday. A more mature or experienced person would have insisted that an official be found, but for a very naive and inexperienced seventeen year old there was nothing to do but to hitchhike back to the airport and await the Tuesday flight without food or accommodation.

Luckily, towards evening she noticed a lady reading a copy of the *Weekly Times*.

'Are you English?' she asked hesitantly, trying to keep back her tears.

The lady looked at her haughtily. 'Of course I am. What's the matter?'

Lindley told her.

'Damn disgrace. As soon as my husband arrives, I'll take you home. I know the UN and Embassy officials very well. Don't worry about immigration.'

The most delightful part of the whole affair, Lindley said, was listening to Mrs Stanley tell the UN and British Embassy exactly what she thought of them.

'THEY LITTLE KNOW OF ENGLAND...'

Eighteen months after my arrival, on my 58th birthday, I waved goodbye to Mary and the kids and boarded a plane to Rome, content that the project was off to a good start and could only get better. That, of course, was before the Cubans arrived.

I had a glorious week in the Italian capital, meeting old friends, and sipping *cappuccinos* on FAO's rooftop cafeteria where I could look down over the ruins of the oval chariot track, the Circo Maximo, and the hot baths of Caracalla. It was easy to imagine the Roman elite discussing 'form' while they soaked themselves in the marble-lined pools. As always, the atmosphere of this Mediterranean city, the gaiety of its curbside *trattorias*, and the sculptured reminders of its long history, stirred a romance within me that no other city could.

A week later I was in England to spend a couple of weeks with Shannon, Lys and Kerry, and to look for possible houses against the time four years hence, when I was due to retire. England inspired a different set of feelings to Italy, a sense of orderliness and common sense, of social responsibility under a well-oiled and sympathetic administration, and in the countryside, a deep harmony with nature.

I drove the hired car from Heathrow to my friend's cottage amongst the trees and meadows of a secluded Surrey hamlet. It was a late June evening, and already the first star had appeared. Birds were still chirping, lazily, otherwise all was still. Even the traffic on the

593

secondary road, half a mile away, seemed hushed and unhurried. Lights from neighbouring parlours twinkled between the trees.

My friend was out. A note on the door told me that beer was in the fridge and that we would eat later at the pub. No-one, apparently, bothered to lock their doors in this part of the country.

I walked to the garden fence. A meadow of tall grass stretched to a far line of beeches: timothy, foxtail, cocksfoot, freckled with wild flowers now almost colourless in the fading light. A mare and her foal raised their heads at my approach.

Slipping through the wire, I flung myself face down into the green-scented carpet.

'They little know of England, who only England know,' I murmured. It was a moment of intense and aching satisfaction and love of heritage, like sipping an elixir distilled from the pens of John Moore, H.E. Bates and Laurie Lee. Nothing in the world could touch the magic of an English summer evening, especially if you were returning from another planet – Mozambique.

COMRADES LOVE COMMITTEES

A few weeks after I returned from leave, Carlos announced that 40 Cubans were coming to join us. 'Some are vets, others farm managers. We must decide how we can best use them.'

I was elated. We urgently needed more professionals to train our field staff. Soon, the corridors were thick with pungent cigar smoke and loud voices. On the whole, they were a jolly, 'hail fellow, well met' lot, but it was their influence on the administration and livestock policy that was so disastrous.

Their daily lives appeared to be dominated by party political commissars, and their professional opinions by their 'Little Blue Book'. Like Comrade Mao's little red one, the blue version gave procedures to be followed in all animal health situations. Since the book had been compiled for use in Cuba, which had few epizootics, it entirely ignored Africa's lavish contribution to the catalogue of devastating diseases which might be encountered in Mozambique. Their conception of pasture production also showed their lack of adaptation to local conditions. In Cuba, land is at a premium, pastures have to be intensively managed and full use made of sugar-cane tops and other cultivated forages. In Mozambique, land was almost unrestricted, and grazing, even if sometimes poor, was unlimited. Furthermore, there were no easily available forage crops other than grass. We continually found ourselves at odds with their recommendations.

But our biggest grouse at the Cuban invasion was the further loss of direct contact with our Ministry counterparts. I already had difficulty in arranging meetings with Carlos, now I found there was a Cuban through whom all approaches to the Director would have to be made. It was as if FAO was no longer trusted.

Since other Project Managers were suffering in the same way, we decided to ask the Minister if we could meet with him, informally, once a month, so that he could brief us on developments, and we could tell him how our work was progressing, without the cumbersome Cuban connection. To my surprise he agreed, so together with the other five Project Managers I walked up to the fourth floor on the appointed day and were shown into the conference room with a table the size of a yacht's deck.

'T'would have been a sight more cosy in his office,' I commented. I was wrong. It would have been far too cosy. About half an hour later, 25 officials, some we'd never seen before, filed in, shaking hands with each of us before taking their seats. The small, friendly, *tête-à-tête* we had anticipated was clearly not to be!

'This will be a shambles,' whispered Renato, an Italian Project Manager.

His opinion was soon confirmed. The Minister's deputy entered, apologized for the delay and told us that as the Minister had been called away, he would take his place. He then asked each Project Manager to give a progress report. When the last of us had had his say, he asked whether any of the Ministry officials had any questions. There were none. He then thanked us for doing a magnificent job and the meeting closed.

'What was all that about, then?' asked Jim, the Irish Land Use Project manager.

'God knows,' I replied. 'Bloody waste of an afternoon.'

We tried several more times to talk to the Minister, as a small group, but to no avail. *Tête-à-têtes* simply weren't the way things were done in Communist countries!

The constant succession of lengthy, unproductive meetings was a bane of Ministry life. *Reuniaões* were called at all hours without notice or agenda.

One Thursday, Carlos rang to say that the Minister required the next year's estimates by Monday. There would be a *reunião* in the morning to consider the draft proposals. Could I have mine ready by then?

I spent the rest of the day and half the night making a resumé of our programmes with costs, staffing and general objectives. Friday morning, we sat from nine till six in the evening, while each section head went through the details of his work. Poultry specialists listened in bored silence to details of milk and beef production or tsetse control measures until they, in turn, had an opportunity to bore everyone else with their own statistics of eggs and broiler production.

On Saturday, Rudi and I left before breakfast for Namaacha, to see the reconstructed cattle sheds and discuss the extension of the forage areas. Afterwards, we called at the Lubombo Hotel for a beer.

'I've a tennis game this afternoon,' I explained, refusing a second bottle.

I had left my car at the Ministry. As we drove into the car park, I saw Carlos arriving.

'*Temos reunião as duas e meia*,' he called.

Another meeting? My watch said ten to two. No time to eat lunch and get back by two-thirty. Hell, I hadn't even had breakfast – only a beer. Oh, well, it would probably be over in time for a set before dark. I rang Mary and joined the others in the conference room. There was one thing about Mozambique that differed from Peru, there was no *hora Moçambiquana*. Meetings usually started on time. I wished that they'd end as promptly.

I had no tennis, not even a game. I reached home just after ten that night, tired, starved and in a very bad temper. The meeting, like the one the day before, had been an utter waste of time. I was so angry at the end that I left without speaking to anyone.

Everyone seemed particularly bleary-eyed on Monday morning.

'What's the problem?' I asked.

'Didn't get out of the meeting till eleven last night.'

'What meeting?'

'The continuation of Saturday's.'

'Thank God I left before anyone told me about it,' I grinned.

'No-one missed you. They spent the whole day talking about rabbits, ducks, buffalo, and dip tank inspection.'

I noticed that the longer a meeting lasted, the less it achieved. Only short snappy meetings produced a result. I sent Carlos a memo suggesting that no meeting should be held without an agenda being circulated at least 24 hours beforehand, and should never last more than an hour. He agreed enthusiastically, but of course it made no difference. Ineffectual meetings droned on just as before.

The main trouble with Communism, I realized, was that it was so damn boring!

A HERO BITES THE DUST

I had only to push my office chair a couple of feet to the right to bring the National Monument into view in the centre of the *Praça dos Heróis* below me.

It was not an imposing structure. White reflecting panels (glass? perspex? aluminium? – I was never close enough to determine) were laid in the shape of a centrally elevated star on a mound at the hub of the *Praça*.

Excavations had started shortly after I had arrived, had stopped, and now had begun once more, leaving a large hole surrounded by an earthen rampart. Towards the end of 1978, activities increased; builders began working round the clock and a wooden palisade was erected, behind which technicians and inspectors with scrolls and clipboards would disappear.

About this time, several dozen volunteers could be seen painting lurid murals on a high white wall which had been erected for 50 metres along one side of the *Praça dos Heróis*, as well as on the Ministry building itself. They depicted, in bright crude frescos, the origins and achievements of FRELIMO. They certainly brightened the otherwise dull arena and lent a gay backdrop to the pompous ceremonies which were frequently held there.

Early in the New Year, it was announced that the National Monument would be inaugurated on 3 February, the Day of the Heroes. Towards the end of January, processions of dark-suited officials following flag-draped coffins, would slow-march up the concrete pathway to disappear beneath the star-shaped roof. These coffins, we were told, held the bodies of Mozambican Heroes brought home from Tanzania and other places to be interred in their country's national shrine. Eddie, the son of Mozambique's first president, Eduardo Mondlane, told us that his father's body was amongst them.

We all felt it wiser not to go to office on the day of the inauguration. It would mean going very early to get through the crowds and troops, and it would be impossible to leave till it was over, and that might be late.

Driving to office the following day, I was surprised to see two cars in front of me stop as they neared the *Praça*, their occupants alight and stand at attention. It had long been the custom at six each evening, for traffic to stop and drivers alight while the national flag was lowered from official buildings, carefully folded and paraded away like a haggis on Burns Night, after which the traffic would continue. But why at this hour, and why here? Then I noticed a detachment of soldiers, arms at the slope, slow-marching along the arc of road between the Ministry building and the National Monument. Turning up the concrete path, they arrived at the entrance to the mausoleum where two of them swopped places with two already on guard. The posse then slow-marched back to the Ministry and traffic resumed its way. The whole procedure, I estimated, had lasted about ten minutes.

One could, perhaps, have forgiven such a ceremony once or twice a day, but hardly had I stirred my coffee, which Fernanda brought as soon as I arrived, when a bugle blew and the whole pageant was repeated. Every hour throughout the day saw another change of guard and stoppage of traffic.

'This is bloody ridiculous,' I said. 'It's the nearest thing I've seen to "economic sabotage"' – a phrase beloved by comrades to describe anything that interfered with national productivity.

'Don't worry,' Fernanda laughed. 'They'll soon get over it.'

As always, she was right. Soon the interval for changing the guard was increased from one to two hours. Then the traffic was halted only while the soldiers were actually marching on the road. In the end, the soldiers wandered across the grass to assemble on the concrete path directly in front of the monument, and the traffic was left uninterrupted. Three months later, no-one took any more notice.

My sympathies were for the poor lads who stood guard, motionless, in the grilling sun for two hours at a time.

'Someone's going to keel over one of these days,' I predicted.

It happened as I looked up from the report I was writing. The left-hand guard swayed, then fell forward, flat on his face, his rifle clattering onto the concrete apron.

For a moment, his companion remained motionless. I expected him, at least, to drag his unconscious buddy into the shaded entrance of the tomb, but no, instead he turned and bellowed across to the Ministry, where some off-duty carabineers were playing dice on the front steps. Three or four of them ambled across the *Praça*, grabbed the unfortunate musketeer's arms and dragged him, accompanied by much laughter and badinage, across to the protection of the Ministry building.

No ceremony this time, only ribald shouts and catcalls as the victim's highly polished boots raised little puffs of dust from the dry soil of the *Praça*.

I witnessed many a visiting dignitary from my perch on the second floor. The Presidents of Angola, Algeria, the Soviet Union and Tanzania, all marched slowly up to the monument to lay their tributes of flowers, while a military band played suitably doleful music. I now regret that I lacked the courage to take photos, with a telescopic lens it would have been easy. But to have been seen would have invited a bullet or at least arrest and probable deportation. It wasn't worth it.

But if I had been brave, or foolish enough, the scene I would have chosen above all others, would have been that of the limp, capless corporal – perhaps himself a future 'Hero of the Republic' – churning up the dust as his fellow warriors hauled him across the *Praça*.

TIME FOR A CHANGE

No recently liberated country has shaken off the last bonds of colonialism until it has uprooted all references to its former imperialist masters, starting with the names of its towns.

Salisbury soon became Harare, Blantyre was now Lilongwe, and even the obscure little settlement of Abercorn in Northern Rhodesia, where I had started my career, had been named Mbala when that country became Zambia. So it was not surprising that the ancient and romantic name of Lourenço Marques – the mere mention of which conjured up all that was most exciting and illicit in Southern Africa – was changed to the more ethnic title of Maputo. The new name was so like the Portuguese word for prostitute that one could hardly blame some of the more dissenting residents for referring to 'Maputo, son of a '*ma-puta*'! Other towns followed. Vila Pery became Chimoio, Porto Amelia became Pemba, João Belo was now Xai-Xai, and the dormitory town of Salazar, outside Maputo, was, wisely, renamed Matola.

Not only its name but most of Maputo's anatomy was also relabelled. Any street name that smacked of the old colonialism or religious subservience was ruthlessly eradicated and supplanted by the name of a more recent tyrant or neighbouring dictator or of a revolutionary anniversary. Victorious Portuguese generals and explorers bit the dust, ousted by the young upstarts of socialism – Karl Marx, Engels, Kim Il Sung and the like. Avenida Pinheiro Chagas bowed out to Eduardo Mondlane. Antonio Enes to Julius Nyerere. Avenida Nossa Senhora de Fatima (where the UN had its office) became Kenneth Kaunda. Many of the new names were Bantu – Magaia, Luthuli, Magumbwe – presumably heroes of the FRELIMO war.

Changes didn't stop at street names. Tourists who had navigated the city using statues in place of stars now found their landmarks also gone. But it didn't really matter as these days there were no longer any visitors!

'I've just seen the most extraordinary thing,' Fernanda was

599

obviously excited. 'I was up at the APIE stores (APIE would have been spelled PWD in British Africa). All the old statues from the city are in one of their backyards – hundreds of them. Even Queen Victoria, I saw.'

To remove some of the city's finest memorials just because there was a change in politics, was, I felt, a childish, vengeful act. Poor old Queen Victoria, toppled off her pedestal by that bedraggled little man Marx, who had spent so much of his time in her beloved British Museum plotting against kings and queens in general, and whose name had now been given to the very avenue down which she had frowned for over half a century. Shame!

One further change remained before the Portuguese reins could be severed entirely.

'Got any escudos?' Fernanda asked as I walked in the door one June morning.

'I think so. How many do you want?'

'I don't want any. I'm just telling you that as from today they are illegal. The currency has been changed. You have two days to swop all your escudos for meticais.'

'For what?'

'Meticais, the plural of metical, the new coinage. We have about six thousand escudos in the FAO imprest petty cash. I'm going to change them right away.'

I gave her what cash I had on me, so did the others in the office. She didn't return till after midday.

'Chaos, absolute chaos,' she groaned. 'Queues for hundreds of metres, some people even arrested for trying to exchange too many escudos.'

An arbitrary limit had been placed on the amount of cash any one person could exchange, reputedly 50,000 escudos. More than that signified that you were a profiteer or dealer on the black market. It was obvious that very little thought had been given to the switch-over.

I had to spend the next two days in the Chokwe area with an expert from the foot and mouth research laboratories in England, evaluating the efficacy of the vaccine we were using in cattle. We might as well have stayed at home. No-one was working. All field staff were swelling the queues in front of the banks in Magude, Chokwe and Chibuto, queues which were still enormous at eight o'clock the night we drove back to Maputo. The new coins of aluminium alloy were a sorry substitute for the solid old ones of copper and silver, and had soon worn into smooth, unrecognizable discs.

600

Country folk, who only heard of the change weeks afterwards, trekked in to the banks, their small savings clutched tightly in hot, sweaty hands, only to have their precious little hoards confiscated and their notes torn up in front of them by boneheaded officials, bent on fulfilling the law to the letter. An eventual dispensation for country areas and for persons who had been abroad at the time of the change was small comfort to those who already had had their notes ripped up.

I found several 500-escudo notes in my filing cabinet, placed there in a moment of affluence as a reserve, and forgotten. I still have them. Perhaps, some day, a collector will buy them off my grandchildren at a price equivalent to their face value in 1980!

TACKLING TUBERCULOSIS

It was ages since I had looked down a microscope, let alone handled a Petri dish or spayed a cat. In fact, the only veterinary work I had done in the last 15 years or so had been to put down unwanted pets. So, when Rui, who had taken over from Carlos as Director of Veterinary Services, asked me to help with the campaign against bovine tuberculosis, the prospect of donning a bush jacket, shorts and *velskoen*, and actually touching animals once more, filled me with happy expectations.

Tuberculosis, I was told, occurred mainly in European breeds on the big farms and rarely in the indigenous, peasant stock. Lately, however, reports of TB in village cattle had become more frequent, probably, I thought because more attention was being paid to the peasant farmer.

Another possible reason, I felt, was that the out-of-date test used by the Portuguese veterinarians, that of injecting the tuberculin into the eyelid instead of into the skin fold under the tail or on the neck, as was done in every other country, had proved unreliable. The infection therefore could have been building up for years.

We started testing the State farms around Dondo on the railway line from Beira to Rhodesia. This would provide a convenient opportunity for me to demonstrate the techniques of the test to the District Veterinarians of the North, most of whom were still students.

Leaving our hotel in Beira at four each morning in a rickety, square-wheeled Land Rover, we'd arrive at the selected farm at first light to find the cattle already packed into the testing crush. Some of the farms still had a Portuguese manager, who would give us a welcome breakfast of tea, rolls and toasted local cheese.

The cattle crushes in Mozambique were, on the whole, superior to those I'd seen elsewhere in Africa. Instead of stakes, the sides were built of bricks covered with cement to make a smooth-walled chute just over a metre high and some 70 centimetres wide. Sometimes a frisky animal would jump out or an obstinate one lie down, but it was easier to raise a prone beast in these crushes than in the stake-walled ones.

As usual, we used the injection site under the tail in preference to the neck. After the cattle were packed into the crush, too tight to turn around, a herder would pass up the line from the last animal to the first, pulling their tails, and thus their rumps, to the left side. Another lad followed with a sponge and bucket of water and washed the grosser dirt from the injection site under the tail. This done, an assistant, starting at the back end of the crush, would hold each tail up high, stretching the skin beneath and creating two folds. The inoculator would grasp the right-hand fold of skin between finger and thumb and inject a single drop of tuberculin into it, raising a pea-like bleb under the skin as evidence of correct delivery.

Finally, a spot of white paint would be dabbed on the animal's rump to confirm that it had been injected. Should the tail site have too many ticks or cuts, or lumps which might confuse the interpretation of the test, the injection would be given in the skin of the neck and a white blob of paint daubed on its head, indicating the site used was on the neck. In this way we could test 20 to 25 animals in under five minutes.

Unfortunately for me, on the very first day, a large Zebu bull swung its head round and caught me in the ribs with its horn. I lay on the ground gasping for breath, certain I was going to die. That night, I had to crawl to my bed on my knees, flop my body onto it, then pull my legs up, one by one. In the morning the process of getting up was reversed and much more painful. In spite of the elastic bandage I had wound round my chest, journeys to the farms each day were nothing less than excruciating.

Three days after injecting each herd, we would return to 'read' the test. Those animals with any swelling at the injection site would have a dollop of red paint splashed on their heads, or be branded with a 'T' on the jaw, and sent to the slaughterhouse.

After two weeks and 3,000 head, of which about 10 per cent reacted positive to TB, I flew back to Maputo, my chest still strapped up but the pain slightly eased. I never did get an X-ray, and to this day I don't know whether I broke a rib or merely bruised it. Either way, there was nothing more I could have done.

Another area was the district of Isla Josinha Machel, 100 kilometres north of Maputo, a low-lying grassland with patches of higher ground which became islands in the rainy season, on which the animals would crowd, making it easy for TB to spread. All 5,000 head of cattle in the district were peasant-owned.

I would pick up Marietta, the young Dutch *co-operante* veterinarian who was in charge of the area, each morning before dawn, so as to try and finish the daily quota before the sun had reached its zenith. Paulinho, the *Assistente Técnica Pecuária*, or ATP, a sort of livestock inspector, would have the crush already packed, awaiting our arrival. Since it was fairly near Maputo, a busload of veterinary students would sometimes join us to assist and learn.

A major obstacle was the behaviour of the herdsmen. Each herdboy wielded a stick or whip, which was continually in action. Often I would see one belabouring the animal's rump while another would be bashing its head, accompanied by yells and curses, so that the poor beast had no idea what to do and usually charged off into the bush, followed by a band of shrieking dervishes. This is nothing new to anyone who has worked in Third World countries. Herding, it seems, is a form of machismo. Certainly, it had been the same in every country in which I had worked. Animals were regarded as inanimate objects, the more and harder one hit them, the better the herdsman you were.

All through my career, I had been wrenching whips from crestfallen herdsmen. Surprisingly, it had often been effective, and the owner, who normally left management entirely to his herdsmen, would thank me and promise that no herder of his would ever be allowed to carry a stick or whip in future. Promises, I'm afraid, that were all too soon forgotten!

One day I lost my temper and told Paulinho to round up the herdboys for an *ndaba*. When they had all shuffled up, I told him to take away every stick or whip and place them in a pile which we stoked with dried grass and set fire to. Then he, Marietta and I, with the help of a couple of students or unarmed herdboys, a few low whistles and encouraging calls, packed the crush in a matter of minutes.

As with the herds at Dondo, niceties in interpreting the test had to be dispensed with. There was no way we could designate an animal as 'suspicious' and retest it in three months' time, as was the custom on well-managed farms. Any swelling, whatsoever, at the injection site, was regarded as 'positive' and the animal eliminated.

603

The number of positive reactors was only slightly higher than the Dondo herds, but the high incidence in the working steers was distressing, for these would be needed for ploughing and thus the ultimate survival of the family. Although the Ministry had arranged to replace all cattle slaughtered, it was little comfort to the owner who had spent years training his oxen, to receive a cow or untrained ox, with the rainy season just round the corner.

During a test along the South African border near Goba, I remarked that a beer would go down well.

'I'll get you one,' said the ATP brightly.

'Beer?'

'Yes, and soft drinks. It'll take about half an hour.'

I gave him some escudos, and he disappeared, taking a couple of herdboys with him.

'I'd no idea you could buy beer and soft drinks in the middle of the bush,' I said as they returned with boxes on their heads. 'You certainly can't in Maputo.'

'There's a store just across the border in South Africa, about two kilometres away,' replied the ATP. 'They accept either escudos or rand. Many people go across the border to work in South Africa each day.'

That was late 1978. Before long, most of the border had been mined by the Mozambique army as an East-West explosive curtain, and later the anti-FRELIMO rebels, the RENAMO, began to make any journey through the bush a hazardous affair, eventually putting an end to all field activities, including the tuberculosis campaign. Politics once again had overruled technology.

RHODESIAN RAIDERS

Ian Smith and his well-trained Rhodesian marauders were a daily threat. A mere 'The Rhodesians are coming' was enough to send everyone scrambling for safety.

Although the raids were usually targeted on specific FRELIMO bases, several civilian friends considered themselves lucky to have escaped unharmed. A district veterinarian was cruising along a country lane near Chokwe one morning, unaware that a Rhodesian raid was taking place nearby and oblivious of the helicopter gunship hovering overhead. Suddenly, a bullet pierced the cab roof and went through the seat between his legs, narrowly missing some vital parts!

604

Another time, a party from the Ministry were strafed by a heli-copter, and spent 15 minutes dodging about in a cane field as it raked them with bullets. Roger was caught in one raid but, luckily, only on the edge. Werner, my East German Veterinary friend from Chimoio, had the most harrowing experience of all.

He had kept my phone number and, as he had promised, gave me a ring on his next trip to Maputo.

'Turn right as you leave the Cardoso hotel,' I told him. 'You'll see the Natural History Museum in front of you on the left. I'll pick you up in front of it in a green Hi-Ace in half an hour.' We had to be sure that his compatriots didn't see him. Later, over a beer on our patio, he recounted his adventures.

He and another East German colleague had been taking blood samples for a brucellosis test on a State farm 20 kilometres from Chimoio and about the same distance from the Rhodesian border.

'It was early morning, and we had just finished the first crushful when someone shouted "Helicopters". Some of the helicopters landed close by and a lot of white soldiers jumped out. "Rhodesians" every-body yelled, and we headed for the bush.'

Deciding to walk back towards Chimoio through the forest, they soon regretted their decision. Both were shirtless and without docu-ments of any sort, having left everything in their Land Rover. After struggling through thorn bush and swamp until late afternoon, they realized that they were lost and that night would soon overtake them. They had heard an occasional vehicle over to their right, so they headed in that direction and eventually hit a road. Everything seemed very quiet until, with great relief, they saw a truck approach-ing and flagged it down. Their reception was hardly cordial. The truck was full of FRELIMO soldiers, who naturally assumed that the two wanderers were some of Ian Smith's men who had been left behind.

It was logical. Two white men alone in the bush, immediately after a Rhodesian raid; shirtless, streaked with blood, with no identifica-tion and gabbling something about helicopters and Rhodesians, in broken Portuguese? There was no doubt these were Smith's men!

'I thought they were going to shoot us,' Werner said, 'so we kept repeating "*co-operantes; Ministério da Agricultura*", and they even-tually took us into Chimoio, where we were identified and freed. I tell you, it wasn't funny.'

Another Rhodesian raid in the Xinovane area, which destroyed several rice harvesters, provided an amusing sequel. The Rhodesian salesman in an Agricultural supply house in Swaziland whom I visited frequently for equipment and spares, sent me a telegram a few days later.

'UNDERSTAND YOU NEED NEW RICE HARVESTERS. HAVE SEVERAL WELL ARMOURED VERY CHEAP QUICK DELIVERY.'

My reply was limited to two words, one very rude.

RABIES AGAIN

Britain's strict six-month quarantine laws regarding the importation of dogs, cats and other carnivores may seem a bit severe to Fido-owners who wish to bring their pets back from Bahrain to Basingstoke, or from Maputo to Manchester. Believe me, they are not! One has only to brush lightly with rabies to appreciate the wisdom of these regulations which have kept the British Isles free from the scourge for over 70 years.

I have described my terrifying encounter with this ghastly disease in Abercorn on my first appointment, the misunderstanding with Joan Crawford's miniature apricot poodle in Jamaica, as well as the more serious affair of my friend's son, bitten by a suspected rabid dog, and taken by his father to the Amazon jungle, ignoring my pleas to have him vaccinated. Now I was to have a further intimate collision with this wretched disease.

Christiana, the German Associate Expert in Sheep and Goats in Pemba, was visiting us for a few days. On the last evening, she brought home a six-week-old puppy which Herman, Rudi's Associate Expert at Namaacha, had given her. It was an adorable Labrador cross. Our kids and their friends were all over it – and vice-versa.

Ten days later, at two o'clock in the morning, we were awakened by a hefty thumping on the front door.

'Sorry to wake you so late,' apologized Christiana, 'the plane broke down in Nampula and we've only just arrived. I have to go to Johannesburg tomorrow to meet a friend from Germany. I hope you got my telegram.'

'Telegram? No, but come in. There's a spare bed in Melanie's room. We'll probably get your telegram in a couple of days.'

At breakfast, we chatted over events in the north, and Shevaughne asked how the puppy was getting along.

'It died,' Christiana told her sadly. 'I took it for a run on the beach and it must have picked up some poison. It was very wobbly that night, and the next evening it died.'

Cries of sympathy gushed from all round the table.

'When did this happen?' I asked.

'About a week ago. Please ask Herman if he has another he can spare me.'

I took Christiana to the airport and went on to the office. A little later Herman popped in,

'Christiana is asking whether you have another puppy you can give her, the last one died,' I told him.

'That's why I came in. My bitch died yesterday, and a puppy last week.'

'What were the symptoms?' I asked.

'I found the puppy dead, but the bitch was weak for a day or two, wouldn't eat and could hardly stand.'

Ping ... ping ... ping. An alarm was sounding. We discussed the symptoms for a few moments.

'Look, Herman,' I said at last. 'I don't want to scare you or Ineke, but I think that both of you had better be vaccinated against rabies as soon as possible.'

'Rabies?'

'Yes, it's a definite possibility, I'm afraid. The symptoms in your bitch are very suspicious, so were those in Christiana's puppy. What beats me is that if it is rabies, how the hell did they get it – unless you have rabid rats.'

Herman's face paled as he stared at me with a half-open mouth.

'My God, Pat. I've just remembered. A stray dog came into the garden some weeks back and attacked the pups. The bitch went for it.'

I felt my stomach twist.

'Rabies is no longer just a possibility,' I told him grimly. 'It's more or less a certainty. Any puppies left?'

'Two.'

'Bring them in to Roger for observation. They will have to be put down anyway. Sorry, but that's the only course to take.'

Some months before, Roger had asked me to import the latest French human rabies vaccine, to protect the staff at the Research Institute. I rang him. He still had 15 full courses left. I told Herman to collect one each for himself and Ineke, and start the injections immediately.

Christiana was my chief worry. She had been in closer contact than anyone else, but she was now somewhere in Johannesburg and wouldn't be back for two or three days. And – oh my God. All those children, including my own, who had played so lovingly with the little puppy in my house that evening. What about them? That had been two weeks ago. There was no time to lose. I rang Roger again.

'I want all the rabies vaccine you have, and please alert Pru to be ready to inject about a dozen kids this afternoon.'

As soon as my three 'Muskatelles' returned from school that midday, I made them write down the names of all their friends who had played with Christiana's puppy. There were eight.

I spent the next two hours phoning parents and explaining, as best I could, in several languages, the necessity to vaccinate their child. I told them that if they were undecided they should consult a doctor, as I was only a vet. None objected.

By four o'clock we had the house swarming, not only with trembling, and in some cases tearful, youngsters, but also with their friends who had come, they said, to give them support but, I suspected, more to see the fun and games. By the greatest of good luck, not a single parent showed up.

I packed all eleven vaccinees into my Hi-Ace and took them round to Pru's clinic wondering, fearfully, what the outcome of the whole affair would be. The kids were remarkably brave. Rabies is not a pleasant injection, but tears were minimal. Predictably, Shivy created the only rumpus of the lot. Afterwards, Pru gave each child an ice-cream.

'Next injection, day after tomorrow,' she warned as we left. Ice-creams were licked furiously and laughter was a bit more nervous, but no-one grumbled.

That night, Shivy had a high temperature. She always was a highly strung kid. I just hoped that no-one else would react badly. It might jeopardize the completion of the vaccinations.

Two days later, the same gang, quieter and considerably more apprehensive, presented their skinny arms for a second shot. It took Mary and I all our strength to hold Shivy. In fact, she almost succeeded in diverting the injection into Mary's arm instead of hers.

'See you all one week from today,' Pru told them. 'It'll be the last shot.'

Mary, who took them on the last sally, reported no problems. It was, in my opinion, one of Pru's greatest triumphs. Three painful jabs within ten days of each other in a bunch of volatile youngers, half of whom were highly excitable Latins, with hardly a squeak – if you discount our Shivy. That was no ordinary achievement!

Having Christiana vaccinated was more of a problem than we had anticipated. Instead of overnighting in Maputo on her return, she had grabbed a vacant seat on the plane to Pemba.

Communication with the north was difficult. Phones were unreliable, and telegrams could take three days. Eventually we got through to the Provincial Agricultural Office and told them to warn Christiana that vaccine was being sent on the next plane, two days hence, and she was to start inoculations immediately. We confirmed this by telegram. I gave the vaccine to the pilot and asked him to hand it to Christiana, personally if possible. I prayed that she would receive at least one of the messages in time. She did. The telegram arrived an hour before the plane, but the Agricultural Office never gave her my message. Big Brother still hadn't forgiven her!

Any possible doubt as to the diagnosis was soon dispelled. The day after Pru had finished the vaccinations, Roger phoned.

'One of the puppies Herman brought in died yesterday. We confirmed rabies. I've put down the other.'

Well, we'd done what we could and, thank God, all turned out well – that is if you discounted the anxiety, the sleepless nights, the aching arms and churning stomachs!

RENAMO RANSACKS MUABSA

Muabsa was soon flourishing under the energy and drive of George, the Associate Expert from Sierra Leone. He had made his home in Inhambane, a seaside town 250 kilometres south of Muabsa, the nearest place suitable for a family within weekend commuting distance.

It was always a delight to be welcomed by his large grin, unfolding like a rose from behind a curly black beard that seemed to have trickled down from his sideburns. Sylvia, a striking blond from the Black Forest, would conjure up delicacies I'd never heard of – let alone tasted.

Within a year, George and Mussagy, the station manager, had built a laboratory, classroom and dormitory for the students, installed a generator and started training courses. The trypanocidal drug experiments had been redesigned and fodder crops planted to help feed the experimental herd. The trees from the newly cleared land had been used to create a charcoal operation. A low-level aerial survey (during which we were all thoroughly airsick) had helped us plan future strategy to thwart Mrs Tsetse's southward invasion, and the *picadas* along which the fly-boys rode their bicycles were cleared of undergrowth, allowing spraying operations to be resumed. Muabsa was soon being described as the most effective tsetse research and training centre south of the Equator.

When John left, George moved down to Maputo to take his place as director of the trypanosomiasis programme, and Will, a young Dutch veterinarian and his biologist wife took over the work at Muabsa.

We were proud of our efforts. It had not been easy to create training facilities in the middle of the bush, 700 kilometres from Maputo. But technical difficulties are only a small part of the problem of disease control in Third World countries; the human obstacles of ignorance, apathy and irresponsibility, are far greater impediments; and, of course, civil strife is the greatest of all. Just as everything at Muabsa was blooming, RENAMO, the anti-FRELIMO guerilla movement, began to increase their activities, and after they had killed two FAO personnel in Chimoio, the UN decided to evacuate all its staff from vulnerable areas. Will and his wife were told to return to Maputo.

It was as well they did. Shortly afterwards RENAMO destroyed the Centre, killing a couple of fly-boys in the process. It was probably the greatest setback to animal disease control since the FRELIMO war.

ONE TO HELP, ONE TO HINDER

During a visit to Rome, I had been introduced to a small, puckish individual with a humorous twinkle in his eyes and tufts of grey Pickwickian hair sprouting from the sides and back of his almost bald head.

'Look him over,' I was told. 'He's been proposed as Administrative Officer for the future FAO office in Mozambique. We'd like to send him out at once.'

Good, I thought. Looks like the first step.

Five minutes sipping *cappuccinos* at a curbside *trattoria* convinced me that Maurice was exactly the person we needed. A Turk from Istanbul, he had once bartered hides and skins in the market place before serving FAO in Central and West Africa. Both his English and French were fluent, and he spoke several other tongues.

Maurice knew the FAO 'bible' – that two-volume Manual of Operations – like the inside of his mouth, and was in addition a born diplomat. What better person to look after our affairs in Mozambique?

'Any news on the appointment of an FAO Representative?' I asked him.

'Yes, they've already selected someone, but I'm afraid he's a bad

610

choice. I worked with him in Central Africa. He's a good field man but hopeless as a leader.'

'Can't we get someone else?' I suggested, a bit alarmed.

'Very difficult. The Italian Communist Party are behind his candidature, and they have a lot of influence in FAO, especially with Mozambique affairs.'

Maurice was already in Mozambique when I returned, and Nicolo, the new FAO Rep, arrived a few months later. It was soon very evident that Maurice's forebodings were well justified. Nicolo certainly did not fit in with our idea of an FAO Rep. Vociferous, ebullient, over-friendly, with myopic eyes blinking eagerly through horn-rimmed, bottle-glass lenses, he was far too excitable to inspire confidence in his leadership.

There was no doubt that he was sincere and that he tried his very best to fulfil his duties as FAO's Representative. He was simply miscast. He craved to make a good impression and show Government what marvellous things FAO could do for Mozambique but, unfortunately, his gushing eagerness merely antagonized everyone from the Minister to the UN Res Rep. He rushed into my office one morning, bubbling with excitement, having just returned from the north.

'Guilbride, I've just been to Cabo Delgado – miles and miles of bush and no livestock at all.' He hadn't stopped to consider why there was this lack of animals. 'I'm drafting a scheme for FAO to buy thousands of head of cattle in the south and ship them to Pemba, where they can be distributed to the *aldeas comunais* (communal villages), to start milk and beef production.'

He leaned back in my visitor's chair, his face broken up by his eager smile, awaiting my acclamation. I could only gape.

'We'll talk about it, Nicolo. There may be problems.'

He laughed, as if to assure me that problems only arose with other people's plans, not with his well-thought-out schemes. Unfortunately, the problems were real and insurmountable. Cabo Delgado province, except for the few spots where livestock were already raised, was infested with tsetse fly. Even if we could have found the cattle and arranged the shipping (there being no adequate through road), it would have been impossible to introduce cattle willy-nilly and expect them to survive.

Delightful fellow though he was, Nicolo was far too impetuous to be a diplomat, far too eager to please everyone, and quite incapable of weighing the pros and cons and taking a balanced decision. It was this burning desire to cooperate fully with Mozambique's Marxist policy that finally brought things to a head.

611

One morning, an incredibly naive circular over his signature appeared on the desk of each FAO member. In it, Nicolo laboured the importance of full cooperation with the Ministry at all levels, even to attending their political meetings, which were held weekly to explain the concepts of Marxism and denigrate the racialistic Rhodesians, South Africans, Americans and Israelis.

We were horrified. His suggestion was directly contrary to our terms of employment. One of our specific instructions was to stay clear of anything political. We were international technicians and diplomats, first and last. Politics were out of bounds. Neither did the Ministry officials appreciate his patronizing political efforts on their behalf, and many openly regarded him as a buffoon. Our situation was now worse than before. We felt angry and very frustrated. Something had to be done – and done quickly. So, one evening, I and the other five Project Managers discussed our problem around the ornately worked, leather-topped Peruvian coffee table in my lounge.

'Nicolo's screwing up everything we've worked for,' complained Nabil, the Egyptian crop production leader. 'I'll be in Rome next week, if you all agree, I'll tackle the Divisional Director.'

We drafted and signed a confidential letter for Nabil to take with him, pointing out the importance of an experienced official with diplomatic manners to represent us, and suggesting a speedy replacement of the present incumbent.

I was a little staggered at the rapidity of the result. A few weeks later Nicolo left 'on urgent medical leave'. To have his eyes treated, so they said, and the following day the UN Res Rep asked me to come and see him.

'I want you to act as FAO Rep while Nicolo is on leave,' he informed me.

Six weeks later, I was told that Nicolo was not coming back and that FAO was sending a top official to look into the whole matter and discuss it with the Minister of Agriculture.

The top official arrived, assured us that FAO had a couple of excellent candidates, and told me to carry on acting.

Oh, well; I was due for leave in a few months. Surely it would be fixed by then. But by the time I left, nothing more had been heard of the new FAO Rep.

'Don't worry,' I assured Jim, who had been asked to sit in my chair and answer letters until I returned. 'The new bloke should be here any day.'

He didn't seem convinced.

LUANDA

'We would like you to visit Angola on your home leave next month, and report on their veterinary requirements.' FAO hoped to start operations there soon.

At noon one Saturday, I took off in a *Lineas Aereas Moçambiquanas* plane for Lusaka and Luanda.

It was impossible to match the high-rise city I saw from the circling plane with the straggling, one-street settlement I had once known as Lusaka. The modern, concrete airport must have been a hundred times the size of the unpretentious sheds of 1946. But for all its size and modernity, it could not conceal the country's obvious economic woes. The floors were unswept, the windows uncleaned, and there were none of the usual airport shops except for one tourist stall selling badly carved bone and wood ornaments.

Some old friends were out in force to meet me. The descendants of those mosquitoes which had made my life a misery 35 years before were just as big and aggressive as their ancestors had been. I added a few more red splotches to the already besmeared whitewashed walls of the Gents.

After two more hours of flying over endless bush, a thin, yellow band began to separate the muddy green of the land from the misty blue of the South Atlantic.

Like Maputo, the Angolan capital, Luanda, was built half on a narrow coastal plain and half on the ridge behind it, where a fort-like structure looked down over the tall modern buildings of the town centre. Inland, the bush was freckled with thatched huts, linked together by eroded yellow paths, like a spider's web. To the south of the city, a stretch of white beach curled out to a sandy headland.

I had expected an easy passage through immigration, as befitted a visiting United Nations official, but although the other three passengers slid comfortably through without let or hindrance, I was not so lucky. I handed the official my *Laissez Passer*.

'*O senhor não tem visa?*' he asked.

I explained that the usual procedure was for the UN office to bring the visa to the airport when they met visiting officials. The problem was that no-one had come. The immigration officials, both youngsters and very sympathetic, looked up the UN in the telephone directory, but it was Saturday afternoon – no answer.

The immigration cubbyhole was extremely stuffy and unbelievably hot but, luckily, I had a good book. When I had discarded all the clothes permissable for a diplomatic gent to part with, one of the youngsters brought me a bottle of pop. It was warm and flat, but nectar could not have been more welcome. A couple of hours later, when I was wondering whether I would have to stay there till Monday morning, a car screeched to a halt in front of the entrance and a stunning brunette pushed through the swing doors.

'I'm very sorry,' she said in Portuguese. 'I came to meet you at three-thirty, but they said the plane was two hours late.'

'Don't worry,' I told her. 'Mozambique is no better.'

Since there would be no hotel rooms available till Monday, I was billeted on the UN Accountant, a short, sad-faced but charming Portuguese with a wide mouth, the image of Peter Lorre of 1940s screen fame. I was dying for a beer, but the Accountant's ration of one small *porón*, or barrel, a month was finished and there was nowhere to obtain more, so after watching a surprisingly good TV programme on garbage collection in Luanda, I, his wife and two children got into his car to *dar uma volta* of the city.

My host would certainly not have passed a driving test in any civilized country, and at the end of the evening I still wasn't sure on which side of the road one drove in Angola, but the view from the floodlit Fort of San Miguel, which I had seen from the plane, down over the twinkling lights of the city and along the shore to the tourist hotel at the point, made up for any deficiencies in his skills of *condu-ção*. One tall building stood up from the city centre.

'That's the best block of apartments in Luanda – now occupied by Cubans – of course.' There was evident disgust in his tone. No-one seemed to like Castro's carabineers.

There was only one bathroom-cum-toilet in the Accountant's house. Competition was acute. The first morning I was up before five, but the water hadn't yet been turned on. Later, when the rush had subsided, the water was off.

The Hotel Turismo, next door to the UN office in downtown Luanda, offered me a room on Monday morning. Amazingly, it had an air conditioner – and still more amazing, it worked. Just as well, it was terrifyingly hot, and somewhere along the corridor a drain was blocked. The air conditioner both cooled the room and blew away the smells!

Priority number one was drinking water. The taps were dry, save for an hour in the early morning and again in the evening. In any case, the water was far from potable. To have drunk it would have invited all sorts of problems. To overcome this, the UN provided its staff with a large bottle of drinking water from the office refrigerator each day.

'We employ a girl to boil and filter water, full time,' the Res Rep told me.

614

Back at the hotel, I rolled my precious bottle in a wet towel and propped it in front of the air conditioner, which kept it icy cold. It was a life saver. There were no bottled beverages to be had. Food, too, was severely rationed. As I walked into the hotel dining room at lunchtime, a waiter asked me if I was registered.

'Yes, room 414.'

'But are you registered in the dining room?'

Each guest, apparently, had to register separately with the dining room to get a meal. It was soup, rice and beans for lunch that day, followed by two very small, very sour, oranges. Supper was again soup, rice and two small fish, followed by the small sour oranges. Breakfast was the only meal with some excitement. Two excellent rolls with a generous glob of butter (Danish Aid, the waiter said), and real coffee, helped one to face another hot humid day.

I had been warned that travelling would be impossible, even to Huambo to see the Veterinary Research Institute a few hundred kilometres to the south.

'UNITA troops are all around,' Fernando, the youthful Director of Veterinary Services, told me. 'We can only travel by air, but all seats are booked for weeks. We'll have to make do with nearby farms.'

We spent several hours working out what was wanted for the forthcoming vaccination campaigns and for the Research Institute. Cattle diseases in Angola were similar to those in Mozambique – anthrax, blackleg, foot and mouth, and one we didn't have, bovine pleuropneumonia. Rabies in dogs was another serious problem.

We estimated that about 1,500,000 cattle and 50,000 dogs would need to be vaccinated. Apart from this, there was an urgent need to test the herds for tuberculosis and to organize general tsetse and trypanosomiasis control measures, all of which only highlighted their acute shortage of syringes, needles and transport.

I telexed Roger, asking if he could supply Angola with 50,000 doses of rabies vaccine from his Institute. He replied that it would be no problem. It was the first of several such consignments. The other vaccines would be ordered through Rome. Just how Fernando's Veterinary Services were going to carry out the campaigns once all the vaccines had arrived, was not at all clear to me. I presumed they would fly them to the larger centres and treat the animals within a safe radius, otherwise the vaccinators would be the ones more likely to be vaccinated – with bullets!

I explored some of Luanda's poorer residential districts. The lovely old buildings, carved doorways, enclosed balconies and steep narrow streets had a lot in common with Olinda, that small seaside town just north of Recife. The Luanda citizens were wonderfully friendly, and I would often find a man or small boy walking beside me, telling me about his family and asking about mine. They were particularly interested in my British nationality.

'Do you allow black people into England?' many asked. I assured them that we did – in large numbers.

'Can you get me a job there?' would usually be the next question. I explained the difficulties and that, in any case, I lived in Mozambique. This didn't impress them much. They had always regarded Mozambique as Angola's poor relation.

There was no doubt that Luanda was now a sad city, dirty and depressing, its architectural attractions marred by huge, overflowing garbage carts parked at nearly every corner. That TV documentary on garbage collection we had watched the previous evening, excellent as it was, had been unable to include the distinctive smells of downtown Luanda! I saw no restaurants or bars open, and the occasional food shop had long, belligerent queues outside. In one of the larger department stores, rows of empty glass shelves occupied its three floors. A few assistants still stood awaiting customers, but about the only things I could see for sale were spare parts for an American make of refrigerator. It was like a description of Uganda I had heard from a visiting consultant. 'Shops are full, old man; but only with packets of Harpic – no food.'

The UN Res Rep was not in his office when I went to present my draft report.

'He won't be in this morning,' his secretary informed me, 'he's dirty.'

'Dirty?'

'That's the message I got. He's asking you to go to his house.'

A grubby, unshaven, but smiling Head of Mission welcomed me on the verandah of his large home. In front, a well-laid-out, but very dry garden separated it from the waters of the bay. He apologized for his absence at the office.

'The water heater blew up, and I have no water in the house. I've been trying to fix it for the last two hours. You have to do these things yourself if you want them done.'

I had to admit that Luanda was a lot worse than Maputo.

* * *

I was glad to have seen even a small part of Angola, and especially to have met the Angolans. Although worse off than their brothers in

616

Maputo, they were more relaxed, more outspoken, more alive. I felt that it only needed the smallest flame to make the country sizzle again. How sad that the politics and obsessions of a few selfish tyrants, thousands of miles away, who had never even seen the country, had turned it, like Mozambique, into a land of misery.

MONKEY BUSINESS

It sat there, quizzing me from the top of the stairs.

'What in God's name is that?' I demanded, putting down my suit-case and hoping my fears were unwarranted.

'That's Freak,' Fuffy exclaimed excitedly. 'She's a baby vervet. Lindley bought her at the Zoo.'

'The one pet we will never have,' I'd often told the children, 'is a monkey. They're dirty, destructive and dangerous.' True, I had once broken the rule myself when I had rescued Bimbo, the kitten-sized *léoncito* from a street urchin in Iquitos. But that had been an emergency, an unpremeditated, humanitarian act. Bimbo hadn't been dirty, destructive or dangerous, but *had*, in the short time he was with us, won our hearts and dominated our lives. Never again would I let that happen. Now this creature sat there, smugly defying me in my own house!

'Sorry, darling.' Mary was a bit sheepish. 'When Lindley asked me I just couldn't say no, and they were starving in those cages.'

'The keepers were eating them,' piped in Shivy. 'She'd soon have been cooked.'

I didn't doubt it. The Zoo was no longer a show place. The animals were starving, many had died and some – like the monkeys – were providing free meals for their hungry attendants.

'She's really very sweet,' Mary persisted, 'and Lindley has promised to look after her.' Big deal, I thought, just like all the other pets hugged into the house as babies, all too soon to outgrow their cute-ness and be left to the care of Mary and myself.

But what could I do? It was a *fait accompli* of several weeks' duration. I couldn't have a showdown the minute I returned from leave, and I had to admit, it did look rather appealing. All the same, it was really a bit hard. Only in the last five of the 22 years we had been married, had we been able to leave ornaments and breakables within reach of the children. Our home, if not exactly tidy, now at least had a modicum of order about it. We had even felt it safe to display our antique glass and our family heirlooms. All we needed was a small, mischievous monkey to wreak havoc with our treasures

617

and place us in a situation far worse than anything our darlings could ever have dreamed up.

Freak's escapades could fill a book – maybe, one day, they will. Destructiveness, I'm afraid, would dominate the tales, but there would be lots of love and humour to offset the many acts of pure devilment.

Her first months were unrestricted. She jumped in the trees that fringed the garden or sat and sunned herself on the verandah or roof, or played with the dogs and cats on the patio. Lindley took her everywhere, the furry little arms tight around her 'mummy's' neck as she and Zeca (now Lindley's constant companion) sped south on his motorcycle along the sandy road to Ponta de Ouro, or north along the highway to his parents' home at Palmeira. While water-skiing at Bilene, Freak showed her concern when Lindley came to grief, diving off the launch and swimming to her.

Every evening she joined Lindley in the shower, at first sitting on the partition, chattering continuously, then clinging to Lindley's neck and finally sliding down to the floor, where she would sit, eyes shut, arms outstretched, wallowing in the warm, luxurious cascade. At night she cuddled up to Lindley, waking her at first light with butterfly kisses or ear nibbles, or by putting a long, furry finger up Lindley's nose. At this stage, she was anything but housetrained and regarded the pillow as good a place as any. The only solution was for Lindley to wake before Freak and shove her outside the window until she had performed.

Lindley has many stories of her simian daughter. Perhaps the most poignant was when she and Zeca had water-skied across the lagoon at Bilene to the sandy, pine-covered strip which separated it from the sea. It was dusk before they started to return and Freak, who was up a tree, was too frightened to come down. They had had to leave her.

Next morning, they went back to fetch her. The sun was already hot, and for an hour they called her name, searching every tree. Then, in the distance, Zeca spied a little grey object plodding laboriously through the hot soft sand. They stumbled towards it. As soon as Freak recognized them, she sat back on her haunches, stretched up her arms and wailed. Lindley could hardly see her for tears.

When Lindley left for Europe, Freak transferred her affections to Mary. She also started to wander. One day, an irate Swiss Ambassador, whose residence fronted ours, informed us that our monkey had absconded with a valuable trinket from his lounge. Luckily, we found it in one piece. Then the secretary to the Romanian Embassy, adjacent the Swiss, complained that our little monster had filched a highly sensitive document from his Ambassador's desk and delivered it to the Cuban Embassy, two houses further down the road!

Reluctantly, we were forced to restrain her. We made a belt from a small dog's collar to fasten round her waist and attached it to a 20-metre cord. Late in the afternoon, when the sun approached the horizon, we let her loose, knowing that with night at hand she would go no further than our roof or a nearby tree.

Every morning, after a night snuggled up in our bed, Mary would put her on the loo. She very soon got the idea. Then she would breakfast with us on our bedroom verandah, where she devoured a bowl of cereals and banana 'pennies'. Sometimes she slipped her belt, or jumped out of bed too early and disappeared. One of her favourite haunts when she escaped, was the pool at the Polana Hotel, 200 metres away up a grassy slope. Here she cavorted with the bathers, projecting herself off the side like a cannonball and clutching any swimmer that came within reach.

Popular though Freak was with most of the guests, it was inevitable that sooner or later her playfulness would bring down the wrath of the establishment. Snitching morsels off the plates of guests lunching round the pool, or in one case robbing an irate American lady of her prescription dark glasses, was more than any hotel could tolerate. We were warned that further visits would be acted upon, but our friend João, the Polana gardener, promised he would let us know immediately if he saw Freak heading that way.

Occasionally she would disappear for a day or more. Once she was brought back by a school friend who found her half across Maputo, and another time she was 'ape-napped' by a man who found her in the street and took her home. Good detective work by Mary led first to his flat and then to the person to whom he had sold her. Here, Mary found the little creature chained to a second-floor verandah railing, crying for her mummy – whether human or simian, I'm not sure.

One day, Corinne found Freak outside the gate dragging one leg. A femur was broken, probably from a slingshot. I took her to the Veterinary Faculty clinic, where we used their last three plaster of Paris bandages to set it, anaesthetizing her in a bucket with halothane gas. Freak was very proud of her cast; all the children's friends signed it, and she would sit for hours trying to scratch out their names with her long nails. We anticipated trouble when the time came to remove it, but she forestalled us. We had let her go untied while she had the cast on, and one evening she didn't come in. There was a terrific storm that night and early next morning in she jumped through the

619

window, walking well and minus her cast. I was amazed that her bone could have set in a little over two weeks.

Whenever she went missing, it was like losing a child. The relief of seeing her jump through the window to be hugged and cuddled, and to listen to her gurgles of delight at being back home, still gives me a lump in the throat.

Freak soon became famous in the international community – even President Samora Machel knew of her. She loved to sit at the end of her lead outside the car porch while passers-by fed her sweets or photographed her as she searched their heads for edible titbits. Only the Eastern Bloc citizens regarded her with suspicion, hurrying their children past on the other side of the road, as if she was some kind of capitalist hobgoblin.

Freak's taste for alcohol grew rapidly. Beer, sherry, but especially gin and tonic, were like a magnet, and with her taste for cocktails grew her passion for cherries and olives. Many a guest found themselves fighting to retain the fruit in their 'Old Fashioneds' or martinis. To leave the drinks cupboard open was disastrous; Freak could unscrew any bottle or pull any cork.

Mary often took Freak to the beach at Costa do Sol, where a troop of vervets lived in the Casuarina trees, hoping that they might accept her, but the little monkey's only reaction was fear, especially of the ferocious leader with his five-inch fangs and the confident way he advertised his purple appendages. When he wasn't there, Freak would sit on the roof of the Hi-Ace while the others accepted peanuts and fruit from Mary's palm, but as soon as he appeared, they both had to jump back inside while Mary frantically rolled up the windows. Furious and frustrated, the scowling male would press his nose flat against the glass, bobbing up and down and emitting a fearsome 'clack, clack, clack' before following the car for a couple of kilometres down the road.

I read, somewhere, that the cheapest pet to keep was a monkey. It ate scraps of bread and fruit from the table, there were no other expenses. Whoever wrote that nonsense never kept a vervet – except in a cage. We reckoned that our friendly and much loved apelet cost us upwards of $5 a day in mangled pens and pencils, devoured pills, emptied liquor bottles, broken ornaments, detaped cassettes, chewed spray-can nozzles and a thousand other valuable or useful articles which she lost or destroyed. Hardly a breakable was left intact after her first six months with us.

And, of course, there was always the danger of her nipping someone outside the family, until I removed her eye teeth. But this didn't stop her chewing the telephone cord or Mary's silver thimbles and other sewing accessories, or ripping the mosquito gauze on the windows, or peeling the wallpaper, or opening and emptying my whisky bottles, all of which she did just as easily without her front fangs.

Freak has wrought havoc with our lives, lost us friends, cost us dearly in lost articles and in repairs, restricted our movements both inside and outside the house, and caused us as much anxiety as any child, but she is now one of the family and has made up for everything by her unwavering trust and adoration of her two stupid foster parents.

Today, 15 years later, fat and less inquisitive and with six acres of garden, tall blue gums, a large orchard and plenty of roofs to romp on, she is quite free. At dusk she puts herself to bed in the linen cupboard until she hears our bed creak, when she comes bounding in, chuckling and purring, to snuggle up to Mary for the night.

As soon as it is time to get up, Mary pops her on the loo, where she has learned to oblige before creeping back, all chuckles, for an extra snooze while we drink our tea. Later, she sits on the roof, climbs the plane tree outside the sitting-room, or parks herself on the driver's seat of our old Hi-Ace, which she now considers she owns, her two little paws gripping the steering wheel, her head resting between them, eyes closed, dreaming perhaps of the many trips she made in it and the many adventures she had in Mozambique. As I write this, she is snuggled up on the couch with one of the cats, like a somnolent Garfield, her paunch sagging to one side, her head on a cushion, content in the certainty that she still rules the household and commands our total love.

But don't be fooled. Anyone who even considers having a monkey for a pet wants their head examined!

VIVA INTERNATIONAL AID

Of course, there had been no permanent FAO Rep when I returned from leave – moreover, Nicolo's old office now housed a new section dealing with commerce.

For the following months, acting as unpaid FAO Rep, I moved from office to office, depending on who was on leave, and for a short time sat in the chair of the UN Res Rep himself, until the only room left was the library – if you could call a cubbyhole heaped higgledy-piggledy with books, periodicals and reports, a library.

The whole issue of a separate FAO office had now been shelved till a permanent FAO Rep had been appointed. Maurice, the FAO

Admin Officer, had long ago moved to a room in Nabil's project at the Agricultural Research Institute, where I would meet with him whenever necessary.

I had cleared a space in the sea of books and was settling in, rather uncomfortably, when I was told that the library was going to be reorganized and I would have to find another place to sit. Pru, Roger's Nursing Sister wife, said there was an attic in the UNICEF building where she had her clinic, and that the Director of UNICEF would let me use it as a temporary FAO office. I moved the only authentic piece of FAO property, the filing cabinet, into my new attic home, which I found was being partitioned into several offices. The fact that the telephone was on the floor below, seemed to fit the general picture.

On top of my in tray, on the first morning back from leave, I had found a file labelled 'Flood Victims'. I flipped through it. Following the devastating floods of the previous year, a philanthropic Dutch government had purchased 400 tons of seed maize for distribution to the afflicted peasant farmers of the Zambezi valley, to replace their losses. Pinned to the outside of the file was a note dated a few days previously from the Maputo Port Authority, advising us that 200 tons of this Katumani maize from Tanzania, addressed to FAO, was on the docks awaiting collection.

I saw from the file that this Katumani maize was a very special variety – drought-resistant and high-yielding. After a bit of a hunt on the docks, we found two stacks of hessian bags, one in an open shed and the other lying unprotected on the wharf.

'About time someone came,' grumbled an official. 'The stuff's been here for months.'

Many of the bags had been ripped open, presumably by rats. The official handed me some documents that had accompanied the maize. They showed that it had been shipped in November from Dar-es-Salaam – it was now June. The documents also showed that it should have been off-loaded in Beira.

'Well it wasn't,' said the grumpy official, 'and now it's here, and I wish you would take it away.'

Back in the office, I rang CNAC, the Government Department which dealt with natural disasters such as floods and droughts. They knew nothing about any seed, but hoped we could soon send it to Zambezia. The section in the Ministry of Agriculture responsible for the importation of all seeds, also denied any knowledge of the Katumani maize, and made it quite clear that it was none of their business. Even less interest was shown by the other half-dozen government Departments I rang. It seemed that flood victims were no longer a priority.

The first thing was to see if the seed was actually worth sending anywhere. It was already over eight months old and would be over a year old before the next rainy season when it could be planted. If it already had a very low fertility, there was no point in transhipping it.

Nabil told me that *Senhorina* Linette in the Agricultural Research Institute did regular fertility tests, so I collected her and went down to the docks again. In 30 bags we sampled, fertility ranged from 1 to 12 per cent. We decided to sow some of the best samples immediately under irrigation, harvest the seed and send that up to the Zambezia peasants to sow the following year.

I made a resumé of the whole affair, indicating what we had done, and sent copies to the Minister of Agriculture, CNAC, and to the Dutch Embassy, who had brought the Katumani seed to Mozambique in the first place.

A couple of days later, the balloon went up. I was summoned to the fourth floor. There I found the Minister, the top officials in CNAC (suddenly expressing extreme interest), the man responsible for seed importations in the Ministry (now rather sheepish), and a representative of the Dutch Embassy, trying to swallow his diplomatic fury, all gathered in the conference room.

FAO was ridiculed for not advising the Ministry the moment the seed had arrived (the ministry official concerned kept silent), the CNAC officials were berated for not sending the seed to Zambezia immediately, and the well-worn phrase 'economic sabotage' was bandied about.

I pointed out the low fertility of the seed and the high cost of transport to Zambezia, but no-one took much notice. I was told to send all the papers to the Minister and, within an hour, I had delivered them personally to his office.

That we received no thanks for trying to save a portion of the seed to sow next year, didn't worry me. I was too delighted that the Ministry had taken the seed off my hands.

I heard rumours that the seed was eventually sent to the north, but a clue to a much more likely fate was given me on a later visit to the docks, when a smirking official pointed to the oily waters below the wharf and drew his finger across his throat.

Whatever the truth, I was pretty certain that the Zambezia flood victims never benefited by a single grain of that Katumani maize seed.

A telegram from Beira, some weeks later, said that another

623

consignment of maize awaited our collection. I advised the Ministry within minutes. When the officials got round to dealing with it, it also had disappeared, probably to join the rest in Davy Jones' locker.

Under the circumstances, this might have been the safest solution, for the temptation to eat it would have been great, and there was no way an ordinary person could tell that it had been treated with a poisonous insecticide – until he was dead!

Viva International Aid!

I was not through with seeds. Another saga was about to unfold.

The thousands of refugees who had fled the bush war in Rhodesia were now herded into camps throughout Mozambique under the general care of ZANU, Mr Robert Mugabe's Zimbabwe African National Union, as opposed to ZAPU, the Zimbabwe African Peoples Union, of his cousin, Mr Joshua Nkomo.

A great deal of International Aid for ZANU's refugee camps was channelled through FAO and ultimately across my desk, and I became friendly with several of the ZANU officials. I found them intelligent, well-educated and cooperative. There was, however, one unfortunate drawback. Since I was still shuffling between offices in the UN building and had few facilities for visitors, I found it more practical to have discussions on ZANU affairs at their offices. No problem there – except that their pitch was on the eleventh and twelfth floors, and the elevator had long since succumbed to over-work and under-maintenance. Often, after puffing up those interminable stairs on a hot humid afternoon, I would find that no-one else had turned up for the meeting I had confirmed that morning. Even if the ZANU officials were intelligent, well-educated and pleasant, they were certainly not reliable.

My immediate business with them at this time was the purchase of seeds – millet, maize, vegetables, wheat and grass, for their refugee camp farms, a matter, I was told, of the highest priority. The agricultural supply firms in Swaziland promised to buy the seeds from Rhodesia and South Africa (FAO being prohibited from dealing directly with these two racialistic countries), and deliver them to the border at Namaacha. As soon as the delivery date was fixed I rang Mr Kamedze, one of my ZANU contacts.

'Our truck will be there,' he assured me.

The day before the seeds were to arrive I rang him again. Yes, all was prepared.

I collected Alf, the husky young Danish Associate Expert working on pastures at the Namaacha Dairy Training Centre, and drove to the border post. No truck of any sort was visible, but we were still half an hour early. An hour later, neither the supply company's truck nor ZANU's five-tonner had appeared, but a moment later a large lorry passed through no-man's land and pulled up beside us.

'We'll have to wait a moment or two,' I told the Swazi driver, 'the ZANU truck hasn't come yet.'

'OK,' he replied, 'as long as I get home tonight. I've a long trip tomorrow.'

Half an hour later, I rang the ZANU office in Maputo. It took 15 minutes to get through, and there was no answer. Must be on their way, I thought hopefully.

'We'll give them another fifteen minutes,' I told Alf, 'then we'll have to start unloading. See if you can rustle up a couple of lads.'

We waited a quarter of an hour while Alf tried to find someone to help us. He couldn't find a solitary soul willing to sweat a bit, nor was there any sign of ZANU's truck. There was nothing for it but to start unloading, so Alf, I and a grudging Swazi driver unloaded closed on two-and-a-half tons of seeds. It took us two hours. As we finished, a fat little customs officer came tripping out to inspect the sacks, now piled up against his office wall.

'When are you going to remove them?' he nagged.

'ZANU will collect them tomorrow, I expect,' I answered, now quite sure that he would be lucky to see their truck inside a week.

'I hope so,' he pouted. 'It is not permitted to leave goods here.' I longed to tell him where to shove them, but I was too bushed.

I just made it back to Maputo, every muscle in spasm. After a few beers and a bath with Badedas, I flopped into bed. Heaving dozens of sacks around was hardly a recommended sport for a desk-bound 60-year-old.

Thereafter, each time I passed the border, I would gaze unbelievingly at the undisturbed pile of sacks. It may not have been permissible to leave them there, but there they remained until, with the ending of the guerilla war and the lifting of sanctions against Rhodesia, ZANU decided that there was nothing to stop the refugees from returning to their new land, Zimbabwe, so the seed would no longer be required in Mozambique.

In due course, I heard, it was reloaded onto a ZANU truck and sent back to the party headquarters in the newly named capital, Harare.

The Katumani tradition was alive and flourishing!

GUESTS OF BIG BROTHER

As members of an United Nations Agency, we were protected from political harassment and from the consequences of our official actions, should these be contrary to Government policy. Not so our national colleagues or those foreigners without diplomatic umbrellas, as for instance, Abreu.

I had known the tall, dark, good-looking Portuguese engineer since the earliest days when, in his capacity as head of the Agricultural Mechanization Department in the Ministry, we had drafted the original NORDIC AID project for the recuperation for abandoned farm machinery. Both he and his young Dutch wife, Sylvia, the same girl who had accompanied us as interpreter during the visit of the NORDIC AID mission, had become good friends of our family.

On Christmas Eve, 1978, two slimy gentlemen arrived at their home.

'You're under arrest,' they announced and bundled Abreu into a police car. It was no use asking why, ten to one they didn't know themselves.

I was stunned. Abreu had been a very respected leader, open, hard-working and well able to solve the ghastly mess his department had inherited. But, unfortunately for Abreu, there had been a change of Ministers. My old friend, who had so delighted to rib me about FAO, had received the boot, apparently for being too liberal – to the point of keeping a mistress.

'I'm probably for the high jump, Pat,' Abreu confided, soon after the change.

'Why?' I protested, 'you were always a favourite with the fourth floor.'

'Exactly,' he replied. 'The previous minister and I thought alike. This new fellow is a political pimp. Last year, when he was Minister of External Trade, I accompanied him to East Germany to buy tractors. The tractors they offered us were rubbish, so I advised him to buy Massey Ferguson from the West. He was furious and called me a capitalist and a lot of other names. So I reckon my number's up.'

The charges, made known some weeks later, were vague and mentioned an imbalance in his department's finances, with the additional, veiled accusation that Abreu had been bribed by Western firms. I was told that he had been incarcerated on the personal order of the Minister of Agriculture.

As soon as he was allowed visitors, I went to see him at the Central Prison on Avenida Kim Il Sung. He was well, but furious at the charges.

'What did I tell you, Pat? That bastard has concocted the whole thing, even to having me arrested on Christmas Eve. It's pure spite. Anyway, they are investigating it, so I should be out soon.'

What worried him most was that Sylvia was expecting their first child any week, and he wouldn't be there to hold her hand.

Days grew to months, then to a year. I would visit him about twice a month. On the anniversary of his arrest, Mary baked him a Christmas cake with one candle on it.

After some months he became a 'trusty', and would act as guard on the front gate. Trusties had other perks as well. They were allowed out for 'haircuts' and visits to the hospital. A warder would accompany two or three favoured inmates, ostensibly on a visit to the barber, leave them to their own devices for a couple of hours and then escort them back. Abreu even had a night out now and then. The impression I had formed on my visits to Lui, two years before, was strengthened. The Kim Il Sung jail was probably as amenable as any in Africa.

But as time went on, Abreu became more and more despondent. In spite of all his friends could do to push what legal processes still existed, nothing was moving. The enquiry into the missing funds had long since been completed, and nothing had been found amiss. But it was despotism, not justice that ruled the legal system. The Minister was too powerful a member of FRELIMO's inner circle; the investigating accountant was rusticated to the north, out of harm's way.

'Could you get me across the border if I met you outside?' Abreu asked me one day.

'No,' I replied. 'I'm a UN employee. I can't trespass that far on diplomatic privilege.'

'Well, I've got to do something. Think about it.'

I did, often. Eventually I said I'd be prepared to drop him on the Swaziland border, if he could meet me at some pre-arranged spot. The thought made my stomach heave.

Luckily, we never had to carry out the plan. A few visits later, he told me that the President had ordered an investigation of his case, and shortly afterwards Sylvia rang us 'to come and meet an old friend and celebrate.'

No formal charges were ever made, the result of the investigation was never released, nor was he given any explanation or offered any apologies.

'But they've given me a month's overseas leave and offered me my job back. Bloody hope!'

A few months later, he wrote from West Africa where he was

working for a Dutch firm. The last thing I did for him was to send on his trophies, won in happier days when he was National Swimming Champion, and which the Customs had refused to let him take out.

During my visits, Abreu had introduced me to a couple of coloured South Africans who had been in the jail for almost two years.

'See what you can do, Pat. They've no-one fighting for them.'

Jackie was a cadaverous, light brown man in his late thirties, with a black toothbrush moustache and a wispy, straggling excuse for a beard. His friend, Johannes, was younger, better-built and darker-skinned.

Their tale, like most tales of those entertained against their will by the People's Republic, was ludicrous to Western ears. Both were South Africans and members of the PAC, the Pan African Congress, originally a splinter group of the ANC, or African National Congress. The headquarters of the PAC were in Tanzania. Jackie and Johannes, neither of whom were permitted to enter South Africa, were on their way to Swaziland where they had arranged to meet their families. They had been given visas to cross Mozambique, but at Namaacha, the border post with Swaziland, they had been stopped.

'Your transit visas expired yesterday.'

'Yes, but the bus from Beira (the road was still open in those days) broke down.'

'Sorry. You'll have to return to Maputo and have your visas renewed.'

Their passports and luggage were taken away and they were put in a police Land Rover.

'We weren't taken to immigration, we were brought here, to jail, and we've lost everything – money, luggage, passports.'

'What about the Tanzanian Embassy?' I asked.

'We've sent many messages, but they never reply.'

'OK,' I agreed, 'let me see what I can do.'

The Tanzanian Ambassador was not much help.

'Yes, yes, I know about them, but there are problems. We would be only too pleased to send them back, but we have no money and the PAC headquarters in Dar-es-Salaam refuse to send their fares.'

I heard afterwards that there had been some in-fighting in the PAC and Jackie and his friend were on the side that had lost. Next, I tried the UN High Commissioner for Refugees. He was quite a different proposition and asked immediately when he could see them.

'I'm visiting my friend on Saturday afternoon,' I told him. 'Why not come with me?'

A few days after our visit he rang me.

'I think I've solved the problem of your friends. The Tanzanians don't want them to return to Dar, and they can't go back to South Africa, so I have put them down for refugee scholarships to Nigeria. Tell them when you next see them that we should have them out of jail in about two weeks.'

I felt justifiably pleased with myself when I entered the prison yard the following Saturday and hailed Abreu.

'Fantastic,' he exclaimed, 'except that they have already gone.'

'Gee, that was quick,' I laughed. 'The High Commissioner is certainly a live wire.'

'Except that it was SNASP who took them, not the High Commissioner!' SNASP were the secret police. 'We hear they are in Machava,' he added. Machava was the high security jail.

I rang the High Commissioner. He was furious.

'I'll try leaning on Government, but God knows how long it will take.'

Two months later, a thin figure passed the open door of my office.

'Hey, Jackie! Looking for me?' He came in smiling.

'We were released last week. I'm seeing the High Commissioner again this afternoon. I came to thank you.'

From his account he must have cursed me many times. Soon after the High Commissioner's visit, he and Johannes had been whisked off to the high-security jail at Machava. There they had been tied up with wire for hours at a time, while a series of East Germans and Cubans, accompanied by blows and kicks, interrogated them. They spent the next seven weeks in solitary confinement until, one morning, they were told they could go and were shoved out through the main gate. Their first call was the High Commissioner, who gave them funds and a place to stay.

Jackie came to see me regularly. His scholarship took longer to arrange than anticipated, meanwhile he married a Mozambique girl. Before he left, Abreu, who had just been released, gave a party for him and his wife. That was the last I saw or heard of Jackie. I hope he is happier now than when we first met.

Johannes, Jackie told me, scathingly, had made a deal with the South African Authorities and returned home. He has my prayers, too. He probably needs them more!

Until then, all our friends had been incarcerated in the Central Prison, popularly called the 'Hotel Machel', on Kim Il Sung. It was a holiday resort compared to the high-security jail at Machava, on the outskirts of Maputo. Mary had heard enough about the place to be shocked when Anagrette, Rudi's wife, rang to tell her that Inga, one of Mary's best friends, and her husband Lori, had been arrested.

'We think they are in Machava,' she blurted out. 'Their cookboy came and told us.'

That morning, just as Lori opened the door of his car, four young men approached, told him they were from SNASP, the secret police, and bundled him into a white Colt (most of the SNASP cars seemed to be white Colts). Another two entered the house, collected Inga and drove her away in Lori's car. The West German Embassy was inundated with enquiries, but it was two weeks before the Government admitted that they were in Machava.

Inga and Lori were a colourful pair. They had come to Mozambique from Germany after the war. Lori boasted that he had been the youngest U-boat Commander in the German Navy. If he was correct, it meant that I had met the youngest submarine commanders on both sides, as Jack, an Anglo-Chilean friend in Jamaica, had claimed a similar status for the Royal Navy.

Now an industrial consultant to the Government, Lori was reputed to earn a very adequate salary, and move in exalted political circles. Inga, 20 years his junior, with flaming red hair, curvaceous body and sharp wit, had run a cine unit until Independence. Their two teenage children were at school with Lindley and Melanie in Swaziland.

We were not altogether surprised to hear that Inga was in trouble. She had a disconcerting way of bragging about her high-up friends in the Mozambique Government as well as her contacts in Ian Smith's Rhodesia and in South Africa, two of Mozambique's bitterest enemies. Only a few days previously, she had treated us to a lobster and prawn dinner at the Polana.

'Next week I go to Jo'burg and then to Salisbury. I have very important friends there, and they are anxious for news.' The implication was obvious.

'Hush, Inga,' we whispered. 'You don't know who is listening.' SNASP had its ears and eyes everywhere.

There was very little you could do for friends unlucky enough to land in Machava. We bought concentrated vitamin tablets and toiletries in Swaziland, and drove across a large parade ground to the studded, castle-like gate of the jail. The guard was polite, smiled condescendingly and promised to give them to the commandant. I suspect that this gentleman and his buddies became healthier and cleaner than ever before in their lives, for neither Inga nor Lori ever

630

saw a single one of our gifts. Meanwhile, they were both incommunicado. No-one heard anything.

Five months later, Mary answered the phone.

'Inga! Where are you?'

'At the airport. We leave in half an hour. We've been deported.' Mary had just enough time to kiss her goodbye and promise to visit them the following week in Johannesburg.

The story they told was similar to that of many others who had passed in through Machava's grim portals and had been lucky enough to pass out again. They had been interrogated continually by East Germans. The food was minimal and atrocious, the warders surly and unsympathetic, the mosquitoes appalling and hygiene non-existent.

In addition to physical discomforts, loudspeakers in the yard outside their cells continually broadcast accounts of their alleged crimes, adding comments from a 'people's court', who shouted 'Kill them, kill them'.

To this day, nobody knows why they were arrested. Perhaps Inga's overconfident and foolishly audible boasts had been taken as a threat to national security, or perhaps Lori was meddling with foreign exchange, or perhaps it was a devious way of acquiring Lori's new apricot BMW, which was soon seen cruising the streets of Maputo with sleazy young men inside. Or perhaps not even the authorities themselves knew!

Even if the reason for their incarceration was not known, their release probably hinged on a visit by the West German Head of Sate, and was linked to continued West German Aid. Whatever the truth, it was not an experience either would choose to repeat.

* * *

The last of our friends to grace Machava's cells, was Paul, a British wildlife specialist with South African residency.

We were all staggered. His work had been praised by the Minister himself, especially his latest escapade when he had brought a female hippo from the Gorongosa National park to Maputo Zoo. Not such a great feat, you say, until I tell you that three hundred of that 1,200 kilometre journey was through RENAMO controlled territory and could only be traversed, at considerable risk, in a military convoy.

The convoy that day had been guarded by a single army landrover, behind which were some twenty civilian vehicles of various sizes and capabilities. The troops in the landrover were as scared as anyone else and from the word go the driver had his foot flat on the floor.

Nor, I imagine, did he once look back at the straggly line of trucks and cars, desperately trying to keep him in sight.

Paul soon realized that his ancient Ministry truck was no longer fit for high speeds, especially with a ton of hippo swaying around in the back. After a few kilometres, he saw the last of the stragglers disappear into the distance and found himself quite alone. He considered turning back, but he wasn't that sort of person and he felt that Miss Hippo had suffered enough already. Every few kilometres he would come across burnt out trucks, peppered with bullet holes; most had army markings.

'I've never been so terrified in my life,' he confessed. 'Talk about a sitting duck – or should I say hippo.'

Against all odds, he eventually arrived at the FRELIMO control post on the banks of the Save river, two hours after the rest of the convoy.

'We thought the rebels had got you,' the officer in charge told him, nonchalantly. 'For all the help you gave us, I can't understand how they didn't,' Paul replied, hotly.

So when Paul was told, on arrival at the office one morning, that the police had been asking for him, he immediately, and unsuspectingly, contacted them – and disappeared for nearly two months.

Ironically, it was his adopted country which was responsible. A month earlier, the South African Defence Force had carried out a nightraid on the ANC base in Matola, Maputo's dormitory town. Coincidentally, both Mary and I had passed through Matola that day, Mary as she returned from Swaziland, and I to show the Deputy Director of the World Food Programme, the milk processing plant there.

It would be impossible to imagine a quieter, sleepier little town. Wide dirt streets, flanked by red-tiled bungalows and large gardens, where mango, frangipani, hibiscus and the occasional jacaranda or clump of bananas helped to soothe the effect of the hot sun and create an oasis of peace.

This soporific charm of Matola must have lulled the nearby headquarters of the Armoured Division into a deep sleep, for it took them several hours to mobilize after the alarm was raised, by which time the raiders had long since skipped back across the border to South Africa.

In the weeks that followed, everyone trod warily. Borders were closed, troops were everywhere and 'suspects' were paraded before mass meetings. A great witch hunt began, with the Americans and their friends as witches and the East Germans, Russians and Cubans as the hunters. It was East *versus* West with no holds barred.

I arrived back from a trip to Muabsa, to find the international community abuzz. Many Mozambicans and foreigners had been arrested the night before. Tilak, roused in the early hours, pointed out that he was a United Nations employee and immune to such indignities. The police left to confer with their superiors and Tilak rang Ida, UN's personnel officer, who rushed round, semi-attired, in time to tear strips off the returning SNASP officials. They apologized, grovelled and departed. Sergio, an FAO expert from Colombia, was less fortunate and had a 24-hour sojourn inside Machava's gloomy precincts before the UN extricated him.

Quite inexcusable was their attitude towards the chief of the Mozambique NORDIC AID Program. MONAP was pumping in millions of dollars to improve Mozambique's agricultural production. Per, the Swedish Co-ordinator, happened to be in Europe, but his wife was dragged out of bed and his house ransacked, including a valuable collection of classical tapes. Even the roof was searched.

The common factor in all these arrests seemed to be friendship with three of the younger American diplomats. Photos of these gentlemen, all of whom had already left the country, appeared in the press with accusations of being CIA agents and organizing the Matola raid. What made the charges even less believable was that the photos above the names did not correspond in any way with the young diplomats we all knew so well.

But back to Paul. One afternoon, seven weeks after his disappearance, he turned up at our house, smiling, and the next day was back at work as if nothing had happened. But it was not a time he is likely to forget. For all the discomfort and anxiety he had experienced, his account was humorous enough.

'The bastards handcuffed me to a chair when they started the interrogation. Then they went away and forgot all about me for three hours. My arms were quite numb. But they had the decency to apologize. Incidentally, they asked about you and Mary.'

'What did you...?'

'Simple. I told them that you liked Scottish dancing, beer and tennis and one of your children was a monkey. They wrote it all down. No sense of humour.'

Paul's first act, in jail, was to identify the inmates of his corridor, whom he could hear but not see, with the names of game animals. It kept up their spirits and confused the warders.

His cell measured two by one and a half metres. His cot, a hard board with a thin mattress occupied one side. By running two steps, turning, running two steps, he could cover several kilometres in a morning, although it made him a little giddy at first. To pass the time, he mixed toothpaste with tobacco ash, both of which his girl-friend had persuaded the guards to give him, and drew pictures of wild animals on the whitewashed walls with the resulting mush. The commandant was so impressed with his murals that he had an official photographer record them.

His other occupation was playing chess – with himself. The chess-men he made from his meagre ration of bread which he chewed and shaped into pawns, knights and castles, one set containing tobacco ash to make them grey.

Paul is still in Mozambique with a wildlife project on the Bazaruto Islands and we often see his cheery face on South African television.

By an extraordinary coincidence, just after we had retired to South Africa, I learned the inside story of the Matola raid. Sitting next to a sturdy young man at a neighbour's drinks party in the Natal Midlands, the conversation turned to Mozambique.

'Do you know Matola?' asked the young lad.

'Certainly,' I replied. 'Why?'

'I went there once but it was dark at the time – couldn't see much.'

'You went to Matola in the dark? Whatever for?'

'Well it was sort of an uninvited visit...' and then the penny dropped.

His account shattered my high opinion of South African military intelligence. The raiders crossed the border near Ressano Garcia (Komatipoort) and took a back road – the same one on which Kerry and his friends had got stuck some years before – hitting the main road again near Boane, where the FRELIMO army had their training centre. This consisted of an enclosed parade ground surrounded on all sides by barracks. The entrance was a massive metal studded gate set in a brick archway.

'Our guide was pretty confused and thought we had arrived at Matola, so we banged on the gate till they let us in, then we drove round the parade ground. No-one took much notice since we were wearing FRELIMO uniforms and the trucks had Mozambiquan Army insignia, but by now we realized our mistake and drove out again and on to Matola. The guide, re-orientated once more, pointed out the ANC houses, and we took them out. In the confusion two of our lads were killed, probably by our own crossfire. Anyway, after fifteen minutes or so, we whizzed back along the main road to the border, acknowledging salutes at the road blocks, and were back at base before sun-up. All rather amusing.'

I wonder if Paul and the others would have agreed!

POLITICS SOUR THE MILK

We were becoming a bit fed up with the Cubans. They were pleasant enough, and Danny, my Cuban veterinary friend, could not have been more friendly, co-operative and eager to learn, but the contingent was a wedge between us and our protégés. Instead of discussions with our Mozambiquan colleagues, we now found ourselves reporting to one of the dark-haired, moustachioed Latins who strutted noisily through the corridors flourishing Churchillian cigars and sprinkling ash over the floor as well as down their white, well-starched *guayaberos*. Although less knowledgeable and experienced than the FAO team, they were Eastern Bloc-orientated and therefore more politically trustworthy than us capitalistic Westerners.

I blew my top when a newly appointed co-ordinator for the Cuban group called me into his office and asked me, like a headmaster accusing a slothful student, why my report was late.

'I'm not here to send you reports,' I told him angrily.

'You must send me a report each month on the activities of all your FAO staff so that I can include the information in my report to the Director.'

'Up you!' I replied. 'If Dr Rui wants a monthly report from me, he must ask me for one. I already give him a copy of my three-monthly reports to Rome.'

I contemplated slamming the door as I stormed out, but that would have been incompatible with the restrained diplomatic side of my position.

The Cubans now also dominated the meetings of the *Colectivo Veterinário* (a sort of advisory panel to the Director) with their ideological, narrow-minded opinions and their atrocious, half-swallowed Spanish. Few of them in the Ministry attempted to speak Portuguese.

Once, when discussing the creation of a regional investigation and diagnostic service, I reiterated my conviction that what we needed were competent all-round field veterinarians with a good knowledge of microbiology, pathology, parasitology, toxicology and metabolic disorders, who could investigate any suspicious condition, do the autopsy, take the right specimens for laboratory confirmation and send anything they couldn't cope with to the Institute in Maputo. It was a system similar to the one we had had in Jamaica, based on the Veterinary Investigation Service in Britain, probably the best in the world.

'We do not have such persons.' The Cubans shook their heads as if to say 'and if *we* don't, nobody does.' 'We have pathologists and parasitologists and physiologists and specialists in microbiology and poultry diseases, but not all together. We will have to put several specialists in each centre.'

I had come across this situation many times in South America. As soon as they graduated, South American veterinarians became specialists, either in poultry diseases, or equine surgery, or small animals, or sheep infertility, or liver fluke control, or any one of the numerous facets of veterinary medicine; but rarely could you find an investigator with sufficient knowledge of each subject to help the farmer sort out his problems.

Jamaica was different; Roger and Tom had established a very competent veterinary clinical and investigation service, but in Peru, except for Manuel and Saul, it had been almost certain that the result of a field investigation would follow the speciality of the investigator. Parasitologists would be certain to diagnose parasites as the cause, a microbiologist would return convinced that the problem was an infectious disease, or the nutritionist that it was a mineral imbalance or plant poison. Very few would be sufficiently competent to arrive at solutions other than those covered by their speciality.

An incident that epitomized this mania for specialization was when a *co-operante* asked whether I could get him a job with FAO.

'I am a specialist in the blood transfusion of horses,' he told me proudly.

'Nothing else?' I enquired, thinking he must be joking.

'No, but I can transfuse dogs as well, if necessary.'

It took a little while to convince him that these were not techniques usually needed in FAO livestock development projects in Third World countries!

Keith, the dynamic, outspoken Australian Chief of FAO's Animal Health Division, once told the Director of Peru's Livestock Extension Service, 'You've got some dandy vets, I'll say that much, but frankly, your service to the farmer bloody well stinks!' That put it in a nutshell.

Another time, the *Colectivo* were discussing an ambitious and quite absurd proposal for a gigantic beef production unit near Beira.

'Even if we *could* find the thirty thousand animals, who is going to run the unit?' I asked. 'This will be ten times the size of anything in the country. We have no one with that sort of experience.'

'We will station one of senior veterinarians to supervise it,' the Cubans told us confidently.

I was aghast. Such an operation would need half a dozen competent managers as well as full back-up services, but the real crux would be the person in overall charge.

636

'Well, I do know of someone who could probably handle the job successfully,' I admitted, 'but he's awfully busy.'

'Who?' several of the *Colectivo* asked eagerly.

'God,' I answered.

Only Rui, the Director, smiled.

At the end of 1980 there was a partial Cuban withdrawal, and we reverted to our original status, chatting directly to our counterparts without having to go through the Cuban curtain. Meetings of the *Colectivo* became relaxed and more productive. A sort of 'end of term' feeling prevailed. Big Brother had left!

The respite was short. Another gang of Castro's *co-operantes* arrived a few months later, but by then we knew how to get along in spite of them.

I was sorry to see Danny, one of the cubans, go. Over a last cup of coffee, we discussed our futures. He would return to the section of animal quarantine and border security in Cuba, and I was retiring to South Africa the following year. I gave him a letter to an old Cuban veterinary friend who had been kind to me at a conference in Havana 25 years before. Although we promised to keep in touch, I never heard from him again. I remember him often.

* * *

The FRELIMO symbol of capitalism – an earringed, high-heeled, flower-shirted layabout – was usually caricatured stretched beneath a shady tree, bottle in hand, puffing a cigar and listening to his Walkman transistor.

Xiconhoca (pronounced Shikonyorka), the 'little snake', was all that a good Marxist was not. Indolent, indulgent, sloppy and

although not exactly an elite, something equally as bad – an individualist. Flamboyant, eccentric, with dark glasses, a gaudy shirt open to the ostentatious buckle on his wide leather belt, he was the ultimate rascal, deviationist and capitalistic pig. But often, I felt, the secret envy of many a Mozambican.

The supposed abolition of elitism by the Communist way of life was, of course, a farce. The higher one climbed the Marxist tree, the greater the perks, no different from the higher branches of the capitalist jungle. Special shops, special houses (grouped together and heavily guarded), special amenities for education and holidays, they were all to be had if you could climb high enough. It was not that I grudged the centurions their hand-outs, in my opinion many probably deserved them, but to talk about equality of life and opportunity under Communism while spitting at capitalism, was pure humbug.

Another thing about Marxism that seemed to me incongruous was the far more rigid pecking order than that to which I was accustomed. Capitalist chiefs could joke and quip with their underlings and discuss matters at friendly *tête-à-têtes* – not so the Marxist masters. Friendly chit-chats with one's superiors were impossible, even *tête-à-têtes* were strictly formal. Politicians and administrators were endowed with divine rights.

Rudi and Herman had been running two-week training courses at Namaacha, teaching groups of six to eight workers from State Dairy Farms to care for calves, make silage, adopt hygienic milking methods and other accepted dairying practices. Between courses they followed up the trainees on their home ground, making sure that the procedures learned at Namaacha were carried out correctly; a most important part of the programme.

One morning, just after we had finished programming the courses for the next six months, Herman rang. Fury gushed out of the earpiece.

'They've cancelled all our training courses,' he spluttered.

'Who have? Why?' I was flabbergasted.

'The Ministry. They're introducing five-month courses for fifty students at a time.'

'We can't cope with fifty students – where do they think they are going to live?' This was ridiculous.

We arranged a meeting with all concerned. The Ministry representative was an East German, grey-haired and sharp-faced, who had, I always thought, been on our side. He explained that the new courses would include general education, maths, Portuguese, as well as a sizeable chunk of political indoctrination.

'But the whole idea is to teach milk production,' insisted Rudi.

638

'They can learn arithmetic and politics at school or on an ATP course. We want to teach them practical dairy management. How can we do that with so many students running around and spending half their time on politics. Anyway, where are they going to sleep?'

'We will start building classrooms and dormitories immediately,' the spokesman assured us. 'We have the funds.'

'This is a retrograde step,' Herman remonstrated. 'We'll lose the personal touch and the practical application of our teaching, We won't have time to follow them up on the State Farms, and there'll be no time for our research. It's an idiotic idea!'

'I agree, it's a huge mistake,' Rudi added.

'Idiotic? Mistake? No, no you don't understand. This was decided by the Minister himself.'

'I don't care who made the decision,' I told him angrily, 'the idea is stupid.'

I think our East German colleague expected the roof to fall in or the secret police to burst through the door and arrest me. His face was as grey as his hair.

'But the Minister said . . .' God had spoken!

Of course, the new buildings didn't start for eight months, and took another seven to finish. Meanwhile we were not allowed to continue with our small two-week courses and so lost some 50 urgently needed dairymen for that year.

It was one of many incidents when a frank discussion with our superiors could have resolved the problem – but discussions are only for the free.

'I think we had better concentrate on cheese-making at Namaacha,' Rudi announced as we left.

'Why?' I asked, a little taken aback.

'Because with all the politics that are going to be flying around Namaacha, the milk will be permanently sour.' He had a point.

For those people who felt like deviating, there was always the fear of the 'Kangaroo Court', or the 'Rogues' Gallery', to keep them in line. In the former, the accused would be tried by his *Grupo Dinamizador* in front of his workmates, fined, dismissed or handed over to the police. Sentences were harsh. A chauffeur at the Veterinary Research Institute, found guilty of making a detour to pick up some vegetables for his family, lost his job – after 20 years' service!

The 'Rogues' Gallery' was nearly as bad. Walking into the Ministry one morning, I noticed a number of photos on a board by the entrance. Several friends stared, unsmiling, from the green baize. Under each was a note of his alleged misdeeds.

639

'Worked for the Colonial Secret Police.'

'Admitted to helping the army against FRELIMO.'

It didn't seem to matter that they were now in responsible Government jobs; once a deviationist, always a deviationist. Their colleagues had to be warned to keep an eye on them – 'help them to conform' was, I believe, the phrase used.

CENTURIONS FROM ROME

Brigitte, a tall, attractive, blonde Swede, sat on a borrowed chair in my attic office. She had arrived the day before – unannounced.

'Rome sent me to help you,' she explained. 'I'll be the assistant to the new FAO Rep when he comes, a sort of Associate Expert on the administrative side. I don't know much about FAO routine, I'm afraid. This is my first job for them.'

I wasn't too sympathetic. I only hoped our new FAO Rep would turn up soon, I already had quite enough to do trying to cope with FAO's perverse ways as well as my own project, without having to break in some administrative rookie.

'Exactly when is this mythical Rep supposed to arrive?' I asked scathingly. 'We've been waiting nearly a year.'

'No-one knows, but there is definitely someone in the pipeline. I think he is a Cuban.'

'Well, there are plenty of his countrymen here, he shouldn't feel lonely.' Sarcasm seemed to be in order.

'This should make you happy,' she laughed, one December morning, handing me a Foodagram.

'DIRECTOR-GENERAL VISIT PLANNED EARLY NEXT YEAR. SUGGEST TAKE OPPORTUNITY OPEN NEW FAO OFFICES. DETAILS FOLLOW. REGARDS TERI.'

'What FAO offices?' I exploded. 'We have only a desk, a chair and a filing cabinet – oh, and the FAO flag.'

'We could always find an empty house, move in some furniture and hoist the FAO flat outside.' Brigitte thought it a big joke.

'Be serious,' I pleaded. 'The Director-General is on a par with heads of state, he commands purple carpet treatment, motorcycle escorts, front page headlines. I've got to find limousines, luxury suites and an FAO headquarters in less than a month!' I sent Rome a caustic telex.

'HAVE BORROWED HALF A ROOM FOR OFFICE. WILL TRY BORROW EXTRA CHAIR FOR DG. CONSIDER VISIT HIGHLY INOPPORTUNE THIS TIME.'

The reply ignored my flippancy.

'DG VISIT PERSONAL INVITATION MINISTER NOW SCHEDULED LAST WEEK JANUARY. HOPE VISIT YOU EARLY NEW YEAR FINALIZE ARRANGEMENTS. HAPPY XMAS.'

'And the same to you,' I growled petulantly.

I rang the UN Res Rep. He knew nothing. I wasn't surprised. For some peculiar reason, Rome had a habit of keeping their actions secret from the UN.

Brigitte, in her calm and logical way, came up with the obvious solution. 'Why don't you speak to the Minister himself? After all, it was he who invited the DG.'

Of course. My panic began to subside. I phoned Margarida, head of International Cooperation in the Ministry, who confirmed that arrangements for the visit were well advanced. I was to do nothing. It was all in the hands of the Minister. Greatly relieved, I took Brigitte home for an early drink. She'd earned it.

'Why the hell didn't the Ministry or Rome tell me all this long ago?' I grumbled. 'After all, I *am* supposed to be the acting bloody FAO Rep.'

An emissary from Rome came and discussed the visit with high officials.

'Miguel, the new Rep will be here in a day or two,' he told me as he said goodbye at the airport. 'It's his first job as a Rep. He's a Cuban. He'll look after everything.'

'*And* find an office for the DG to inaugurate?' I flung after him. He waved acknowledgement of my childish barb and disappeared through the gate.

I had prejudged Miguel on the basis of the Cubans I knew in the Ministry; either 'hail fellow, well met' types or political crustaceans. Neither sort would fit the part of FAO Rep. God forbid that we should be saddled with another Nicolo. I needn't have worried, Miguel was quite different. Rather short, plump with a strong face and intelligent, humorous eyes behind his hornrims. I judged him to be in his mid-forties.

'*Qué tal?*' he smiled, the first time we met. 'I'm glad someone here speaks Spanish.' There was no need to speak Spanish to him, his English was impeccable; but it was a friendly gesture that indicated we both played for the same team.

Although his figure belied it, his passion was fast motorcycles. An enormous Japanese steed of colossal power and cylinder volume was one of the first items of luggage to arrive. I couldn't imagine how he would ever get his short legs round the massive engine.

'I must meet with the Minister at once,' he said. 'I've a rather delicate matter that needs an urgent decision.'

This was a difference of opinion between the Director-General of FAO and the Minister. The latter wished to show off some well-laid-out *aldeas comunais* and a large state rice production operation at Chokwe, 200 miles to the north. The only way that this could be fitted into the DG's visit was to fly there by helicopter. The DG, however, was adamant that he would never step inside a Mozambican helicopter.

'I've seen hundreds of community villages and crop schemes all over the world,' he had told Miguel. 'I'm not going to risk my life seeing another!'

I thoroughly agreed. Too many friends in FAO had taken one trip too many in an ill-maintained local plane or vehicle, at the whim of a boastful politician.

Miguel waited three days to see the Minister, pacing my office and growing more and more frustrated as the meeting was postponed from a.m. to p.m., to the next morning, the next afternoon. Finally he was summoned to the fourth floor and an hour later descended, triumphant, to telex the DG that the Chokwe trip was cancelled.

'I'm going to Angola tomorrow to meet the Director-General and accompany him here. See you next week,' he told me and was off.

The following days were chaotic. Far from 'doing nothing', I attended endless meetings in the Ministry, Foreign Affairs and the UN, as well as lengthy sessions with FAO colleagues on how we could best exploit the DG's visit. But at the end of it all we still had no idea why he was coming, there was still no FAO office to baptize, and no-one had seen an agenda. Screw it, I thought, as I downed a last beer and headed for the airport. Why worry? This is the Minister's affair. The DG's plane was due at ten that night.

At two a.m., together with Miguel and other FAO knights, the DG arrived, shook hands insouciantly with the yawning band of welcomers, gave a brief press conference – there was only one reporter/photographer – and scribbled a draft agenda for the morrow.

The first item next day was a general gathering of all the FAO staff in the *Camara Municipalidad*, a huge white edifice, adorned with an eight-metre-high portrait of President Samora Machel above the entrance, which looked down over the circular *Praça Mouzinho de Albuquerque* (now *Praça Independencia*) to the bay beyond.

It was strictly an FAO family affair. As far as I could see, no government officials nor anyone from the UN were there. The 50 or so experts sat eagerly awaiting his eminence the DG and the pearls that would undoubtedly drop from his lips.

He arrived punctually, followed by his slim, elegant private secretary (an Italian Count, I was told), Teri, Miguel and – thank God he'd been invited – the UN Res Rep. We rose, as is only proper when greeting a high priest, and then settled down to hear his long-awaited sermon. He wouldn't have come all this way without a special message for us – would he?

The noble Italian acolyte approached and placed a folder on the table in front of his master. I wondered what he'd talk about. FAO's future? The new FAO offices in Maputo? New projects? The DG opened the file and examined the first page. We waited.

'Please would each expert stand up when I call his name,' he pronounced, at last. 'Dr Roger...' As Roger's surname began with 'A', it headed the alphabetical list. Roger stood up.

'I see you've been here since 1978...'

'1976, actually,' Roger put in.

'Oh, it says here 1978.' He took out a pen and made an alteration. 'I see that you are...' and so it went on. Each expert stood up in turn, confirmed his period of service and his present duties and sat down. He was gracious enough when my turn came to thank me for acting as his Representative, but no wise words were scattered amongst us, no strategies or new policies divulged. We began to wonder why we had been assembled. Surely, we merited something better than a roll-call.

After the last expert had sat down, he asked whether we had any questions.

'About what?' murmured Rudi, next to me.

'No idea,' I whispered back.

'Well, you're the senior one. You'd better think of something, quick.'

I hesitated a moment, then stood up and asked him to tell us about the newly instituted 'task forces' which FAO sent out to deal with special problems, and which I knew were dear to his heart.

He was obviously relieved to have something to talk about and became so carried away that his satellite secretary had to remind him of his next appointment. We filed out, greatly disappointed. After all the build-up to the visit, we'd expected some hint at future developments and strategy, or at least a reference to the proposed FAO office in Mozambique.

On the eve of his departure, the Minister of Agriculture gave a buffet supper in honour of his guest. Perhaps, we thought, this might be the occasion for our leader to open up. The Polana Hotel (now part of the Ministry of Internal Commerce, with all the resources it needed to make a luxury spread) excelled itself. King prawns by the bushel, crab *piri-piri*, lobsters the length of your arm, and every conceivable *bocadita* were laid out for the hundred or so selected male guests – no wives!

It was over an hour before the Minister appeared with the DG beside him. There were no speeches, which in one way was a relief. The two principal actors squatted on a settee in the corner, like royalty, while the rest of us plebs showed our appreciation of the Polana's culinary achievements. Once only was someone summoned to converse with the deities, other than that there was no contact at all between the potentates and the 'impotentates'.

Finally, the Minister stood up, thanked the DG for his visit, thanked the hotel for the goodies, thanked us for eating them, and left, without his guest of honour uttering a single word.

Maurice looked at me and grimaced. Another let-down, but at least this time, the food had been worth coming for.

There was no doubt that our Director-General was good at his main job, that of squeezing funds from the richer countries and private enterprise, and soft-soaping the Agricultural Ministers of member states, so as to keep FAO's wheels grinding through the mud and sand of Third World development programmes, but to us minor minions, and to our government counterparts who had expected someone special, he appeared aloof, unsympathetic and out of touch.

A FINCH TOO FREQUENT

The *Quelea quelea* is a small African finch with an insatiable appetite for grass seeds or, if these run out, for grain crops.

Like locusts, the little tawny birds move in swarms, migrating from region to region or country to country as crops mature. Flocks of *Quelea* can be as destructive as a swarm of locusts or a plague of rats.

Millions and millions of these tiny red-billed robbers would cross the border each year and settle down for a month's orgy on the rice fields around Chokwe. Shooting a few thousand or scaring them away had virtually no effect. The only successful method was to spray them with poison from low-flying aircraft.

This could only be done at night. In the daytime, the birds were too widely scattered and feeding on the rice, which the spray would contaminate and make unfit for human consumption. At night, however, the flocks nested in the surrounding bush, where they could be sprayed without fear of crop pollution, and since they returned to the same resting places each night, it was only a matter of identifying these sites and attacking them.

It wasn't an easy operation. To be effective, the planes had to fly at 200 kilometres an hour, five metres above the forest canopy. It was not a job for the unskilful or timid.

'Only one in three of the pilots we test finally make the grade,' the German owner and chief pilot of General Air Swaziland, who had perfected the technique, told me. 'And an awful lot have to change their pants after their first run!'

Once the resting places had been defined, radio beacons with flashing lights were placed to mark their limits. Shortly after sundown, the planes would take off from a nearby airstrip, home in on the beacons and spray the snoozing *Quelea*.

Quelea spraying had provoked a keen debate in the Ministry, not because of any ethical concern over the mass slaughter, but because of the cost. Why should Mozambique pay General Air Swaziland thousands of dollars every year to spray the little blighters when, with their own plane, some suggested, the Government could clobber *Quelea* at half the cost? FAO was approached and in due course I was asked to report.

From the first, I was vehemently against any idea of running our own spraying operation. It was hard enough to get a Land Rover serviced in Maputo, let alone maintain an aircraft. No, even if it did cost twice as much, it would be far better to let the private enterprise do it; they had the planes, the maintenance facilities and the trained pilots. All Mozambique could muster were a couple of ancient Aerocommanders, stored in an airport hangar, which would cost upwards of $30,000 apiece to convert for spraying – and God knew how much in annual maintenance. In spite of all my arguments, the high-ups in FAO decided that one of these old planes should be adapted immediately, a pilot recruited and trained at an aerial spraying operation in Tanzania, and that Mozambique would, in future, do their own *Quelea*-bashing. The Minister, I could see, was lukewarm. I'm sure his fears were no less acute than mine. Nevertheless, he and the DG duly signed an agreement during the latter's visit, for the conversion of one Aerocommander and for the training of a pilot – all at FAO's expense. There was nothing more I could do.

Nor, as it happened, did I have to. Somebody more influential than I must have painted the Minister a vivid picture of his one and only aircraft disappearing into a flock of *Quelea*, or diving into the unlit forest, for the day following the DG's departure from Mozambique, a contract was arranged with General Air Swaziland for the coming season's slaughter! It was one of the few times I saw eye to eye with the Minister.

General Air Swaziland was using the same night-flying technique to spray tsetse fly in northern Botswana, and invited us to witness it. Lucia, chief of Animal Health in the Ministry, together with an expert from the Land Use Project, Brigitte and myself, squeezed into a small Islander of Mozambique Airlines and flew north for five hours to Maun, a dusty, scattered hamlet on the borders of the fabulous Okavango swamps.

There were three aircraft spraying, and we were offered a free trip to experience the technique at first hand. Lucia and Brigitte, like the intrepid females they were, jumped at the opportunity. The Land Use lad and I firmly refused. I don't remember what his excuse was, probably the same as mine – pure funk – but besides being scared, I had only a couple more months before retirement, with four kids still at school. Anyway, I had only brought one pair of trousers!

Using a modified Dambusters technique, with twin searchlights gauging the height above the forest canopy, they flew along the lines between the flashing radio beacons, set earlier that day by Land Rovers. Fifteen feet is not a lot of leeway if a small *kopje* or extra-tall tree suddenly decides to jump up at you, but all went well, and half an hour after disappearing into the night sky, Lucia and Brigitte arrived back safely for a well-deserved drink.

The trip back to Maputo proved to be even more hazardous than flying in the spray planes. Our Land Use friend decided that it would be a good opportunity to visit a dentist in Johannesburg. Please could he be dropped off? No problem, said our pilot, and set course for Lenasia airfield, near Pretoria, circling a couple of times and landing about three o'clock in the afternoon. We were met by a very stern-faced official.

'Where's the bloody pilot?' he demanded.

Our fellow stepped forward proudly.

'You're wanted in the control tower, NOW,' he growled. I offered to go with him, as his English was fragmentary, and if the official's behaviour was any kind of barometer, the future looked a bit stormy.

'Do you realize that you nearly caused a serious accident?' a furious controller asked our now somewhat abashed pilot. 'We called you continually. You were on a crash course with a military Hercules. Luckily, he was able to deviate at the last moment.'

The pilot didn't quite understand all this, so I repeated it in Portuguese. He looked thoroughly alarmed.

'Just tell the idiot to keep his radio on in future, and get him out of here at once. We're taking no responsibility for his flight back, he'll be on Visual Flight Rules from now on. Now get going. All we need is a clot like him cluttering up our airspace.'

We set off again at four-thirty, minus the Land Use fellow whose teeth had pitched our pilot in the manure heap. For the first half an hour, we were in sight of the ground, the pilot flying by compass and sightings. Then cloud descended and, shortly afterwards, the night. For an hour we bumped through milk and Bovril.

'We'll never make it,' Brigitte moaned. I was inclined to agree. My faith in our pilot was now pretty low. Then, just as I had given up hope of seeing the family again, the clouds parted and there, sparkling below us, like a Golden City, was Maputo – and home!

A MEDAL FOR THE MINISTER

The large silver disc with the FAO slogan, '*Fiat Panis*', on one side and a commemorative inscription on the other, arrived from Rome with instructions that I should present it to the Minister of Agriculture on behalf of the Director-General of FAO. The ceremony, it was emphasized, should have as much publicity as possible, since the medal was both a token of esteem as well as the celebration of FAO's 30th year of operations.

A printed speech was included, which I was asked to translate into Portuguese, adapt to local conditions, and read to the Minister at the presentation ceremony.

I felt a complete hypocrite. There was no-one, in my opinion, less deserving of a medal than our unloved Minister. Hadn't he had Abreu incarcerated for nearly two years on the flimsiest of excuses? And even when the investigation had shown no evidence of the alleged misdemeanours, hadn't he put further obstacles in the way of his release? Wasn't he the one who had tried to scuttle the Peasant Farmers' Milk Collection scheme on purely political grounds? And there had been several other things, like the rice fiasco, when the whole of the Ministry staff, amongst others, were shipped off in panic to Chokwe for a week, to help harvest the rice crop by hand, because the Bulgarian-built rice harvesters, which Abreu had long ago told him were the wrong type, had let them down.

As far as we were concerned, he'd been a disaster since his first general meeting with the Ministry staff, when instead of inspiring and encouraging us, he harangued us all on the way we dressed. No more shorts or jeans to be worn in the Ministry, men to wear jackets and ties, no slacks for women, sandals forbidden in either sex.

No, I thought. Sack him by all means, but don't give him a medal.

The medal, of course, was purely a political gimmick and had nothing to do with his accomplishments in the field of agriculture. Some mean-minded persons even suggested that it was a well-camouflaged bribe, because the next year the Director-General would come up for re-election. Candidates for the post of DG were voted into office by the Governments (in effect the Ministers of Agriculture) of the member States. Each geographical region – the Americas, Africa, India and the Far East – had its preferred candidate. A medal here and there might swing the odd vote.

Fernanda thoroughly enjoyed translating the speech. From time to time she would ask my advice. 'Should I say "contribution" or "confusion"?' she'd ask, referring to a passage praising the Minister's efforts on behalf of Mozambique's agriculture; or, 'Should I write "stupid" instead of "stupendous"?'

The presentation was scheduled for a Friday morning at eleven. That was fine, I was due to pick up Lindley and Melanie from school the next day, Saturday, in Mbabane; Mary was in Canada. Roland, the then 'Godfather' of our project, on a routine visit from Rome, agreed to accompany me to the ceremony.

Attired in our best 'Sunday-go-to-Meeting' suits, we waited in my office, I was going over the speech to get the pronunciation perfect. At ten-thirty we were told that the presentation had been postponed till three that afternoon. At two-thirty we were told that the Minister was too busy but would be ready at nine the next morning. Two more postponements carried us through to one o'clock. Visions of my making Mbabane in time to pick up the kids began to fade.

At last the call came, and we were ushered into the conference room, where we sat for half an hour until the Minister, his Deputy and several other officials, bustled in, a photographer and a young lady with a tape recorder slung over her shoulder, in their wake.

We rose, exchanged greetings, and I introduced Roland. Then, as no-one seemed to know quite what to do next, I got up and read the speech with growing conviction, as if I believed all the rosy compliments it contained. When I had finished, I presented the medal to his

Excellency, still lying in its red morocco case. I had considered hanging it around his neck, but decided against this in case my feelings got the better of me and I strangled him!

I wasn't quite prepared for the Minister's reply. He began by thanking the Director-General and then went on to praise the work FAO was doing in Mozambique, especially that of my project. I listened with increasing surprise – and embarrassment – as he praised the beef and dairy schemes, the tsetse fly and trypanosomiasis research and, of all things, the Peasant Farmers Milk Collection Co-operative, which he now held up as a victory of 'scientific socialism' and FAO's farsightedness!

Had I misjudged him? Perhaps, beneath that sour face, he appreciated more than we realized. Perhaps he could even recognize and learn from his mistakes: I remembered how he had finally squashed the DG's ridiculous proposal to buy an aeroplane for *Quelea quelea* spraying. Perhaps I should withhold my judgement for a while – but I still didn't think he deserved a medal!

Every Minister of Agriculture in every developing country where FAO operated was, I knew, also receiving a similar medal. Perhaps they deserved their decorations even less! Anyway, who was I to talk? Hadn't Uganda presented me with a medal, by post, for services rendered and in commemoration of Uganda's Independence? The tea-stained, cyclostyled letter accompanying it began, 'Dear Sir/Madam'. No-one had even taken the trouble to ascertain my sex!

Perhaps the Minister and I had something in common, after all!

BULLS FROM COMRADE CASTRO

'Pat, I need your help.' Roger flopped into the chair in front of my desk, the deep lines on his rugged face even deeper.

'Sure,' I replied cheerfully, 'What can I do?'

'To start with, a vehicle for about two months and a lot of antibiotics, syringes and other equipment.'

'No problem. I was looking for an excuse to visit Swaziland and see the kids. I'll go across tomorrow and buy them. Why the urgency?'

'There's a shipload of Brahman bulls arriving from Cuba in three weeks' time. Two hundred will be off-loaded in Maputo and another two hundred taken to the north. The Ministry have been negotiating the deal for months, evidently, and this morning they tell me I'm in charge of the whole bloody operation.'

'Bit inconsiderate,' I commented, although I wasn't really surprised. Those who actually did the dirty work were always the last to be told.

'Damn right it's inconsiderate, especially as there's nowhere to put the wretched beasts. They'll have to be quarantined and immunized against tick-borne diseases, or they'll be dead within a month – and you know exactly who'll be held responsible if that happens. Rui says they are planning a quarantine station at Belulane. I'm going there with him this afternoon. Like to come?'

'Love to. Where the hell is Belulane?'

'Somewhere behind Machava, I think.'

Apart from the logistical problems of moving animals from country to country, there is always the danger of introducing new diseases (foot and mouth disease in cattle and rabies in dogs are classic examples) which can be spread from one country to another by apparently healthy animals. We weren't too worried that the bulls would bring something nasty with them from Cuba; there were many more dangerous diseases that could be taken out of Africa than could be brought in, so our problem was just the reverse. The Cuban bulls, reared on a comparatively disease-free island, would be highly susceptible to many of the diseases they would encounter in Mozambique.

The most dangerous was heartwater, a tick-transmitted killer, the main symptom of which was usually sudden death. A greatly enlarged heart sac helped to confirm the diagnosis at autopsy and gave the disease its name. Cattle born and raised in heartwater-infected areas picked up the infection soon after birth while still protected by antibodies in their mothers' milk. As they grew older, constant exposure to infection acted as a vaccination process, increasing their immunity. The Cuban bulls, which were between two and three years old, had never encountered heartwater and therefore had no immunity. The only answer was to vaccinate them while in quarantine and hope for the best!

Belulane proved to be an overgrown, abandoned dairy farm sweltering beside the little-used railway line to Boane and Goba. A mud-brick farmhouse in reasonable repair and several barns and outbuildings in advanced disrepair peeped out of the invading bush. A couple of old retainers were cooking, listlessly, beside a small fire.

Pastures there had been in plenty when the farm was producing milk, before the owner fled to Portugal, but now the paddocks were overgrown with bushes and the fence lines were only discernible by the few ant-eaten posts that poked up through the long grass and weeds. An encouraging find was a dipping bath, badly designed, but half full of a muddy liquid, which proved that it could still hold water.

Dr Rui tried to be enthusiastic.

'We'll start clearing the pastures of weeds and putting up fences at once,' he announced. 'We'll put an ATP in the farmhouse as supervisor. Shouldn't take long.'

I drove to Swaziland the following day, and bought the drugs and equipment. The vaccines against heartwater and other tick-borne diseases would be obtained later from the Onderstepoort Veterinary Research Institute in South Africa *via* Swaziland, of course. But in spite of all that Roger and his team could do to hasten matters, it was obvious that Belulane would not be ready in time to receive the bulls.

It was George who saved the day.

'If you supply food and shelter,' he assured us, 'I'll get Mussagy and the fencing gang down from Muabsa. They'll have the whole thing finished in a week.'

A few days later they arrived, and when the bulls docked, the station was as good as complete.

I had grown to love Brahmans in Jamaica. To my mind, Zebus are the most beautiful of all the cattle breeds. Their massive size, their short sleek coats, their wavy dewlaps, their flowing lines and the lanky, rippling elegance of their movements, made them aristocrats amongst bovines. The consignment from Cuba certainly upheld my opinion. Like those in Jamaica, they were predominantly white, due to their Nellore ancestry, with charcoal-grey humps and heads, and a dark tassel at the end of their tails. I watched them, loping along the fence lines, their pendulous dewlaps swinging, long ears flopping and humps bouncing from side to side, as they sniffed out the boundaries of their new domain.

The following weeks were not enjoyable; they were dusty, hot and tiring. Each morning at four, Roger, with other members of his team who were on duty that day, Don (the new beef cattle expert), Ali (another Associate), Danny (my Cuban friend), and often myself, would bump along the ten kilometres of pot-holed track which connected Belulane to the main road. We would find the bulls packed tightly into the crushes and the ATPs already inserting thermometers under their tails, recording their temperatures. It was extremely important to know the normal temperature of each animal (all animals differ slightly), because a certain rise, after vaccination, might be our only evidence of a 'take'.

Being January, the hottest and most humid time of the year,

temperature-taking had to be completed in the cool of the early morning, at the latest by eight o'clock.

Heartwater vaccine had to be given into a vein. Any vein would have done, but the ear vein was the most convenient. The animal's head was firmly roped to the side of the crush, bull-tongs clipped into its nostrils, and a firm grip taken of the base of the ear to swell the blood vessel before a teaspoonful (5ml) of the heartwater vaccine was injected.

It wasn't always easy to slip in the needle without going right through the vein if the bull decided to object. They were young, extremely strong and lively animals, and however well we thought they were immobilized, there were sure to be one or two who felt strongly enough to send the syringe – and often the vaccinator – flying into the bush!

I don't know how many thermometers and syringes we went through, dozens certainly, but no operators – not permanently, anyway. Every day, one of the five herds, in rotation, was put through the dip bath. No hassles there. They loved it. The problem was to keep an adequate interval between each animal as they trotted up the race to the tank. A slight hesitation at the rim was followed by a frantic leap to plunge halfway down the long narrow tank, followed by a short swim to the exit ramp. In that heat, I envied them.

Ten days after the injections, we began to pay special attention to any rise in temperature which might indicate a successful 'take'. If the reaction was severe, the bull was given a large dose of antibiotic as a precaution against it dying of heartwater, otherwise it was left to get over it by itself. As soon as all the bulls had recovered from their reactions, vaccination against two other tick-borne diseases – redwater (babesiosis) and gallsickness (anaplasmosis) – was begun. Injections for these were made under the loose skin over the ribs or in the neck, and were a piece of cake compared with the ear vein inoculations. The need for less restraint, however, made the handlers careless, and a sudden jump as the needle pricked the skin, or a swing of the hundred-pound head and horns, crushed several fingers.

Examination of the bulls' semen for fertility completed the operations, and by mid-March they were ready to prove themselves on the local talent.

Roger took a couple of weeks off in February, to inspect the other 200 bulls which had gone straight to Nampula, 1,000 kilometres to the north, leaving me in charge. Up till then, I had gone out to the quarantine station perhaps twice a week, now I had to rise at three-thirty every day for a straight two weeks, and spend six to eight hours in the blazing sun, struggling with enraged Zebu bulls. It was something I felt I was getting a little too old for – even if Roger was a year older than I!

The only comic relief was supplied by Danny who, either from desire or duty, or both, never seemed to miss the frequent lively parties at the Cuban Embassy, almost opposite our house. One morning, I found him on our doorstep, head in hands, the pallor of his face exaggerated by his jet-black hair and drooping moustache. He could barely stagger to the car but insisted on accompanying me to Belulane, where he lay for the rest of the day, groaning under a shady tree, swigging iced water from the canister which contained the vaccine! Judging by the piles of empty beer and wine bottles (all from despised South Africa) outside the Embassy when I returned that afternoon, it must have indeed been a superlative binge.

We had estimated that, with luck, we wouldn't have more than a dozen bovine casualties. As it turned out, only one poor beast provided us with steaks, and that was because another, following too closely, jumped on top of it in the dip tank and drowned it. For the hungry herdsmen, it was a most popular demise!

Everyone felt very pleased and proud when the Minister, so impressed by the smoothness and success of the operation, awarded Roger a special accolade and flew him and Pru to Paradise Island off the coast at Vilancoulos, one of the country's most beautiful resorts, for a two-week, all expenses paid, holiday. He had certainly earned it.

PUT OUT TO GRASS

I was two years short of compulsory retirement.

Retirement! It had crept up so swiftly that Mary and I had not yet decided where we would like to spend our golden years. Roger and Pru had retired to their Spanish villa on the Costa del Sol, and we had considered following suit, but with four children still at school and others ready for university, educational options would be limited and far too expensive on a pension – even one from the UN.

Jamaica had crossed our minds, but education opportunities would be worse than Spain, also Ken and Marjorie, the only people there we still knew, told us that the island we remembered had long since disappeared. Canada, where we both had relatives, was, like Australia and New Zealand, half a globe away. Britain, for long our first choice, had, after a depressing month house-hunting, offered little. A ghastly climate, matchboxes with 'master' bedrooms scarcely large enough for the beds, and pokey, soggy gardens, at inflationary prices, were all we could have afforded in the semi-urban areas which provided an accessible Comprehensive for the children.

Combing Devon lanes and Welsh hills and nearly every other country district in the south (the north and Scotland we considered too cold), had coughed up only one possible house in Essex, on the edge of the village sports ground.

'What about South Africa?' Mary suggested. 'It's a lovely country, it's cheap and the climate's stupendous, and it's just across the border. We can drive there.'

'Try around Pietermaritzburg,' Jim, the Land Use Project Manager, suggested. 'Most people in Natal speak English.'

A couple of weekends later, Mary and I took off to investigate, and three days later we had found ourselves a large house with six acres of garden and paddocks, plus a cottage and half a hundred peach, plum and apple trees, in the rolling foothills of the Drankensberg 60 kilometres north of Pietermaritzburg. The cost was a third of that quoted for the house in Essex.

Of course, we were well aware of South Africa's image abroad, but our frequent forays into the Republic to buy essentials had convinced us that by no means everything there was amiss; the judiciary was independent, the public services worked, and it was obvious that apartheid was already doomed. There was an old-fashioned air about the place – a nostalgic echo of pre-war Britain. How different to the fear-ridden, restrictive ideology of the Eastern Bloc satellite we were leaving.

Mary had another, equally compelling reason for suggesting South Africa. Her attempts to introduce our little vervet, Freak, into the monkey troupe at the Costa do Sol had failed. There was no way we would take her back to the Zoo, Britain would impose a six-month quarantine, and we had no-one to leave her with. It was South Africa or curtains for the little ape. After several letters (which only Mary can write) and a personal visit to Pretoria, we obtained the necessary import permits from the Natal Parks Board and Veterinary authorities, and Freak's fate – and ours – was sealed!

There were no farewell parties for me in the UN or FAO offices, no friendly handshakes, kind speeches or cheery goodbyes. Retirement to racialistic South Africa was considered an almost traitorous act for a senior field official of a United Nations Agency. Only the Ministry personnel took it upon themselves to acknowledge their appreciation at a farewell dinner.

I had been taken ill ten days before our intended departure, so Kerry had given up his job in England and flown out to help us move. Without him and Tilak, who had taken it on himself to arrange the truck to transport our goods across the border and sort out the red tape, we would never have made it.

We had intended to start early in the day in case of hassles at the border, but it was afternoon before we had managed to complete the last chores, rope the last of our luggage to the overloaded roof-rack, collect the six children, three dogs and monkey, and were ready to leave.

All morning there had been a growing roar of motorcycles in the street outside our house. By noon, it was jammed with machines and their riders, sporting dark mafioso-like sunglasses. At three o'clock, they formed themselves into a cavalcade, 50 metres long, which would have done credit to President Machel himself, and with a last cacophonous cheer from the bystanders which almost drowned the revving Kawasakis and Hondas, we were off.

Our outriders accompanied us all the way to the border – that is, those who still had sufficient petrol (now strictly rationed) after a morning of revving and showing-off. Many, however, had to turn round during the 80-kilometre journey, bidding us a honking farewell.

I was not so naive as to imagine that this show of affection had anything to do with me. This was a family send-off, and 'family' in this case meant the kids and Mary; but it made up in some way for the UN office's offhand rejection of their longest-serving FAO official.

As we waved goodbye at Namaacha and watched the Libombo hills fade into the dusk, I realized that this was indeed the end of the saga that had begun almost exactly 38 years before, when that naive youngster had landed at Cape Town and headed north to Abercorn and the Northern Rhodesian bush.